ELEMENTARY
STRUCTURAL
ANALYSIS

McGraw-Hill Series in Structural Engineering Mechanics

RAY W. CLOUGH, *Consulting Editor*

NORRIS AND WILBUR · Elementary Structural Analysis

GERARD · Introduction to Structural Stability Theory

ELEMENTARY
STRUCTURAL
ANALYSIS

CHARLES HEAD NORRIS, Sc.D.

Professor of Civil Engineering
University of Washington
Fellow, American Society of Civil Engineers

JOHN BENSON WILBUR, Sc.D.

Consulting Professor of Engineering
Massachusetts Institute of Technology
Fellow, American Society of Civil Engineers

SECOND EDITION   1960

McGraw-Hill Book Company   NEW YORK   TORONTO   LONDON

ELEMENTARY STRUCTURAL ANALYSIS

THE MAPLE PRESS COMPANY, YORK, PA.

V

47255

Preface

Since this book was first published in 1948, there have been many developments in the various aspects of structural engineering. Improved fabrication and construction techniques have led to more efficient utilization of established constructional materials such as steel, concrete, and wood. Use of structural aluminum has expanded, due particularly to the development of various types of prefabricated elements. Plastics have been introduced, primarily into building construction. Post-elastic behavior of structures is now recognized and structural design procedures are in the process of being modified to utilize this behavior where appropriate. The use of electronic computers in structural analysis and design calculations is being expanded by leaps and bounds.

The major changes which have been introduced into this second edition of Elementary Structural Analysis reflect the influence of this era of rapid technological development. Four major units have been added: a foreword, in which an attempt is made to place the various aspects of structural engineering, and the past, present and future of this field into a proper perspective; Chapter 15, which is a brief introduction to matrix analysis of structures; Chapter 16, which is a discussion of certain aspects of the plastic behavior of structures; and Chapter 17, which is an introduction to advanced structural mechanics.

Engineering education, like all other aspects of technology, is in an era of rapid change and development. At the undergraduate level, more emphasis is being placed on fundamentals and less on professional subjects. This new edition, like the original, also emphasizes fundamentals rather than practice, and attempts to correlate the various procedures of structural analysis with the principles of applied mechanics on which they are based.

The scope of this book is restricted to the field of structural analysis, and must be supplemented by a book on structural design. Herein it is emphasized and reemphasized that *the function of a structural engineer is to design—not to analyze;* and that analysis is a means to an end rather than the end itself. Today there are a number of fine textbooks available covering various aspects of structural design, to which the reader is referred.

In the preparation of this second edition, the authors were assisted by Martha M. Norris, the wife of one of them, who typed the manuscript; and by Harold D. Smith, who prepared the new figures. For their valued and loyal support, the authors are very grateful.

The authors wish to continue to acknowledge with appreciation the contributions of those who assisted in the preparation of the first edition: Mrs. Grace M. Powers, who typed the manuscript; Prof. Donald R. F. Harleman, who prepared the figures; and Prof. Myle J. Holley, Jr., who proofread the manuscript.

Both authors are also deeply grateful to those responsible for their education in structural engineering, particularly to Prof. Charles Milton Spofford, and to the late Prof. Charles Church More. They likewise acknowledge with appreciation the help they have received from their colleagues, **Prof.** Eugene Mirabelli and the late Profs. W. M. Fife and J. D. Mitsch.

Charles Head Norris
John Benson Wilbur

Contents

CONTENTS

CONTENTS

List of Symbols

Symbols are defined where they appear. The principal symbols are listed here for convenience. Note that some symbols have several definitions depending on the context in which they are being used.

A cross-sectional area of member

C carry-over factor in moment distribution method

D flexural rigidity of plates and shells, $Eh^3/12(1 - \nu^2)$

D_m joint displacement component used in displacement method of structural analysis

DF distribution factor in moment distribution method

E Young's modulus of elasticity (in tension or compression)

E_t tangent modulus of elasticity

F force in general; axial force or axial resisting force acting on a cross section of a member

$\mathfrak{F}$ form factor of cross-sectional area, **Z/S**

FEM   fixed-end moment of member used in slope-deflection method and in moment distribution method

G modulus of elasticity in shear

H horizontal component of force; total shear acting on story of building frame; horizontal component of cable tension

I moment of inertia of cross-sectional area

J sidesway-factor used in moment distribution method

K stiffness factor for flexural member, I/L for prismatic members

K^R reduced stiffness factor for flexural member

K' true stiffness factor for flexural member

K'^R true reduced stiffness factor for flexural member

eff K   effective stiffness factor for flexural member

L length of member; span length

M	moment of force (or couple); bending moment; resisting moment; end moment of member; bending or twisting stress-couples in plate and shell theory
M_{yp}	resisting moment of cross section corresponding to stress condition where bending stress in extreme fiber has just reached the yield-stress, $M_{yp} = \mathbf{S}\,\sigma_{yp}$
M_{pl}	resisting moment for a cross section which is fully plasticized in pure bending, $M_{pl} = \mathbf{Z}\,\sigma_{yp}$
N	membrane stress-resultants used in plate and shell theory
P	external load
P_m	joint force component used in displacement method of structural analysis
P_{cr}	critical load (for buckling)
P_{yp}	load which produces yield point stress in most highly stressed fiber
P_{ult}	ultimate load (in plastic behavior considerations, load at which excessive deflections impend)
Q	imaginary external load used in application of method of virtual work; transverse shear stress-resultant used in plate and shell theory
R	reactive force; resultant
S	shear force (shear) in member; shear resisting force
$\mathbf{S}$	section modulus of cross-sectional area
T	cable tension
V	vertical component of force
W	weight of body
W_d	internal virtual work of deformation
W_R	external virtual work done by reactions
W_s	external virtual work done by external force system (loads and reactions)
W_E	external work done by external force system
W_I	internal work (or strain energy) stored by deformation of structure
W_m	elastic load (or weight) at joint m used in bar-chain method of computing truss deflections
X	redundant force (or couple) used in analysis of statically indeterminate structures
X,Y,Z	coordinate components of a force
X,Y,Z	coordinate components of body force used in theory of elasticity
$\overline{X},\overline{Y},\overline{Z}$	coordinate components of surface forces used in theory of elasticity
$\mathbf{Z}$	plastic modulus of cross-sectional area which is fully plasticized in pure bending

a dimension of length; radius of curvature of shell

b dimension of length; width of cross section; number of members in a frame or framework

c dimension of length; distance from centroid to extreme point of cross section

d dimension of length; depth of cross section; deflection of point on elastic curve from tangent at another point

d_{ml} deflection (or flexibility) coefficients used in superposition equations expressing deflection m of a structure

e lineal strain of a longitudinal element of member

$e_0, e_1,$ etc. lineal strain of longitudinal element of centroidal axis of member

e_a, e_b, e_c lineal strains of a strain rosette

g acceleration of gravity

h cable sag at mid-span of cable curve; story height of building; thickness of plate or shell

k stiffness of a linear spring (force required to produce unit change of length of spring)

k_{ml} stiffness coefficient used in the displacement method of structural analysis

l dimension of length

n number of joints of a frame or framework

p intensity per unit length of distributed loading on beam

q intensity per unit area of distributed load applied to a plate or shell

r number of independent reaction elements of a frame or framework; principal radius of curvature of shell; radius of gyration of cross-sectional area, $(I/A)^{1/2}$

s dimension of axial length of member

t uniform change of temperature; time

w intensity of uniformly distributed loading

u, v, w displacement components corresponding to x, y, and z coordinate directions, respectively

x, y, z orthogonal coordinates

α angle; rotational displacement; central angle subtended by line element of middle surface of shell

α_t coefficient of thermal expansion

γ shearing strain

Δ deflection; increment of a quantity

δ deflection; unit deflection used in superposition equation method for analyzing statically indeterminate structures

ϵ lineal strain

$\epsilon_x, \epsilon_y, \epsilon_z$ coordinate components of lineal strain

θ angle; rotation of tangent elastic curve with respect to original direction of axis of member; sag ratio of cable, h/L

ν Poisson's ratio

σ normal stress

σ_{yp} yield point stress in tension

τ shear stress; rotation of tangent to elastic curve with respect to chord of elastic curve

ϕ angle; curvature of flexural member

χ change in curvature or twist of middle surface of shell

ψ angle; rotation of chord of an elastic curve with respect to original direction of axis of a member

ω natural frequency of vibration

Notice to the Student Reader

Several suggestions regarding two of the major revisions incorporated in this new edition of "Elementary Structural Analysis" may be helpful to the student reader.

1. A Foreword has been inserted prior to the detailed technical presentation starting with Chap. 1. Essentially it is a summary of the historical development of structural engineering, a short statement of the present status of the field, and a suggestion of some of the future trends. An attempt has been made to emphasize that a structural engineer's primary objective is to design structures, *not* to analyze them; to describe the philosophy of structural design; and to show how the principles of the analysis of structural behavior introduced in this book are used to assist the structural engineer in arriving at his design.

Please read this Foreword carefully before starting your study of the detailed technical presentation. In your first reading, there will be many statements and generalities which will be difficult to appreciate and comprehend. Therefore, please reread this Foreword frequently as you progress through this book and as you develop your capabilities to analyze and understand structural behavior.

2. Answers are supplied for approximately half of the problems in this book (those problems preceded by an asterisk). These are intended to help make your studying more efficient by enabling you to identify quickly whether you have made either a careless computational error or perhaps a fundamental error in the solution of the problem. Please do not use these answers as a crutch. If you do so and do not develop your capability to check yourself, you will prolong your infancy as a structural engineer and will not be able to walk and run as a responsible professional as soon as you should. A good structural engineer continually makes approximate calculations to check himself. Get in the habit of making an approximate estimate of the answer to a problem before you start your detailed calculations. You will find such exercise invaluable in developing your judgment and intuition for structural behavior.

Foreword

Historical Review. Doubtless the planning, design, and construction of structures is essentially as old as man himself since nature provides on this planet a suitable environment for man, but seldom are the detailed natural forms of this environment exactly suitable to his needs, convenience, and desires. Early man could probably find a natural cave or a hollow tree which would give him partial shelter from the elements, but it most likely would not be situated properly with respect to his source of food and water. So man started to alter nature to meet his needs—and thereby built his first structure. Was his first structure a crude shelter, or may it have been a bridge made of a log beam or a stone slab or a vine?

Historical records tracing the evolution of structural engineering from its very early beginnings to the present are much poorer than those documenting the spiritual, philosophical, political, economic, and artistic development of man. On the other hand, archeological exploration has given us some limited physical evidence of the structures produced by early engineering even though the concepts and ideas behind their construction are lost and can only be inferred.

Man's basic needs for food and shelter of course are unchanging with time, but the standards which he accepts for the fulfillment of these needs continually change with the capabilities of his civilization. Fortunately for progress and the advancement of civilization, man's ambitions and desires always exceed his achievements. Sometimes the differential between these two is so great that it drives him to try to accomplish his objective before he can really define what his objective is, or why he desires it, or what techniques or methods he should use to achieve it. The highlights of man's history are the record of his most daring efforts— sometimes the record of a sensational advance or breakthrough, other times the record of a catastrophic failure.

Down through the centuries, master builders and structural engineers have practiced their art assisted by, but not completely dependent upon, the mathematical and scientific knowledge available to them. Mathe-

1

matics and science when available are convenient tools which the designer uses to determine the detailed proportions and dimensions of his structures. When theoretical knowledge has not yet been developed to satisfy his needs, the designer must rely on his experience, field and/or laboratory tests, or his intuition and feeling for structural behavior. The accomplishments of a successful builder are *really* bounded by *only* four limitations: the functional requirements and needs of his civilization; the properties of the materials available to him; the constructional techniques which are practical and economical for him to employ; and the creativity and imagination with which he applies his talents, knowledge, experience, and intuition.

The nineteenth and twentieth centuries have produced very impressive mathematical, scientific, material, and mechanical advances in the field of structural engineering. So impressive is the store of knowledge which has been accumulated during this period that far too many structural engineers have been inclined to limit their designs to those which are encompassed by codes, standard practices, and available mathematical formulations. In such a professional atmosphere, the truly outstanding efforts of modern master builders such as Maillart, Freyssinet, Torroja, and Nervi seem even more impressive in comparison with the work of their contemporaries.[1] All these outstanding engineers have possessed creativity, imagination, and intuition to a very unusual degree, but it is noteworthy that all of them have likewise supplemented their mathematical and scientific knowledge generously with the intelligent and extensive use of not only their own and others' experience but also field and laboratory testing.

The careers of these outstanding men reveal the same lesson that can be drawn from such historical records as are available regarding the development of structural engineering and mechanics, namely, that the mathematical and scientific evaluation of a structural behavior or phenomena almost invariably antedates, rather than precedes, the initial application of such ideas in actual design and construction.

The earliest construction forms of which we have any real knowledge are the lake dwellings at the bottom of some of the Swiss lakes.[2]   These

[1] For descriptions of work of these outstanding engineers see: Eduardo Torroja, "Philosophy of Structures" (English version by J. J. Polivka and Milos Polivka), University of California Press, Berkeley, 1958; Eduardo Torroja, "The Structures of Eduardo Torroja," F. W. Dodge Corporation, New York, 1958; Pier Luigi Nervi, "Structures" (translated by Giuseppina and Mario Salvadori), F. W. Dodge Corporation, New York, 1956; Leonard Michaels, "Contemporary Structure in Architecture," Reinhold Publishing Corporation, New York, 1950.

[2] There are a number of excellent books tracing the history and development of structural mechanics and structural engineering, among which are: Stephen P. Timoshenko, "History of Strength of Materials," McGraw-Hill Book Company, Inc.,

were very primitive houses erected on piles and date back to the Paleolithic Age. There are earlier megalithic remains in Europe and Asia, but these show almost no evidences of a true structural art. Archeological exploration and restoration has given us considerable evidence of Egyptian, Greek, and Roman construction as well as that of the numerous ancient civilizations of Asia and Asia Minor.

Perhaps the structural forms used by early builders which are of greatest interest to structural engineers of today are the following: the post and

Figure F.1 Pont du Gard (*Bettmann Archive*)

lintel constructions of the classic Greek architecture, dating from about 500 B.C.; the Roman contributions to the development of the arch, the vault, the dome, the wood truss, and concrete; the groined vault and vault rib developed by Romanesque builders between A.D. 500 and 1000; and the pointed arches and flying buttresses used by the Gothic builders in the magnificent cathedrals constructed in Europe during the Middle Ages between A.D. 1000 and 1500. Even in comparison with modern structures, a Roman aqueduct or bridge such as the famous Pont du Gard or the dome roof of the Santa Sophia cathedral in Istanbul (built about A.D. 540) is an impressive and inspiring sight. All the more is this so when one realizes the "state of the art" when such structures were designed and built.

1953; H. M. Westergaard, "Theory of Elasticity and Plasticity," Harvard University Press, Cambridge, Mass. (John Wiley & Sons, Inc., New York), 1952; David B. Steinman and Sara Ruth Watson, "Bridges and Their Builders," Dover Publications, Inc., New York, 1957.

No doubt the Egyptians and other ancient builders had formulated empirical rules based on their previous experience to guide them in planning a new structure, but there is no evidence that they had developed even the beginnings of a theory of structural behavior. The Greeks further advanced the art of building, but their contribution to structural theory was limited to that of certain of their philosophers such as Archimedes (287–212 B.C.), who laid the basis of structural mechanics by formulating certain fundamental principles of statics. The Romans were

Figure F.2 Santa Sophia dome (*Bettmann Archive*)

primarily builders and became very competent in developing and using certain structural forms. However, they apparently had little knowledge of the stress analysis of these forms. For example, they apparently did not know how to establish the proper shape of their arches and usually used semicircular short-span arches.

Most of the knowledge that the Greeks and Romans accumulated concerning structural engineering was lost during the Middle Ages and has been recovered only since the Renaissance. Leonardo da Vinci (1452–1519) was not only the leading artist of his time but was also a great scientist and engineer. From his notebooks, it is clearly evident that he was very perceptive and understood quite well certain fundamentals of the behavior of structural materials. This work of da Vinci appears to be the real beginning of the development of structural theory, but it was not widely publicized by being published in book form. As a result, Galileo (1564–1642) is properly acknowledged to be not only the founder of modern science but also the originator of the mechanics of materials. For, in his last publication, "Two New Sciences," completed in 1636 and published in 1638, he was the first to discuss the strength of certain structural members, including the failure of a cantilever beam.

Galileo investigated the failure of a beam cantilevered from a wall by rupture in the cross section of the beam adjacent to the wall. He considered the material to be rigid and assumed that, at failure, the compression was concentrated at the lower edge of the ruptured section and the tensile resistance was uniformly distributed over the depth of the section. Such a stress distribution would not be valid in the elastic range of a material following Hooke's law, but could be true under some assumed law for a plastic range of a material. Whereas Galileo's analysis would not lead to a close absolute value of the strength of a cantilever beam, it is interesting to note that it did give him the correct ratio for the strengths of two beams of similar cross sections. Even more interesting to us today is the fact that Galileo (and also da Vinci) were interested in predicting *strengths* of members rather than *stresses* and *strains* developed in the members at loads less than the failure load. If all investigators over the last three hundred years had continued to have an interest in strength, comparable to their interest in elastic behavior of structures, perhaps today the knowledge of structural mechanics would be better balanced between elastic behavior and strength of structures and structural members.

Subsequent investigators such as Hooke (1635–1703), Mariotte (1620–1684), Jacob Bernoulli (1654–1705), John Bernoulli (1667–1748), Daniel Bernoulli (1700–1782), Euler (1707–1783), Lagrange (1736–1813), Parent (1666–1716), and Coulomb (1736–1806) made important contributions to the development of this new field of knowledge. Of these, Coulomb's contributions were particularly outstanding, and his memoir written in 1773 was particularly significant though it did not attract the attention and exert the influence that it deserved. In this paper was presented for the first time a completely adequate elastic analysis for the flexure of beams. He also noted that, under certain conditions at rupture, the neutral axis could have shifted from its elastic position and thereby demonstrated an appreciation for plastic behavior.

It was not until 1826 when the first printed edition of Navier's (1785–1836) book on strength of materials was published that some of the misconceptions corrected by Coulomb were widely publicized and the modern theory of mechanics of materials was established. Thus, Coulomb and Navier should be considered as the founders of this important field which is so basic to structural analysis. Whereas his predecessors in the eighteenth century had measured and calculated ultimate loads for structural members, Navier stated at the very beginning of his presentation that it is very important to know the limit up to which structures behave elastically, and he therefore concentrated on a consideration of the elastic behavior of structures. He suggested that formulas derived for elastic behavior should be applied to existing structures which were behaving satisfactorily in order to establish safe stresses which could be used in design. In retrospect, it is unfortunate that, in this very important and

Figure F.3 Saguenay River aluminum bridge   (*From the files of Engineering News-Record*)

influential treatise, Navier had not also retained a proper interest in post-elastic behavior and ultimate strengths of structures.

The remainder of the nineteenth century after the publication of Navier's book could be considered the "golden age" as far as the development of what is now considered to be the classical theory of structures is concerned. Some important contributors in this era were Lame (1795–1870), Saint-Venant (1797–1886), Clapeyron (1799–1864), Clebsch (1833–1872), Rankine (1820–1872), Airy (1801–1892), Maxwell (1831–1879), Castigliano (1847–1884), Culmann (1821–1881), Mohr (1835–1918), Müller-Breslau (1851–1925), Engesser (1848–1931), Wöhler (1819–1914), A. Föppl (1854–1924), Jourawski (1821–1891), Bauschinger (1833–1893), von Tetmajer (1850–1905), and Jasinsky (1856–1899). These men and their contemporaries did a tremendous job of compiling, developing, and presenting the theories of the mechanics of materials and of structural analysis into substantially the same form as we know them today. Later in this book, as methods which were developed in this era are presented, the names of these men will be identified with some of their important contributions. One of the classical methods discussed here, the slope-deflection method, was developed in the early nineteen hundreds, Bendixen, Maney, and Ostenfeld being the major contributors to this development.

Since 1900, the modern era of structural engineering has been characterized by the following major developments:

1. The publication of a number of excellent books[1] dealing with the theories of elasticity, plasticity, buckling, plates and shells, and vibrations

2. The development of improved machines, instrumentation, and techniques for testing materials and structures, and the increased use of experimental structural analysis in research

3. The development of the moment-distribution method and the related, but generalized, relaxation procedure

4. The renewed interest in ultimate strength and plastic behavior of structures and structural elements and the incorporation of these ideas into structural design procedures

5. The application of the probability theory and statistical methods to a reevaluation of the probability of failure or the probability of inserviceability, and a comparison of these ideas with conventional "factors of safety"

6. The recent advent of the analog and digital electronic computers and the application of modern computational methods and procedures to structural analysis and design

---

[1] Among the fundamental theoretical books which have had a very important influence on the development of structural mechanics, analysis, and design in America in the last fifty years are: A. E. H. Love, "The Mathematical Theory of Elasticity," Cambridge University Press, London, 1892, 4th ed., 1927; A. Föppl and L. Föppl, "Drang und Zwang," R. Oldenburg-Verlag, Munich, 1920, 2d ed., 1928; H. Lorenz, "Technische Elastizitätslehre," R. Oldenburg-Verlag, Munich, 1913; A. Nádai, "Plasticity," McGraw-Hill Book Company, Inc., New York, 1931; S. P. Timoshenko, "Theory of Elasticity," McGraw-Hill Book Company, Inc., New York, 1934, 2d ed. with J. N. Goodier, 1951; S. P. Timoshenko, "Theory of Elastic Stability," McGraw-Hill Book Company, Inc., New York, 1936; S. Timoshenko, "Theory of Plates and Shells," McGraw-Hill Book Company, Inc., New York, 1940, 2d ed. with S. Woinowsky-Krieger, 1960; R. V. Southwell, "An Introduction to the Theory of Elasticity for Engineers and Physicists," Oxford University Press, London, 1936; I. S. Sokolnikoff, "Mathematical Theory of Elasticity," McGraw-Hill Book Company, Inc., New York, 1946; F. Bleich, "Buckling Strength of Metal Structures," McGraw-Hill Book Company, Inc., New York, 1952; W. Flügge, "Statik und Dynamik der Schalen," Springer-Verlag, Berlin, 1934; K. Girkmann, "Flächentragwerke," Springer-Verlag, Berlin, 1946, 4th ed., 1956.

7. The improved understanding of reinforced-concrete behavior, the development of precast and prestressed concrete, and the application of these ideas to design

8. The shell, panel, and stressed-skin construction developed primarily by the aeronautical structural engineers and the increased incorporation of these ideas into civil engineering structural design of not only metal structures but also concrete structures

9. The development of improved structural materials—steels, aluminum, plastics, concretes, processed woods, laminates, sandwiches, and ceramics

10. Last—but far from least—the continued and rapid development of new and improved construction equipment, methods, and techniques pertaining to the fabrication, transportation, erection, and maintenance of structures

Considering only the field of structural analysis, the moment-distribution method presented originally by the late Hardy Cross and the more general relaxation procedures sponsored by Prof. R. V. Southwell are without a doubt the most important contributions of the last fifty years. With the recent development of electronic computers and the rapidly expanding use of them for structural engineering problems, however, the future trends in the field of structural analysis and design are difficult to predict.   Classical methods of analysis which involved large numbers of simultaneous equations and, as a result, had been replaced by relaxation procedures now have become practical to apply with the aid of modern computers.   Under such influences, the relative importance of various computational approaches and techniques can change rapidly.   But this aspect is only one small facet of the demands for continued development of new and improved methods of analyzing structural behavior which will be of maximum assistance and guidance to the structural design engineer.

Modern society is faced with tremendous sociological, political, and economic problems and demands the maximum possible assistance of all its professions.   As its contribution, the structural engineering profession must continually strive to produce improved versions of conventional structures and, when necessary, to develop new structural types to satisfy the changing needs of society.

The Structural Engineering Project.   The structural engineer usually acts in a service capacity to the functional design engineer who normally provides the leadership in carrying out an engineering project. In the civil engineering field, he assists the transportation engineer, or the hydraulic engineer, or the sanitary engineer by providing the structures needed to implement their projects.   In building construction, he is one of the principal collaborators of the architect.   In a similar way, he assists mechanical, chemical, or electrical engineers in designing the heavy

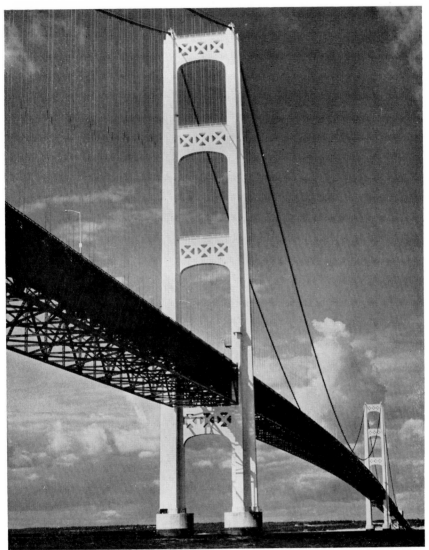

Figure F.4 Mackinac Straits bridge, Michigan. Longest suspension bridge, anchorage to anchorage, 8,614 ft; second longest main span, 3,800 ft (*Photograph furnished and reproduced by courtesy of the designer, Dr. D. B. Steinman, Consulting Engineer, New York*)

machinery or facilities required for their projects. He may shift his entire activity into naval architecture or aeronautical engineering and become a specialist in the design of ship or airplane structures. Today, as the new Space Age is developing, the structural engineer may be involved in providing special structures for launching or servicing space vehicles, or again he may use his knowledge in assisting with the structural design of the vehicle itself. Sometimes, of course, the structure itself may be the major feature of a project, and the structural engineer may provide the leadership for the undertaking, as, for example, in the case of a large bridge or dam, a wharf, or a large industrial facility.

A structural engineering project may be divided into three phases: planning, design, and construction.

The **planning phase** involves a consideration of the various requirements and factors which affect the general layout and dimensions of the structure and leads to the choice of one or perhaps several alternative types of structures, which offers the best general solution. The primary consideration is the function of the structure whether it is to enclose or house, to convey, or to support in space. Many secondary considerations are also involved, including esthetic, sociological, legal, financial, or economic. In addition, there are structural and constructional requirements and limitations which also may affect the structural type selected.

The **design phase** involves a detailed consideration of the alternative solutions evolved in the planning phase and leads to the most suitable proportions, dimensions, and details of the structural elements and connections for constructing each alternative structural arrangement being considered. Usually before the final design stage is reached the best solution has been identified, and final construction plans are prepared for this selection. Occasionally, the choice is dependent on economic and constructional features which cannot be accurately evaluated except by competitive bidding; so final bid plans have to be prepared for the competitive alternatives.

The **construction phase** involves procurement of materials, equipment, and personnel; shop fabrication of the members and subassemblies; transportation of them to the site; and the actual field construction and erection. During this phase, of course, some redesign may be required if unforeseen foundation difficulties develop, or if specified materials cannot be procured, or for any number of other reasons.

Philosophy of Structural Design. As defined above, *structural design* involves determining the most suitable proportions of a structure and dimensioning and detailing the structural elements and details of which it is composed. This is the most highly technical and mathematical phase of a structural engineering project, but it cannot—or certainly should not—be conducted without being fully coordinated with the planning and construction phases of the project. The successful designer is at all times fully conscious of the various considerations which were involved in the preliminary planning for the structure and, likewise, of the various problems which may later be involved in its construction.

Specifically the structural design of any structure first involves the establishment of the loading and other design conditions which must be resisted by the structure and therefore must be considered in its design; then comes the analysis (or computation) of the internal gross forces (thrust, shears, bending moments, and twisting moments), stress intensities, strains, deflections, and reactions produced by the loads, temperature, shrinkage, creep, or other design conditions; finally comes the proportioning and selection of materials of the members and connections so as to resist adequately the effects produced by the design conditions. The criteria used to judge whether particular proportions will result in the desired behavior reflect accumulated knowledge (theory, field and model tests, and practical experience), intuition, and judgment. For most common civil engineering structures such as bridges, buildings, etc., the usual practice is to design on the basis of a comparison of permissible stress intensities with those produced by the service loadings and other design conditions. This traditional basis for design is called **elastic design** since the permissible stress intensities are chosen in accordance with the concept that the stress or strain corresponding to the yield point of the material should not be exceeded at the most highly stressed points of the structure. Of course, the selection of the permissible stresses may also be modified by a consideration of the possibility of failure due to fatigue, buckling, or brittle fracture or by consideration of the permissible deflections of the structure.

Depending on the type of structure, the stress intensities computed for the assumed design conditions may or may not be in close agreement with the stress intensities produced in the structure by the actual conditions to which it is exposed. The degree of correspondence is not important, provided that the computed stress intensities can be interpreted in terms of previous experience. By the selection of the service conditions and the permissible stress intensities, a margin of safety against failure is provided. The selection of the magnitude of this margin depends on the degree of uncertainty regarding loading, analysis, design, materials, and construction and on the consequences of failure. For example, if a permissible tensile stress of 20,000 psi is selected for structural steel with a yield stress of 33,000 psi, the margin of safety (or factor of safety) provided against tensile yielding is 1.65 (i.e., 33,000/20,000).

There is a growing tendency in structural design to base the design on the ultimate strength of the structure. This approach goes under the name of **limit analysis or limit design** in reinforced-concrete-design literature and of **limit design or plastic design** in steel-design literature. When proportioning is done on this basis, the anticipated service loading is first multiplied by a suitable "load factor" (greater than 1), the magnitude of which depends upon the same considerations as enumerated above for the margin of safety. Sometimes, of course, the various separate contributions to the anticipated service loading are multiplied by different load factors, depending on the certainty with which the contribution is known, the frequency with which it acts on the structure, etc.   The structure is then proportioned so that, depending on the governing conditions, the increased load would (1) cause a fatigue failure, or (2) just produce yielding at one internal section (or simultaneous yielding at several sections), or (3) cause elastic-plastic displacement of the structure, or (4) cause the entire structure to be on the point of collapse.

Proponents of this latter approach argue that it results in a more realistic design with a more accurately provided margin of strength over the anticipated service conditions.   These improvements result from the fact that nonelastic and nonlinear effects which become significant in the vicinity of ultimate behavior of the structure may be accounted for.

In recent years, there has been a growing concern among many prominent engineers that not only is the term "factor of safety" improper and unrealistic, but worse still a structural design philosophy based on this concept leads in most cases to an unduly conservative and therefore uneconomical design, and in some cases to an unconservative design with too high a probability of failure.   They argue that there is no such thing as certainty, either of failure or of safety of a structure, but only a *probability* of failure or a *probability* of safety.   They feel therefore that the variations of the load effects and the variations of the structural resistance should be studied in a statistical manner and the probability of survival or the probability of serviceability of a structure estimated.[1] It may not be practical to apply this approach to the design of each individual structure.   However, it is believed to be practical to do so in framing design rules and regulations.   It is highly desirable that building codes and specifications plainly state the factors and corresponding probabilities that they imply.

Structural Materials.   Of course, the availability of suitable structural materials is one of the principal limitations on the accomplishments of an experienced structural engineer.   Early builders depended almost exclusively on wood, stone, brick, and concrete.   Although iron had been used by man at least since the building of the Egyptian pyramids, use of it as a structural material was limited because of the difficulties of smelting it in large quantities.   With the industrial revolution, however, came both the need for iron as a structural material and the capability of smelting it in quantity.

[1] A. L. Johnson, Strength, Safety and Economical Dimensions of Structures, *Royal Inst. Technol., Bull.* 12, *Div. Statistics and Structural Eng.*, Stockholm, 1953; A. M. Freudenthal, The Safety of Structures, *Trans. ASCE*, vol. 112, p. 125, 1947; A. M. Freudenthal, Reflections on Standard Specifications for Structural Design, *Trans. ASCE*, vol. 113, p. 269, 1948; A. M. Freudenthal, Safety and Probability of Structural Failure, *Trans. ASCE*, vol. 121, p. 1337, 1956; O. G. Julian, Synopsis of First Progress Report of Committee on Factors of Safety, *J. Structures Div., Proc. ASCE*, vol. 83, no. ST4, Paper 1316, July, 1957.

John Smeaton, the English civil engineer, was the first to use cast iron extensively as a structural engineer in the mid-eighteenth century; but another Englishman, Abraham Darby, constructed the first cast-iron bridge in 1776–1779, the Coalbrookdale arch bridge with semicircular cast-iron arches. Cast-iron girders were unreliable, and a number of fatigue and brittle failures occurred under heavy moving loads. Malleable iron was developed as a more reliable material and was widely used after 1841. Iron-plate girders were very commonly used for short-span bridges. Since suspension bridges were too flexible for long-span rail road bridges, it was necessary to develop a more rigid type of structure, and the malleable-iron tubular design was evolved for the famous Britannia and Conway tubular bridges built in England just prior to 1850. At about this same time, the development of iron-truss construction started in the United States, England, and Europe. Incidentally, the first iron chain suspension bridge had been built in England in 1741.

Whereas malleable iron was superior to cast iron, there were still too many structural failures and there was a need for a more reliable material. Steel was the answer to this demand. The invention of the Bessemer converter in 1856 and the subsequent development of the Siemens-Martin open-hearth process for making steel made it possible to produce structural steel at competitive prices and triggered the tremendous developments and accomplishments in the use of structural steel during the last hundred years.

Ordinary structural carbon steel is almost a perfect structural material. It can be manufactured reliably and economically and rolled into a large variety of suitable shapes and sizes. It can be fabricated and erected by a number of techniques and procedures without changing its physical properties appreciably. It has essentially the same strength in tension or compression. Up to over half of its strength, it behaves in a linearly elastic manner, and over this range it exhibits a high modulus of elasticity. At the end of this initial range of high stiffness, the steel will yield at constant stress for a strain of $1\frac{1}{2}$ to 2 per cent, thereby allowing stresses to equalize themselves at locations where loading or fabrication or erection has caused high stress concentrations. Following this yield range, the material regains some of its original stiffness—a small fraction, true, but enough to arrest sufficiently the rate of increase in deflection in many cases. Before actual fracture occurs in a tensile test, the specimen will have stretched 15 to 25 per cent of its original length. Refer to Fig. F.5 for the stress-strain diagrams of various materials.

Structural silicon steel exhibits similar characteristics to structural carbon steel, and in addition has about 50 per cent more strength. Since its price per pound is only slightly higher than carbon steel, this alloy is widely used in long-span structures. Silicon steel is not available in all sizes and shapes, and compared with structural carbon steel there is a somewhat greater variation in its physical properties. Nickel steel, manganese steels, heat-treated steels, and other special steels are also available—usually marketed under the proprietary brands and specifications of the manufacturer.

Figure F.5 Stress-strain diagrams for various materials

The most serious disadvantage of steel is that it oxidizes easily and must be protected by paint or by some other suitable coating. When steel is used in an enclosure where a fire could occur, the steel members must be encased by a suitable fire-resistant enclosure such as masonry, concrete, vermiculite concrete, etc. Normally, steel members will not fail in a brittle manner unless an unfortunate combination of metallurgical composition, low temperature, and bi- or triaxial stresses exists.[1]

[1] Brittle fracture of steel is a question which is not fully solved even though its mechanics are fairly well outlined. For an excellent summary of the status of knowledge in this field, see M. E. Shank (ed.), "Control of Steel Construction to Avoid Brittle Failure," Plasticity Committee of Welding Research Council, New York, 1957.

Structural aluminum is still not widely used in civil engineering structures, though its use is steadily increasing. By a proper selection of the aluminum alloy and its heat-treatment, a wide variety of strength characteristics may be obtained. Some of the alloys exhibit stress-strain characteristics similar to structural steel, except that the modulus of elasticity for the initial linearly elastic portion is about 10,000,000 psi, or about one-third that of steel. Lightness and resistance to oxidation are of course two of the major advantages of aluminum. Because its properties are very sensitive to its heat-treatment, care must be used when riveting or welding aluminum. In recent years, several very exciting techniques have been developed for prefabricating aluminum subassemblies which can be readily erected and bolted together in the field to form a number of beautiful and well-designed shell structures. This general procedure of prefabrication and field assembly by bolting seems to be the most promising way of utilizing structural aluminum.

Reinforced and prestressed concrete share with structural steel the position of the most important civil engineering structural material. Natural cement concretes have been used for centuries. Modern concrete construction dates from the middle of the nineteenth century, though artificial portland cement was patented by Aspidin, an Englishman, about 1825. Although several builders and engineers experimented with the use of steel-reinforced concrete in the last half of the nineteenth century, its dominant use as a building material dates from the early decades of this present century. The last quarter century has seen the rapid and vigorous development of prestressed-concrete design and construction, founded largely on early work by Freyssinet in France and Magnel in Belgium.

Plain (unreinforced) concrete not only is a heterogeneous material but has one very serious defect as a structural material, namely, its very limited tensile strength, which is only of the order of one-tenth its compressive strength. Not only is tensile failure in concrete of a brittle type, but likewise compression failure occurs in a relatively brittle fashion without being preceded by the forewarning of large deformations. (Of course, in reinforced-concrete construction, ductile behavior can be obtained by proper selection and arrangement of the reinforcement.) Unless proper care is used in the selection of aggregates, and in the mixing and placing of concrete, frost action can cause serious damage to concrete masonry. Concrete creeps under long-term loading to a degree which must be considered carefully in selecting the design stress conditions. During the curing process and its early life, concrete shrinks a significant amount, which to a degree can be controlled by properly proportioning the mix and utilizing suitable construction techniques.

With all these potentially serious disadvantages, engineers have learned to design and build beautiful, durable, and economical reinforced-concrete structures for practically all kinds of structural requirements. This has been accomplished by careful selection of the design dimensions and the arrangement of the steel reinforcement, development of proper cements, selection of proper aggregates and mix proportions, careful control of mixing, placing, and curing techniques, and imaginative development of construction methods, equipment, and procedures.

The versatility of concrete, the wide availability of its component materials, the unique ease of shaping its form to meet the strength and functional requirements involved, together with the exciting potential of further improvements and developments of not only the new prestressed and precast concrete construction but also the conventional reinforced-concrete construction, combine to make concrete a strong competitor of other materials in a very large fraction of structures contemplated for the future. The use of precast-concrete elements which can be produced under carefully controlled plant conditions and then assembled in the field using prestressing techniques is bound to expand tremendously, particularly in this country with its high ratio of labor to material costs.

Wood of course was the only material used by early builders which had more or less equal tensile and compressive strength. Wood is characterized by its nonhomogeneity due to its grain, knots, and other defects; by its anisotropic strength properties parallel and perpendicular to its grain; and by its poor durability due largely to its susceptibility to variations in humidity and moisture and to attack by bacteria, fungi, and insects. While its tensile and compressive strength is much less perpendicular than parallel to the grain, the most serious aspect of its anisotropic strength characteristics is its much smaller shear resistance parallel to the fibers than transverse to them. Wood also exhibits considerably lower strength under long-duration loadings. Wood deforms considerably under load, exhibiting essentially linear stress-strain characteristics at low stresses with a modulus of elasticity of about half that of concrete (and about a twentieth that of steel). Compression failures are not abrupt, but tension failures are—less so than concrete, however. The design of wood structures must allow properly for dimensional changes caused by temperature and moisture variations. The major design problem, however, is providing adequate, dependable, and practical connections.

In modern times, with the increased use of steel and reinforced-concrete construction, wood was relegated largely to accessory use during construction, to use in temporary and secondary structures, and to use for secondary members of permanent construction. Modern technology in the last thirty-odd years has revitalized wood as a structural material, however, by developing vastly improved timber connectors, various treatments to increase the durability of wood, and laminated wood made of thin layers bonded together with synthetic glues using revolutionary gluing techniques. Plywood with essentially nondirectional strength properties is the most widely used laminated wood, but techniques have also been developed for building large laminated-wood members which for certain structures are competitive with concrete and steel.

Last to be discussed here, but far from least as far as future possibilities are concerned, are the engineering plastics[1] and the exotic metals[2] such as beryllium, tungsten, tantalum, molybdenum, chromium, vanadium, and niobium. There are many different plastics available, and the mechanical properties exhibited by this group of materials vary over a wide range which encompasses the range of properties available among the more commonly used structural materials. Thus in many specific design applications it is possible to select a suitable plastic material for an alternative design. Experience with the use of plastics outdoors is limited. Generally speaking, however, plastics must be protected from the weather. This aspect of design is therefore a major consideration in the use of plastics for primary structural elements. One of the most promising potential uses of plastics is for panel and shell-type structures. Laminated or sandwich panels have been used in such structures with encouraging results which indicate an increased use in this type of construction in the future.

Perhaps the exotic metals will never be widely used and competitive with steel and aluminum for terrestrial structures. These materials are currently being developed for use in long-range missiles and in space vehicles. Whereas a few years ago the idea of building structures on the moon, in space, or on other planets appeared fantastic, the Space Age *is here* and we may expect the actual building of a lunar base within 5 to 10 years. Environmental conditions of space structures cannot be accurately defined at the present time, but present knowledge definitely indicates that new metallic materials such as beryllium alloys will be needed for space structures.[3]

Modes of Structural Failure and Inadequacy. The most obvious mode of failure of a structure is collapse due to insufficient strength to resist the loads and other effects imposed on it. In addition, however, a structure may be unserviceable because of its stiffness and vibrational characteristics. For example, a structure may be so flexible that sensitive equipment or machinery supported by it cannot operate satisfac-

---

[1] For summary of engineering properties of currently available plastics, see C. H. Adams, Plastics: Engineering Materials, *J. Eng. Mech. Div.*, ASCE, Paper 1072, October, 1956.

[2] See S. L. Hoyt, Metal Properties, "ASME Handbook," 1954; and H. R. Ogden, Future Metals, *Chem. Eng. Progr.*, vol. 54, no. 11, November, 1958.

[3] R. Szilard, Structures for the Moon, *Civil Eng.*, October, 1959, pp. 46–49.

torily, or so flexible that unsightly cracks develop in plaster or other superficial finishes, or so flexible that many people using the structure are disturbed by its movement or by the visual appearance of its deflected shape. On the other hand, the structure may have vibrational characteristics which are poorly matched to the frequency of the dynamic loads acting on it.

Collapse of a structure may be triggered by any of the following modes of failure: rupture or plastic deformation of the material in a ductile manner, rupture of the material in a brittle manner, buckling, or fatigue of the material.

Seldom is the collapse of a structure triggered by rupture of the material in a ductile manner, since such rupture is preceded by such large strains that excessive deflections would become apparent. Under normal types of loading, there would therefore be opportunities to relieve the structure either by unloading it partially or by shoring it or strengthening it temporarily. Of course, in catastrophic situations—such as earthquakes, windstorms, floods, fires, and bomb blasts—there is no opportunity to relieve the structure and collapse could be triggered by ductile rupture or excessive plastic deflection. Many collapsed structures show evidence of ductile rupture or excessive plastic deformation at a number of points, but these usually have developed during the collapsing process and did not trigger the failure.

Brittle fracture is much more likely to trigger the collapse of a structure than ductile fracture. Certain steels (and perhaps other alloyed metals), depending upon their metallurgical composition and manufacture and upon the minimum temperature of their environment, may be susceptible to this type of failure. This is particularly so if the member is designed and detailed so that at the location of potential failure a pronounced bi- or triaxial stress condition exists, thereby inhibiting plastic flow and permitting a cleavage type of fracture to occur. In reinforced-concrete structures, a brittle behavior can occur when portions are over reinforced and the compressive strength of the concrete is reached before significant yielding occurs in the tensile steel. In such cases if the compression steel and stirrups are not detailed so as to prevent cracking off of large chunks of the compression zone, the member may fail in a precipitous brittle manner. Such behavior may also occur if the diagonal tension reinforcement is inadequate.

In civil engineering structures where the dominant loading is usually substantially static, the most common cause of collapse is a buckling failure. Buckling may occur locally in a manner that may or may not trigger collapse of the entire structure, such as in outstanding flanges, or in flange or web plates of compression members, or in the web or compression flange of girders, etc. Compression members or beams may buckle as individual members, or structures as a whole may buckle. Occasionally in civil engineering structures, the buckling is an *elastic buckling* wherein the portion recovers its original shape if unloaded. Such buckling resistance depends on the elastic flexural rigidity and the unsupported length (or sometimes the width) of the portion, but not on the stress intensities involved.   More often, however, because of the slenderness ratios commonly used, *plastic buckling* is involved wherein the member or portions of it are stressed beyond the proportional limit of the material.   Then, the stress intensities are a significant factor in the behavior, because the strain and flexural rigidity beyond the proportional limit depend upon the value of the stress.   Sometimes, when elastic buckling occurs, the load on the portion is relieved as a result of the buckling displacements.   In other cases, however, such relief does not occur, and under continued action of the load additional deflections are developed which may involve substantial plastic deformation and subsequent collapse of the structure.

Fatigue failures seldom occur in conventional civil engineering structures.   When heavy dynamic loads or severe vibrations are involved, however, the possibility of fatigue failure must be considered.   Elastic fatigue failures are of a brittle type, symptoms of which can be detected only by refined inspection techniques.   So-called plastic fatigue can also occur, though it is rare.   This is the phenomenon involved when one breaks a wire or nail by bending it into the plastic region, first in one direction and then the other.   Obviously, it is seldom that a civil engineering structure is subjected to large reversible loadings which could cause this type of failure.   Such possibilities should be recognized and considered, however.

The structural engineer must therefore design his structures so as to obtain a suitable improbability that they will collapse or become unserviceable.   He must be prepared to analyze the behavior of the various structural forms which he uses so as to estimate the possibilities of collapse or poor performance under the loading and environment to which they are subjected.   If the theory is inadequate for such predictions, he must make his evaluations and design decisions on the basis of his experience and model and/or field tests.

Structural Forms.   The most important design decision made by a structural engineer is the selection of the most suitable structural form to satisfy the various requirements and objectives of a particular project. Most often, he is not able to identify immediately *the* best solution, and he must continue to consider several alternative structural types throughout the planning and design phases of the project until he is able to identify the best of the alternatives.   The most suitable structural form is the one which satisfies the functional, economic, sociological, aesthetic, and other requirements to the highest degree and which may be economically and reliably built using the structural materials and construction methods which are the most appropriate of those which are available or can be devised.

Structural forms may be classified as being of one of the two following types according to the dominant stress condition developed under their most important design loads and conditions:

1. **Uniform—stress forms** in which the stress is uniform over the depth of a member, or over the thickness of a panel as, for example, cables, arches, truss members, membranes, shells, etc.

2. **Varying—stress forms** in which the stress varies over the depth or thickness, usually from a maximum tensile stress at one surface to a maximum compressive stress at the other as, for example, beams, rigid frames, slabs, plates, etc.

Obviously uniform-stress forms utilize the available strength of material more efficiently than the varying-stress forms in which under elastic conditions the material between the outside faces is understressed except in regions where there are high shear stresses. Where functional requirements permit, therefore, the structural designer tries to use a uniform-stress form. Of course, sometimes the fabrication and/or construction difficulties involved in achieving the desired shape for the structure cost more than the material saved through its more efficient use, so that over-all economy cannot be realized.

Steel cable structures illustrate a very efficient structural form. Cables are almost perfectly flexible, that is, they may be assumed to have no flexural strength and, therefore, *must* carry their loads by simple tension. As a result, they must adjust their shape to conform to the equilibrium polygon of the loads applied to them (see Chap. 10). This adjustment in shape is a significant geometrical change in shape, not simply the small deflections resulting from the stress-strain characteristics of deformable bodies. As shown by the solid-line position in Fig. F.6a, a cable has the shape of a catenary under its own dead weight. If a large load P (compared with its own weight) is now imposed on the cable, it shifts its shape markedly to the dashed-line position which is substantially two straight line segments. On the other hand, as shown in Fig. F.6b, a load P small compared with the weight of the cable would require only a very small change in shape of the cable if it were applied. The principle is clear, however, from a consideration of the equilibrium of a small portion of the cable: the only two ways a cable can maintain simultaneously both vertical and horizontal equilibrium are (1) to change its tension and (2) to adjust its slope (i.e., its shape). In other words, *one* unknown (the cable tension) cannot in general satisfy *two* equations simultaneously—two unknowns (the cable tension and cable slope) are required to do so. If for functional reasons substantial changes in shape of cable structures cannot be tolerated, a stiffening truss, as illustrated in Fig. F.6d, must be connected to the cable to distribute large concentrated loadings.

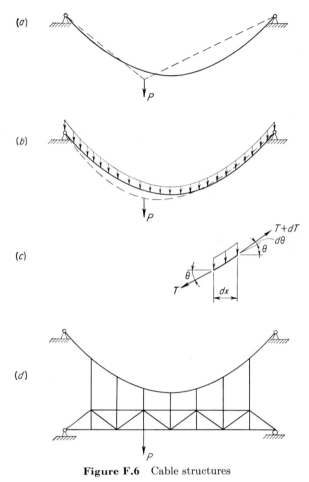

Figure F.6 Cable structures

A **flexible membrane** such as shown in Fig. F.7a at first glance seems to be the same as a large number of cables side by side, and it *would* be essentially this situation if the curved edges of this cylindrical membrane were unsupported. However, the generation of shear stresses between adjacent cable elements constitutes a very important difference between the cable and the membrane, which becomes apparent from a consideration of the equilibrium of a differential element of the membrane shown in Fig. F.7b. In the case of the differential element of the membrane, there are *three* equilibrium conditions which must be satisfied—summation of forces in the longitudinal, the circumferential, and the radial directions must each equal zero—compared with only *two* conditions in the case of the cable. Note, however, that there are *three* forces N_l, N_ϕ, and $N_{\phi l}$ in the case of the membrane which by incremental changes in their values can satisfy these *three* equilibrium equations for the element *without* the necessity of changing its shape beyond the small strains or deformations associated with its stresses. This characteristic of the

Figure F.7 Cylindrical membrane

three-dimensional membrane surface makes it essentially different structurally from the two-dimensional cable. Such surfaces are true uniform-stress structural forms which are structurally stable and adequate and capable of supporting distributed loadings with no changes of shape except the small deflections associated with the deformation of the material. Of course, concentrated loadings on a flexible membrane—being discontinuities in the loading—can be supported only by violent localized changes of shape of the membrane similar to those changes required of a cable.

An **arch,** such as shown in Fig. F.8a, is somewhat like an inverted cable provided that its shape conforms to the equilibrium polygon for the loading imposed on it. Even though the arch, unlike the flexible cable, possesses flexural stiffness and strength, it would carry such a loading essentially with a uniform stress condition over each cross section and no flexure. Now, as shown in Fig. F.8b, if a completely different loading is applied to this arch, the arch tries to change its shape—just as a cable—to that of the equilibrium polygon for the new system of loading. Because of its flexural stiffness, however, it cannot change its shape without bending. As a result, therefore, it bends and changes its shape slightly— sufficiently, in fact, so that a varying-stress condition is developed in the

(*a*) Shape of arch axis selected to coincide with
shape of equilibrium polygon for applied loading

(*b*) Arch of same shape as (*a*) but subjected to
different loading, which causes arch axis to
bend into shape something like exaggeration
shown by dashed line

Figure F.8   Two-hinged arch

arch whereby the arch carries the load partly by flexural stresses and partly by thrust. That is, the arch thrust cannot in general satisfy both horizontal and vertical equilibrium without the assistance of bending stresses and the transverse shear stresses associated with them. Of course, the one case where an arch does not bend materially is for the loading with an equilibrium polygon of the same shape as the arch.

From a design standpoint, the arch form may be an economical solution for cases where there is one predominant loading condition, the equilibrium polygon of which is used to define the shape of the arch.

For this loading, the arch acts substantially as a uniform-stress structural form; for other loadings which may be relatively less important and infrequently applied, the arch acts satisfactorily, but less efficiently, as a varying-stress structural form.

The **shell** is to the membrane as the arch is to the cable. That is, a shell is a membrane which has flexural stiffness and strength, just as an arch is related in the same way to a cable. Most often, civil engineering shells are the inverts of shapes such as shown in Fig. F.7a so that they carry their loads primarily by compressive rather than tensile stresses and are often made of reinforced concrete as a result. A shell which was the invert of the membrane shown in Fig. F.7a would act distinctly differently than a series of arches side by side for exactly the same reason that a membrane would act differently than a series of cables as discussed above.

The shell even though it may have flexural stiffness and strength possesses the basic structural stability and adequacy of its corresponding membrane shape as far as satisfying equilibrium requirements is concerned. That is, the *three* membrane forces available in the shell—N_l, N_ϕ, and $N_{\phi l}$—can satisfy the *three* equations of equilibrium without the assistance of bending stresses. As a result, as long as the loading is distributed, it carries the loading primarily by a membrane type of stress condition even though the shape of the shell may not correspond to the shape of the equilibrium surface for the loading involved. Because of the slight tendency of the membrane surface to deform and, hence, change shape, some slight secondary bending is induced. Only adjacent to the supports, however, where it is usually impossible to supply exactly the supporting forces required by the membrane stresses, do significant flexural stresses develop. Of course, if concentrated loadings or abruptly varying distributed loadings are applied to the shell, large localized flexural stresses are developed in the shell just as violent changes in shape occur in membranes under such conditions. Bending also occurs adjacent to abrupt changes in shell thickness or shape.

Another very important uniform-stress structural form is the **planar truss** (or **planar framework**). Of course, a single concentrated load P could be supported by the two-member arch form shown in Fig. F.9a, the axis of which conforms to the shape of the equilibrium polygon for such a load. If, however, the foundations were not suitable to provide the necessary horizontal reactions H, this resistance could be provided at both a and c by a tensile force H in the third member ac added as shown in Fig. F.9b to form, with the other two, a simple triangular truss. Additional concentrated loads at d and e could be supported as shown in Fig. F.9c by using two bars to connect each of these joints in turn to the framework already formed. It is quite apparent that such an arrangement permits the members to support a system of joint loads by uniform-stress conditions in each of the members—equivalent to tensile forces in some members and to compressive forces in others.   If the load system to be supported does not lie in a plane but is three-dimensional in character, a suitable **space framework** can be arranged to connect the points of loading by starting with a tetrahedronal nucleus consisting of four

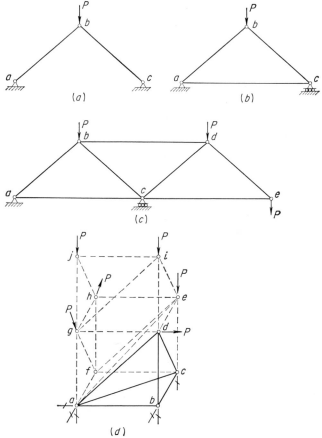

Figure F.9   Planar and space frameworks

joints and six bars, as shown by the heavy lines in Fig. F.9d.   Three bars are used to connect each additional joint to the framework.

In Fig. F.9, the encircled joints indicate frictionless pin joints for the planar truss (or planar framework) and ball joints for the space framework.   Such joints are all that is needed for structural adequacy.   Actually it is convenient and economical in modern truss fabrication and erection to use essentially rigid joint connections, using rivets, bolts, or welds. Doing so actually prevents the framework from carrying its loads by purely axial forces in its members. This is apparent when one considers that the members of an idealized pin- or ball-jointed framework change their lengths slightly in developing their axial forces. As a result, the angles between the members change slightly as there is displacement of the joints consistent with these changes of length in the members. If the members are rigidly connected together, however, at the joints, the angle changes cannot occur and slight bending of the members is necessary to accommodate the joint displacements. In a well-designed truss, the stresses associated with this flexure of the members are small compared with the uniform axial stresses and are, therefore, in fact, referred to as *secondary stresses*.

It is interesting to note that in a sense rigid-jointed frameworks are very closely related to shell structures. Basically they want to belong to the uniform-stress family and try to act as pin- or ball-jointed frameworks, but because of their deformation they cannot do so exactly and thereby induce some nominal amount of flexure. Basically, shells want to act as membranes, but because of their flexural stiffness and the support arrangement along their boundaries they cannot deform as membranes and thereby induce flexural action which is usually of secondary importance except in the region adjacent to the edges.

It should also be noted that frameworks cannot be loaded directly on their members between joints without developing large flexural stresses in the members so loaded and in other nearby members connected to them. In other words, trusses prefer concentrated joint loadings, not distributed loadings; but conversely, shells and membranes prefer distributed loadings, not concentrated loadings.

Very often for reasons based on considerations of function, economy, or construction, varying-stress structural forms such as **beams, frames, plates,** and **slabs** are used, particularly in bridge and building design. The relative inefficiency of such forms in the utilization of the potential strength of all the material may be minimized by the selection of proper proportions for the cross sections of such members. For example, in the hypothetical case of pure bending shown in Fig. F.10a, all the material could be divided between the two flanges since, there being no shear, no web is required. In actual situations, of course, both bending and shear are involved and web material is needed as shown in Fig. F.10b. As a result, manufacturers of rolled-steel and aluminum beams have developed a number of series of standard I and W (wide flange) beam sections which in many practical situations result in quite efficient use of material at least at the *most critical cross sections*. In recent years, considerable attention has been given to the fact that, because of the inefficient use of material in flexural members, many beam and frame structures possess considerable load-carrying capacity beyond the loading which develops the yield stress at the most highly stressed point. Ductile structures made of structural steel or reinforced concrete may be subjected to further loading which simply produces plastic deformation at locations where yield stresses have already been reached, while mobilizing the full strength of less critical locations. Considerations and utilizations of such behavior are variously labeled ultimate strength design, limit design, or plastic design, as mentioned previously.

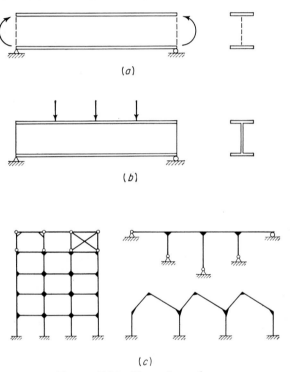

Figure F.10   Flexural members

Of course, many heavily loaded long-span beams exceed the capacity of the standard rolled-metal sections. In such cases, the required flexural strengths are obtained by designing special built-up sections out of plates, angles, and other standard shapes, these elements being connected together by rivets, bolts, or welds. Much more consideration could, and perhaps should, be given to the evolution of beam sections of reinforced concrete, wood, and other materials. Space limits the present discussion, and the reader is referred to standard textbooks on structural design for such information.

Sometimes beams are cantilevered or end-supported, as shown in Fig. F.10a, b. More often in modern construction, however, they are continuous over several intermediate supports or are connected to other members to form so-called **framed structures.** Everyone sees daily numerous examples of the almost infinite variety of configurations used in frame construction, some of which are indicated by the line diagrams in Fig. F.10c. Almost always these framed structures are three-dimensional assemblages of members, though often planar portions may be isolated, as depicted in the figure, for purposes of design and analysis. Sometimes the joints of these frames are detailed using rivets, bolts, and welds so as to be substantially *rigid* so that the ends of all members connected must not only translate but also rotate essentially identical

Figure F.11   Plate behavior

amounts. Sometimes lighter connections are provided which are only *semirigid*. Rarely are the members actually pinned together at the joints, but sometimes the riveted or bolted joint details are so *flexible* that they transmit only negligible moments through the connection. In such cases, it may be necessary to add knee braces or diagonal bracing, as shown in the top story of the frame in Fig. F.10c, in order to stabilize the frame.

The members of framed structures are primarily flexural members subjected principally to bending moment and shear. In addition, the members are subjected to axial forces though these are not large except in members such as the vertical columns of these frames.

The last varying-stress form to be considered is the **slab** or **plate element.** The structural behavior of a plate may be visualized as being similar to that of two layers of beam strips, each layer consisting of strips which are cemented together side by side. The layers are then oriented so that the directions of the strips are perpendicular as the layers are placed one on top of the other, as shown in Fig. F.11. If the edges of such a plate are supported and it is then subjected to a transverse (i.e., vertical) loading, both layers will collaborate in resisting the load, each layer bending and transmitting the load into the pair of edge supports at the ends of its beam strips. (It should be noted that, for the visualized behavior to be correct, the thickness of each layer should be considered to be equal to the full thickness of the plate.) It is of interest to consider the behavior of a relatively long and narrow plate in terms of the beam-strip-layer analogy. In such a case, the layer with the long beam strips will be much less stiff than the layer with the short beam strips spanning in the narrow direction. As a result, most of the load is carried by the short beam strips, with practically no two-way plate action involved. In other words, to benefit significantly from two-way plate action, the length-width ratio of the plate should be 2 or less.

Analysis of Structural Behavior. One of the important assets of a structural engineer is his ability to analyze mathematically the behavior of a proposed structure for the specified design conditions. If he has available a theory which is correlated with and corroborated by laboratory and field experimentation, and by observed performance of existing structures, he then has a logical and rational basis for extrapolating his current knowledge and previous experience to new situations. Of course, when no theory is available, the successful engineer is prepared to use a combination of model and field experimentation, previous experience, judgment, and intuition to guide him in arriving at his design.

The structural engineer should be able to analyze[1] three basic aspects of structural behavior:

1. Stress, strain, and deflection characteristics under static or quasi-static loading or deformation conditions
2. Response and vibrational characteristics under dynamic loading conditions
3. Buckling characteristics usually under static loading conditions, but occasionally under dynamic loading conditions

In each of these respects, he must compare the limiting capabilities of the structure for each of the potential modes of failure which obtain, with the corresponding behavior of the structure for the design conditions.

Obviously, categorizing these aspects of structural behavior in this manner is somewhat arbitrary. It could be argued that aspects 2 and 3 would actually be included in 1 if dynamic loading conditions were

---

[1] The analysis of the stress, strain, and deflection characteristics of structural behavior is referred to as **structural analysis.** The analysis of simply the internal force and stress condition in a structure is referred to as **stress analysis.**

included in the description of 1—and this is true. However, analysis of aspects 2 and 3 requires specialized techniques beyond those used for 1; so it seems desirable to consider these aspects separately. Moreover, civil engineering structures must usually be designed so that there is sufficient improbability of brittle or ductile failure associated with the behavioral characteristics categorized under 1 and so that there is an *even greater* improbability of fatigue or unsuitable vibrational properties or of buckling failure associated with the behavioral characteristics categorized under 2 and 3, respectively.

Analysis of buckling and vibrational characteristics is beyond the scope of the present discussion, which will be focused on the analysis of the stress, strain, and deflection characteristics of a structure when it is subjected to static or quasi-static loading or deformation conditions. To solve such a problem completely it is necessary to obtain the unknown stresses and displacements throughout the structure so as to satisfy the governing equations and the known force and displacement conditions on the boundaries. These unknowns may be obtained by formulating a suitable number of independent equations which are obtained from the three following types of relations or conditions which govern the behavior of the structure:

1. Conditions for static equilibrium of the internal and external forces (and couples) acting on the structure
2. Relations between stress and strain of the material involved
3. Geometrical relations between strains and displacements of points on the structure

Of course, it is easy to combine relations 2 and 3 so as to eliminate the strains and obtain thereby direct relations between the stresses (or internal forces) and the displacements. Some analysts may therefore prefer to say that there are only two types of relations involved, namely:

1. Conditions for static equilibrium
2, 3. Relations between stresses (or internal forces) and displacements

It really makes no difference which point of view is preferred since in either case one of two basic approaches may be used to formulate the solution of the problem.

The two basic approaches are the *force*[1] *method* and the *displacement*[1] *method*, which may be described as follows. These approaches are described in a generalized fashion as they would apply to a *member*-type *structure*.[2]

---

[1] In these instances, the terms *force* and *displacement* are used in a generalized sense. *Force* may be interpreted to refer to either a force or a couple. *Displacement* may be interpreted to refer to either a lineal or a rotational displacement.

[2] For purposes of analysis, a structure may usually be classified as being either a

1. *Force Method*

    a. First, the number of independent unknown forces (both external and internal) is established and compared with the number of independent equations of static equilibrium which may be written involving these unknowns. If the number of unknown forces is identical to the number of equilibrium equations, the problem is said to be *statically determinate* since the unknown forces can be determined directly from these equilibrium equations. If, however, the number of unknown forces exceeds the number of equilibrium equations, the problem is said to be *statically indeterminate* to a degree equal to this excess. In such a case, a number of the unknown forces equal to the degree of indeterminancy are designated as *redundant forces* and imagined to be removed as restraints on the actual structure to obtain a statically determinate (and stable) residual structure, called the *primary structure*. One equation may be written for each redundant force in which the displacement of its point of application on the primary structure is expressed in terms of the known forces and the unknown redundant forces. These equations may then be solved simultaneously for the unknown redundants.

    b. Once all the forces acting on the primary structure have been determined, the stresses can be computed throughout. Then the structural analysis can be easily completed by computing the strains from the stress-strain relations and the displacements using either the stress-displacement relations or the strain-displacement relations.

---

member structure or a *panel structure*, though occasionally it is a mixture of these two types.

    1. A **member structure** consists of one or more members which are connected in some manner at their ends, and then the whole assemblage is supported in some fashion at certain discrete locations. Each member of such a structure is relatively long compared with its cross-sectional dimensions. The equilibrium or displacement conditions of a member structure may be defined by a certain number of algebraic equations involving the loads and reactions, the independent force components in the members, and/or the independent displacement components of the joints.

    2. A **panel structure** consists of one or more panels which are connected together continuously along their edges or sizable portions thereof. The assemblage may be supported either at discrete points, or continuously over sizable areas, or along lines of considerable length. Each panel of such a structure may be either flat or curved, but of a thickness which is small compared with the length of its edges. The equilibrium or displacement conditions of a panel structure may be defined by a certain number of partial differential equations which involve continuous functions defining the internal stresses and the displacements throughout the structure. The solution of these equations must satisfy any prescribed condition regarding the external forces or displacements on the boundaries of the structure.

2. *Displacement Method*

    a. First, the independent unknown displacement components involved in the structure are identified and considered as the basic unknowns involved in the problem. The internal forces in the structure may then be expressed in terms of these unknown displacements, using the stress-displacement relations. For each unknown displacement component, a corresponding equilibrium equation may be written in terms of known external forces and the unknown internal forces which have been expressed in terms of the displacements. These equations, equal in number to the unknown displacements, may then be solved simultaneously for their values.

    b. Once the displacements have been determined, the internal forces may be back-figured. Thus all the forces will have been computed except the unknown external forces, and these may easily be computed by using the remaining equilibrium equations which were not used initially in setting up the equations for the solution of the unknown displacement components.

Most of the methods of structural analysis that have evolved over the years are classified as force methods. The slope-deflection method and Castigliano's first theorem, to be discussed later in Chaps. 12 and 13, are both displacement methods, however.

Whether a force method or a displacement method is a more efficient method depends on several considerations. Up to the present time, force methods have been much more widely used in the field of civil engineering structures for a number of reasons. First it should be noted that in most cases a complete structural analysis of stresses and also displacements of all points of the structure has not been necessary for design purposes. A complete picture of the stresses has been needed, but only a few representative deflections have been computed. In addition, many civil engineering structures are substantially statically determinate; or if they are statically indeterminate, the degree of indeterminacy is considerably less than the number of unknown displacement components. There are of course certain structures such as many rigid frames where there are fewer unknown displacement components than the degree of indeterminacy. In such cases, the slope-deflection method (that is, one of the displacement methods) has been the preferred classical method of solution. What the future may portend with regard to preferred methods of structural analysis will be discussed further in the next section.

There is one more very important truism which should be recognized regarding analysis of structural behavior. The majority of the actual structures which must be designed by the structural engineer are not susceptible to precise analysis. This is particularly true of structures involving complicated space frames and frameworks, slabs, shear walls, and shells. In such cases, several idealized and simplified versions of the actual structure are analyzed rather extensively to furnish a basis for designing the actual prototype. Where there is a backlog of experience with a particular type of structure, such simplifications are justified and provide a satisfactory basis for a new design when tempered by the judgment and intuition of an intelligent and experienced engineer.

When appraising the results of his analysis, the engineer must never forget that the results must satisfy the equilibrium requirements. To be "exact," the results must also satisfy the stress-displacement relations. A structure designed on the basis of an analysis which satisfies statics, but only approximately satisfies the stress-strain relations, will seldom be in serious trouble provided that the designer has been conservative with respect to satisfying buckling and vibrational requirements and has detailed the structure so that it is not susceptible to brittle failure. A structure so designed may deflect somewhat more and in a different manner than really desired. It may even crack or develop plastic deformations at lower loads than anticipated from the analysis. But, if an avenue is provided with sufficient strength to satisfy static equilibrium for the ultimate loading, given sufficient ductility and buckling resistance the structure will mobilize the strength provided before it collapses.

Computational Procedures. The advent of the modern analog and digital computers has already had a significant effect on the practice of structural engineering. The extent to which these computing aids will affect the future of structural engineering is difficult to predict. Certainly they will have a tremendous effect, and they could revolutionize present practice.

When considering the potential impact of modern computers, one must recognize that the development of structural analysis until very recently has taken place in the context of hand-computation techniques (logarithms, slide rules, and desk calculators). As a result, methods which involved extensive computation (such as the solution of large numbers of simultaneous equations) were impractical to apply except for unusual or very important situations encountered in practice. Approximate methods and procedures were developed to handle common problems. Relaxation methods and other successive-approximation techniques were developed to obtain answers which converged on the solution to problems which, when solved by classical methods, involved large numbers of simultaneous equations. In fact, the most significant developments of the last thirty years have been in this latter category.

Now, however, with the availability of the "automatic" electronic computers the engineer has the assistance of computing aids which are several *orders* of magnitude faster than those he had previously. Obviously, even if new methods of analysis and design are not developed, he immediately realizes certain benefits. By using these machines, the cost of computations is reduced to a small fraction (one-quarter is often quoted) of the cost of manual computation. This saving permits the engineer to do more professional engineering and less subprofessional computation. As a result, he is able to refine and optimize his designs. Even more important, he is able to consider potential designs which previously he was unable to analyze or able to do so only very crudely. If the structural engineer does no more than reap these obvious benefits, he will fall far short of achieving the full potential benefits which the electronic computers almost certainly make available to him.

The challenge here is to develop *completely new* methods of structural analysis and design which most efficiently use the full computational capacity of these electronic computers. In general, the analytical procedures which have been evolved over the years for efficient manual computation cannot be expected to be equally effective for machine computation. What is needed is that the structural engineering profession look objectively at its future problems as little prejudiced as possible by the practices and procedures which have been evolved in a completely different computational context in the past.

At present it appears that the simplest approach to the organization of structural calculations for machine solution is the matrix formulation of structural theory using the notations and operations of matrix algebra. Future considerations and developments may in fact demonstrate that this is *the* approach which the profession seeks for machine computation. Intuitively it seems, however, that this approach is too traditional and that completely new concepts and procedures are needed to utilize the full potential of machine computation. Many authors, primarily from the aeronautical structural field, have been contributing to the development of matrix methods of structural analysis over the last two decades. Actually this approach was apparently first suggested many years ago by Edward Study in 1903. It attracted very little interest, however, at that time because of the extensive computations involved.

Whereas the electronic computers will have a greater and greater effect on the developments in structural engineering, the engineer of the future will still need his slide rule and his desk calculator and many of his present methods of analysis and design. He will not discard these any more than the machinist will discard his bench tools because the automatic-programmed machine tools have been developed. He will, however, add the new machine computer to his equipment and learn how to use it efficiently and effectively.

Scope of This Book. This book is focused sharply on an elementary treatment of the analysis of structural behavior. Admittedly analysis is a means to an end—not the end itself—since the primary objective of the structural engineer is to design, *not* to analyze. Concentration on analysis to the exclusion of the larger and more important problem of design allows the structural engineering student to develop his capacity for logical, rational, analytical thinking, and also to cultivate his appreciation, feeling, and intuition for structural behavior. Of course, he will never benefit fully from this educational experience unless he correlates it with a parallel study of structural design. By studying design, the student develops his judgment, his perception, his imagination, and his creativity—in short his ability to synthesize.

The first ten chapters of this book are devoted almost exclusively to a consideration of statically determinate structures. These considerations are based almost entirely on fundamentals previously introduced in physics, mathematics, engineering mechanics, and materials. Here these fundamentals are reviewed and reemphasized as they apply to problems of structural analysis. Since this material is in the nature of a restatement and review, the student will progress through this portion quite rapidly, depending on the thoroughness with which he has assimilated the fundamentals in earlier courses.

Chapters 11 to 14 are devoted to the computation of deflections and the stress analysis of statically indeterminate structures. This will be substantially new material to the normal student, although he will have been introduced briefly to these ideas earlier in his mechanics and materials courses. Although this is an elementary treatment, the student will find it quite rigorous and comprehensive so that, having mastered it, he should have no particular difficulty studying more advanced books devoted exclusively to this aspect of structural analysis.

Chapter 15 is a very elementary introduction to the matrix formulation of structural theory. It is this approach which at the moment appears to be the simplest one to the organization of structural calculations for machine solution. Several books devoted entirely to this approach have been or are currently being published. To date it is not clear to what extent a book such as this one should be revised to incorporate matrix methods. Perhaps future developments will require a much more extensive revision in this respect than is being incorporated in this current edition.

Up to Chap. 16, the emphasis will have been on the analysis of linearly elastic structures. With the increased interest in structural design on the basis of ultimate strength, it becomes necessary to consider post-elastic behavior. Chapter 16 is therefore devoted to the plastic behavior of structures. This treatment covers only the *analysis* of this behavior—*not* the methods and principles of the plastic *design* of structures.

Modern structural engineering has become increasingly involved with not only more complex structural forms but also more refined design of both these complex forms and conventional standard structural forms. It is therefore important for the structural engineer to become familiar with the analysis of plate and shell structures and with the analysis of buckling, dynamic response, and stress distribution for various structures and structural elements. Chapter 17 is a very brief introduction to the principles of the advanced structural mechanics involved in such an analysis. This is intended merely to serve as a transition from this elementary book to advanced books in these areas.

Chapters 18, 19, and 20 present a condensed treatment of model analysis of structures. To date, model analysis has been used primarily as a research and an educational tool. However, this is one of the important tools available to the design engineer which he should use much more than he has in the past. Model analysis may be used as a check on a complex mathematical analysis of his design; or in cases where mathematical analysis is impractical or impossible, model analysis may be the only analytical approach available. European engineers in Spain, Portugal, Italy, and Switzerland have made important uses of model analysis in connection with actual structural design. In the United States, only a few organizations such as the U.S. Bureau of Reclamation have done so.

1

Introduction

1.1 Engineering Structures. The design of bridges, buildings, towers, and other fixed structures is very important to the civil engineer. Such structures are composed of interconnected members and are supported in a manner such that they are capable of holding applied external forces in static equilibrium. A structure must also hold in equilibrium the gravity forces that are applied as a consequence of its own weight. A transmission tower, for example, is acted upon by its own weight, by wind and ice loads applied directly to the tower, and by the forces applied to the tower by the cables that it supports. The members of the tower must be so arranged and designed that they will hold these forces in static equilibrium and thus transfer their effects to the foundations of the tower.

There are many kinds of structures in addition to those mentioned above. Dams, piers, pavement slabs for airports and highways, penstocks, pipelines, standpipes, viaducts, and tanks are all typical *civil engineering* structures. Nor are structures of importance only to the *civil engineer.* The structural frame of an aircraft is important to the *aeronautical engineer;* the structure of a ship receives particular attention from the *naval architect;* the *chemical engineer* is concerned with the structural design of high-pressure vessels and other industrial equipment; the *mechanical engineer* must design machine parts and supports with due consideration of structural strength; and the *electrical engineer* is similarly concerned with electrical equipment and its housing.

The analysis of all these structures is based, however, on the same fundamental principles. In this book the illustrations used to demonstrate the application of these principles are drawn largely from civil engineering structures, but the methods of analysis described can be used for structures that are important in other branches of engineering.

1.2 Structural Design. A structure is designed to perform a certain function. To perform this function satisfactorily it must have sufficient strength and rigidity. Economy and good appearance are further objectives of major importance in structural design.

The complete design of a structure is likely to involve the following five stages:

1. Establishing the general layout to fit the functional requirements of the structure

2. Consideration of the several possible solutions that may satisfy the functional requirements

3. Preliminary structural design of the various possible solutions

4. Selection of the most satisfactory solution, considering an economic, functional, and aesthetic comparison of the various possible solutions

5. Detailed structural design of the most satisfactory solution

Both the preliminary designs of stage 3 and the final detailed design of stage 5 may be divided into three broad phases, although in practice these three phases are usually interrelated. First, the loads acting on the structure must be determined. Next, the maximum stresses in the members and connections of the structure must be analyzed. Finally, the members and connections of the structure must be dimensioned, i.e., the make-up of each part of the structure must be determined.

That these three steps are interrelated may be seen from considerations such as the following: The weight of the structure itself is one of the loads that a structure must carry, and this weight is not definitely known until the structure is fully designed; in a statically indeterminate structure, the stresses depend on the elastic properties of the members, which are not known until the main members are designed. Thus, in a sense, the design of any structure proceeds by successive approximations. For example, it is necessary to assume the weights of members in order that they may be properly designed. After the structure is designed, the true weights may be computed; and unless the true weights correspond closely to those assumed, the process must be repeated.

In designing a structure, it is important to realize that each part must have sufficient strength to withstand the maximum stress to which it can be subjected. To compute such maximum stresses, it is necessary to know, not only *what* loads may act, but the exact *position* of these loads on the structure that will cause the stress under consideration to have its maximum value.

Thus, when a railroad locomotive crosses a bridge, a given portion of the bridge receives its maximum stress with the locomotive at a given position on the bridge. A second part of the structure may be subjected to its maximum stress with the locomotive in another position.

In this book, the emphasis is placed on structural analysis. But, in order to discuss structural analysis satisfactorily, it is desirable to give some attention to the loads acting on a structure and to the design of members and connections.

In the Foreword, it was noted that the conventional basis for structural design is so-called **elastic design.** The design loads, permissible stresses, and other design requirements according to this approach are defined in various ways in standard design specifications and building codes, such as those issued by the following well-known organizations:

American Association of State Highway Officials (AASHO)

American Railway Engineering Association (AREA)

American Institute of Steel Construction (AISC)

American Concrete Institute (ACI)

Some specifications and codes have permissive clauses under which structures may be proportioned by **plastic-design** methods, provided that such designs are defended to the satisfaction of the proper authorities who grant permission for deviations. Up to the present time, however, the authors know of no American codes which have incorporated plastic-design principles into their standard specifications. Since these ideas have merit when used properly, there is no doubt that they will eventually achieve the recognition which they deserve.

1.3   Dead Loads. The dead load acting on a structure consists of the weight of the structure itself and of any other immovable loads that are constant in magnitude and permanently attached to the structure. Thus, for a highway bridge, the dead load consists of the main supporting trusses or girders, the floor beams and stringers of the floor system, the roadway slabs, the curbs, sidewalks, fences or railings, lampposts, and other miscellaneous equipment.

Since the dead load acting on a member must be assumed before the member is designed, one should design the members of a structure in such a sequence that, to as great an extent as is practicable, the weight of each member being designed is a portion of the dead load carried by the next member to be designed. Thus, for a highway bridge, one would first design the road slab, then the stringers that carry the slab loads to the floor beams, then the floor beams that carry the stringer loads to the main girders or trusses, and finally the main girders or trusses.

In designing a member such as a floor slab, stresses due to dead loads are likely to be only a small percentage of the total stress in a member, so that, even if dead loads are not very accurately estimated, the total stress can be predicted with fair accuracy and hence the first design can be quite satisfactory. For main trusses and girders, however, the dead loads constitute a greater portion of the total load to be carried, so that it is more important to make a reasonably accurate first estimate of dead weights. Often data concerning the dead weights of other similar structures will serve as a guide to the designer. Many investigations have been carried out with the purpose of presenting such data in a convenient form.[1] It should be emphasized, however, that the original dead-weight estimate is tentative, whatever the source of the data may be. After a structure is designed, its actual dead weight should be accurately computed and the stress analysis and design revised as necessary. This is necessary for safety and desirable for economy.

If the dimensions of a structure are known, dead loads may be computed on the basis of unit weights of the materials involved. Unit weights for some of the materials commonly used in engineering structures are readily available in many books and handbooks.[2]

1.4 Live Loads—General. As contrasted to dead loads, which remain fixed in both magnitude and location, it is usually necessary to consider live loads, i.e., loads that vary in position. It is sometimes convenient to classify live loads into movable loads and moving loads. Movable loads are those which may be moved from one position to another on a structure, such as the contents of a storage building. They are usually applied gradually and without impact. Moving loads are those which move under their own power, such as a railroad train or a series of trucks. They are usually applied rather rapidly and therefore exert an impact effect on the structure.

When live loads are involved, attention must be given to the placing of such loads on a structure so that the stress in the structural member or connection under consideration will have its maximum possible value. Thus, while we speak of dead stresses due to dead loads, we refer to maximum live stresses due to live loads.

1.5 Live Loads for Highway Bridges. The live load for highway bridges consists of the weight of the applied moving load of vehicles and pedestrians. Actually, the traffic over a highway bridge will consist of a multitude of different types of vehicles. It is designed, however, for a train of standard trucks, so chosen that the bridge will prove safe and economical in its actual performance. The live load for each lane of the roadway consists of a train of heavy trucks following each other closely. The weight and weight distribution of each truck vary with the specifica-

[1] The student is referred to pp. 79 and 91 of "Structural Theory" (John Wiley & Sons, Inc., New York, 1950) by H. Sutherland and H. L. Bowman for excellent summaries of formulas giving the weights of roof trusses and bridges. Charts dealing with the weights of railroad bridges, highway bridges, and signal bridges are given in chap. I of C. M. Spofford's "Theory of Structures," 4th ed., McGraw-Hill Book Company, Inc., New York, 1939.

[2] The student is referred, for example, to the section on Weights and Specific Gravities in "Steel Construction," American Institute of Steel Construction, New York.

tion under which one designs, but a typical example is afforded by the H-series trucks specified by the AASHO.

These H-series trucks are illustrated in Fig. 1.1. They are designated H, followed by a number indicating the gross weight in tons for the standard truck. The choice as to which of the H-series trucks shall be used for the design of a given structure depends on circumstances such as the importance of the bridge and the expected traffic.

It is seen that the loading per lane of roadway consists of a series of concentrated wheel loads. The stress analysis involved in computing

Figure 1.1   AASHO H-series truck

maximum live stresses due to a series of concentrated live loads may become rather complicated. Under some conditions it is permissible to substitute for purposes of stress analysis an equivalent loading consisting of a uniform load per foot of lane, plus a single concentrated load. Thus, for the H-20 loading, the equivalent live load consists of a uniform load of 640 lb per lin ft of lane, plus a concentrated load of either 18,000 lb or 26,000 lb, depending on whether live moments or shears, respectively, are being computed. This equivalent live load is not exactly equivalent to the series of concentrated wheel loads, but it permits a simpler computation of maximum stresses that correspond closely enough to those which would be computed from the actual loads to be used for design purposes.

1.6   Live Loads for Railroad Bridges. The live load for railroad bridges consists of the locomotives and cars that cross them. The live load for each track is usually taken as that corresponding to two locomotives followed by a uniform load which represents the weight of the cars. To standardize such loadings a series of E-loadings was devised by Theodore Cooper. These loadings are designated by the letter E, followed by a number indicating the load in kips[1] on the driving axle. The loads on other axles always bear the same ratio to the load on the driving axle. The uniform load following the two locomotives always has an intensity per foot of track equal to one-tenth the load on the driving axle. The wheel spacings do not vary with the Cooper's rating. Figure 1.2 illustrates a Cooper's E-50 loading. Modern railroad bridges

Figure 1.2   Cooper's E-50 loading

are designed for at least an E-60 loading and often for an E-72 or even a heavier loading. It should be noted that the wheel loads for these heavier Cooper's loadings can be obtained from Fig. 1.2 by direct proportion.

Simplified equivalent loadings are sometimes used in place of Cooper's wheel loadings to represent live loads on railroad bridges.

1.7 Live Loads for Buildings. Live loads for buildings are usually considered as movable distributed loads of uniform intensity. The intensity of the floor loads to be used depends on the purpose for which the building is designed, as indicated in Table 1.1

Table 1.1

	Minimum live load, lb per sq ft
Human occupancy:	
Private dwellings, apartment houses, etc.	40
Rooms of offices, schools, etc.	50
Aisles, corridors, lobbies, etc., of public buildings	100
Industrial or commercial occupancy:	
Storage purposes (general)	250
Manufacturing (light)	75
Printing plants	100
Wholesale stores (light merchandise)	100
Retail salesrooms (light merchandise)	75
Garages:	
All types of vehicles	100
Passenger cars only	80
Sidewalks	250 lb per sq ft or 8,000 lb concentrated, whichever gives the larger moment or shear

---

[1] To facilitate computations, loads are usually given in units of kips, 1 kip being equal to 1,000 lb.

When floors are to carry special live loads of known intensities greater than those suggested above, these special loads should of course be used in design.

1.8 Impact. Unless live load is applied gradually, the deformation of the structure to which the live load is applied is greater than it would be if the live load were considered as a static load. Since the deformation is greater, the stresses in the structure are higher. The increase in stress due to live load over and above the value that this stress would have if the live load were applied gradually is known as impact stress. Impact stresses are usually associated with moving live loads. For purposes of structural design, impact stresses are usually obtained by multiplying the live-load stresses by a fraction called the impact fraction, which is specified rather empirically. The determination of a wholly rational fraction for this purpose would be very complicated, since it depends on the time function with which the live load is applied, the portion of the structure over which the live load is applied, and the elastic and inertia properties of the structure itself.

For highway bridges, the impact fraction I is given in the specifications of the AASHO by

$$I = \frac{50}{L + 125} \qquad \text{but not to exceed 0.300} \qquad (1.1)$$

in which L is the length in feet of the portion of the span loaded to produce the maximum stress in the member considered. For example, suppose that the maximum live positive shear at the center of a 100-ft longitudinal girder of a highway bridge equals 1,000,000 lb and occurs with the live load extending over half the 100-ft span. Then the loaded length L is 50 ft; the impact fraction $I = 50/(50 + 125) = 0.286$; the impact shear is obtained by multiplying the live shear by the impact fraction and therefore equals $1,000,000 \times 0.286 = 286,000$ lb. The total effect of the live load, i.e., lives hear plus impact shear, equals 1,000,000 lb plus 286,000 lb, or 1,286,000 lb.

The Specifications for the Design and Construction of Steel Railway Bridges, published by the AREA, treat impact as follows (note that impact percentage discussed equals 100 times the impact fraction as previously defined):

"To the maximum computed static live-load stresses, there shall be added the impact, consisting of:

1. The rolling effect:

A percentage of the static live-load stress equal to $\dfrac{100}{S}$

S = spacing, in feet, between centers of longitudinal girders, stringers, or trusses; or length, in feet, of floor beams or transverse girders

2. The direct vertical effect:
With steam locomotives (hammer blow, track irregularities, and car impact) a percentage of the live-load stress equal to:

a. For beams, stringers, girders, floor beams:

For L less than 100 ft $\qquad\qquad\qquad\qquad\qquad\qquad 60 - \dfrac{L^2}{500}$

For L 100 ft or more $\qquad\qquad\qquad\qquad\qquad\qquad \dfrac{1,800}{L - 40} + 10$

b. For truss spans $\qquad\qquad\qquad\qquad\qquad\qquad\qquad \dfrac{4,000}{L + 25} + 15$

With electric locomotives (track irregularities and car impact), a percentage of static live-load stress equal to:

For L less than 80 ft $\qquad\qquad\qquad\qquad\qquad\qquad 40 - \dfrac{3L^2}{1,600}$

For L 80 ft or more $\qquad\qquad\qquad\qquad\qquad\qquad \dfrac{600}{L - 30} + 16$

L = length, in feet, center to center of supports for stringers, longitudinal girders, and trusses (chords and main members)
or L = length of floor beams or transverse girders, in feet, for floor beams, floor-beam hangers, subdiagonals of trusses, transverse girders, and supports for transverse girders"

To illustrate the application of the foregoing impact specification, let us assume that the longitudinal girder described in the previous example is one of the two main girders of a steam-railroad bridge and that these two girders are spaced at 18 ft center to center. Then, for the rolling effect, since S = 18, the percentage impact equals $100/18$ = 5.5%; for the direct vertical effect, since L = 100, the percentage impact equals 1,800/(100 − 40) + 10 = 40.0% (note that in this case L = 100 because this is the span of the girder, whereas in the previous example we used L = 50 because the loaded length of the girder was 50 ft); thus the total percentage impact equals 5.5 + 40.0 = 45.5%; the impact shear equals 1,000,000 × 0.455 = 455,000 lb; the total effect of the load, i.e., live shear plus impact shear = 1,000,000 + 455,000 = 1,455,000 lb.

Other specifications give still other rules for determining impact, but the two methods discussed are perhaps the most important of those in common use. They illustrate, moreover, the type of impact equations specified elsewhere.

It is usually unnecessary to consider impact stresses in designing for movable live loads such as the live loads for buildings. Moreover, when a structure is designed of timber, impact is often ignored. This is largely because timber, as a material, is much stronger in resisting loads of short duration than in resisting permanently applied loads, and it therefore can use this reserve of strength to carry impact loads.

1.9 Snow and Ice Loads. Snow loads are often of importance, particularly in the design of roofs. Snow should be considered as a movable load, for it will not necessarily cover the entire roof, and some of the members supporting the roof may receive maximum stresses with the snow covering only a portion of the roof. The density of snow, of course, will vary greatly, as will the fall of snow to be expected in different regions. In a given locality, the depth of snow that will gather on a given roof will depend on the slope of the roof and on the roughness of the roof surface. On flat roofs in areas subjected to heavy snowfalls, snow load may be as large as 60 or even 90 lb per sq ft. Whether or not snow and wind loads should be assumed to act simultaneously on a roof is problematical, since a high wind is likely to remove much of the snow.

Ice loads may also be of importance, as, for example, in designing a tower built up of relatively small members which have proportionately large areas on which ice may gather. Ice having a density equal approximately to that of water may build up to a thickness of 2 in. or more on such members. It may also build up to much greater thicknesses, but when it does it is apt to contain snow or rime and hence have a lower density. When ice builds up on a member, it alters the shape and the projected area of the member. This should be considered in computing wind loads acting on members covered with ice.

1.10 Lateral Loads—General. The loadings previously discussed usually act vertically, although it is not necessary that live loads and their associated impact loads shall act in that direction. In addition, there are certain loads that are almost always applied horizontally, and these must often be considered in structural design. Such loads are called lateral loads. We shall now consider some of the more important kinds of lateral loads.

Wind loads, soil pressures, hydrostatic pressures, forces due to earthquakes, centrifugal forces, and longitudinal forces usually come under this classification.

1.11 Wind Loads. Wind loads are of importance, particularly in the design of large structures, such as tall buildings, radio towers, and long-span bridges, and for structures, such as mill buildings and hangars, having large open interiors and walls in which large openings may occur. The wind velocity that should be considered in the design of a structure depends on the geographical location and on the exposure of the structure. For most locations in the United States, a design to withstand a wind velocity of 100 mph is satisfactory.

Design loads for wind recommended in various specifications, like design loads for live load, should not be considered as attempts to represent actual wind loadings. Experience has shown that use of the recommended values generally results in a design of adequate strength and also of adequate rigidity.

The AASHO specifies that the wind force on the superstructure of highway bridges shall be assumed as a movable horizontal load equal to 75 lb per sq ft for trusses and arches and 50 lb per sq ft for girders and beams. These forces are for a wind velocity of 100 mph. The exposed area is the sum of the areas of all members, including floor system and railing, as seen in elevation at 90° to the longitudinal axis of the structure. When combined with live load on the structure, the wind-load intensity is reduced by 70 per cent. For the substructure, wind forces are specified for varying angles of wind direction so as to provide for both longitudinal and transverse wind forces.

For buildings, the specifications of the AISC state that the frame of a building must be designed to carry a wind pressure of not less than 20 lb per sq ft on the vertical projection of exposed surfaces of the finished structure.

For buildings with gabled or rounded roofs, more exact data for wind loads on roofs should be used. The student is referred to a report entitled Wind Bracing in Steel Buildings,[1] where, for convenience, roof pressures (and suctions) are expressed in terms of q, the velocity pressure, which is defined by

$$q = \tfrac{1}{2}mV^2 \tag{1.2}$$

in which m is the mass of a unit volume of air and V is the velocity of the wind in units corresponding to m. For average conditions, and where the wind velocity is expressed in mph, the velocity pressure in pounds per square foot may be taken as

$$q = 0.002558V^2 \tag{1.3}$$

For gabled roofs, it is recommended that the following loadings shall be adopted for the windward slope:

1. For slopes of 20°, or less, a suction (uplift) of $0.7q$
2. For slopes between 20 and 30°, a suction of

$$p = (0.07\alpha - 2.10)q \tag{1.4}$$

in which α is the roof slope in degrees.

3. For slopes between 30 and 60°, a pressure of

$$p = (0.03\alpha - 0.90)q \tag{1.5}$$

4. For slopes steeper than 60°, a pressure of $0.90q$

It is suggested that the wind load on the leeward slope of a gabled roof shall be taken as a suction of $0.6q$ for all slopes. All pressures and suctions are perpendicular to the surfaces on which they act.

The American Society of Civil Engineers (ASCE) report to which reference has been

[1] *Proc. ASCE*, March, 1936, p. 397.

The recommendations of this report are undoubtedly more consistent with the actual aerodynamic forces acting on a roof than the wind forces often used in the design of roofs. The practice often followed in determining wind pressures on surfaces which are not vertical is to follow a formula such as that of Duchemin, whereby $P_n = P\dfrac{2\sin i}{1 + \sin^2 i}$, in which P_n is the intensity of normal pressure on a given surface, P is the intensity of pressure on a vertical surface, and i is the angle made by the surface with the horizontal. Such a procedure leads to wind pressure on the windward slope of a gable roof and makes no attempt to account for suction on the leeward slope.

made also discusses the magnitude and distribution of wind pressures on rounded roofs, such as are used on hangars.

In the AISC specifications for wind loads on buildings, it is assumed that the entire pressure specified acts on the windward vertical surface of the building. This procedure is satisfactory for the design of typical tall buildings, although the actual lateral load due to wind consists of pressure on the windward side and suction on the downwind side. This matter also is discussed in the ASCE report.

1.12 Soil Pressures. Loads on retaining walls, on walls of buildings, and on other structures due to the pressure of soil must frequently be considered by the structural engineer. The lateral pressure caused by soil on a wall varies when the wall yields. After a small movement of the wall, the soil pressure reaches a minimum value known as the active pressure. If, on the other hand, the wall is forced into the backfill, the pressure between the wall and the backfill increases to a maximum value known as the passive pressure. Under usual conditions, the active pressure at any depth is about $\frac{1}{4}$ the vertical pressure, and the passive pressure is about 4 times the vertical pressure. Since the lateral pressure would equal the vertical pressure if the material were a fluid, the approximate values of $\frac{1}{4}$

Figure 1.3   Retaining wall

and 4 are sometimes called "hydrostatic-pressure ratios" for the active and passive cases, respectively.

According to the above discussion, any wall that may yield without detrimental results may be designed on the basis of active pressure, although the pressure that will actually act on the wall will in general be somewhat above this value. Further, the distribution of pressure over such a wall may be assumed to be triangular, although this assumption is not strictly correct.

For cohesionless soils, the total resultant force corresponding to active soil pressure acting on a strip of wall 1 ft long may be computed on the basis of the theory developed by Coulomb, which assumes failure of soil by rupture along an inclined plane through the soil. Referring to Fig. 1.3, this total resultant force is denoted by P, which acts two-thirds of the way down from the top of the wall, in a direction making the angle ϕ' with a line perpendicular to the face of the wall, ϕ' being the friction angle of the soil on the masonry. H is the vertical depth of soil above the base of the wall. The angle that the surface of the soil makes with the horizontal is defined by i. The batter of the wall is defined by the angle θ.

The total force P in pounds, according to Coulomb's theory, is expressed by

$$P = \frac{1}{2}\gamma H^2 \left[\frac{\csc \theta \sin (\theta - \phi)}{\sqrt{\sin (\theta + \phi')} + \sqrt{\dfrac{\sin (\phi + \phi') \sin (\phi - i)}{\sin (\theta - i)}}} \right]^2 \quad (1.6)$$

where γ is the weight of the earth in pounds per cubic foot, ϕ is the angle of internal friction of the soil (easily obtained by shear tests in a laboratory, and with typical values of from 30 to 40°), and ϕ', the friction angle of soil on masonry, has about the same value as ϕ for a rough wall but is somewhat less than ϕ for a smooth wall.

If $i = 0$, $\theta = 90°$, and $\phi = \phi'$, Eq. (1.6) reduces to

$$P = \frac{1}{2}\gamma H^2 \left[\frac{\cos \phi}{(1 + \sqrt{2} \sin \phi)^2} \right] \quad (1.7)$$

If, for example, we consider a sand for which $\phi = \phi' = 30°$, and $\gamma = 100$ lb per cu ft, acting on the back of a vertical wall 10 ft high, the resultant thrust on a strip of wall 1 ft long, by Eq. (1.7), is given by

$$P = \frac{1}{2}(100)(10)^2 \left\{ \frac{0.867}{[1 + 1.414(0.500)]^2} \right\} = 1,490 \text{ lb}$$

This resultant force acts 3.33 ft above the base of the wall, in a direction toward the wall and downward, making an angle of 30° with the horizontal.

For a more complete treatment of soil pressures, the student is referred to books on soil mechanics.

1.13 Hydrostatic Pressures. Dams, tanks, etc., are subjected to hydrostatic loads that as a rule may be easily computed in accordance with the elementary principles of hydraulics. Hydrostatic loads should in general be considered as movable loads, inasmuch as critical stresses in a structure do not necessarily occur when the liquid involved is at its highest possible level. In some structures, the presence of certain hydrostatic pressures actually relieves stresses in a structure. Thus an underground tank might be more likely to collapse when empty than when full, or a tank built above the ground might undergo a critical-stress condition when it is only partly filled.

It is sometimes necessary to consider hydrodynamic loads, such as occur when water traveling at a high velocity strikes a bridge pier or a caisson.

1.14 Earthquake Forces. Important structures located in regions subject to severe earthquakes are often designed to resist earthquake effects. During an earthquake, structural damage may result from the fact that the foundation of the structure undergoes accelerations. Such accelerations are largely horizontal, and vertical components of acceleration are usually neglected. The rate of horizontal acceleration of the foundations may be of the order of magnitude of one-tenth the acceleration due to gravity, that is, 3.2 ft per sec², and is commonly referred to as 0.1g. If the structure is assumed to act as a rigid body, it will accelerate horizontally at the same rate as its foundations. Hence each part of the structure will be acted upon by a horizontal inertia force equal to its mass multiplied by its horizontal acceleration, or

$$\text{Lateral force} = \text{mass} \times \text{acceleration} = \frac{\text{weight}}{g} \times 0.1g$$
$$= \text{one-tenth of its weight}$$

Structures are often designed to resist earthquakes on the foregoing basis, although it is quite approximate, inasmuch as the assumption that the entire structure accelerates as a rigid body is usually not particularly valid. Actually, the structure will undergo elastic deformations that will affect the acceleration of its various members.

The horizontal acceleration of a structure such as a dam will produce not only horizontal inertia forces due to the mass of the dam but also hydrodynamic forces as the dam moves rapidly into the water that it retains.

1.15 Centrifugal Forces. In designing a bridge on which the tracks or roadway are curved, vehicles crossing the structure exert centrifugal force that may be of sufficient magnitude to require consideration in design. Such centrifugal forces are lateral loads and should be considered as moving loads.

If a weight W travels at velocity V around a curve of radius R, the centrifugal force C (which acts through the center of gravity of the object of weight W) is expressed by

$$C = \text{mass} \times \text{circular acceleration} = \frac{W}{g} \cdot \frac{V^2}{R} \qquad (1.8)$$

1.16 Longitudinal Forces. For a bridge, horizontal forces acting in the direction of the longitudinal axis of the structure, i.e., in the direction of the roadway, are called *longitudinal forces*. Such forces are applied whenever the vehicles crossing the structure increase or decrease their speed. Since they are inertia forces resulting from the acceleration or deceleration of vehicles, they act through the centers of gravities of the vehicles. The magnitude of such forces is limited by the frictional forces that can be developed between the contact surfaces of the wheels of the vehicles applying these forces to the roadway or track and the surface of the roadway or track.

For railway bridges, the AREA specifications state that longitudinal forces shall be assumed to act 6 ft above the top of the rail and that such forces shall be considered as being applied by the live load on one track only. For that track, longitudinal forces shall be taken as the larger of the following: (1) due to braking, 15 per cent of the total live load, without impact; (2) due to traction, 25 per cent of the weight on the driving wheels of the locomotive, without impact.

For highway bridges, the AASHO specifications state that provision shall be made for the effect of a longitudinal force of 5 per cent of the live load on the structure, acting 4 ft above the roadway.

1.17 Thermal Forces. Changes in temperature cause strains in the members of a structure and hence produce deformations in the structure as a whole. If the changes in shape due to temperature encounter restraint, as is often the case in a statically indeterminate structure, stresses will be set up within the structure. The forces set up in a structure as a result of temperature changes are often called thermal forces. In addition to considering the forces set up by changes in temperature, it is important to take into consideration the expansion and contraction of a structure, particularly in connection with support details.

In a moderate climate, one should consider a variation in temperature of 0 to 120°F. In cold climates, this range should be extended to from −30 to 120°F.

1.18 Make-up of Girders. In a structure built of structural steel, rolled sections such as standard I beams or wide-flanged beams are

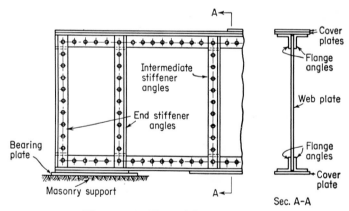

Figure 1.4 Plate girder components

commonly used to support loads across a span. When rolled sections can be used, they are economical because they require less fabrication than built-up girders. For longer spans and for heavier loadings, however, the bending moments and shears will be found to be too large to be carried safely by rolled sections, and built-up girders must be used. The most important parts of a typical built-up plate girder, as shown in

Fig. 1.4, are the web plate, the top flange, which is composed of flange angles and cover plates, and the bottom flange, which is similarly composed. Over the end bearing plates are vertical angles called end stiffeners, while at other points along the span it is usually necessary to have further vertical angles, which are called intermediate stiffeners. The component parts of the girder shown in Fig. 1.4 are riveted together. Welding is often used instead of riveting, in which case the details of the girder differ somewhat, but the essential component parts, viz., the web, top and bottom flange, and web stiffeners, must still be provided.

1.19 Make-up of Trusses. Fabrication, shipping, and erection considerations usually limit the depth of built-up girders to about 10 ft.

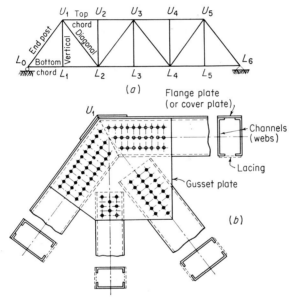

Figure 1.5   Riveted truss components

When bending moments and shears are so large that they cannot be carried by a girder of that depth, it becomes necessary to employ a truss. The layout of a typical truss is shown in Fig. 1.5a. Members L_0L_1, L_1L_2, . . . , L_5L_6 are called bottom chords; members U_1U_2, U_2U_3, . . . , U_4U_5 are called top chords; members L_0U_1 and U_5L_6 are called end posts and are often included as top-chord members; members U_1L_2, L_2U_3, . . . , L_4U_5 are called diagonals; members U_1L_1, U_2L_2, . . . , U_5L_5 are called verticals. Figure 1.5b shows a typical connection detail for the members of a riveted truss and the make-up of typical truss members. The plates to which the members intersecting at a joint are connected are called gusset plates. For long-span trusses, members are sometimes connected at a joint by a pin passing through the webs of the members themselves or through pin plates connected to these webs. Trusses may be welded rather than riveted.

1.20 Make-up of Floor Systems. For a plate-girder railroad bridge, if the girders are not too far apart and if the track is located at

Figure 1.6   Deck girder bridge

the top of the girders, it is economical to have the ties rest directly on the cover plates of the top flanges of the girders, as shown in Fig. 1.6. Such bridges are called deck structures. As the distance between girders becomes larger, such construction becomes uneconomical. It is moreover obvious that it cannot be followed if the tracks are to be located below the tops of the girders. Under either of the foregoing circumstances, it becomes necessary to build up a floor system composed of stringers and floor beams, as shown in Fig. 1.7. If such a built-up floor system is at the top of the girders or trusses, the bridge is still called a deck structure; if it is at the

PLAN VIEW
(*a*)

TRANSVERSE SECTION
(Railroad bridge)

(*b*)

TRANSVERSE SECTION
(Highway bridge)

(*c*)

Figure 1.7   Girder bridge cross sections

bottom of the girders or trusses, the bridge is called a through structure; if it is at an intermediate elevation, it is called a half-through structure. Figures 1.7*a* and *b* illustrate a half-through single-track railroad bridge and show the make-up of floor systems for such bridges. The ties rest directly on members called stringers, which are parallel to the main girders. These stringers frame into members called floor beams, which are transverse to, and frame into, the main girders. Thus a load applied to the rails is transferred by the ties to the stringers, which carry the load to the floor beams. The floor beams carry the load to the girders, which in turn transfer the load to the foundations of the structure.

Figure 1.7c shows a transverse section through a typical highway bridge with a floor system. Such a floor system is similar to that described for a railroad bridge, with the floor slab of the bridge resting on stringers that frame into floor beams, which in turn frame into the main girders.

Similar framing may be used for the floor of a building, as shown in Fig. 1.8. In this case the floor slab would rest on the floor beams and girders as well as on the stringers, but loads applied to the floor slab directly over a stringer would be carried by the stringer to the floor beams, thence to the girders, thence to the columns, and finally to the foundations.

Figure 1.8 Floor framing of building

For bridges in which the main load-carrying elements are trusses rather than girders, floor systems are always used. The floor beams are located at the panel points (joints) of the loaded chord, so that the members of the truss will not be subjected to transverse loads and thus undergo primary bending.

1.21 Bracing Systems. Trusses, girders, floor beams, stringers, columns, etc., which are designed primarily to carry vertical loads, are often referred to as the main members of a structure. In addition to the main members, most structures require bracing systems, which serve a number of purposes, the most important of which are that of resisting lateral loads and that of preventing buckling. The most important bracing systems of a typical through truss bridge are shown in Fig. 1.9. The top-chord lateral system lies in the plane of the top chords and consists of a cross strut at each top-chord panel point and diagonals connecting the ends of these cross struts. The bottom-chord lateral system lies in the plane of the bottom chords and consists of the floor beams, which occur at each bottom-chord panel point and which serve as cross struts, and diagonals connecting the ends of the floor beams. In the planes of the end posts is the so-called "portal" bracing, which stiffens the end posts laterally.

1.22 Permissible Stresses. When a structure is being designed by the *conventional elastic-design method*, the structural analyses are performed for the various design loading conditions to obtain the bending moments, the twisting moment, the shear forces, and the axial force at various cross sections throughout the structure.   From this information, it is possible to compute the intensities of the normal and shear stresses on these cross sections.   In order that the structure shall perform satisfactorily, it is necessary that these stresses which have been developed by the design load shall not exceed certain permissible or allowable limits which have been specified for the material being used.   These

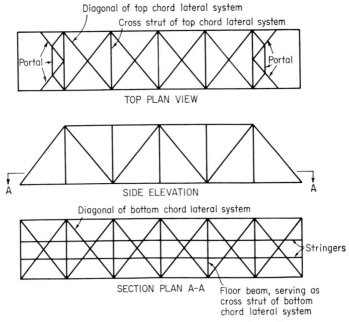

Diagonal of top chord lateral system
Cross strut of top chord lateral system

Portal   Portal

TOP PLAN VIEW

SIDE ELEVATION

Diagonal of bottom chord lateral system

Stringers

SECTION PLAN A-A   Floor beam, serving as cross strut of bottom chord lateral system

Figure 1.9   Lateral bracing systems of through truss

limiting values which have been specified are called **permissible stresses** (or **allowable stresses**).[1]

In any practical problem there are always certain ambiguities regarding the physical dimensions which should be used in the calculations.   The various assumptions which may be made in order to rationalize such difficulties can, of course, have a marked effect on the values computed.

[1] **As used here, stress (or stress intensity) denotes force per unit area, such as pounds per square inch.**   Usage of this term is not uniform in structural engineering literature.   Sometimes, for example, the total tensile or compressive force acting on the cross sections of a truss member is referred to as the *stress* in the member. In fact, in the first edition of this book, in an effort to avoid confusion, the authors elected to use the term *stress intensity* to denote force per unit area, and the term *stress* to denote the total force on a cross section.   This usage did not prove to be so effective as they had hoped.   Therefore, here in the second edition, the term *stress* denotes force per unit area, and the term *force* denotes the total of the stresses integrated over the area of a cross section.

Specifications therefore not only state values for permissible stresses, but also define certain aspects of the basis on which they should be compared with the stresses developed by the design loads. For example, a transverse section through a structural member is likely to pass through rivets. Since a well-driven rivet is tight and substantially fills the rivet hole, it is customary to assume that in transferring compressive stresses the member is not weakened by rivet holes. The area of a transverse section, with no deduction made for rivet holes, is called the "gross area." Even though the rivet is well driven, however, it is not customary to assume that tensile stresses can be transferred across the rivet hole. The area of a transverse section, reduced by the area of those rivet holes located where the section is in tension, is called the "net area." In defining permissible stresses, it is necessary to define whether they are applicable to the net or gross area (or section).

In riveted fabrication, the rivet hole is punched $\frac{1}{16}$ in. in diameter greater than the diameter of the rivet itself, and it is assumed that the material punched is damaged to a diameter $\frac{1}{16}$ in. greater than the hole itself. Thus, in computing net areas, the effective diameter of the hole is taken as $\frac{1}{8}$ in. greater than the diameter of the rivet.

The following allowable stresses for structural steel[1] are specified by the AISC for structural-steel buildings, with all values in pounds per square inch:

Tension: Structural steel, net section   20,000
    Rivets, on area based on nominal diameter   20,000
    Bolts and other threaded parts, on nominal area at root of thread   20,000
Compression: Columns, gross section
    For axially loaded columns with values of l/r not greater than 120

$$17,000 - 0.485\frac{l^2}{r^2}$$

    For axially loaded columns with values of l/r greater than 120

$$\frac{18,000}{1 + (l^2/18,000r^2)}$$

    in which l is the unbraced length of the column and r is the corresponding radius of gyration of the section, both in inches
Bending (based on gross moment of inertia): Tension on extreme fibers of
    rolled sections, plate girders, and built-up members   20,000
    Compression on extreme fibers of rolled sections, plate girders, and
    built-up members,
        with ld/bt not in excess of 600   20,000
        with ld/bt in excess of 600 $\dfrac{12,000,000}{ld/bt}$

    in which l is the unsupported length, and d the depth, of the member;
    b is the width, and t the thickness, of its compression flange; all in inches

[1] Note that the specified minimum yield stress for structural carbon steel (ASTM A-7 steel) is 33,000 psi.

Shearing: Rivets		15,000
Pins, and turned bolts in reamed or drilled holes		15,000
Unfinished bolts		10,000
Webs of beams and plate girders, gross section		13,000

	Double shear	Single shear
Bearing: Rivets	40,000	32,000
Turned bolts in reamed or drilled holes	40,000	32,000
Unfinished bolts	25,000	20,000
Pins	32,000	32,000
Contact areas		
Milled stiffeners and other milled surfaces		30,000
Fitted stiffeners		27,000

Permissible structural-steel stresses for highway and railroad bridges vary somewhat from the foregoing values. For such values, the student is referred to the specifications of the AASHO and the AREA, respectively. Permissible stresses in concrete, timber, and other structural materials are available in various specifications and handbooks.

1.23 Factor of Safety. In the Foreword, it is noted that the values of the permissible stresses used in the conventional elastic-design method are chosen so as to provide an adequate *margin of safety* against exceeding the stress or strain corresponding to the yield point of the material being used. Of course, the selection of the permissible stresses, design loads, and other design restrictions may also be modified by consideration of the possibility of failure due to fatigue, buckling, or brittle fracture, or by consideration of the permissible deflections. If for the design conditions a structure has been designed to utilize exactly the permissible tensile stress of 20,000 psi for structural steel with a specified yield stress of 33,000 psi, the margin of safety (or *factor of safety*) provided against tensile yielding is 1.65 (i.e., 33,000/20,000).

It should be obvious that in actuality this margin of safety cannot be defined this precisely. The actual loads on a structure, particularly those of certain types, cannot be predicted or defined with much precision. Certain simplifying assumptions are always made in the stress analysis, so that even for the assumed design loads the computed stresses are not precise. Even though care is used in manufacturing and fabricating the structural materials employed, some variations in the properties of these materials exist, even when the materials are new. With the passage of time, partial disintegration must be expected. There are always therefore certain variations in the estimates of the actual stress in the structure and of the stress at which it starts to yield. Thus, ideally, the margin of safety should be studied in a statistical manner to ascertain if there is a satisfactorily small probability that the possible variation in the calculated design stress overlaps the possible variation in the yield stress.

Conventionally, the factor of safety is defined as above. That is, the factor of safety against yielding is the ratio of the yield stress of the material employed to the permissible design stress. Admittedly this is a rather crude way of handling this matter. It must be kept in mind, however, that the factors of safety implied in current standard specifications reflect years of experience during which design procedures have been correlated with the actual behavior of structures, usually successful behaviors but occasionally unsuccessful.[1]

The magnitudes of the *load factors* used in the plastic-design methods depend upon the same considerations as noted above for the factor of safety.

1.24   Practical and Ideal Structures.   Rarely if ever does an actual structure correspond to the idealized structure that is considered in its

(a)   *(b)*

Figure 1.10   Idealized structure

analysis. The materials of which the structure is built do not have the exact properties assumed, nor do the dimensions correspond exactly with their theoretical values. Structural details such as lacing bars and gusset plates introduce effects that might make an analysis very complicated indeed; but because they have little actual effect, they are usually neglected in the analysis of stresses in main members. Because of the width of members, considerable difference may exist between clear spans and center-to-center spans which are ordinarily used in analyses. Support details may vary considerably from the idealized type assumed

---

[1] See discussion on p. 12 of Foreword.

for purposes of analysis.   A member may not actually be prismatic, and yet it may be assumed to be, to simplify computations.

The practical structure of Fig. 1.10a, for example, might be analyzed on the basis of the idealized structure of Fig. 1.10b, in which the footing has been assumed to be perfectly fixed, although it could not be so in nature; the extra column area of the anchorage detail and the material of the gusset plate have been ignored; the gusset plate has been assumed as a truly rigid connection, whereas it will actually permit some rotational yielding between the column and the horizontal girder; the effective height of the column has been taken as the distance from the top of the bedplate to the center line of the girder; and the effective span of the girder has been measured from the center line of the column to the center of the applied load.

It is necessary to idealize a structure in order to carry out a practical analysis.   Experience and judgment are necessary in determining the idealized structure that should be used in a given case.   In important structures, where doubt exists as to the most logical assumptions to be made in idealizing a structure, it is sometimes desirable to compute stresses on the basis of more than one possible idealized form, and to design the structure to resist the stresses corresponding to all the analyses.

1.25   Problems for Solution

Problem 1.1   An end-supported girder with a span of 50 ft carries a dead load of 500 lb per ft and a live load of 600 lb per ft.   The dead load extends over the entire span of the girder, and maximum live moment at the center of the girder occurs with the live load extending over the entire span.

(a) Assuming that the intensity of dead load varies directly with the girder span but that live-load intensity remains constant, compute the total maximum moment (dead plus live) at mid-span, for spans varying from 20 to 100 ft, based on 10-ft intervals.

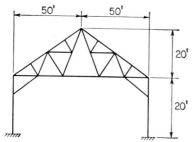

Figure 1.11   Problem 1.3

(b) Assuming that by the use of light-weight alloys the dead load is reduced by 40 per cent, what is the percentage reduction in total moment at mid-span for each span specified in part a?

*Problem 1.2   Compute the impact moments corresponding to Prob. 1.1a in accordance with the specifications of the AASHO.

*Problem 1.3   Figure 1.11 shows the bent of a mill building.   These bents are spaced 20 ft, center to center.   Determine the wind loads for which an intermediate bent should be designed, basing your load determination for vertical surfaces on the specifications of the AISC and the loadings for inclined surfaces on the recommendations of the ASCE for a wind velocity of 100 mph.

* An asterisk in front of a problem number indicates that the answer to this problem appears in the Answer section at the end of the book.

Problem 1.4 (a) Considering a strip 1 ft long of the dam of Fig 1.12, determine the moment, about point *a*, of the total hydrostatic pressure acting on the upstream face of the dam.

(b) The dam of Fig. 1.12 is subjected to an earthquake involving horizontal accelerations of the foundation of $0.1g$. Treating the dam as a rigid body and assuming the reservoir to be empty, determine the moment, about point *a*, of the lateral forces to which a 1-ft strip of the dam is subjected.

Figure 1.12   Problem 1.4

*Problem 1.5** The compression flange of a girder consists of two angles, each $6 \times 6 \times \frac{1}{2}''$, and one cover plate, $14 \times \frac{1}{2}''$. The girder is 10 ft deep. It has a span of 96 ft, and the top flange is braced laterally at intervals of 16 ft. In accordance with the AISC specifications, what stress would be permissible in the design of the compression flange?

2
Reactions

2.1 Definitions. The major portion of this book will be devoted to the analysis of so-called *planar structures,* i.e., structures that may be considered to lie in a plane that also contains the lines of action of all the forces acting on the structure. Such a structure is by far the most common in structural analysis. The analysis of three-dimensional, or space, structures involves no new fundamental principles beyond those required for planar structures, but the numerical computations are greatly complicated by the additional geometry introduced by the third

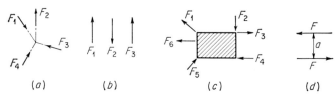

Figure 2.1   Coplanar force systems

dimension. For these reasons, the emphasis will be placed on planar structures, and a limited discussion of space structures will be reserved for later portions of the book.

Since the discussion in this chapter is limited to planar structures, all the force systems will be so-called *coplanar force systems,* i.e., systems consisting of several forces the lines of action of which all lie in one plane. Some of these systems have special characteristics, and it will be found convenient to classify them accordingly and to identify them by special names.

A *concurrent coplanar force system* is shown in Fig. 2.1a. This system consists of several forces the lines of action of which all intersect at a common point. A *parallel coplanar force system* consists of several forces the lines of action of which are all parallel, as shown in Fig. 2.1b.

A *general coplanar force system* consists of several forces the lines of action of which are in various directions and do not intersect in a common point, as shown in Fig. 2.1c. Another important system, a couple, is shown in Fig. 2.1d. A *couple* consists of two equal and opposite parallel forces that do not have a common line of action.

Since, in a planar structure, the lines of action of all the forces lie in the plane of the structure, each of the forces F could be resolved into two components F_x and F_y, where the x and y reference axes may be taken in any directions as long as they do not coincide. It is almost always desirable to select x and y axes that are mutually perpendicular, in which case F_x and F_y are called rectangular components. Further, it is usually most convenient to take the x axis horizontally and the y axis vertically.

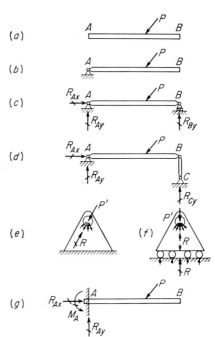

Figure 2.2   Support reactions

2.2 General—Conventional Supports. Most structures are either partly or completely restrained so that they cannot move freely in space. Such restrictions on the free motion of a body are called restraints and are supplied by supports that connect the structure to some stationary body. For example, consider a planar structure such as the bar AB shown in Fig. 2.2. If this bar were a free body and were acted upon by a force P, it would move freely in space with some combined translatory and rotational motion. If, however, a restraint were introduced in the form of a hinge that connected the bar to some stationary body at point A, then the motion of the bar would be partly restricted and could consist only of a rotational movement about the hinge. During such a rotation, point B would move along an arc with point A as the center. Instantaneously, point B could be considered to move normal to the line AB, or, in this case, vertically. If, therefore, another restraint were introduced that would not allow point B to move instantaneously in a vertical direction, the rotation about the hinge at point A would be prevented and thus the free motion of the bar would be completely restricted. It is evident that this type of restraint would be supplied by the supports shown at B in either c or d of Fig. 2.2.

The supports at A and B, in restricting the free motion of the bar, are called upon to resist the action that the force P imposes upon them through the bar. The resistances that they thus develop to counteract the action of the bar upon them are called *reactions*. The effect of the supports may therefore be replaced by the reactions that they supply to the structure.

In future discussions, it will be necessary to deal continually with the reactions that different types of supports supply, and it therefore will be convenient to use a conventional symbol for describing these different types. A *hinge support*, as shown in Fig. 2.2e, is represented by the symbol ⚊. In such a support, if it is assumed that the pin of the hinge is frictionless in the pinhole, then the contact pressures between the pin and its hole must remain normal to the circular contact surface and must therefore be directed through the center of the pin. The reaction R that the support supplies to the structure must completely counteract the action of the force P', and therefore R and P' must be collinear and numerically equal but must act opposite to one another. It is therefore evident that a hinge support supplies a reactive force the line of action of which is known to pass through the center of the hinge pin but the magnitude and direction of which are unknown.[1] These two unknown elements of such a reaction could also be represented by the unknown magnitudes of its horizontal and vertical components, R_x and R_y, respectively, both acting through the center of the hinge pin.

A *roller support*, as shown in Fig. 2.2f, is represented by either the symbol ⚊ or ⚊. In the same manner as above, it may be reasoned that the reactive force of a roller support must be directed through the center of the pin. In addition, however, if the rollers are frictionless, they can transmit only a pressure which is normal to the surface on which they roll. Hence, a roller support supplies a resultant reactive force which acts normal to the surface on which the rollers roll and is directed through the center of the hinge pin. It is therefore evident that a roller support supplies a reactive force which is applied at a known point and acts in a known direction, but the magnitude of which is unknown. Roller supports are usually detailed so that they can supply a reaction acting either away from or toward the supporting surface.

Consideration of the *link support BC* shown in Fig. 2.2d shows that for small movements it effectively reproduces the action of the roller support shown at B in Fig. 2.2c. By the same approach as used above, it

---

[1] According to this terminology, the "direction of a force" is intended to define the slope of its line of action, while the "magnitude" indicates not only its numerical size but also the sense in which the force acts along this line of action, i.e., whether toward or away from a body.

may be reasoned that, if the pins at the ends of this link are frictionless, the force transmitted by the link must act through the centers of the pins at each end. Therefore, a link support also supplies a reaction of a known direction and a known point of application but of an unknown magnitude. A link support is denoted by the symbol ⊥.

One other common type of support used for planar structures is that shown at A in Fig. 2.2g and called a *fixed support*. Such a support encases the member so that both translation and rotation of the end of the member are prevented. A fixed support therefore supplies a reaction, the magnitude, point of application, and direction of which are all unknown. These three unknown elements may also be considered to be a force, which acts through a specific point but has an unknown magnitude and direction, and a couple of unknown magnitude. For example, the three unknown elements could be selected as a couple and a horizontal and a vertical force, the two latter acting through the center of gravity of the end cross section. A fixed support is designated by the symbol ⊨.

The external forces acting on a body therefore consist of two distinct types—the applied loads P (shown thus →) and the reactions R (shown thus ↠). A reactive force at support a will be designated as R_a, while its x and y components will be called R_{ax} and R_{ay}. A reactive couple at support a will be called M_a.

2.3 Equations of Static Equilibrium—Planar Structures. If the supports of a planar structure are considered to be replaced by the reactions that they supply, the structure will be acted upon by a general coplanar force system consisting of the known applied loads and the unknown reactions. In general, the resultant effect of a general coplanar force system could be either a resultant force acting at some point and in some direction in the plane or a resultant couple.

A body that is initially at rest and remains at rest when acted upon by a system of forces is said to be in a **state of static equilibrium. For such a state to exist, it is necessary that the combined resultant effect of the system of forces shall be neither a force nor a couple; otherwise, there will be a tendency for motion of the body.** In order that the combined resultant effect of a general system of forces acting on a planar structure shall not be equivalent to a resultant force, it is necessary that the algebraic sum of all the F_x components shall be equal to zero and likewise that the algebraic sum of all the F_y components shall be equal to zero. In order that the combined resultant effect shall not be equivalent to a couple, it is necessary that the algebraic sum of the moments of all the forces about any axis normal to the plane of the structure shall also be equal to zero. The three following conditions must therefore be fulfilled simultaneously by the loads and reactions of a planar structure for the structure to remain in a state of static equilibrium:

$$\Sigma F_x = 0 \qquad \Sigma F_y = 0 \qquad \Sigma M = 0 \qquad (2.1)$$

These equations are called the **equations of static equilibrium** of a planar structure subjected to a general system of forces.

In the special case where a planar structure is acted upon by a concurrent system of loads and reactions, it is impossible for the resultant effect of the system to be a couple, for the lines of action of all the forces of a concurrent system intersect in a common point. Therefore, for the structure to remain in static equilibrium in such a case, it is necessary only that the two following conditions be satisfied:

$$\Sigma F_x = 0 \qquad \Sigma F_y = 0 \qquad (2.2)$$

These equations are the equations of static equilibrium for the special case of a planar structure subjected to a concurrent system of forces.

Quite often in the discussions that follow, structural members will be referred to as being *rigid bodies*. In an exact sense, a rigid body is one in which there is no relative movement between any two particles of the body. Of course, any structural element is never absolutely rigid since it is made of materials that deform slightly under the loads imposed on them. However, such deformation is so slight that the changes of dimension, the shifting of the lines of action of forces, etc., may usually be neglected during the investigation of the condition of equilibrium of the body. Thus, in most problems, in applying the equations of static equilibrium to structural elements, it will be assumed that they are rigid bodies for all practical purposes and hence that the geometry after application of the loads is essentially the same as before.

2.4 Equations of Condition. Many structures consist of simply one rigid body—a truss, frame, or beam—restrained in space by a certain number of supports. Sometimes, however, the structure may be built up out of several rigid bodies partly connected together in some manner, the whole assemblage then being mounted on a certain number of supports. In either type of structure, the force system consisting of the loads and reactions must satisfy the equations of static equilibrium if the structure is to remain at rest. In the latter type of structure, however, the details of the method of construction used to connect the separate bodies together may enforce further restrictions on the force system acting on the structure. The separate parts may be connected together by hinges, links, or rollers in some way, and in each case these details can transmit only a certain type of force from one part of the structure to the other.

Figure 2.3 illustrates this type of structure. It is composed of two rigid members *ab* and *bc* connected together by a frictionless hinge at point *b* and supported by hinge supports at points *a* and *c*. Since a frictionless hinge cannot transmit a couple, its insertion imposes the condition that the action of one portion of the structure on the other portion connected by the hinge can consist only of a force acting through the center of the hinge pin. Therefore, the algebraic sum of the moments of the loads and reactions applied to any *one* such portion of the structure taken about an axis through the center of the hinge pin must be equal to zero. Such conditions introduced by the method of construction (other than the manner in which the supports are detailed) result in so-called *equations of construction or condition*.

Figure 2.3
Three-hinged arch

2.5 Static Stability and Instability—Statically Determinate and Indeterminate Structures Not Involving Equations of Condition.

Consider first a planar structure which is acted upon by a general system of loads and into which no equations of construction have been introduced. If the supports are replaced by the reactions that they supply to the structure, the structure will be acted upon by a general system of forces consisting of the known loads and the unknown reactions. If the structure is in static equilibrium under these forces, the three equations of static equilibrium may be written in terms of the known loads and the unknown elements defining the reactions. The simultaneous solution of these three equations will in certain cases determine the magnitude of the unknown reaction elements. Whether or not these three equations are sufficient for the complete determination of the reactions, they must be satisfied for the structure to be in static equilibrium, and therefore they form a partial basis for the solution to obtain the reactions of any structure that is in static equilibrium.

If there are fewer than three unknown independent reaction elements, there are not enough unknowns to satisfy the three equations of static equilibrium simultaneously. Fewer than three unknown reaction elements are therefore insufficient to keep a planar structure in equilibrium when it is acted upon by a general system of loads. Under such condition, a structure is said to be statically unstable.

Under certain special conditions, a planar structure having fewer than three unknown independent reaction elements may be in static equilibrium. Of course, if the system of applied loads acting on the structure is in equilibrium itself, no reactions are required; also, if the loads and reactions have certain mutual characteristics, fewer than three reaction elements may be sufficient for equilibrium. For example, considering the bar shown in Fig. 2.2*b*, if the resultant effect of the applied loads is a force whose line of action goes through the center of the hinge pin at point A, the forces acting on the structure are concurrent and the horizontal and vertical components of the reaction at A will be capable of maintaining static equilibrium. Moreover, if the bar were supported at both points A and B by rollers which rolled on horizontal surfaces, the reactions supplied by such supports could maintain in a state of static equilibrium any system of applied loads of which the resultant effect is either a couple or a vertical force. Such structures, although stable under special types of loading but unstable under the general case of loading, are said to be in a state of *unstable equilibrium* and are still classed as unstable structures.

Since three unknowns can be obtained from the solution of three independent simultaneous equations, the reactions of a stable planar structure having exactly three unknown reaction elements may be obtained from the simultaneous solution of the three equations of static equilibrium. In such a case, the reactions of the structure are said to be statically determinate. However, if there are more than three unknown independent reaction elements supplied to a stable planar structure, the three equations of static equilibrium are not sufficient to determine the unknown reactions. This is evident since all but three of the unknowns could be assigned arbitrary values and then the remaining three determined from the simultaneous solution of the three equations of static equilibrium. In such cases, there are an infinite number of related sets of values for the unknown reactions that could satisfy the conditions of static equilibrium. The correct values for the reactions cannot therefore be determined simply from these three equations but must also satisfy certain deformation conditions of the structure, as will be discussed later in this book. **If the unknown reaction elements cannot be determined simply by the equations of static equilibrium, the reactions of the structure are said to be statically indeterminate. The structure is then said to be indeterminate to a degree equal to the number by which the unknowns exceed the available equations of statics.**

From the above discussion it may be concluded that at least three independent reaction elements are *necessary* to satisfy the conditions of static equilibrium for a planar structure acted upon by any general system of loads. It may easily be demonstrated, however, that three or more elements are not always *sufficient*, and therefore a planar structure having three or more independent reaction elements may still be unstable. This is the reason why a *stable* planar structure was specified in the discussion of the previous paragraph.

The question of sufficiency of the reactions for stability may be discussed by an extension of the approach used in the early part of Art. 2.2. For example, the bars shown in Figs. 2.2c and d are stable when supported by the horizontal and vertical components of the reaction at A and the vertical reaction at B. These structures are equivalent to that shown in Fig. 2.4, where the hinge support has been replaced by two links attached to the hinge pin at point A. These two links may be in any directions as long as they are not collinear. This structure would be stable as long as the line of action of the link at B did not also pass through the center of the hinge pin at A. If this line of action did pass through A, the structure would be only partly restrained and therefore unstable under the general system of loads because there would be nothing to prevent the instantaneous rotation of the structure about the hinge at point A. **In such cases, where there are nominally sufficient reaction elements but the geometrical arrangement is such that the structure is unstable, the structure is said to be geometrically unstable.**

Figure 2.4 Stable structure   **Figure 2.5** Geometrically unstable structure

One other case where three independent reaction elements are not sufficient for stability should be discussed. Consider a bar supported by three parallel links as shown in Fig. 2.5. It is apparent that there is no restraint to prevent a small translation of the structure normal to the direction of the links. Hence, if the resultant effect of the applied loads has a component in this direction, motion will be produced and such a structure must be classed as geometrically unstable. These and similar considerations lead to the following conclusion: *If the reactions are equivalent to those supplied by a system of three or more link supports that are either concurrent or parallel, they are not sufficient to maintain static equilibrium of a planar structure subjected to a general system of loads even if there are three or more unknown reaction elements.* In other words, **the stability of a structure is determined not only by the number of reaction elements but also by their arrangement.**

It should be noted that unstable structures having three or more independent reaction elements usually could also be classed as statically indeterminate. Consider the structure shown in Fig. 2.5. While it is unstable and starts to translate horizontally under the load P, it is not completely unrestrained. Instantaneously the bar translates horizontally, and the three links rotate about points A', B', and C', respectively. After a finite rotation of the links, points A, B, and C will have moved vertically as well as horizontally. A vertical movement of these points can be accomplished only by making the bar AC bend and by stretching the links. The final equilibrium position is determined not only by the geometry of the structure but also by its elastic deformation due to the stresses developed in the links and the bar. In this final position, the links will have moved through such finite rotations that the algebraic sum of the horizontal components of the internal forces in the links is equal to the horizontal component of the load. Hence, the analysis of this structure in its final equilibrium position involves not only the equations of static equilibrium but also its deformation properties, and the structure may therefore be classed as statically indeterminate. The structure shown in Fig. 2.4 also falls into this same category if the line of action of the link at B passes through the hinge at A.

If the structure shown in Fig. 2.5 were acted upon by a system of vertical loads, there would be no tendency for it to move horizontally, i.e., the structure would be in unstable equilibrium. In such a case, note that the reactions would also be statically indeterminate.

2.6 Stability and Determinancy of Structures Involving Equations of Condition. So far the discussion has been restricted to structures in which no special construction conditions have been introduced. If, however, such conditions are introduced into a planar structure, a like number of equations of condition are added to the three equations of statics. It is then necessary for the loads and reactions acting on the structure to satisfy simultaneously both the equations of static equilibrium and the equations of condition. If the number of unknown reaction elements is fewer than the total number of equations, the structure is statically unstable or possibly in unstable equilibrium for certain special conditions of loading. If the number of reaction elements is more than the total number of equations, the structure is classed as statically indeterminate. If, however, there are the same number of reaction elements as there are equations, the structure is statically determinate unless the reactions are so located and arranged that geometrical instability is possible.

Such a condition of instability may be simply illustrated by a consideration of a structure of the type shown in Fig. 2.3. The structure shown there is, of course, stable; but if the hinge at b lay on the line joining points a and c, there would be no restraint to the instantaneous rotation of members ab and bc about points a and c, respectively. After a certain finite rotation of both members, tensile forces will be developed in members ab and bc that in view of the new slopes of the members will have vertical components that will keep the load P in equilibrium. The computation of the equilibrium position of joint b and the resulting tensile forces that are developed involves a consideration of the deformation properties of the structure. Therefore, this structure is not only unstable in its original position but also statically indeterminate.

Geometrical instability similar to that just illustrated is most likely to occur whenever equations of construction are introduced into an originally stable structure. It is therefore evident that care must be used in introducing construction hinges, etc., so that geometrical instability is not produced. Such a condition will always be apparent, for solution of the combined equations of static equilibrium and equations of condition will yield inconsistent, infinite, or indeterminate values for the unknown reaction elements.[1]

2.7 Free-body Sketches. In the previous discussion, it is shown that the unknown reaction elements of a statically determinate and stable structure may be computed from the simultaneous solution of the equations of static equilibrium, augmented, in certain cases, by equations of condition. All the equations involve some or all of the forces acting on the structure, including both the applied loads and the reactions supplied by the supports. To assist in formulating these equations, it is desirable to draw so-called *free-body sketches* of either the entire structure or some portions of it. The importance of drawing an adequate number of these free-body sketches cannot be overemphasized to the student. Such sketches are the basis of the successful stress analysis of structures. The student should be admonished that *it is impossible to draw too many free-body sketches* and that time spent in so doing is never wasted.

A free-body sketch of the entire structure is drawn by isolating the structure from its supports and showing it acted upon by all the applied loads and all the possible reaction components that the supports may supply to the structure. Such a sketch is illustrated in Fig. 2.7b. In this same manner, any portion of the structure can be isolated by passing any desired section through the structure, and a free-body sketch drawn showing this portion acted upon by the applied loads and reactions, together with any forces that may act on the faces of the members cut by the isolating section. Any force the magnitude of which is unknown may be assumed to act in either sense along its line of action. The assumed sense is used in writing any equation involving such a force. When the magnitude of such a force is determined from the solution, if the sign is positive, the force is then known to act in the assumed sense; if negative, in the opposite sense.

Sometimes it becomes desirable to isolate several portions of the structure and to draw free-body sketches of these portions. In such cases, it is necessary to show the internal forces acting on the internal faces that have been exposed by the isolating section. If free-body sketches are drawn for two adjacent portions of the structure and the

---

[1] For a discussion of this subject, see W. M. Fife and J. B. Wilbur, "Theory of Statically Indeterminate Structures," art. 8, p. 9, McGraw-Hill Book Company, Inc., New York, 1937.

internal forces have been assumed to act in certain senses on an internal face of one portion, the corresponding forces must be assumed to act with the same numerical values but in *opposite* senses on the matching face of the adjacent portion. This is evident since the action and reaction of one

body on another must be numerically equal but opposite in sense. Such free-body sketches are shown in Fig. 2.6. If this practice is not followed, equations of static equilibrium, written using two such free-body sketches, will not be consistent with one another and it will be impossible to obtain a correct solution from them. It is of course obvious that any particular reac-

Figure 2.6   Free-body sketches

tion which is assumed to act in a certain sense on one sketch must be shown in the same sense on all other sketches in which it appears.

2.8 Computation of Reactions. If no equations of condition have been introduced into a statically determinate structure, the computation of the reactions involves only a straightforward application of the equations of static equilibrium. Such computations may be illustrated by considering the simple end-supported beam shown in Fig. 2.7a. The unknown reaction elements may be taken as the vertical and horizontal components of the reaction at A and the vertical component of the reaction at D. These may be assumed to act as shown in the free-body sketch, Fig. 2.7b.

To obtain these three unknowns there are available the three equations of static equilibrium $\Sigma F_x = 0$,

Figure 2.7   Computation of reactions

$\Sigma F_y = 0$, and $\Sigma M = 0$, and therefore such a structure is statically determinate. It is possible to write the following three equations of static equilibrium and solve them simultaneously for the three unknowns R_{Ax}, R_{Ay}, and R_{Dy}:

$$\Sigma F_x = 0, \xrightarrow{+}, \; R_{Ax} - 36 = 0$$
$$\Sigma F_y = 0, \uparrow+, \; R_{Ay} + R_{Dy} - 60 - 48 = 0$$
$$\Sigma M_C = 0, +), \; 12R_{Ay} - 6R_{Dy} - (60)(6) = 0$$

While such a solution is always possible, it is not very ingenious and it is inefficient, particularly in a complicated structure. Consider the advantages of proceeding as follows: By taking the summation of moments

about an axis through point A, the only unknown entering the equation
will be R_{Dy}, and a direct solution for it will be possible.

$$\Sigma M_A = 0, +\rangle, (60)(6) + (48)(12) - (R_{Dy})(18) = 0$$
$$\therefore R_{Dy} = {}^{936}\!/_{18} = 52 \text{ kips } \updownarrow$$

In the same manner, R_{Ay} may be found directly from

$$\Sigma M_D = 0, +\rangle, (R_{Ay})(18) - (60)(12) - (48)(6) = 0$$
$$\therefore R_{Ay} = 1{,}008/18 = 56 \text{ kips } \updownarrow$$

Of course, these values should satisfy the equation $\Sigma F_y = 0$, and the
following check is obtained:

$$\Sigma F_y = 0, \uparrow+, 56 + 52 - 60 - 48 = 0 \qquad \therefore \text{ O.K.}$$

From $\Sigma F_x = 0$, R_{Ax} is obtained directly,

$$\Sigma F_x = 0, \xrightarrow{+}, R_{Ax} - 36 = 0 \qquad \therefore R_{Ax} = 36 \text{ kips } \nrightarrow$$

Thus, by ingenuity in applying the equations of static equilibrium, the
solution for the reactions is facilitated.

To enlarge on this discussion, **it should be noted that the three conventional equations of static equilibrium $\Sigma F_x = 0$, $\Sigma F_y = 0$, and
$\Sigma M = 0$ may always be replaced by the independent moment
equations $\Sigma M_A = 0$, $\Sigma M_B = 0$, and $\Sigma M_C = 0$, when points A, B,
and C are three points which do not lie on a straight line.** This
may be verified in the following manner: If a system of forces satisfies
any one of these moment equations, such as $\Sigma M_A = 0$, then the resultant
effect of the system cannot be a couple but may be a resultant force acting
through point A. If the system also satisfies the equation $\Sigma M_B = 0$,
then the resultant effect of the system may still be a resultant force; but,
if so, such a force can act only along the line joining points A and B.
If in addition, however, the system also satisfies the equation $\Sigma M_C = 0$
(where C does not lie on a line going through A and B), this eliminates the
possibility of the resultant force existing and acting along the line AB.
Therefore, if the system satisfies all three moment equations, its resultant
effect can be neither a couple nor a resultant force and the system must
be in a condition of static equilibrium.[1]

[1] **Important Questions:**

1. If two moment equations were obtained, first from $\Sigma M_A = 0$ and then from
$\Sigma M_B = 0$, would a third independent equation be obtained by summing up the force
components perpendicular to the line AB and setting this sum equal to zero? Why?
Would summing up the force components in any direction other than parallel to AB
result in a satisfactory independent equation?

2. It has been shown that it is often desirable to replace a force equilibrium equation
with a moment equilibrium equation in the case of a planar structure subjected to a

This principle may often be used to advantage in writing equations of static equilibrium, for it is often possible to select a moment axis so that only one unknown reaction element is involved in the summation of moments about that axis, thus leading to a direct solution for that one unknown. The student should study the illustrative examples in Art. 2.11 in conjunction with this article, since methods of arranging the computations and applying the above general approach will be discussed

Figure 2.8 Three-hinged arch

with a view to facilitating the numerical computations.

2.9 Computation of Reactions— Structures Involving Equations of Condition. Whenever special conditions of construction have been introduced into a structure, the evaluation of the reactions involves both the equations of static equilibrium and the equations of condition. Even when such structures are statically determinate, the computation of the reactions is more difficult and requires more ingenuity than cases where no equations of condition have been introduced.

To illustrate the method of attack in such cases, consider the structure shown in Fig. 2.8. This structure is of a type already discussed and may be shown to be statically determinate and stable. There are four unknown reaction elements, but in addition to the three equations of static equilibrium there is the equation of condition introduced by the frictionless hinge at point b. As discussed previously (Art. 2.4), such a hinge is capable of transmitting a couple neither from the portion ab to the portion bc nor vice versa. It is therefore necessary that the algebraic sum of the moments about an axis through point b of all the forces acting on *either* the portion ab *or* the portion bc add up to zero. Stating this in equation form,

$$\overset{ab}{\sum} M_b = 0 \quad \text{or} \quad \overset{bc}{\sum} M_b = 0$$

At first glance, a student might infer from this that such a hinge really introduces two independent equations of condition. This is not so. There is only *one* independent equation introduced, as may easily be

general system of forces. Is the following statement valid in the case of a planar structure subjected to a concurrent force system?

The two conventional equations of equilibrium $\Sigma F_x = 0$ and $\Sigma F_y = 0$ may be replaced by the two moment equations $\Sigma M_A = 0$ and $\Sigma M_B = 0$ if the point of concurrency does not lie on the line through points A and B.

shown by the following reasoning: One of the equations of static equilibrium requires that for the entire structure the summation of the moments about any axis of all the forces shall be equal to zero, and hence, with b as an axis, $\Sigma M_b = 0$. If one then writes the equation of condition that, for the portion ab, $\overset{ab}{\sum} M_b = 0$, it immediately implies that the algebraic sum of the moments about b of all the remaining forces acting on the remainder of the structure bc must add up to zero. Therefore, $\overset{bc}{\sum} M_b = 0$ is not an independent relation—it is simply equal to the equation $\Sigma M_b = 0$ minus the equation $\overset{ab}{\sum} M_b = 0$. The student should constantly keep these ideas in mind when setting up the equations of condition of the structure. He should never be fooled into thinking that he has more independent equations than he actually has. In this case any two of these three equations—$\Sigma M_b = 0$, $\overset{ab}{\sum} M_b = 0$, $\overset{bc}{\sum} M_b = 0$—can be used independently, but the remaining one is not an independent relation.

To proceed now with the solution of this example, the reactions may be obtained easily if ingenuity is used in setting up the equations of statics.

$$\Sigma M_a = 0, \curvearrowright, (20)(15) + (40)(55) - 80R_{cy} + 15R_{cx} = 0$$
$$\therefore R_{cy} = 31.25 + \tfrac{3}{16}R_{cx} \tag{a}$$

$$\overset{bc}{\sum} M_b = 0, \curvearrowright, (40)(15) - 40R_{cy} + 45R_{cx} = 0$$
$$\therefore R_{cx} = \tfrac{8}{9}R_{cy} - 13.33^{*} \tag{b}$$

Substituting for R_{cy} from Eq. (a) into Eq. (b),

$$R_{cx} = \tfrac{8}{9}(31.25 + \tfrac{3}{16}R_{cx}) - 13.33 \qquad \therefore R_{cx} = 17.33 \text{ kips} \leftleftarrows$$

And then substituting back in (a),

$$R_{cy} = 34.5 \text{ kips} \Updownarrow$$

In a similar manner,

$$\Sigma M_c = 0, \curvearrowright, 80R_{ay} + 15R_{ax} - (20)(65) - (40)(25) = 0$$
$$\therefore R_{ay} = 28.75 - \tfrac{3}{16}R_{ax} \tag{c}$$

$$\overset{ab}{\sum} M_b = 0, \curvearrowright, 40R_{ay} - 30R_{ax} - (20)(25) = 0$$
$$\therefore R_{ax} = \tfrac{4}{3}R_{ay} - 16.67 \tag{d}$$

---

* Numbers such as 13.333 · · · will often be written 13.3̇, the dot over the last digit indicating that it may be repeated indefinitely.

Then substituting from Eq. (c) into Eq. (d),

$$R_{ax} = \tfrac{4}{3}(28.75 - \tfrac{3}{16}R_{ax}) - 16.67 \qquad \therefore R_{ax} = 17.33 \text{ kips} \rightarrow$$

And substituting back in (c),

$$R_{ay} = 25.5 \text{ kips} \updownarrow$$

Using equations $\Sigma F_x = 0$ and $\Sigma F_y = 0$ for checks on the solution,

$$\Sigma F_x = 0, \xrightarrow{+}, 17.33 - 17.33 = 0 \qquad \therefore \text{O.K.}$$
$$\Sigma F_y = 0, \uparrow+, 25.5 - 20 - 40 + 34.5 = 0 \qquad \therefore \text{O.K.}$$

If the supports of a and c of this structure had been on the same elevation, it is evident that the solution of the reactions would have been much easier, for in that case a direct solution for the vertical components of the reactions would be obtained from the equations $\Sigma M_a = 0$ and $\Sigma M_c = 0$. From a consideration of some of the illustrative examples in Art. 2.11, it will be apparent that the solution of the reactions of complicated structures involving special conditions of construction may be expedited in some cases by isolating internal portions as free bodies and applying the equations of static equilibrium to those portions. It should again be emphasized to the student, however, that such a technique does not add any new independent equations besides the three equations of static equilibrium for the entire structure plus the equations of condition resulting from the special conditions of construction. The equations used may be in a different form, but they are not new independent ones.

2.10 Examples for Classification. In this article, examples are discussed illustrating the methods of determining whether a structure is stable or unstable and whether it is statically determinate or indeterminate with respect to its reactions. Note that all beams are represented by straight lines coinciding with their centroidal axes and that their depth is not shown in the sketches of Fig. 2.9. This will be common practice in the remainder of the book whenever the depth does not essentially affect the solution of the problem.

Consider the beam shown in Fig. 2.9a. The unknown independent reaction elements are the magnitude and direction of the reaction at A and the magnitude of the reaction at B or a total of three. These elements may also be considered as the magnitude of the horizontal and vertical components of the reaction at A and of either the horizontal or vertical component at B. Note that, if the point of application and the direction of a reaction are known, the one unknown element of this reaction may be considered as the magnitude of the resultant reaction itself or the magnitude of either its vertical or horizontal component, since either component may be expressed in terms of the other, using the known direction of the reaction. Since the reaction supplied by the support at B does not pass through point A, this structure is stable. The three unknown reaction elements may therefore be found from the three available equations of static equilibrium, and the structure is statically determinate.

Consideration of the beam in Fig. 2.9b shows that there are only two unknown reaction elements—the magnitude of the reactions at A and B. These two unknown elements may also be considered as either the horizontal or the vertical component of each reaction. Since the three equations of static equilibrium cannot be satisfied simultaneously by these two independent unknown reaction elements, this structure is statically unstable under a general system of applied loads. The lines of action of the two reactions intersect at point O. If the resultant effect of the applied loads is a resultant force whose line of action also passes through point O, the two reactions will be capable of keeping such a special system of loads in equilibrium. While the structure is still classed as unstable, it will be in a state of unstable equilibrium under this loading and its reactions can be determined by the equations of static equilibrium.

If a roller support is added at point C, as shown in Fig. 2.9c, the reactions of the structure will be equivalent to three links whose lines of action are neither concurrent nor parallel. The structure will therefore be stable and also statically determinate, for the three unknown reaction elements—the three unknown magnitudes—can be found from the three equations of static equilibrium. On the other hand, if the link support is applied at point C in Fig. 2.9d, the structure will be geometrically unstable since the supports will consist of three links whose lines of action all intersect at point O. The structure is not completely unrestrained, of course, but will rotate instantaneously about point O through some finite angle until equilibrium is attained. Since the new position assumed by the structure is a function of the deformations of the structure, the reactions acting on the structure in its displaced position are considered to be statically indeterminate.

The structure shown in Fig. 2.9g is obviously stable and has a total of six unknown reaction elements—a horizontal and vertical component and a couple at each support. Since there are only three equations of static equilibrium available, the structure is indeterminate to the third degree. The insertion of the hinge in the structure shown in Fig. 2.9j introduces one condition equation and therefore makes the structure indeterminate to the second degree. The insertion of the roller in Fig. 2.9k makes it possible to transmit only a vertical force from one part of the structure to the other. This in effect introduces two equations of condition, one that the sum of the moments about a of the forces acting on *either* portion shall be equal to zero and the other that the sum of the horizontal components of the forces acting on *either* portion shall be equal to zero. As a result, this structure is indeterminate to the first degree only.

In the figures from *p* on, all the truss portions should be considered as rigid bodies whose bar forces are statically determinate once the

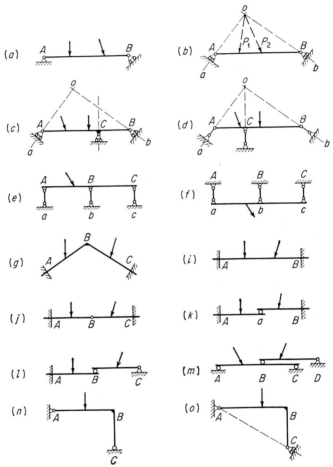

Figure 2.9   Examples for classification

reactions have been calculated. The arrangement of the bars of a truss necessary for stability, etc., is discussed in detail in Chap. 4. For the purposes of the present discussion, the trussed portions may be considered as solid bodies. The structures in Figs. 2.9*p* and *q* are easily seen to be stable and statically determinate under any general system of loads. In Fig. 2.9*r*, the structure has four unknown reaction elements—the magnitude of the reactions at the link supports *A* and *B* and both the magnitude and direction of the reaction of the hinge support at C. To solve for these four unknowns there are only three equations of static equilibrium. The structure is therefore stable and statically indeterminate to the first degree.

For structures similar to that shown in Fig. 2.9s, it is often better to use a different approach to determine their stability or statical determinancy. In such structures, the counting of the available equations may be awkward and obscure. Suppose instead that the structure is

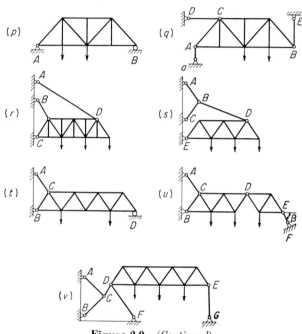

Figure 2.9   (*Continued*)

broken up into separate parts and the solution for the forces connecting each part to the rest of the structure is considered. If in this case an isolating section is passed through the link BD and the hinge support at E is replaced by the horizontal and vertical reaction components that it supplies, the truss portion will be isolated as a free body acted upon by the applied loads and three unknown forces—the link force and the two components of the reaction at E. If this free body is to be in equilibrium, these three unknowns may be determined so as to satisfy the three equations of static equilibrium. Taking $\Sigma M_E = 0$ on the free body will yield an equation involving the link force as the only unknown. Knowing the force in the link BD, we can find the forces in links AB and BC by $\Sigma F_x = 0$ and $\Sigma F_y = 0$ applied to hinge B isolated as a free body. The reactions of this structure may therefore be found by the equations of static equilibrium, and the structure is thus said to be stable and statically determinate.

2.11 Illustrative Examples of Computation of Reactions. The student should study the following examples carefully. All the structures are statically determinate, but the student should investigate them independently for practice.

Example 2.1 *Determine the reactions of the beam ab.*

Method A:

$\Sigma M_a = 0,\ \curvearrowright{+}$
$(60)(4) - (40)(12) + (40)(20) - (R_{by})(24) = 0$ $\qquad \therefore R_{by} = {}^{560}\!/_{24} = \underline{\underline{23.3^k}}\ \Updownarrow$
$\qquad\qquad\qquad\qquad\qquad\qquad\qquad\qquad\qquad\qquad\qquad R_{bx} = \tfrac{3}{4}R_{by} = \underline{\underline{17.5^k}}\ \mathrel{+}\mathrel{+}$

$\Sigma M_b = 0,\ \curvearrowright{+}$
$(R_{ay})(24) - (60)(20) + (40)(12) - (40)(4) = 0$ $\qquad \therefore R_{ay} = {}^{880}\!/_{24} = \underline{\underline{36.6_k}}\ \Updownarrow$
$\Sigma F_x = 0,\ \xrightarrow{+},\ R_{ax} - 30 - 17.5 = 0$ $\qquad \therefore R_{ax} = \underline{\underline{47.5^k}}\ \mathrel{+}\!\!\rightarrow$
Check: $\qquad \Sigma F_y = 0,\ \uparrow{+},\ 36.6 - 60 + 40 - 40 + 23.3 = 0$
$\qquad\qquad\qquad\qquad\qquad\qquad\qquad\qquad 0 = 0 \qquad \therefore\ O.K.$

Method B:

$\Sigma M_b = 0,\ \curvearrowright{+}$

	+	−
$-(60)(20) =$		$1,200$
$+(40)(12) = 480$		
$-(40)(4) =$		160
	$+\ \overline{480}$	$-\ \overline{1,360}$
		$+\ \ \overline{480}$
$R_{ay} = \underline{\underline{36.6^k}}\ \Updownarrow =$	$-$	$\dfrac{880}{24}$

$R_{ax} = \underline{\underline{47.5^k}}\ \mathrel{+}\!\!\rightarrow$

$\Sigma M_a = 0,\ \curvearrowright{+}$

	+	−
$+(60)(4) =$	240	
$-(40)(12) =$		480
$+(40)(20) =$	800	
	$+\ \overline{1,040}$	$-\ \overline{480}$
		$-\ \ \overline{480}$
$R_{by} = +$	$\overline{560}$	$= \underline{\underline{23.3^k}}\ \Updownarrow$
	$\dfrac{}{24}$	

$R_{bx} = = \tfrac{3}{4} \times 23.3 = \underline{\underline{17.5^k}}\ \mathrel{+}\mathrel{+}$

Method C:

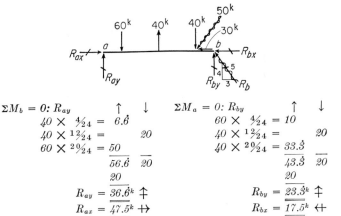

$$\Sigma M_b = 0: R_{ay} \qquad \uparrow \quad \downarrow$$

$$40 \times \tfrac{4}{24} = 6.\dot{6}$$

$$40 \times 1\tfrac{2}{24} = \qquad 20$$

$$60 \times 2\tfrac{0}{24} = 50$$

$$\overline{56.\dot{6} \quad 20}$$

$$20$$

$$R_{ay} = \underline{36.\dot{6}^k} \; \Updownarrow$$

$$R_{ax} = \underline{47.5^k} \; \rightarrowtail$$

$$\Sigma M_a = 0: R_{by} \qquad \uparrow \quad \downarrow$$

$$60 \times \tfrac{4}{24} = 10$$

$$40 \times 1\tfrac{2}{24} = \qquad 20$$

$$40 \times 2\tfrac{0}{24} = 33.\dot{3}$$

$$\overline{43.\dot{3} \quad 20}$$

$$20$$

$$R_{by} = \underline{23.\dot{3}^k} \; \Updownarrow$$

$$R_{bx} = \underline{17.5^k} \; \leftarrowtail$$

Discussion:

The three methods of solving for the reactions are all fundamentally the same and differ only in the details of the arrangement of the computations. Method A is probably the best way to organize the computations for an unusual or complicated structure. However, the systematic arrangement of either method B or C will be found most useful for the simple or conventional types of beams and trusses.

Note that it is usually extremely convenient to replace inclined forces by their horizontal and vertical components and to use these components instead of the forces in writing the equations of static equilibrium.[1]

The computer should clearly indicate his results by underlining them and also by indicating the units and directions of the forces. Remember that if an answer comes out plus, the force was assumed acting in the correct direction on the free-body sketch; if the answer comes out minus, the force acts opposite to the direction assumed.

Note that in this problem two moment equations and one force equation were used in the solution. The check equation $\Sigma F_y = 0$ gives a check on the vertical components of the reactions but does not check the horizontal components. If $\Sigma M = 0$ were written about any axis that did not lie on a line through a and b, a check would be obtained on the values of the horizontal reactions.

[1] If both a force and its components are shown on a free-body sketch, a wavy line should be drawn along the shank of the force arrow, thereby indicating that the force has been replaced by its components.

Example 2.2   *Determine the reactions of this structure.*

Solution:

Isolate *ab*:   **Isolate** *bd*:

$\Sigma M_c = 0,\ \overset{\curvearrowright}{}$ $+$ $-$

$\Sigma M_b = 0,\ \overset{\curvearrowright}{}$ $\Sigma M_d = 0,\ \overset{\curvearrowright}{}$ $-(17.7)(6) =$ 106.6

$(9)(R_{ay}) - (40)(5) = 0$ $-(17.7)(18) =$ -320 $-(40)(3) =$ 120

$\therefore R_{ay} = 22.2^k \uparrow$ $-(40)(15) =$ -600 $+(4 \times 8)(4) =$ 128

$-(4 \times 8)(8) =$ -256 $+(30)(10) =$ 300

$\Sigma M_a = 0,\ \overset{\curvearrowright}{}$ $+428$ -226.6

$(40)(4) - (S)(9) = 0$ -226.6

$-(30)(2) =$ -60

$S = 17.7^k \uparrow$ $R_{cy} = 103^k \uparrow = \dfrac{-1,236}{12}$ $R_{dy} = \dfrac{+201.3}{12} = 16.7^k \uparrow$

$\Sigma F_x = 0$ $\Sigma F_x = 0$

$\therefore R_{ax} = 30^k \twoheadleftarrow$ $\therefore F = 30^k \leftarrow$

Check: $\Sigma F_y = 0,\ \uparrow +,$ *for entire structure*

$$22.2 - 40 - 40 + 103 - 32 - 30 + 16.7 = 0$$
$$142 - 142 = 0 \qquad \therefore O.K.$$

Discussion:

When isolating the two portions ab and bd from one another, imagine that the hinge pin is removed. The hinge may transmit a force acting in any direction through the center of the hinge pin. If the horizontal and vertical components of this force are designated by F and S and assumed to act as shown on the portion ab, they must act in the opposite senses on the portion bd. Note that an independent check could be obtained on both the horizontal and the vertical reactions by taking $\Sigma M = 0$ about some axis which does not lie on the line through a and d.

Example 2.3   *Determine the reactions of this beam.*

$\Sigma M_b = 0, \curvearrowright$
$$(R_{ay})(20) - (40)(12) - (30)(6) + (44.72)(6) - (R_{cy})(12) = 0$$
$$20R_{ay} = 12R_{cy} + 391.68$$

$\Sigma F_x = 0, \rightarrow +, \quad \frac{3}{4}R_{ay} - 22.36 - \frac{4}{3}R_{cy} = 0 \qquad R_{cy} = 0.5625R_{ay} - 16.77$

$\therefore 20R_{ay} = 6.75R_{ay} - 201.24 + 391.68 \qquad R_{ay} = +14.37^k \uparrow \qquad R_{ax} = \underline{10.78^k} \nrightarrow$

and $R_{cy} = 8.08 - 16.77 = -8.69 \qquad R_{cy} = \underline{-8.69^k} \updownarrow \qquad R_{cx} = \underline{-11.59^k} \nrightarrow$

$\Sigma M_a = 0, \curvearrowright$
$$(40)(8) + (30)(14) - (R_{by})(20) + (44.72)(26) + (8.69)(32) = 0$$
$$R_{by} = 109.04^k \uparrow$$

Check: $\Sigma F_y = 0, \uparrow +$
$$14.37 - 40 - 30 + 109.04 - 44.72 - 8.69 = 0$$
$$123.41 - 123.41 = 0 \qquad \therefore O.K.$$

Check: $\Sigma F_x = 0, \xrightarrow{+}$
$$10.78 - 22.36 + 11.59 = 0$$
$$-22.36 + 22.37 = 0 \qquad \therefore O.K.$$

Example 2.4   *Determine the reactions of this structure.*

Isolate bc:

$$\Sigma M_b = 0, \; \curvearrowright, \; (2)(10)(5) - (R_{cy})(10) = 0 \qquad \therefore R_{cy} = 10^k \uparrow$$
$$\Sigma M_c = 0, \; \curvearrowright, \; (S)(10) - (2)(10)(5) = 0 \qquad \therefore S = 10^k \uparrow$$

Isolate ab:

$$\Sigma M_a = 0, \; \curvearrowright, \; (10)(12) + (6)(9) + (8)(6) - M_a = 0 \qquad \therefore M_a = 222^{k1} \curvearrowleft$$
$$\Sigma F_y = 0, \uparrow +, \; R_{ay} - 8 - 6 - 10 = 0 \qquad R_{ay} = 24^k \uparrow$$

Check: $\Sigma F_y = 0$, *applied to entire beam,*

$$24 - 8 - 6 - 20 + 10 = 0$$
$$\therefore 0 = 0 \qquad \therefore O.K.$$

Example 2.5   *Determine the reactions of this truss.*

$$\Sigma F_a = 0 \qquad R_{bx} = 24^k \longleftarrow$$
$$\Sigma M_b = 0, \; \curvearrowright, \; (R_{ay})(40) - (40)(37.5) = 0 \qquad R_{ay} = 37.5^k \uparrow$$
$$\Sigma M_a = 0, \; \curvearrowright, \; (40)(12.5) - (24)(30) - (R_{by})(40) = 0 \qquad R_{by} = -5.5^k \updownarrow$$
Check: $\qquad \Sigma F_y = 0, \uparrow +, \; 37.5 - 32 - 5.5 = 0 \qquad \therefore O.K.$

Discussion:

In problems such as this, first compute the loads acting on the structure. This may be done by isolating the roller, which is in equilibrium under its own weight, the tension in the cable, and the reaction of the truss on the roller. The loads acting on the structure having first been determined, it is a straightforward problem to determine the reactions. Note that it has been assumed that there is no friction between the roller and truss and therefore that the interacting force between the two acts normal to the line ab and is directed through the center of the roller.

Example 2.6   *Determine the reactions of this structure.*

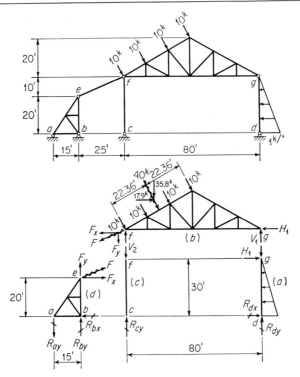

Free-body sketch a:

$$\Sigma M_d = 0, \; \curvearrowright, \; (H_1)(30) - \frac{(1)(30)}{2}(10) = 0 \qquad H_1 = 5^k \nrightarrow$$

$$\Sigma M_g = 0, \; \curvearrowright, \; \frac{(1)(30)}{2}(20) - (R_{dx})(30) = 0 \qquad R_{dx} = 10^k \nrightarrow$$

Free-body sketch b:

$\Sigma M_f = 0, \; \curvearrowright, \; (40)(22.36) - (V_1)(80) = 0 \qquad V_1 = 11.18^k \uparrow \qquad \therefore R_{dy} = \underline{11.18^k} \; \Updownarrow$

$\Sigma F_x = 0, \; \rightarrow, \; 17.9 - 5 - F_x = 0 \qquad F_x = 12.9 \leftarrow \qquad \therefore F_y = \frac{2}{5}(12.9) = \underline{5.16^k} \; \Updownarrow$

$\Sigma M_g = 0, \curvearrowright, \; (17.9)(10) - (35.8)(60) - (5.16)(80) + (V_2)(80) = 0 \qquad V_2 = 29.77 \uparrow$

$\therefore R_{cy} = \underline{\underline{29.77^k}} \; \Updownarrow$

Check: $\Sigma F_y = 0, \; \uparrow+, \; -5.16 + 29.77 - 35.8 + 11.18 = 0$

$\therefore \; -0.01 = 0 \qquad \therefore \text{ O.K.}$

Free-body sketch d:

$$\Sigma M_b = 0, \ \curvearrowright, \ (12.9)(20) - (R_{ay})(15) = 0 \quad \therefore R_{ay} = 17.9^k \ \big\downarrow$$

$$\Sigma M_a = 0, \ \curvearrowright, \ (12.9)(20) - (5.16)(15) - (R_{by})(15) = 0 \quad \therefore R_{by} = 12.04^k \ \big\uparrow$$

$$\Sigma F_x = 0 \qquad R_{bx} = 12.9^k \ \leftarrow\!+$$

Check on structure as a whole:

$$\Sigma F_x = 0, \ \xrightarrow{+}, \ -12.9 + 17.9 + 10 - \frac{(1)(30)}{2} = 0 \quad \therefore 0 = 0 \quad O.K.$$

$$\Sigma F_y = 0, \ \uparrow\!+, \ -17.9 + 12.04 + 29.77 - 35.8 + 11.18 = 0 \quad -0.01 = 0 \quad O.K.$$

$$\Sigma M_a = 0, \ \curvearrowright, \ -(12.04)(15) - (29.77)(40) - (11.18)(120) + (17.9)(40)$$

$$+ (35.8)(60) - \frac{(1)(30)}{2}(10) = 0$$

$$-2,863 + 2,864 = 0 \quad O.K.$$

Discussion:

In problems of this type, the structure is broken up into its separate structural elements, and the free-body sketches are drawn for each element. The interacting forces between elements may be assumed to act in either sense, but they must act in opposite senses on two adjacent elements. For example, if force F is assumed to act down to the left on sketch b, it must act up to the right on sketch d. Since the structure as a whole is in equilibrium, each of its elements must be in equilibrium. The equations of static equilibrium for each element must be satisfied, and they therefore form a basis for the solution of the unknown reactions and unknown interacting forces.

Note that when all the unknown reactions have been obtained the results may be checked by applying the equations of static equilibrium to the structure as a whole to see whether or not they are satisfied.

2.12 Superposition of Effects. At this point, a brief discussion of the *principle of superposition* is appropriate. This principle is used continually in structural computations. As a matter of fact, its use has already been implied in the solution of Example 2.1 by method C. There the reactions due to each of the three loads were computed separately and added algebraically to obtain the reactions due to all three loads acting simultaneously. In other words, the separate effects were superimposed to obtain the total effect.

Such a procedure is usually permissible. However, there are two important cases in which the principle of superposition is *not* valid: (1) when the geometry of the structure changes an essential amount during the application of the loads; (2) when the strains in the structure are not directly proportional to the corresponding stresses, even though the effect of change in geometry can be neglected. The latter case occurs whenever the material of the structure is stressed beyond the elastic limit or when it does not follow Hooke's law through any portion of its stress-strain curve.

In Art. 2.3, it is pointed out that usually the deformations of a structure are so slight that it is permissible to consider the structure as a rigid body in applying the equations of static equilibrium and therefore to neglect the effect of slight changes in geometry on the lever arms of forces, the inclinations of members of the structure, etc. However, consider the structure shown in Fig. 2.10. In this case, all three hinges lie along the same straight line in the unloaded structure. It will be found necessary to consider the alteration of the geometry caused by the deformation of the structure, for the lever arms, slopes of the members, etc., are changed by an important amount. As a result, it will be found that the forces and deflections in the structure are not directly proportioned to the load P even though the material of the structure may follow Hooke's law. This is therefore an illustration of the first case noted above where the principle of superposition is not valid. In this

Figure 2.10 Nonlinear structure

structure, the effects of a load $2P$ are not twice the effects of a load of P, nor are the effects of a load equal to $P_1 + P_2$ equal to the algebraic sum of the effects of P_1 and of P_2 acting separately. From applied mechanics, a more important case may be recalled where superposition is not valid—the case of a slender strut acted upon by both axial and transverse loads. There the stresses, moments, deflections, etc., due to an axial load of $P_1 + P_2$ are not equal to the algebraic sum of the values caused by P_1 and P_2 acting separately. Fortunately, most cases of this type where superposition is not valid are easily recognized.

It is mentioned above that superposition is not valid in cases where, although the effect of change in geometry can be neglected, the material of the structure does not follow Hooke's law. If such structures are also statically determinate, then quantities that can be found by statically determinate stress analysis (such as reactions, shears, and bending moments) may be superimposed but stress intensities and deflections cannot be superimposed. For example, in the case of an end-supported cast-iron beam, the reactions and the shear force and bending moment on the transverse cross sections are statically determinate quantities and may be superimposed. However, the stress intensities and deflections produced by the bending moment due to a load $2P$ are not equal to twice those due to load P, and hence such quantities cannot be superimposed. If the reactions of a cast-iron beam are statically indeterminate, then none of these quantities may be superimposed, since the stress analysis is then a function of the deformation of the structure.

2.13 Problems for Solution

*Problem 2.1 Classify the structures shown in Figs. 2.9e, f, i, l to o, and t to v as stable or unstable and statically determinate or indeterminate. Discuss and state reasons for your answer.

*Problem 2.2   Determine the reactions of the beams of Fig. 2.11.

Hint: Only a vertical force can be transmitted through
the roller at point d

Hint: Find the reactions
on the beam ab by
cutting cable between
A and B and C and E.
Find cable tension by
isolating pulley D

Figure 2.11   Problem 2.2

*Problem 2.3   Determine the reactions of the structures of Fig. 2.12.

Figure 2.12   Problem 2.3

Problem 2.4 It is sometimes difficult to convince a student that there are only a certain number of independent equations. To demonstrate this, consider the structure shown in Fig. 2.8. Draw three free-body sketches—one of the entire structure, one of the portion ab, and one of the portion bc. Write three equations of static equilibrium for each sketch. Compare and combine these nine equations containing six unknowns, and show that there are only four independent equations containing four unknowns among them.

Problem 2.5 Determine the reactions of the structures shown in Fig. 2.13.

Figure 2.13   Problem 2.5

3

Shear and Bending Moment

3.1 General. The ultimate aim of all stress analysis is to determine the adequacy of a structure to carry the loads for which it is being designed. The criteria for determining this involve a comparison of the stresses developed by the applied loads with the allowable stresses for the structural material being used. The stresses acting on any cross section may be studied by passing an imaginary section that cuts through the structure along this cross section and isolates *any* convenient portion of the structure as a free body. If all the other forces acting on this isolated portion have already been determined, the required resultant effects of the stresses acting on the cross section being investigated may easily be computed by the equations of static equilibrium.

One of the commonest structural elements to be investigated in this manner is a *beam*, i.e., a member that is subjected to bending or flexure by loads acting transversely to its centroidal axis or sometimes by loads acting both transversely and parallel to this axis. The following discussions are limited to straight beams, i.e., beams in which the axis joining the centroids of the cross sections (centroidal axis) is a straight line, and to beams the cross sections of which are of such a shape that the shear center[1] and the centroid are coincident. It is also assumed that all the loads and reactions lie in a single plane which also contains the centroidal axis of the member and a principal axis of every cross section. If these conditions are satisfied, the beam will simply bend in the plane of loading without twisting.

3.2 Determination of Stresses in Beams. Suppose that, in determining the adequacy of the statically determinate beam in Fig. 3.1, it is necessary to compute the stresses on a transverse cross section *mn*. The reactions necessary for static equilibrium may be computed easily and are shown in free-body sketch *a*. The portions of the beam to the left and right of cross section *mn* may be imagined to be isolated from one another by cutting the structure in two along this section. Free-body sketches *b* and *c* may then be drawn showing all the forces acting on these two portions of the beam.

When one considers the external forces acting on either of the portions *b* or *c*, it is immediately apparent that the portions are not in static equilibrium under the external

---

[1] For a discussion of the location of the shear center of a beam cross section, see standard textbooks on mechanics of materials such as S. H. Crandall and N. C. Dahl, "An Introduction to the Mechanics of Solids," p. 314, McGraw-Hill Book Company, Inc., New York, 1959.

forces acting alone.   If the beam as a whole is in equilibrium, however, then each and every portion of it must be in equilibrium.   It is therefore necessary that there shall be internal forces or stresses distributed over the internal faces which have been exposed by the imaginary cut.   These stresses must be of such a magnitude that their resultant effect balances that of the external forces acting on the isolated portion and therefore maintains the portion in a state of static equilibrium.

The stresses acting on the exposed internal faces may be broken down into two components, one component acting normal to the face and called the *normal stresses*

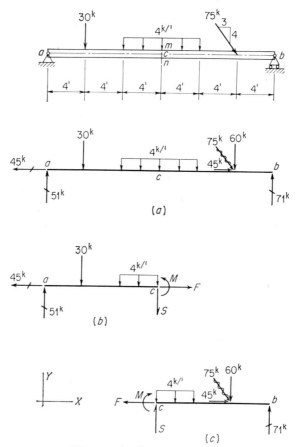

Figure 3.1   Stresses in beams

and the other acting parallel to the face and called the *shear stresses*.   In the free-body sketches b and c, these stresses have been replaced by their resultant effect as represented by the forces S and F, acting through the centroid of the cross section, and the couple M.   Note that the resultant effects S, F, and M of the stresses acting on the portion in sketch b are shown to be numerically equal but opposite in sense to the corresponding effects shown in sketch c.   That this must be so is apparent from the following considerations:

Consider the free-body sketch a showing the entire beam acted upon by all the external loads and reactions.   Suppose that the resultant of all the external forces applied to the beam on the left of section mn is computed in magnitude and position. Suppose that similar computations are made for the resultant of the remaining external forces applied to the right of mn.   Now if the beam as a whole is in equilibrium under *all* the forces acting on it, it must be apparent that the resultant of those forces applied to the left of mn must be collinear, numerically equal, but opposite in sense to the resultant of the remaining forces applied to the right of mn.   It therefore follows that the resultant of the external forces in sketch b must be numerically equal but opposite in sense to the resultant of the external forces in sketch c, and hence the resultant effects of the stresses in sketches b and c must likewise bear the same relation.

It is convenient to assign names to F, S, and M, the resultant effects of the stresses acting on a cross section of a member.   The axial force F acts through the centroid of the cross section and will be called the *axial resisting force*.   The transverse force S will be called the *shear resisting force* and the couple M will be called the *resisting moment*.

In order to satisfy the three equations of static equilibrium for either the portion of the beam in sketch b or the portion in sketch c, the magnitudes of F, S, and M must be such as to counteract the resultant of the external forces acting on the portion considered.   Which portion is used makes no difference theoretically.   The portion having the fewer external forces is ordinarily used so as to simplify the computations. Static equilibrium will be maintained by values computed in the following manner: The axial resisting force F and the shear resisting force S must be equal and opposite to the axial and transverse components, respectively, of the resultant of the external forces acting on the portion of the beam under consideration.   Upon taking moments about an axis through the centroid of the cross section, i.e., the point of intersection of the resisting forces F and S, it is then apparent that the resisting moment M must be equal in magnitude but opposite in direction to the moment of the resultant of the external forces acting on this portion.

Once the axial resisting force, the shear resisting force, and the resisting moment have been determined at any section, the intensities of the normal and shear stresses at any point on the cross section may be computed by using well-known equations given in standard textbooks on the strength of materials.

3.3 Shear and Bending Moment Defined; Sign Convention.   From the previous discussion, it is evident that, in order to determine the magnitudes of the axial resisting force, the shear resisting force, and the resisting moment acting on a cross section of a beam, it is advisable to compute first the magnitude and position of the resultant of the external forces acting on the portion of the beam on either side of that cross section.   It is usually convenient to represent this resultant by its axial component, its transverse component, and its moment about an axis through the centroid of the cross section under consideration.   These three elements are statically equivalent to this resultant and are given the following three names, respectively: *axial force*, *shear force*, and *bending moment*.   The definition of these three terms may therefore be summarized as follows:

Axial Force F.   **The axial force at any transverse cross section of a straight beam is the algebraic sum of the components acting parallel to the axis of the beam of all the loads and reactions applied to the portion of the beam on** *either* **side of that cross section.**

Shear Force (Shear) S.   **The shear force at any transverse cross section of a straight beam is the algebraic sum of the components acting transverse to the axis of the beam of all the loads and reactions applied to the portion of the beam on** *either* **side of the cross section.**

Bending Moment M. The bending moment at any transverse cross section of a straight beam is the algebraic sum of the moments, taken about an axis passing through the centroid of the cross section, of all the loads and reactions applied to the portion of the beam on *either* side of the cross section. The axis about which the moments are taken is, of course, normal to the plane of loading.

While it is not the purpose of the authors to encourage the memorizing of structural principles, formulas, etc., these definitions recur constantly and are so fundamental to structural engineering that students should study and understand them so thoroughly and completely that they are indelibly impressed on their minds.

With these definitions introduced, this discussion may now be summarized by saying that the axial resisting force acting on a cross section will be equal but opposite to the axial force at that section; the shear resisting force will be equal and opposite to the shear force (or shear); and the resisting moment will be equal and opposite to the bending moment.

(+) Axial force

(+) Shear force

(+) Bending moment

Figure 3.2
Beam convention

In subsequent calculations, the following sign convention will be used to designate the directions of axial force, shear, and bending moment at any transverse cross section of a beam. The convention is that ordinarily used in structural engineering. It is clear and simple to employ and will be referred to as the *beam convention.* As shown in Fig. 3.2, axial force is plus when it tends to pull two portions of a member apart, i.e., when it tends to produce a tensile stress on the cross section. Shear force is plus when it tends to push the left portion upward with respect to the right. Bending moment is plus when it tends to produce tension in the lower fibers of the beam and compression in the upper fibers, i.e., to bend the beam concave upward. Many beams are horizontal, and this convention may be applied without confusion. When a member is not horizontal, however, either side may be selected as the "lower side" and the beam convention applied to correspond.

3.4 Method of Computation of Shear and Bending Moment. The procedure for computing the axial force, shear force, and bending moment at any section of a beam is straightforward and may be explained easily by the illustrative problem shown in Fig. 3.3. In this problem, it is desired to compute the axial force, shear, and bending moment at the cross sections at points *b*, *c*, and *d*. The computation of the axial force is simple and needs no explanation in this case, as is true of this computation with respect to most beams. If the couple applied by the bracket at point *c* is assumed to be applied along the cross section at point *c*, there will be an abrupt change in the bending moment at this point and it is necessary to compute the bending moment, first on a cross section an infinitesimal distance to the left of *c* and then on a cross section an infinitesimal distance to the right of *c*.

It will be recalled that the shear and bending moment at any cross section may be computed by considering *all* the external loads and reactions applied to the portion of the beam on *either* side of the cross section under consideration. *Either* portion may be used, but the computations may usually be performed more efficiently by using that involving the smaller number of forces. One portion having been selected, *only the loads and reactions acting on that portion* are included in the summation of the force components or moments.

The left-hand portion of the beam was chosen for computing the shear and bending moment at section *b* and at the sections to the left and right of point *c*. Free-body sketches *b*, *c*, and *d*, respectively, show the portion used in each case. To illustrate the advantage of using one portion instead of the other, the shear and bending moment at section d are computed by using first the left- and then the right-hand portion, as shown in free-body sketches e and f, respectively. Note the simplicity of the computations for sketch f as compared with sketch e.

To explain typical computations, consider those for the shear and bending moment on the cross section just to the left of point c, as shown in sketch c. The shear force at this section is the algebraic sum of the 57-kip reaction, the uniformly distributed load totaling 16 kips, and the concentrated load of 30 kips, where the reaction causes

Sketch a:

$$\Sigma M_e = 0, \curvearrowright + \qquad\qquad \Sigma M_a = 0, \curvearrowright +$$

$(4 \times 4)(22)$	$= -$	352	$(4 \times 4)(2)$	$= +$	32
$(30)(16)$	$= -$	480	$(30)(8)$	$=$	240
$(40)(8)$	$= -$	320	$(6)(4)$	$=$	24
$(60)(4)$	$= -$	240	$(40)(16)$	$=$	640
		$\overline{-1,392}$	$(60)(20)$	$=$	$1,200$
$(6)(4)$	$= +$	24			$\overline{+2,136}$
		$\overline{-1,368}$			

$$\therefore R_{ay} = \frac{1,368}{24} = 57^k \Uparrow \qquad \therefore R_{ey} = \frac{2,136}{24} = 89^k \Uparrow$$

Check: $\Sigma F_y = 0, \uparrow +$
$$57 + 89 - 16 - 30 - 40 - 60 = 0 \quad O.K.$$

Sketch b: $S = 57 - (4)(4) = +41^k$
$\qquad\qquad M = (57)(6) - (16)(4) = +278^{k\prime}$

Sketch c: $S = 57 - 16 - 30 = +11^k$
(*to left of* $M = (57)(12) - (16)(10) - (30)(4)$
point c) $\qquad = +404^{k\prime}$

Sketch d: $S = 57 - 16 - 30 = +11^k$
(*to right of* $M = (57)(12) - (16)(10) - (30)(4)$
point c) $\qquad\qquad + 24 = +428^{k\prime}$

Sketch e: $S = 57 - 16 - 30 - 40 = -29^k$
$\qquad\qquad M = (57)(18) - (16)(16) - (30)(10)$
$\qquad\qquad\qquad - (40)(2) + 24 = +414^{k\prime}$

Sketch f: $S = -89 + 60 = -29^k$
$\qquad\qquad M = (89)(6) - (60)(2) = +414^{k\prime}$

Sketch g: $S = 41 - 30 = +11^k$
$\qquad\qquad M = 278 + (41)(6) - (30)(4)$
$\qquad\qquad\qquad = +404^{k\prime}$

Figure 3.3 Computation of axial force, shear, and bending moment

positive shear (tends to push left portion up) and the two loads cause negative shear (tend to push the left portion down). Hence, the shear force is

$$S = +57 - 16 - 30 = +11 \text{ kips}$$

having a resultant positive effect tending to push the left portion up with respect to the right. For equilibrium, the shear resisting force obviously must be 11 kips acting down on the cross section in sketch c. In the same manner, the bending moment is the algebraic sum of the moments about the centroid of the cross section of the same three forces. Since the reaction tends to produce tension in the lower fibers at the section and the two loads tension in the upper fibers, the bending moment is

$$M = (57)(12) - (16)(10) - (30)(4) = +404 \text{ kip-ft}$$

having a resultant positive tendency to produce tension in the lower fibers. Again for equilibrium, it is necessary for the resisting moment to be 404 kip-ft acting counterclockwise on the cross section in sketch c. The remaining computations are self-explanatory.

It is important to note that, if the axial force, shear, and bending moment are known at one cross section, similar items may be computed at any other cross section by using these known quantities rather than working with all the external forces on the entire portion of the beam on either side of the new cross section. For example, the axial force, shear, and bending moment at c could be computed with the quantities already computed at b. This is apparent since the shear, axial force, and bending

$$57 \times 4 = \quad 228$$
$$-16 \times 2 = -\ 32$$
$$\overline{\quad 196} = M\ @\ f$$
$$41 \times 4 = \quad 164$$
$$-30 \qquad\ \ \overline{360} = M\ @\ g$$
$$11 \times 4 = \quad\ \ 44$$
$$\overline{\quad 404} = M\ @\ c$$
$$24$$
$$\overline{\quad 428} = M\ @\ c$$
$$11 \times 4 = \quad\ \ 44$$
$$-40 \qquad\ \ \overline{472} = M\ @\ h$$
$$-29 \times 4 = -116$$
$$-60 \qquad\ \ \overline{356} = M\ @\ j$$
$$-89 \times 4 = -356$$
$$\overline{\quad\quad\ 0} = M\ @\ e$$

Figure 3.4   Shear and bending-moment diagrams

moment at b are statically equivalent to the resultant of the external forces applied to the left of b. Hence, the contribution of these forces to the resultant effect of all the forces to the left of c may be evaluated by using their statical equivalent rather than the forces themselves. The advantage of this procedure increases with the number of external forces applied to the left of point b. Such computations are illustrated under sketch g of Fig. 3.3, and the forces acting on the isolated portion bc are shown in this sketch.

3.5   Shear and Bending-moment Curves.   When a beam is being analyzed or designed for a stationary system of loads, it is helpful to have curves or diagrams available from which the value of the shear and bending moment at any cross section may readily be obtained. Such curves may be constructed by drawing a base line corresponding in length to the axis of the beam and then plotting ordinates at points along this base line which indicate the value of the shear or bending moment at that cross section of the beam. Plus values of shear or bending moment are plotted as upward ordinates from the base line and minus values as downward ordinates. Curves drawn connecting the ends of all such ordinates along the base line are called shear and bending-moment curves. In Fig. 3.4, shear and bending-moment curves are shown for the beam in Fig. 3.3.

The construction of these curves is quite straightforward, but needs some explanation. The shear on a cross section an infinitesimal distance to the right of point a is $+57$ kips, and therefore the shear curve rises abruptly from zero to $+57$ at this point. In the portion af, the shear on any cross section a distance x from point a is

$$S = 57 - 4x$$

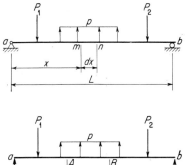

which indicates that the shear curve in this portion is a straight line decreasing from an ordinate of $+57$ at a to $+41$ at point f. Since no additional external loads are applied between points f and g, the shear remains $+41$ on any cross section throughout this interval and the shear curve is a horizontal line as shown. An infinitesimal distance to the left of point g the shear is $+41$, but at an infinitesimal distance to the right of this point the 30-kip load has caused the shear to be further reduced to $+11$. Therefore, at point g, there is an abrupt change in the shear curve from $+41$ to $+11$. In this same manner, the re-

Figure 3.5 Relations between load, shear, and bending moment

mainder of the shear curve may easily be verified. It should be noted that, in effect, a concentrated load is assumed to be applied at a point and hence at such a point the ordinate to the shear curve changes abruptly by an amount equal to the load. Physically, it is impossible for a load to be applied at a point without developing an infinite contact pressure, and it is therefore necessary for such loads to be distributed over a small area. However, for computations such as for shear and bending moment, such inconsistencies are ignored, and it is considered mathematically possible that concentrated loads may be applied at a point.

In the portion af, the bending moment at a cross section a distance x from point a is $M = 57x - 2x^2$. Therefore, the bending-moment curve starts at 0 at point a and increases along a curved line to an ordinate of $+196$ kip-ft at point f. In the portion fg, the bending moment at any point a distance x from point f is $M = 196 + 41x$. Hence, the bending-moment curve in this portion is a straight line increasing from an ordinate of 196 at f to 360 at g. Likewise, in the portion gc, the bending-moment curve is a straight line increasing to a value of 404 at a cross section an infinitesimal distance to the left of point c. However, at a cross section an infinitesimal distance to the right of point c, the bending moment has increased by 24 to 428. Assuming the external couple of 24 kip-ft to be applied exactly on the cross section at point c, there will be an abrupt change in the bending-moment curve similar to the abrupt changes in the shear curve already discussed. In an analogous manner, the remainder of the bending-moment curve may easily be verified. The computations for the controlling ordinates of the curve are shown in Fig. 3.4.

3.6 Relations between Load, Shear, and Bending Moment. In those cases where a beam is subjected to transverse loads, the construction of the shear and bending-moment curves may be facilitated by recognizing certain relationships that exist between load, shear, and bending moment. For example, consider the beam shown in Fig. 3.5. Suppose that the shear S and the bending moment M have been computed at the cross section for any point m. Point m is located by the distance x, which is measured from point a, being positive when measured to the right from that point. Suppose that the shear and bending moment are now computed at the cross section at point n, a differential distance dx to the right of point m. Assuming that a uniformly distributed *upward* load of an intensity p per unit length of beam has been applied to the beam between m and n, the shear and bending moment will have increased by differential amounts to values of $S + dS$ and $M + dM$, respectively.

The new values of shear and bending moment at point n may be computed by using the values already computed at point m, as is discussed in Art. 3.4. Thus,

$$S + dS = S + p\,dx \qquad\qquad (a)$$

$$M + dM = M + S\,dx + p\,dx\,\frac{dx}{2} \qquad\qquad (b)$$

Therefore, from (a) it is evident that

$$\frac{dS}{dx} = p \qquad\qquad (c)$$

and, differential quantities of the second order being neglected, from Eq. (b) it may be found that

$$\frac{dM}{dx} = S \qquad\qquad (d)$$

It should be particularly noted that, in addition to the usual beam convention being used for shear and bending moment, upward loads have been considered as positive and x has been assumed to increase from left to right.

The relationships stated mathematically in Eqs. (c) and (d) are tremendously helpful in constructing shear and bending-moment curves. Consider first Eq. (c). It states that the rate of change of shear at any point is equal to the intensity of load applied to the beam at that point, i.e., that the slope of the shear curve at any point is equal to the intensity of the load applied to the beam at that point. The change in shear dS between two cross sections a differential distance dx apart is

$$dS = \frac{dS}{dx}\,dx = p\,dx$$

Therefore, the difference in shear at two cross sections A and B is

$$S_B - S_A = \int_{x_A}^{x_B} p\,dx \qquad \text{or} \qquad S_B = S_A + \int_{x_A}^{x_B} p\,dx$$

Thus, the difference in the ordinates of the shear curve at points A and B is equal to the total load applied to the beam between these two points.

According to Eq. (c) and the sign convention used in its derivation, if the load is upward, or positive, at a point on the beam, the shear is changing at a positive rate at this point. This means that if the shear is computed on a cross section just to the right of this point, i.e., at a slightly greater distance x from the left support, it will tend to be *more* positive, or algebraically larger, than it was at the first point. Of course, if the load is downward, or negative, at a point, just the reverse will be true. If we think of this interpretation in terms of slope of the shear curve and use the ordinary calculus convention for slope of a curve, if dS/dx is plus, the curve slopes upward to the right, since positive values of S are plotted upward and x increases from left to right. If dS/dx is minus, the shear curve slopes downward to the right.

To apply these ideas, if a uniformly distributed load is applied to a portion of a beam, p will be constant and therefore the shear will change at a constant rate and the shear curve will be a straight sloping line in such a portion. However, if the load is distributed but its intensity varies continuously, the shear curve will be a curved line whose slope changes continuously to correspond. If no load is applied to a beam between two points, the rate of change of shear will be zero, i.e., the shear will remain constant and the shear curve will be straight and parallel to the base line in this portion. At a point where a concentrated load is applied to a beam, the intensity of load will be infinite, and therefore the slope of the shear curve will be infinite, or vertical. At such a point, there will be a discontinuity in the shear curve, and the difference in ordinates from one side of the load to the other will be equal to the concentrated load. These ideas conform to the discussion of the previous article.

Equation (d) may be interpreted in the same manner. It states that the rate of change of bending moment at any point is equal to the shear at that point in the beam, i.e., the slope of the bending-moment curve at any point is equal to the ordinate of the shear curve at that point. The change in bending moment dM between two cross sections a differential distance dx apart is

$$dM = \frac{dM}{dx}\,dx = S\,dx$$

Therefore, the difference in the bending moment at two cross sections A and B is

$$\int_{M_A}^{M_B} dM = M_B - M_A = \int_{x_A}^{x_B} S\,dx \qquad \therefore M_B = M_A + \int_{x_A}^{x_B} S\,dx$$

or the difference in the ordinates of the bending-moment curve at points A and B is equal to the area under the shear curve between the two points.

From Eq. (d) it is evident that, if the shear is positive at a point in a beam, the rate of change of bending moment is also positive at this point. This means that if the bending moment is computed on a cross section just to the right of this point, i.e., at a slightly greater distance x from the left support, it will tend to be *more* positive, or algebraically larger, than it was at the first point. If the shear is negative, just the reverse will be true. In terms of slope of the bending-moment curve, it may be said that if dM/dx is positive (or negative), the slope of the bending-moment curve at this point is upward (or downward) to the right, since positive values of M are plotted upward and x increases from left to right.

If the shear is constant in a portion of the beam, the bending-moment curve will be a straight line in this portion. However, if the shear varies in any manner within a portion, the bending-moment curve will be a curved line. At a point where a concentrated load is applied, there is an abrupt change in the ordinate of the shear curve and, therefore, an abrupt change in the slope of the bending-moment curve at such a point. At a point where the shear curve goes through zero and the ordinates to the left of the point are positive and those to the right negative, the slope of the bending-moment curve will change from positive at the left of the point to negative at the right of the point. Therefore, the ordinate of the bending-moment curve will be a maximum at such a point. If, on the other hand, the shear curve goes through zero in the reverse manner, the ordinate at that point on the bending-moment curve will be a minimum.

3.7 Construction of Shear and Bending-moment Curves. The ideas of Art. 3.6 may be utilized most efficiently in constructing shear and bending-moment curves for beams subjected to transverse loads if the following procedure is adopted: After computing the reactions of a beam, first plot a load curve. The load curve is a curve the ordinates of which show the intensity of the distributed load applied to the beam at any point. In addition, all concentrated loads should be indicated. Upward, or positive, loads should be drawn above the base line and negative loads below. Then the shear and bending-moment curves may be constructed in turn, proceeding from left to right across the beam and establishing the *shape* of the curves by using the following principles, which are summarized from the above discussion:

1. The slope of the shear curve at any point is equal to the intensity of the distributed load at that point.

2. Abrupt changes in the ordinates of the shear curve occur at points of application of concentrated loads.

3. The slope of the bending-moment curve at any point is equal to the ordinate of the shear curve at that point.

4. At points where concentrated loads are applied, there are abrupt changes in the ordinates of the shear curve and, hence, abrupt changes in the slopes of the bending-moment curve.

It is usually necessary to compute the numerical values of the ordinates of the shear and bending-moment curves only at the points where the shapes of the curves change or at points where the maximum or minimum values occur. Such values may usually be most easily computed by direct computation as in Fig. 3.3. Such computations may be checked using the following principles if the value of one ordinate of a curve is known:

5. The difference in the ordinates of the shear curve between any two points is equal to the total load applied to the beam between these two points, i.e., the area under the load curve between these two points plus any concentrated loads applied within this portion.

6. The difference in the ordinates of the bending-moment curve between any two points is equal to the area under the shear curve between these two points.

This method of constructing shear and bending-moment curves will be illustrated in the examples that follow.

Although all these relations and this discussion apply specifically to the case of a beam loaded by transverse loads, it should not be inferred that they are useless in analyzing a beam subjected to a more general condition of loading. The method of handling such cases will be discussed in the examples that follow. For cases of loading involving anything more complicated than transverse loads, it will be seen that a load curve loses its utility and becomes impractical. While some of the above relations may be used to advantage, it will be found that, in most of the more complicated cases of loading, they must be revised. To illustrate, in Example 3.5 it will be seen that abrupt changes in the ordinates of the moment curve occur at points where external couples are applied to the beam. Therefore, the difference in the ordinates of the bending-moment curve between any two points will be equal to the area under the shear curve between these two points plus or minus the sum of any external couples applied to the beam within this portion. However, the student will find that the experience gained in drawing the shear and bending-moment curves for the simpler cases of transverse loadings will enable him to proceed to the more complicated problems with very little difficulty.

3.8 Illustrative Examples—Statically Determinate Beams. The following examples will illustrate the construction of shear and bending-moment curves for statically determinate beams, utilizing the ideas and principles discussed above:

Example 3.1

$$\Sigma M_c = 0, \overset{\curvearrowright}{+}$$
$$-(2)(16)(8) = -256$$
$$+(2)(1\tfrac{2}{2})(1\tfrac{2}{3}) = \underline{+33.3}$$
$$-222.6$$
$$\therefore R_{ay} = 11.13^k \, \text{⇑}$$

$$\Sigma M_a = 0, \overset{\curvearrowright}{+}$$
$$(2)(16)(12) = +384$$
$$(2)(1\tfrac{2}{2})(23.3) = \underline{+233.3}$$
$$+617.3$$
$$\therefore R_{cy} = 30.87^k \, \text{⇑}$$

$$\Sigma F_y = 0, \uparrow+,$$
$$11.13 + 30.87 - 32 - 10 = 0 \quad \therefore \, O.K.$$

Shear:

$$S_c(left) = 11.13 - (2)(16) = -20.87^k$$

Location of point of S = 0 between b and c,

$$S_x = 11.13 - 2x = 0 \quad \therefore \, x = 5.57'$$

Bending moment:

$$M_b = +(11.13)(4) = +44.52^{k'}$$

$$M_c = -\frac{(2)(10)}{2}\left(\frac{10}{3}\right) = -33.3^{k'}$$

Between b and c,

$$M_{max} = (11.13)(9.57) - \frac{(2)(5.57)^2}{2}$$
$$= +75.48^{k'}$$

Discussion:

    In establishing the shape of the shear and bending-moment curves, follow the ideas of Art. 3.7. Starting at the left end of the shear curve, the curve rises abruptly to a value of +11.13. From a to b, since p = 0, the shear curve is horizontal. From b to c, since p = −2, the shear curve slopes downward to the right at a constant slope to a value of −20.87 just to the left of c. At c, the reaction causes an abrupt increase in the ordinate of the shear curve to +10 just to the right of point c. From c to d, since p = −2 + (x/5), the shear curve slopes downward to the right with a slope that varies linearly from −2 at c to 0 at d.

    In the same way, the bending-moment curve starts at 0 at a and progresses from a to b with a constant positive slope (upward to the right). To the right of b, the slope decreases linearly from a slope of +11.13 at b to zero at the point of maximum moment, and further to a slope of −20.87 at c. There is an abrupt change in slope at c to a value of +10 just to the right of c. Between c and d, the slope decreases from +10 to 0 at d.

    The numerical value of the controlling ordinates of the shear and bending moment may be most easily computed by direct computation in the manner discussed in Art. 3.4.

Example 3.2

$$\Sigma F_x = 0, \; \overleftarrow{+}, \; R_{ax} - (1,125)(1\%) = 0 \qquad R_{ax} = 10,125^{\#} \; \text{++}$$

$$\Sigma M_a = 0, \; \overset{\curvearrowright}{+}, \; (1,125)(1\%)(6) - M_a - 0 \qquad M_a = 60,750'^{\#} \; \curvearrowright$$

Shear and bending moment:

$$At \; y = 9': \quad p = -1,125 + (62.5)(9) = -1,125 + 562.5 = -562.2^{\#/\prime}$$
$$S = +(562.5)(\%) = +2,531.3^{\#}$$
$$M = -(562.5)(\%)(3) = -7,593.8'^{\#}$$

Discussion:

After the reactions have been determined, the load, shear, and bending-moment curves may be drawn, the fibers on the right-hand side of the cantilever being considered as the "lower fibers" in applying the beam convention. Then, the uniformly varying load would be considered downward or negative in plotting the load curve.

The shear curve rises abruptly at a to a value of +10,125. Progressing toward b, the shear curve starts downward with a negative slope of 1,125 but gradually flattens out to zero slope as well as a zero ordinate at b.

On the other hand, the bending-moment curve starts from an ordinate of −60,750 at a with a positive slope of +10,125. Proceeding toward b, the magnitude of slope remains positive but steadily decreases until at b both the slope and the ordinate of the bending-moment curve are zero.

The shape of these curves having been established, an ordinate of either the shear or the bending-moment curve at any intermediate point such as y = 9 may most easily be computed directly by considering the portion of the beam between that point and b.

Example 3.3

$\Sigma M_b = 0, \curvearrowleft_+$

$$
\begin{array}{rcr}
30 \times 2 &=& 60 \\
30 \times 8 &=& 240 \\
40 \times 14 &=& 560 \\
40 \times 18 &=& 720 \\
40 \times 22 &=& 880 \\
40 \times 26 &=& 1{,}040 \\
\hline
220 & & 3{,}500
\end{array}
$$

$\therefore R_{ay} = 109.37^k \, \updownarrow$

$\Sigma M_a = 0, \curvearrowright_+$

$$
\begin{array}{rcr}
30 \times 30 &=& 900 \\
30 \times 24 &=& 720 \\
40 \times 18 &=& 720 \\
40 \times 14 &=& 560 \\
40 \times 10 &=& 400 \\
40 \times 6 &=& 240 \\
\hline
& & 3{,}540
\end{array}
$$

$\therefore R_{by} = 110.63^k \, \updownarrow$

$\Sigma F_x = 0, \uparrow, \ 109.37 + 110.63 - 220 = 0$
$+$

$\therefore O.K.$

$$
\begin{array}{rlrll}
S = & 109.4 \times 6 = & 656.4 & \\
& -40 & \overline{656.4} &= M_6 \\
S = & 69.4 \times 4 = & +277.6 & \\
& -40 & \overline{934.0} &= M_{10} \\
S = & 29.4 \times 4 = & +117.6 & \\
& -40 & \overline{1{,}051.6} &= M_{14} \\
S = & -10.6 \times 4 = & -42.4 & \\
& -40 & \overline{1{,}009.2} &= M_{18} \\
S = & -50.6 \times 6 = & -303.6 & \\
& -30 & \overline{705.6} &= M_{24} \\
S = & -80.6 \times 6 = & -483.6 & \\
& -30 & \overline{222.0} &= M_{30} \\
S = & -110.6 \times 2 = & -221.2 & \\
& +110.6 & \overline{0.8} &= M_{32} \\
\hline
& 0 & 0 &
\end{array}
$$

$\therefore O.K. \qquad \therefore O.K.$

Note: M_{max} occurs where shear passes through zero (14 ft from a).

Discussion:

   In computing ordinates to the shear and bending-moment curves for concentrated load systems, it is convenient to arrange the computations in this manner, the ordinates being computed successively from left to right by means of principles 5 and 6 stated near the end of Art. 3.7. Note that a check of the computations is obtained if both curves come back to zero at point b.

Example 3.4

$$\Sigma M_c = 0, \ \overset{+}{\curvearrowright}$$
$$(R_{by})(18) - (32)(5)(10) = 0$$
$$\therefore R_{by} = 88.\dot{8}^k \ \Uparrow$$

$$\Sigma M_b = 0, \ \overset{+}{\curvearrowright}$$
$$-(R_{cy})(18) + (32)(5)(8) = 0$$
$$\therefore R_{cy} = 71.\dot{1}^k \ \Uparrow$$

$$\Sigma F_y = 0, \uparrow +, \ 88.8 + 71.\dot{1} - 160 = 0$$
$$\therefore \ O.K.$$

$$M_b = -(5)(8)(4) = \underline{-160^{k'}}$$
$$M_c = -(5)(6)(3) = \underline{-90^{k'}}$$

In portion b to c,

$$S = 48.\dot{8} - 5x$$

When $S = 0 = 48.\dot{8} - 5x \ \therefore \ x = \underline{\underline{9.\dot{7}'}}$

$$\therefore M_{max} - M_b = \frac{(48.\dot{8})(9.\dot{7})}{2}$$

$$M_{max} = M_b + 239.02$$
$$= -160 + 239.02$$
$$= \underline{\underline{+79.02^{k'}}}$$

Discussion:

   Note that the magnitude of the maximum ordinate of the bending-moment curve between b and c may easily be computed by adding algebraically the area under the shear curve between b and m to the ordinate M_b.   In this case, this is particularly easy because the area under the shear curve is one triangle.

Example 3.5

All pulleys have 2' diameter.

$\Sigma M_a = 0,\ \overset{\curvearrowright}{+}$
$(5)(30) - (4)(30) - (R_{ey})(24) = 0$
$\therefore R_{ey} = 1.25^k$

$\Sigma M_e = 0,\ \overset{\curvearrowright}{+}$
$(R_{ay})(24) - (30)(19) - (30)(4) = 0$
$\therefore R_{ay} = 28.75^k$

$\Sigma F_y = 0,\ \uparrow+,\ 28.75 + 1.25 - 30 = 0$
$\therefore O.K.$

Bending moments:

At b (*just to left*),
$\qquad M_{b_L} = +(28.75)(6) = +172.5^{k'}$

At b (*just to right*),
$\qquad M_{b_R} = (28.75)(6) + (30)(3)$
$\qquad\qquad\qquad = +262.5^{k'}$

At c (*just to left*),
$\qquad M_{c_L} = 262.5 - (1.25)(8) = +252.5^{k'}$

At c (*just to right*), *isolate element of beam*

between two cross sections—one just to left, one just to right of point c. This element will have a differential length, say, of 0+ ft.

$\Sigma M_{c_R} = 0,\ \overset{\curvearrowright}{+}$
$+252.5 - (30)(3) - (1.25)(0+)$
$\qquad\qquad\qquad\qquad - M_{c_R} = 0$
$M_{c_R} = 252.5 - 90 - 0 = +162.5^{k'}$

At d (*just to left*),
$\qquad M_{d_L} = (1.25)(8) + (30)(3) = +100^{k'}$

At d (*just to right*),
$\qquad M_{d_R} = (1.25)(8) = +10^{k'}$

Discussion:

As is evident in Chap. 2, the computation of the reactions of such structures may be carried out without first computing the forces that the individual pulleys apply to the beam. However, for the construction of shear and bending-moment curves and the computation of internal stresses in the beam, it is necessary to compute the detailed manner in which the pulleys apply the loads. The reactions from sketch I and the pulley loads having been computed, sketch II may be drawn, showing the precise manner in which the structure is loaded.

As explained in the latter part of Art. 3.7, it is unwise to attempt to draw a load curve in such problems. Instead, the load curve is replaced by a free-body sketch such as sketch II. The student may now proceed to draw the shear bending-moment curves, using *the fundamental definitions and methods of computation and, of course, utilizing the experience gained in simple problems such as Examples 3.1 to 3.4. All the above calculations may be followed without difficulty.*

Example 3.6

$$\Sigma M_a = 0, \curvearrowright +$$
$$(50)(4) + (10)(6) - (40)(12)$$
$$+ (40)(16) + (40)(20) - (30)(1)$$
$$- (R_{gy})(24) = 0$$
$$200 + 60 - 480 + 640 + 800 - 30$$
$$= 24R_{gy}$$
$$\therefore R_{gy} = \underline{49.58^k} \; \text{↑}$$

$$\Sigma M_g = 0, \curvearrowright +$$
$$(R_{ay})(24) - (50)(20) + (10)(6)$$
$$+ (40)(12) - (40)(8) - (40)(4)$$
$$- (30)(1) = 0$$
$$24R_{ay} = 1{,}000 - 60 - 480 + 320$$
$$+ 160 + 30$$
$$\therefore R_{ay} = \underline{40.42_k} \; \text{↑}$$

$$\Sigma F_y = 0, \; \text{↑}+,$$
$$40.42 + 49.58 - 50 + 40 - 40 - 40$$
$$= 0 \quad \therefore O.K.$$

Bending moment:

$$M_b = 40.42 \times 4 = \quad 161.68 = M_b$$
$$-9.58 \times 4 = \quad \underline{-38.32}$$
$$123.36 = M_c \, (left)$$
$$\underline{+60}$$
$$+183.36 = M_c(right)$$
$$-9.58 \times 4 = \quad \underline{-38.32}$$
$$145.04 = M_d$$
$$30.42 \times 4 = \quad 121.68$$
$$\underline{+266.72} = M_e$$
$$-9.58 \times 4 = \quad \underline{-38.32}$$
$$+228.40$$
$$= M_f \, (left)$$
$$\underline{-30}$$
$$+198.40$$
$$= M_f \, (right)$$
$$-49.58 \times 4 = -198.32$$
$$\underline{0.08} = M_g$$
$$0$$

Discussion:

This example is similar to Example 3.5, and the same comments are applicable. In addition, it should be noted that inclined loads are sometimes applied to the top or bottom edges of a beam, such as the 50-kip load at f. In such cases, it is evident that the horizontal component of such loads will produce a couple which will cause an abrupt change in the ordinates of the bending-moment curve at this point.

Example 3.7

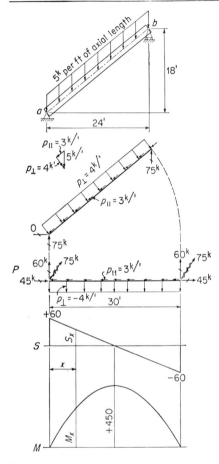

$$\Sigma M_a = 0, \ \overset{\frown}{+}$$
$$(5)(30)(12) - (R_{by})(24) = 0$$
$$\therefore R_{by} = 75^k$$

$$\Sigma M_b = 0, \ \overset{\frown}{+}$$
$$-(5)(30)(12) + (R_{ay})(24) = 0$$
$$\therefore R_{ay} = 75^k$$

Shear and bending moment:

At a distance x from a,

$$S_x = 60 - 4x$$
$$M_x = 60x - 2x^2$$

When $x = 15'$,

$$S_{15} = 60 - 4(15) = 0$$
$$M_{15} = (60)(15) - (2)(15)^2 = +450^{k'}$$

Discussion:

  When inclined beams are acted upon by a uniformly distributed vertical load per unit of axial length, such as their own dead weight, the load intensity may be resolved into components perpendicular and parallel to the axis of the beam.   If the load is applied to the axis of the beam, only the component perpendicular to the axis contributes to shear and bending moment, the component parallel to the axis contributing only to the axial force.   If the reactions are also resolved into components parallel and perpendicular to the axis, the shear and bending-moment curves may easily be constructed in the usual manner.   These curves may be drawn about axes drawn parallel to the member or, for convenience, in the manner illustrated above.   The load curve may also be used to advantage in such problems.

3.9 Illustrative Example—Girders with Floor Beams. In all the previous examples, the loads have been applied directly to the beam itself. Quite often, however, the loads are applied indirectly through a floor system that is supported by girders. A typical construction of this kind is shown diagrammatically in Fig. 1.7 and also in Fig. 3.6. In such a structure, the loads P are applied to the longitudinal members S, which are called *stringers*. These are supported by the transverse members FB, called *floor beams*. The floor beams are in turn supported by the girders G. Therefore, no matter whether the loads are applied to the stringers as a uniformly distributed load or as some system of concentrated loads, their effect on the girder is that of concentrated loads applied by the floor beams at points a, b, c, etc.

Section A-A
Figure 3.6 Girder bridge

To illustrate the construction of the shear and bending-moment curves for girders loaded in this manner, consider Example 3.8. For simplicity, it will be assumed in this example that the loads are applied to stringers supported on the top flange of the girder as shown. The stringers and girder will be assumed to lie in the same plane. It will further be assumed that the stringers are supported as simple end-supported beams, with a hinge support at one end and a roller at the other. As a first step, it is necessary to obtain the stringer reactions and from them to determine the concentrated forces acting on the girder. From this point on, the construction of the shear and bending-moment curves for the girder proceeds as for any beam acted upon by a system of concentrated loads.

The student should study the following questions concerning this type of structure: How do the shear and bending-moment curves differ in the two cases, i.e., with and without the stringers? Is there any notable similarity? If a uniformly distributed load is applied to the structure, how will the shear and bending-moment curves compare with and without stringers? If the stringers are not supported as simple end-supported beams by the girder, will the answers to the previous questions be altered? Problems at the end of the chapter will emphasize some of these points.

Example 3.8

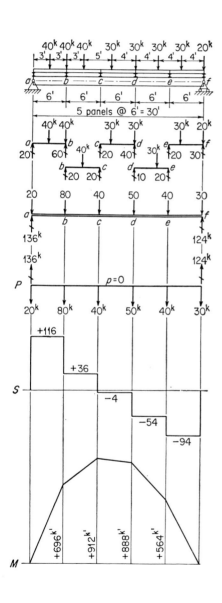

Considering isolated girder acted upon by stringer reactions,

$$\Sigma M_a = 0, \curvearrowright +$$
$$(80)(1P) = 80P$$
$$(40)(2P) = 80P$$
$$(50)(3P) = 150P$$
$$(40)(4P) = 160P$$
$$(5P)(R_{fy}) = 470P$$
$$Net\ R_{fy} = 94^k \Updownarrow$$
$$\underline{30^k}$$
$$Gross\ R_{fy} = 124^k \Updownarrow$$

$$\Sigma M_f = 0, \curvearrowleft +$$
$$(80)(4P) = 320P$$
$$(40)(3P) = 120P$$
$$(50)(2P) = 100P$$
$$(40)(1P) = 40P$$
$$(5P)(R_{ay}) = 580P$$
$$Net\ R_{ay} = 116^k \Updownarrow$$
$$\underline{20^k}$$
$$Gross\ R_{ay} = 136^k \Updownarrow$$

$$\Sigma F_y = 0, \uparrow +$$
$$124 + 136 - (3)(40) - (4)(30)$$
$$- 20 = 0$$
$$260 - 120 - 120 - 20 = 0 \ \therefore\ O.K.$$

These reactions may also be checked by using the applied loads directly.

Shear and bending moment on girder:

$$Gross\ R_{ay} = \quad 136^k$$
$$\underline{-20} \qquad\qquad 0 = M_a$$
$$S_{a-b} = \quad 116^k \times 6 = +696^{k'}$$
$$\overline{+696^{k'}} = M_b$$
$$\underline{-80}$$
$$S_{b-c} = \quad 36 \times 6 = +216$$
$$\overline{+912} = M_c$$
$$\underline{-40}$$
$$S_{c-d} = \quad -4 \times 6 = -24$$
$$\overline{+888} = M_d$$
$$\underline{-50}$$
$$S_{d-e} = \quad -54 \times 6 = -324$$
$$\overline{+564} = M_e$$
$$\underline{-40}$$
$$S_{e-f} = \quad -94 \times 6 = -564$$
$$\overline{0} = M_f$$
$$\underline{-30}$$
$$\underline{-124}$$
$$Gross\ R_{fy} = \underline{+124}$$
$$0$$

Discussion:

Note the terms "gross" and "net" reactions. The gross reaction is the total force supplied by the support and includes any load applied to the beam immediately over the support point. The net reaction is the reaction at a support due to all loads except the one applied right at this support. Note that only the net reaction enters the computations for shear and bending moment.

3.10 Illustrative Examples—Statically Indeterminate Beams. From the discussion in Chap. 2, it will be recalled that the stress analysis of indeterminate structures involves the satisfaction of not only the equations of static equilibrium but also certain conditions of deformation. The analysis of such structures is discussed in detail later in this book. In these later chapters, it will be seen that, after some of the unknown stress components (such as reactions, shears, and moments) have been found so as to satisfy the conditions of deformation, the remaining unknowns may be found so as to satisfy the equations of static equilibrium. That is, the remaining portion of the problem is statically determinate and may be handled by means of the techniques explained in Chaps. 2 and 3 for statically determinate structures.

Once the reactions of a statically indeterminate beam have been determined, the shear and bending moment may be computed at any desired cross section in the same manner as that used for statically determinate beams. The same principles may also be followed in constructing shear and bending-moment curves.

Example 3.9 *This statically indeterminate continuous beam is not only acted upon by the loads shown but is also subjected to certain support movements. The following bending moments have been computed by using methods discussed later for analysis of statically indeterminate structures.*

$$M_a = -85.17^{k'}$$
$$M_b = -60.05^{k'}$$
$$M_c = 0$$

Sketch I:

$$\Sigma M_b = 0, \curvearrowright, (R_{ay})(10) + 60.05 - 85.17$$
$$- (60)(4) = 0$$
$$\therefore R_{ay} = \underline{\underline{26.51^k}} \;\uparrow$$
$$\therefore S_{b_L} = 26.51 - 60 = \underline{\underline{-33.49^k}}$$

Sketch II:

$$\Sigma M_b = 0, \curvearrowright,$$
$$(5)(10)(5) - 60.05 - (R_{cy})(10) = 0$$
$$\therefore R_{cy} = \underline{\underline{19.00^k}} \;\uparrow$$
$$\therefore S_{b_R} = -19.00 + 50 = \underline{\underline{+31.00^k}}$$

Sketch III:

$$\Sigma F_y = 0, \; R_{by} = 33.49 + 31.00$$
$$= \underline{\underline{64.49^k}} \;\uparrow$$

Bending moments:

$$M_e = -85.17 + (26.51)(6)$$
$$= \underline{\underline{+73.89^{k'}}}$$

Between b and c, find M_{max},

$$S_x = 31.00 - 5x$$

When $S_x = 0 = 31 - 5x$,

$$\therefore x = \underline{\underline{6.20'}}$$

$$M_{max} = -60.05 + (31.00)\left(\frac{6.20}{2}\right)$$
$$= \underline{\underline{+36.05^{k'}}}$$

Example 3.10 *The following bending moments have been computed by methods of analysis of indeterminate structures.*

"Lower fibers" considered as being on the side of the member by the dashed lines. (+) Bending moments cause tension in lower fibers

At A end of AB: M = −260.9
At B end of AB: M = − 62.0
At B end of BD: M = − 62.0
At D end of BD: M = −430.0
At D end of DE: M = + 72.6
At D end of DG: M = +502.7

$$\Sigma M_B^{(I)} = 0, \qquad 260.9$$
$$62.0$$
$$R_{Ax} = \frac{198.9}{12} = 16.58$$

$$\Sigma M_D^{(II)} = 0, \qquad 100 \times 16 = 1,600$$
$$62$$
$$\overline{1,662.0}$$
$$-430.0$$
$$S_B = 38.5 = \frac{1,232.0}{32}$$

$$\Sigma M_B^{(II)} = 0, \qquad 100 \times 16 = 1,600$$
$$430$$
$$\overline{2,030}$$
$$-62$$
$$S_D = 61.5 = \frac{1,968}{32}$$

$$\Sigma M_D^{(III)} = 0, \qquad 100 \times 30 = 3,000$$
$$72.6$$
$$R_{Ey} = 122.9 = \frac{3,072.6}{25}$$

3.11 Problems for Solution

Problem 3.1   Draw the shear and bending-moment curves for the conditions of loading of a simple end-supported beam as shown in Fig. 3.7.

Figure 3.7   Problem 3.1

Suggestion: What is the maximum bending moment in each case? If, in part *b*, *k* equals 0.5, what is the maximum bending moment?

*Problem 3.2   Draw the load, shear, and bending-moment curves for the beam of Fig. 3.8.

Figure 3.8   Problem 3.2

*Problem 3.3   Draw the shear and bending-moment curves for the beam of Fig. 3.9.

Figure 3.9   Problem 3.3

Problem 3.4   Draw the shear and bending-moment curves for the beams shown in Probs. 2.2*a* and *b*.

*Problem 3.5   Draw the shear and bending-moment curves for beam *AB* of Fig. 3.10.

Figure 3.10   Problem 3.5

Figure 3.11   Problem 3.6

*Problem 3.6   Draw the shear and bending-moment curves for the beam of Fig. 3.11.

Problem 3.7   Draw the shear and bending-moment curves for beam *ab* of Prob. 2.2*d* and for beams *ab* and *cd* of Prob. 2.2*e*.

Problem 3.8 Draw the shear and bending-moment curves for members *ab* and *bc* of the structure of Fig. 3.12.

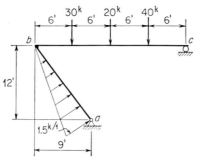

Figure 3.12 Problem 3.8

*****Problem 3.9** Draw the shear and bending-moment curves for girder *ab* of Fig. 3.13.

Figure 3.13 Problem 3.9

Problem 3.10 Draw the shear and bending-moment curves for girder *ab* of Fig. 3.14.

Figure 3.14 Problem 3.10

Problem 3.11   Draw the shear and bending-moment curves for the beams shown in Fig. 3.15.

Figure 3.15   Problem 3.11

Problem 3.12   Draw the shear and bending-moment curves for the beams shown in Fig. 3.16.

(a)

(b)

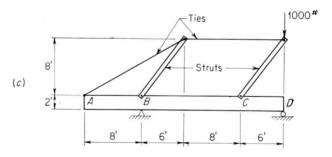

(c)

Figure 3.16   Problem 3.12

4

Trusses or Plane Frameworks

4.1 General—Definitions. In this chapter, the general theory of the stress analysis of trusses is discussed. Consideration is also given to the manner in which the members (bars) of a truss must be arranged in order to obtain a stable structure. In a subsequent chapter, the stress analysis of some of the more important types of bridge and roof trusses under design loading conditions is considered in detail.

A truss or plane framework may be defined as a structure composed of a number of bars, all lying in one plane and hinged together at their ends in such a manner as to form a rigid framework. For the purposes of the discussion in this chapter, it will be assumed that the following conditions exist: (1) The members are connected together at their ends by frictionless pin joints. (2) Loads and reactions are applied to the truss only at the joints. (3) The centroidal axis of each member is straight, coincides with the line connecting the joint centers at each end of the member, and lies in a plane that also contains the lines of action of all the loads and reactions. Of course, it is physically impossible for all these conditions to be satisfied exactly in an actual truss, and therefore a truss in which those idealized conditions are assumed to exist is called an ideal truss.

Any member of an ideal truss may be isolated as a free body by disconnecting it from the joints at each end. Since all external loads and reactions are applied to the truss only at the joints and no loads are applied between the ends of the members themselves, the isolated member would be acted upon by only two forces, one at each end, each force representing the action on the member by the joint at that end. Since all the pin joints are assumed to be frictionless, each of these two forces must be directed through the center of its corresponding pin joint. For

115

these two forces to satisfy the three conditions of static equilibrium for the isolated member, $\Sigma F_x = 0$, $\Sigma F_y = 0$, and $\Sigma M = 0$, it is apparent that the two forces must both act along the line joining the joint centers at each end of the member and must be numerically equal but opposite in sense. Since the centroidal axes of the members of an ideal truss are straight and coincide with the line connecting the joints at each end of the member, every transverse cross section of a member will be subjected to the same axial force but to no bending moment or shear force. **The stress analysis of an ideal truss is essentially completed, therefore, when the axial forces have been determined for all the members of the truss, since the normal stress intensities on the cross sections of the members can then easily be computed.**

Three-dimensional structures composed of a number of bars hinged together in such a manner as to form a rigid framework are called *space frameworks*. Such structures are discussed in detail in Chap. 9.

Trusses and space frameworks are structures which are arranged specifically to carry loads applied at their joints. As a result of these joint loads, the members of such frameworks are subjected primarily to axial forces and to little or no shear and bending. If transverse loads are applied to the members between joints, one of the requirements for truss behavior is violated, and significant shear and bending effects are produced. If the joints are substantially frictionless pin joints or ball joints, these flexural effects are confined to the members which are subjected to the between-joint loads. (Problem 4.6 illustrates such a case.) If, however, the joints are substantially rigid, the structure acts as if it were a rigid frame (see Art. 4.13). In such a case, the flexural effects in the transversely loaded members are transmitted through the joints to other members so that significant shear and bending can be produced in all members of the structure. Methods of analyzing statically indeterminate rigid frames will be discussed in Chaps. 11 and 13.

4.2   Ideal vs. Actual Trusses. While it is true that the ideal truss is hypothetical and can never exist physically, the stress analysis of an actual truss based on the assumption that it acts as an ideal truss usually furnishes a satisfactory solution for the axial forces in the members of the actual truss. The axial forces in the members, or bars, of a truss will be referred to as the *bar forces*. The stress intensities due to the bar forces computed on the basis that the truss acts as an ideal truss are referred to as *primary stress intensities*.

The pins of an actual pin-jointed truss are never really frictionless; moreover, most modern trusses are made with riveted or welded joints so that there can be no essential change in the angles between the members meeting at a joint.[1] As a result, even when the external loads are

[1] See also first three paragraphs of Art. 4.13, Rigid Frames.

applied at the joint centers, the action of the joints on the ends of a member may consist of both an axial and transverse force and a couple. The transverse cross sections of a member may be subjected, therefore, to an axial force, a shear force, and a bending moment. In addition, the dead weight of the members themselves must necessarily be distributed along the members and therefore contributes to further bending of the members. If good detailing practice is followed and care is taken to see that the centroidal axes of the members coincide with the lines connecting the joint centers, additional bending of the members due to possible eccentricities of this type may be eliminated or minimized.

All these departures from the conditions required for an ideal truss not only may develop a bending of the members of an actual truss but also may cause bar forces that are somewhat different from those in an ideal truss. The differences between the stress intensities in the members of an actual truss and the primary stress intensities computed for the corresponding ideal truss are called *secondary stress intensities*. It may be demonstrated, however, that in the case of the usual truss, where it is detailed so that the centroidal axes of the members meet at the joint centers and where the members are relatively slender, the secondary stress intensities are small in comparison with the primary stress intensities.[1] The primary stress intensities computed on the basis that the truss acts as an ideal truss are therefore usually satisfactory for practical design purposes.

In subsequent discussions, the term truss will be used to denote a framework that either is actually an ideal pin-jointed truss or may be assumed to act as if it were an ideal truss.

4.3   Arrangement of Members of a Truss.   In Art. 4.1, it is stated that the members of a truss must be hinged together in such a manner as to form a rigid framework. The term *rigid* as used in this instance has the same significance as when used previously in Art. 2.3, i.e., **a framework is said to be rigid if there is no relative movement between any of its particles beyond that caused by the small elastic deformations of the members of the framework.**   In this sense, a rigid framework may be obtained by arranging the truss members in many different ways. When the bars have been satisfactorily arranged in one of these ways, the entire truss can be supported in some manner and used to carry loads just like a beam.

Suppose that it is necessary to form a truss with pin joints at points a, b, c, and d. If this is attempted by pin-connecting four bars together as shown in Fig. 4.1a, the resulting framework will not be rigid and may collapse in the manner shown owing to the loads P, until, in this case,

---

[1] See J. I. Parcel and R. B. B. Moorman, "Analysis of Statically Indeterminate Structures," chap. 9, John Wiley & Sons, Inc., New York, 1955.

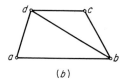

Figure 4.1 Frameworks: (a) nonrigid; (b) rigid

joints a, d, and c are lying along a straight line. After a little thought, it is apparent that any attempt such as this to connect four or more joints together with a like number of bars hinged at their ends will result in a framework which will collapse under all but a few special conditions of loadings. If, however, points a and b are first connected by a bar ab, then two other bars of lengths ad and bd can be hinged at a and b, respectively. If the d ends of these bars are then hinged together at point d, a rigid triangle will be formed connecting joints a, b, and d. Bars of lengths dc and bc can then be connected to the pin joints at d and b, respectively. The c ends of these bars can then be made to coincide at point c and pinned together at this point, thus rigidly connecting joint c to the triangle abd and resulting in a rigid framework of five bars with joints at a, b, c, and d. As alternative arrangements, point c can be con-

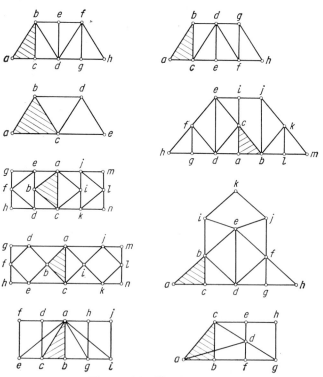

Figure 4.2 Simple trusses

nected to joints a and b by bars ac and bc or to joints a and d by bars ac and dc. Several other alternative arrangements can be used by first forming a triangle with joints a, b, and c; or with a, d, and c; or with b, c, and d. Any of these arrangements will result in a rigid framework capable of withstanding any system of joint loads without collapsing, as long as none of the members buckles or is strained beyond the yield point of the material.

In this same manner, any number of pin joints can be connected together with bars to form a rigid frame-

work. The procedure is first to select three joints that do not lie along a straight line. These three points can then be connected by three bars pinned together to form a triangle. Each of the other joints can then be connected in turn, two bars being used to connect it to any two suitable joints on the framework already constructed. Of course, the new joint and the two joints to which it is connected should never lie along the same straight line. Each of the trusses shown in Fig. 4.2 has been formed in this manner by starting with a rigid triangle abc and using two additional bars to connect each of the other joints in alphabetical order.

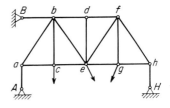

Trusses the bars of which have been arranged in this manner are called *simple trusses*, for this is the simplest and commonest type of bar arrangement encountered in practice.

In all truss diagrams such as those shown in Fig. 4.2, the members will be represented by single lines and the pin joints connecting

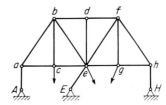

Figure 4.3 Stable and statically determinate simple trusses

them by small circles. Sometimes bars may cross each other but may be arranged in such a manner that they are not connected together by a joint at their point of intersection.

When the members have been arranged to form a simple truss, the entire framework may then be supported in the same manner as a beam. In order to approach the conditions of an ideal truss, the supports should be detailed so that the reactions are applied at the joints of the truss. Upon recalling the discussion in Art. 2.5, it is apparent that, if the supports of the truss are arranged so that they are equivalent to three-link supports neither parallel nor concurrent, then the structure is stable and its reactions are statically determinate under a general condition of loading.   Illustrations of a simple truss supported in a stable and statically determinate manner are shown in Fig. 4.3.

Sometimes it is desirable to connect two or more simple trusses together to form one rigid framework.   In such cases, the composite framework built up in this manner is called a *compound truss*.   One simple truss can be rigidly connected to another simple truss if the two trusses are connected together at certain points by three links neither parallel nor concurrent or by the equivalent of this type of connection.   Hence, two trusses connected in this manner will form a composite framework that is completely rigid.   Additional simple trusses can be connected in a similar

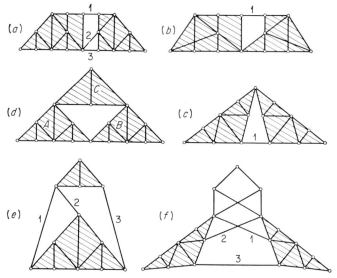

Figure 4.4   Compound trusses

manner to the framework already assembled to form a more elaborate compound truss.

Several examples of compound trusses are shown in Fig. 4.4.   In all these cases the simple trusses that have been connected together are shown crosshatched.   In trusses *a*, *e*, and *f*, the simple trusses have been connected together by bars 1, 2, and 3.   In cases *b* and *c*, the trusses have been hinged together at one common joint, thus requiring only one additional bar to form a rigid composite framework.   In case *d*, the additional bar connecting trusses *A* and *B* together has been replaced by the simple truss *C*.

The members having been arranged to form a compound truss, the entire framework may be supported in the same manner as a simple truss.

4.4 Notation and Sign Convention Used in Truss Stress Analysis.

Before the stress analysis of trusses is discussed, it is necessary to establish a definite notation and sign convention for designating the bar forces in the members of a truss.

The various members of a truss will be designated by the names of the joints at each end of the member. The letter F will be used to denote the bar force in a member. Thus, subscripts being used to denote the bar, F_{ah} denotes the bar force in member ah. The values of the bar forces in the members of a truss are often tabulated or written alongside the various members on a line diagram of the truss. For this purpose, it is convenient to have a **definite convention for designating the character of stress in a member, i.e., whether the internal stress is tension or compression. The most convenient convention is to use a plus (+) sign to designate a tension and a minus (−) sign to designate a compression.** Thus, $+10$ means a tension of 10, and -10 a compression of 10. A plus sign is used to designate tension because such a bar force causes an elongation, or an *increase* in length, of the bar. Thus, a plus force causes a plus change in length. On the other hand, a compression, or minus, bar force causes a decrease, or minus change, in length of a bar.

In the stress analysis of trusses, it is often convenient to work with two rectangular components of a bar force rather than the bar force itself. For this purpose, two orthogonal directions x and y are selected (usually horizontal and vertical, respectively), and the two corresponding components in bar ah are designated as X_{ah} and Y_{ah}. It is particularly important for the student to be completely familiar with the various relationships between a force and its two rectangular components. These relationships are so important in truss analysis that a student must have complete facility with them. For this reason, some of them are reviewed at this time. When it is realized that a bar force acts along the axis of a member, the following statements are self-evident:

1. *The horizontal (or vertical) component of a bar force is equal to the bar force multiplied by the ratio of the horizontal (or vertical) projection of a member to its axial length.*

2. *The bar force of a member is equal to its horizontal (or vertical) component multiplied by the ratio of the axial length of the member to its horizontal (or vertical) projection.*

3. *The horizontal component of a bar force is equal to the vertical component multiplied by the ratio of the horizontal to the vertical projection of the axial length, and vice versa.*

The following principle is also useful and important in dealing with bar-force computations:

4. *For purposes of writing equilibrium equations for a particular isolated*

body, any force may be replaced by its rectangular components as long as the components are both assumed to act at some one convenient point along the line of action of the force.

4.5 Theory of Stress Analysis of Trusses. To determine the adequacy of a truss to withstand a given condition of loading, it is first necessary to compute the bar forces developed in the members of the truss to resist the prescribed loading. The fundamental approach to studying the internal stresses in any body is the same whether it is a beam, a truss, or some other type of structure. In the case of a truss, this approach consists in passing an imaginary section that cuts through certain of the bars and isolates some convenient portion of the truss as a free body. Acting on the internal cross sections exposed by the isolating section will be internal stresses. In the case of a member of an ideal truss, the resultant of these stresses is simply an axial force referred to as the bar force in the member.

If the truss as a whole is in static equilibrium, then any isolated portion of it must likewise be in equilibrium. Any particular isolated portion of a truss will be acted upon by a system of forces which may consist of certain external forces and the bar forces acting on the exposed faces of those members which have been cut by the isolating section. It is often possible to isolate portions of a truss so that each portion is acted upon by a limited number of unknown bar forces, which may then be determined so as to satisfy the equations of static equilibrium for that portion.

This procedure may be explained quite easily by considering a specific example such as the simple truss shown in Fig. 4.5. This truss is supported in such a manner that the reactions are statically determinate and are easily computed, as shown in the figure. Proceeding now with the determination of the bar forces in this truss, suppose an imaginary section is passed around joint *a*, cutting through bars *ah* and *ab* and thus completely isolating joint *a* from the rest of the truss, as shown in free-body sketch *a* of this figure.

Such an isolated joint will be a body acted upon by a concurrent system of forces since the bar forces in the cut bars of an ideal truss and the external forces are all forces the lines of action of which are directed through the center of the isolated joint. The resultant of a concurrent system of forces cannot be a couple, and hence the force system will be in equilibrium if $\Sigma F_x = 0$ and $\Sigma F_y = 0$. Therefore, if there are only two unknown bar forces acting on a given isolated joint and these do not have the same line of action,[1] the two conditions for static equilibrium will yield two independent equations that may be solved simultaneously for the two unknown forces. If there are more than two unknown bar

---

[1] If the two unknown bar forces have the same line of action, will the two equations be consistent and independent?

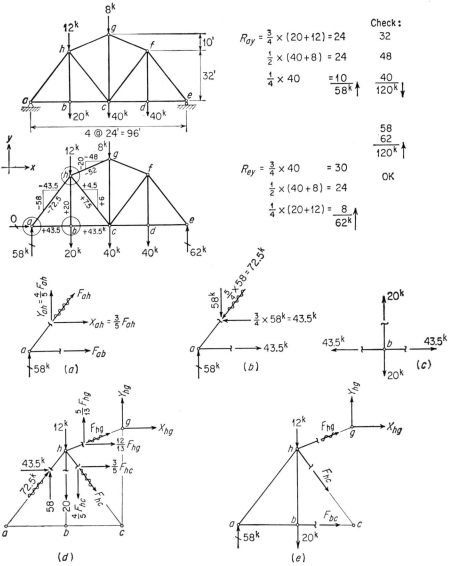

Figure 4.5 Analysis of simple truss

forces, the values of all the unknowns cannot be determined immediately from these two equations alone.

In this particular case, however, the isolated joint a is acted upon by the known reaction and only two unknown bar forces F_{ah} and F_{ab}. The slopes of the members being known, the horizontal and vertical components of the two unknown bar forces may be expressed in terms of the bar force as shown in sketch a. The two equations of static equilibrium may then be written, assuming both F_{ah} and F_{ab} as being tensions,

$$\Sigma F_y = 0, \; +\uparrow, \; 58 + \tfrac{4}{5}F_{ah} = 0 \qquad (a)$$
$$\Sigma F_x = 0, \; \overset{\rightarrow}{+}, \; \tfrac{3}{5}F_{ah} + F_{ab} = 0 \qquad (b)$$

Then, from Eq. (a),

$$F_{ah} = -72.5 \text{ kips} \qquad \text{(compression)}$$

and hence, from Eq. (b),

$$F_{ab} = -\tfrac{3}{5}F_{ah} = -(\tfrac{3}{5})(-72.5) = +43.5 \text{ kips} \qquad \text{(tension)}$$

Then the components of F_{ah} are

$$X_{ah} = (\tfrac{3}{5})(-72.5) = -43.5 \text{ kips}$$
$$Y_{ah} = (\tfrac{4}{5})(-72.5) = -58 \text{ kips}$$

Thus, the minus sign indicates that F_{ah} is opposite to the assumed sense (a compression), while the plus sign indicates that F_{ab} is in the assumed sense (a tension). The sign of the results, therefore, automatically conforms to the sign convention that has been adopted to indicate the character of stress. These results may now be recorded on the line diagram of the truss as -72.5 and $+43.5$, the signs indicating the proper character of stress. The components of the force in ah may be recorded conveniently as shown on the line diagram.

Such conformity in the signs of the results will always be obtained if, in drawing the free-body sketches and setting up the equations of statics, the sense of the unknown bar forces is assumed to be tension. If this is done, then a plus sign for an answer indicates that the assumed sense is correct and therefore tension, while a minus sign indicates that the assumed sense is incorrect and therefore compression. Thus the signs of the results will automatically conform with the established sign convention.

The procedure just used may be applied in principle to solve for the unknown bar forces at any isolated joint that is acted upon by only two unknown bar forces. In this particular truss, the remaining unknown bar forces could be computed easily by isolating the remaining joints one after the other, always selecting the next joint to be isolated so that the forces in all but two (or fewer) of the cut bars have previously been computed. Of course, it is also necessary for these two unknown bar forces to have different lines of action. This technique of passing a section so as to isolate a single joint of a truss is called the *method of joints*.

Sometimes it is more expedient to pass a section that isolates a portion containing several joints of a truss. This latter technique of passing the cutting section is called the *method of sections*. An isolated portion consisting of several joints of a truss will be a body that is acted upon by a nonconcurrent system of forces that may consist of certain external forces and the bar forces in those bars cut by the isolating section. For equilibrium of such a portion, the three equations $\Sigma F_x = 0$, $\Sigma F_y = 0$, and $\Sigma M = 0$ must be satisfied by the forces acting on this part of the truss. Therefore, if there are only three unknown bar forces acting on this part and these three bars are neither parallel nor concurrent, the values of the three unknown forces may be obtained from these three equilibrium equations.

A typical application of the method of sections is shown in free-body sketch *e* of Fig. 4.5. In this case, the cutting section is passed through bars *hg*, *hc*, and *bc*, thus isolating the portion of the truss to the left of this section. The unknown forces in these three cut bars may now be determined by solving the three equations of equilibrium for the isolated portion. In previous discussions of the computations of reactions, it has been demonstrated that it is often possible to expedite the solution in such cases of nonconcurrent force systems by using ingenuity in writing the equations of statics. For example, to solve for F_{ag}, take moments about point *c*, the point of intersection of F_{hc} and F_{bc}, and resolve F_{hg} into its horizontal and vertical components at point *g*. Then only X_{hg} enters the moment equation, and

$$\Sigma M_c = 0, \; \overset{\curvearrowright}{+}, \; (X_{hg})(42) + (58)(48) - (32)(24) = 0$$

whence $X_{hg} = -48$ and by proportion $Y_{hg} = -20$ and $F_{hg} = -52$. In a similar manner,

$$\Sigma M_h = 0, \; \overset{\curvearrowright}{+}, \; (58)(24) - (F_{bc})(32) = 0$$

whence $F_{bc} = +43.5$. Then either $\Sigma F_x = 0$ or $\Sigma F_y = 0$ may be used to obtain the horizontal or vertical component, respectively, of F_{hc}.

$$\Sigma F_x = 0, \; \overset{\rightarrow}{+}, \; X_{hc} + 43.5 - 48 = 0$$

whence $X_{hc} = +4.5$ and by proportion $Y_{hg} = +6$ and $F_{hg} = +7.5$. Of course, any three independent equations of statics could be written and solved for these three unknown forces. However, if ingenuity is not used, the three equations may all contain all three unknowns and have to be solved simultaneously, whereas, as just shown, it is possible to write three equations, each of which contains only one unknown.

4.6 Application of Method of Joints and Method of Sections. In the previous article, the equations involved in applying both the method of joints and the method of sections were set up in a rather formal manner. However, it is often unnecessary to do this. For example, consider joint a, which was used in illustrating the method of joints in the previous article. At the present time, consider this isolated joint as shown in free-body sketch b of Fig. 4.5. By inspection, it is obvious that, for $\Sigma F_y = 0$ to be satisfied, the vertical component in bar ah must push downward with a force of 58 kips in order to balance the reaction. Then, by proportion, the horizontal component and the bar force itself in this bar are equal to 43.5 and a compression of 72.5, respectively, acting in the directions shown. The horizontal component in ah being known, it is now apparent that, for $\Sigma F_x = 0$ to be satisfied, the force in ab must be a tension of 43.5 acting to the right to balance the horizontal component in ah acting to the left.

Since the bar force in ab is known, it is a simple matter to find the forces in bc and bh by passing a section that isolates joint b as shown in free-body sketch c of Fig. 4.5. Again, this simple case may be easily solved in an informal manner to obtain the two unknown bar forces F_{bc} and F_{bh}. To satisfy $\Sigma F_x = 0$, it is apparent that F_{bc} must be a tension of 43.5 and, to satisfy $\Sigma F_y = 0$, F_{bh} must be a tension of 20.

If joint h is isolated in a similar manner, as shown in free-body sketch d, the isolating section will cut through four bars, two in which the bar forces are known and two in which they are unknown. Again these two unknowns may be found from the equilibrium conditions $\Sigma F_x = 0$ and $\Sigma F_y = 0$ for the isolated joint. Assuming the unknown forces to be tension, the two equations may be written as follows:

$$\Sigma F_x = 0, \overrightarrow{+}, \; {}^{12}\!\!/_{13}F_{hg} + {}^3\!\!/_5 F_{hc} + 43.5 = 0$$
$$\Sigma F_y = 0, +\uparrow, \; {}^5\!\!/_{13}F_{hg} - {}^4\!\!/_5 F_{hc} - 12 - 20 + 58 = 0$$

In this case, unfortunately, both equations contain both unknowns, and it is necessary to solve the equations simultaneously for these two values. Of course, the two unknowns can be obtained quite easily in this manner, but consider the advantages of proceeding as follows:

In the discussion of computation of reactions in Chap. 2, it will be recalled that it was often advantageous to replace either or both $\Sigma F_x = 0$ and $\Sigma F_y = 0$ by one or two moment equations. A similar technique is likewise desirable in the present case of the isolated joint h. Suppose that in free-body sketch d the positions of joints a, c, and g are located in space as shown. Then, $\Sigma M_c = 0$ could be used instead of the equation $\Sigma F_y = 0$ or $\Sigma F_x = 0$. Taking moments about point c not only eliminates F_{hc} from the equation but also makes it possible to simplify the computation of the moments of the forces in bars ah and hg. These two bar forces may now be resolved into their vertical and horizontal components at joints a and g, respectively, and then only the vertical component of F_{ah} and the horizontal component of F_{hg} will enter the moment equation and the lever arms of both these components are easily obtained.   In this way,

$$\Sigma M_c = 0, \;\widehat{+}, \; (X_{hg})(42) + (58)(48) - (32)(24) = 0 \qquad \therefore \; X_{hg} = -48$$

and by proportion $Y_{hg} = -20$ and $F_{hg} = -52$.

F_{hg} and its two components being known, it is an easy matter to use either $\Sigma F_x = 0$ or $\Sigma F_y = 0$ and obtain, respectively, either the horizontal or vertical components of the force in hc directly.   For example, since $X_{hg} = -48$, the horizontal component in hc must act to the right with 4.5 kips so as to balance the 43.5 kips in ah and make $\Sigma F_x = 0$.   This means that this bar is in tension and by proportion the bar force and vertical component are $+7.5$ and $+6.0$, respectively.   All these computations may now be checked by seeing whether the results satisfy $\Sigma F_y = 0$.

In the following illustrative examples, additional techniques and "tricks" will be used to expedite the application of the method of joints and the method of sections.   In the first few examples, all the free-body sketches will be shown in detail.   To train the student to visualize free-body sketches when possible, such sketches will be omitted in the later examples.   When desirable, the numerical computations will be carried out in an informal manner.   If the student finds it difficult to follow these short cuts, he should draw the necessary free-body sketches and set up the equilibrium equations in a fundamental manner.   The student should recognize that it is desirable to develop a facility for visualizing free-body sketches and solving equilibrium equations in an informal manner; but he should also recognize that even the expert has to go back to fundamentals—draw sketches and write equations—whenever he is confused or faced with a difficult problem.

The student should also note carefully the technique of drawing free-body sketches of isolated portions of a truss.   Any bar force that is known in magnitude[1] from previous computations should be shown acting with this known magnitude on any sketch that is drawn subsequently.   For example, in drawing free-body sketch d of Fig. 4.5, the forces in bars ah and bh have previously been computed and recorded on the line diagram of the truss as -72.5 and $+20$, respectively.   Hence, the bar forces acting on the stub ends of these two bars should be shown pushing the stub end of ah into joint h and pulling the stub end of bh out of this joint.   Thus the sense of these known bar forces having been indicated by arrows, the forces should be labeled with their numerical value only, viz., simply by 72.5 and 20, not by -72.5 and $+20$.   As suggested in the previous article, the free-body sketch is completed by showing the unknown bar forces as being tensions.

---

[1] Note that magnitude has previously been defined as including the sense in which a force acts.

When the value of a bar force is recorded on the line diagram of the truss, it will be found helpful also to draw arrows at each end of the member, indicating the direction in which the force in the member acts *on the joint*. This procedure will be followed in recording the bar forces in the remaining illustrations of this chapter.

Example 4.1 *Compute the bar forces in members Cc, CD, cd, cD, and DE of this truss, due to the loads shown.*

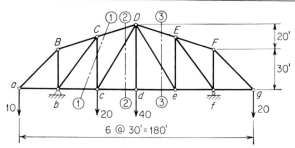

$$\Sigma M_b = 0, \; \curvearrowright^+$$

$$
\begin{array}{rr}
20 \times 1 = & 20 \\
40 \times 2 = & 80 \\
20 \times 5 = & \underline{100} \\
& 200 \\
-10 \times 1 = & \underline{-10} \\
& 190
\end{array}
$$

$$R_{fy} = 47.5 \uparrow$$

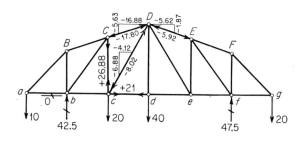

$$\Sigma M_f = 0, \; \curvearrowright^+$$

$$
\begin{array}{rr}
40 \times 2 = & -80 \\
20 \times 3 = & -60 \\
10 \times 5 = & \underline{-50} \\
& -190 \\
20 \times 1 = & \underline{20} \\
& -170
\end{array}
$$

$$R_{by} = 42.5 \uparrow$$

$$\Sigma F_y = 0, \; \uparrow +$$
$$47.5 + 42.5 - 10 - 20 - 40 - 20 = 0$$

$$\Sigma M_m = 0, \; \curvearrowright^+$$

$$
\begin{array}{rl}
10 \times 2 = & +20 \\
42.5 \times 3 = & \underline{-127.5} \\
& -107.5 \curvearrowleft
\end{array}
$$

$$\therefore F_{Cc} = + \frac{107.5}{4} = +26.88$$

$$\Sigma M_e = 0, \; \curvearrowright^+$$

$$
\begin{array}{rl}
42.5 \times 1 = & +42.5 \\
10 \times 2 = & \underline{-20} \\
& +22.5 \curvearrowright
\end{array}
$$

$$\therefore X_{CD} = \frac{-(22.5)(30)}{40}$$

$$= -16.88$$

$$\therefore F_{CD} = -(16.88) \left(\frac{31.63}{30} \right)$$

$$= -17.80$$

Bar *Cc* Section ① - ①
Bar *CD*

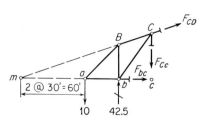

Bar *cd* Section ② - ②
Bar *cD*

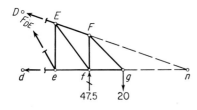

Bar *DE* Section ③ - ③

$\Sigma M_m = 0,$ ↰ ⊕

$$10 \times 2 = \quad +20$$
$$20 \times 4 = \quad \quad 80$$
$$\overline{\quad +100}$$
$$42.5 \times 3 = \quad -127.5$$
$$\overline{\quad -27.5} \curvearrowleft$$

$$\therefore Y_{cD} = \frac{-27.5}{4} = -6.88$$

$$\therefore F_{cD} = -6.88 \times \frac{58.3}{50}$$
$$= -8.02$$

$\Sigma M_D = 0,$ ↰ ⊕

$$20 \times 1 = -20$$
$$10 \times 3 = -30$$
$$\overline{\quad -50}$$
$$42.5 \times 2 = +85$$
$$\overline{\quad +35} \curvearrowright$$

$$\therefore F_{cd} = +35 \times \frac{30}{50} = +21$$

$\Sigma M_e = 0,$ ↰ ⊕

$$47.5 \times 1 = -47.5$$
$$20 \times 2 \quad = +40$$
$$\overline{\quad -7.5} \curvearrowleft$$

$$\therefore X_{DE} = -7.5 \times \frac{30}{40} = -5.62$$

$$\therefore F_{DE} = -5.62 \times \frac{31.6}{30}$$
$$= -5.92$$

Discussion:

Note that, after the force in *Cc* has been found, the vertical component of the force in *cD* can easily be found by isolating joint *c*. Note also that, the force in *cD* being known, the vertical component in *CD* can be found from $\Sigma F_y = 0$ rather than $\Sigma M_c = 0$ for the free-body sketch for section 2-2. The force in *CD* being known, the force in *cd* can be obtained from $\Sigma F_x = 0$ applied to this free-body sketch.

The force in member *DE* can be obtained by isolating the portion of the truss to either the right or the left of section 3-3. The portion to the right was chosen because it has fewer external forces acting on it.

In all these computations, the moments of the vertical forces are computed in terms of panel lengths. When necessary, the panel length of 30 ft is substituted at the end of the computation. The trick simplifies the numerical work in such computations.

Example 4.2   *Determine the bar forces in members dg, eg, gh, and hm.*

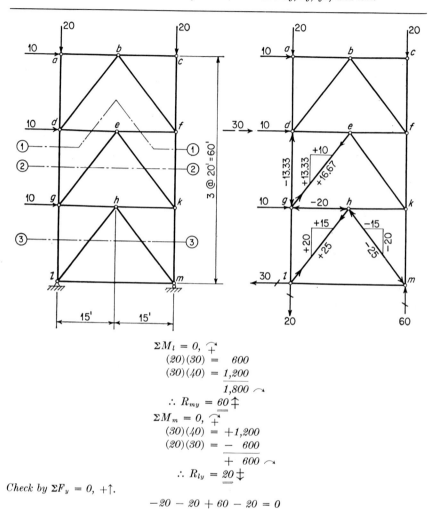

$$\Sigma M_l = 0, \; \overset{\curvearrowleft}{+}$$
$$(20)(30) = 600$$
$$(30)(40) = 1,200$$
$$\overline{ 1,800 \;\curvearrowright}$$
$$\therefore \; R_{my} = 60 \updownarrow$$
$$\Sigma M_m = 0, \; \overset{\curvearrowleft}{+}$$
$$(30)(40) = +1,200$$
$$(20)(30) = - 600$$
$$\overline{ + 600 \;\curvearrowright}$$
$$\therefore \; R_{ly} = 20 \updownarrow$$

Check by $\Sigma F_y = 0, \; +\uparrow$.

$$-20 - 20 + 60 - 20 = 0$$

Bar dg: Section ①-①

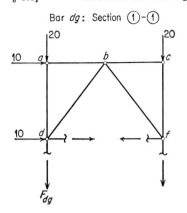

$$\Sigma M_f = 0, \curvearrowright +$$
$$(10)(20) = +200$$
$$(20)(30) = -600$$
$$\overline{ -400} \curvearrowleft$$
$$\therefore F_{dg} = -\frac{400}{30} = -13.33$$

Bar eg: Section ②-②

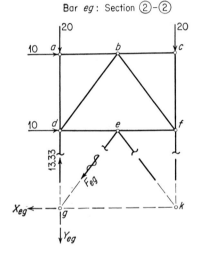

$$\Sigma M_k = 0, \curvearrowright +$$
$$(13.33)(30) = +400$$
$$(10)(20) = +200$$
$$(10)(40) = +400$$
$$\overline{ +1,000}$$
$$(20)(30) = -600$$
$$\overline{ +400} \curvearrowleft$$
$$\therefore Y_{eg} = \frac{400}{30} = +13.33 \qquad X_{eg} = +10$$
$$F_{eg} = +16.67$$

Bar gh: Isolate joint g

Bar hm. Isolate joint h.   Then, consider the portion above isolated by section 3-3.
From $\Sigma F_y = 0$, Y_{lh} must be equal and opposite to Y_{hm}.
Assume that $Y_{lh} = A$; then $Y_{hm} = -A$, etc.

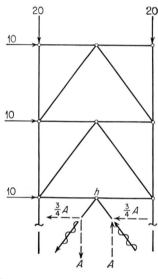

Then $\Sigma F_x = 0$, $\overset{\rightarrow}{+}$

$$10 + 10 + 10 - \tfrac{3}{4}A - \tfrac{3}{4}A = 0 \qquad A = 20$$
$$\therefore X_{lh} = +15 \quad and \quad X_{hm} = -15$$
$$Y_{lh} = +20 \qquad Y_{hm} = -20$$
$$F_{lh} = +25 \qquad F_{hm} = -25$$

Discussion:

If the forces in all the bars are required, the method of joints can be applied, the joints being isolated successively in the following order: a, c, b, d, f, e, g, k, h, l, m.   This is probably the most efficient method of finding all the bar forces in this particular truss. If only a few particular bar forces are required, the computation can be carried out as illustrated in this example.

Example 4.3 *Compute the bar forces in members bc, BC, aC, and bC.*

$$\Sigma M_a = 0, \; \curvearrowright$$

$$
\begin{aligned}
10 \times \tfrac{4}{3}p &= \; +13.\dot{3}p \\
20 \times 1p &= \quad 20 \; p \\
30 \times 2p &= \quad 60 \; p \\
40 \times 3p &= \quad \underline{120 \; p} \\
&\quad +213.3p
\end{aligned}
$$

$$\therefore R_{ey} = 53.\dot{3} \; \Updownarrow$$

$$\Sigma M_e = 0, \; \curvearrowright$$

$$
\begin{aligned}
20 \times 3p &= \; -60p \\
30 \times 2p &= \; -60p \\
40 \times 1p &= \; \underline{-40p} \\
&\quad -160p \\
10 \times \tfrac{4}{3}p &= \; \underline{+13.\dot{3}p} \\
&\quad -146.\dot{6}p
\end{aligned}
$$

$$\therefore R_{ay} = 36.\dot{6} \; \Updownarrow$$

Check:

$$\Sigma F_y = 0, \; \uparrow+, \; 36.\dot{6} - 20 - 30$$
$$- 40 + 53.\dot{3} = 0$$

Bar *bc: Portion to left of 1-1,* $\Sigma M_C = 0, \; \curvearrowright, \; 36.\dot{6} \times 2p = \quad 73.\dot{3}p$
$$20 \times 1p = \; -20.0p$$
$$\frac{53.\dot{3}p + 10 \times 40}{40}$$
$$= F_{bc} = \; +50$$

Bar *BC: Isolate joint A, then B.* $F_{BC} = \; -10$

Bar *aC: Portion to left of 2-2,* $\Sigma F_y = 0$ $\quad \therefore Y_{aC} = \; -36.\dot{6}$

$$\therefore F_{aC} = \frac{\sqrt{3^2 + 2^2}}{2} \, (-36.\dot{6}) = \; -66.1$$

Bar *bC: Portion to left of 1-1, with stress in aC known, then, from* $\Sigma F_y = 0$

$$\therefore Y_{bC} = \; +20$$

or, from joint B, $F_{Bb} = 0;$ *then, from joint b,* $\Sigma F_y = 0$

$$\therefore Y_{bC} = \; +20$$

Example 4.4   *Compute the bar forces in members cd, BC, bm, nf, nF, and md.*

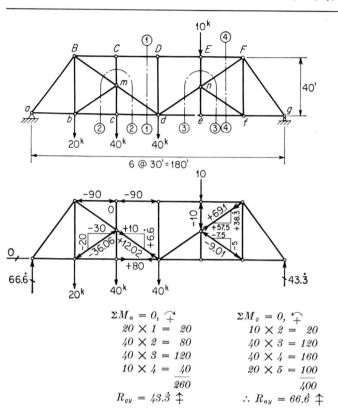

$$\Sigma M_a = 0, \; \overset{\curvearrowright}{+}$$

$$
\begin{aligned}
20 \times 1 &= 20 \\
40 \times 2 &= 80 \\
40 \times 3 &= 120 \\
10 \times 4 &= \underline{40} \\
&\overline{260}
\end{aligned}
$$

$$R_{gy} = 43.\dot{3} \; \text{\Updownarrow}$$

$$\Sigma M_g = 0, \; \overset{\curvearrowleft}{+}$$

$$
\begin{aligned}
10 \times 2 &= 20 \\
40 \times 3 &= 120 \\
40 \times 4 &= 160 \\
20 \times 5 &= \underline{100} \\
&\overline{400}
\end{aligned}
$$

$$\therefore R_{ay} = 66.\dot{6} \; \text{\Updownarrow}$$

Bar *cd:* Portion to left of 1-1, $\Sigma M_B = 0, \; \overset{\curvearrowright}{+}, \; 66.\dot{6} \times 1p + 40 \times 1p = 106.\dot{6}p$

$$\therefore F_{cd} = +80$$

Bar *BC:* Same portion, $\Sigma M_d = 0, \; \overset{\curvearrowright}{+},$

$$66.\dot{6} \times 3p - 40 \times 1p - 20 \times 2p = 120p \quad \therefore F_{CD} = -90$$

$$\therefore \text{ Isolate joint } C, \; F_{BC} = -90$$

Bar *bm:* Isolating joint C shows $F_{Cm} = 0$. Hence, considering portion isolated by section 2-2,

$$\Sigma M_d = 0, \; \overset{\curvearrowleft}{+}, \; +40 \times 1p = +40p$$

$$\therefore Y_{bm} = -20$$

$$\therefore X_{bm} = -30$$

$$\therefore F_{bm} = -36.06$$

Bar nf: *Isolating joint E shows* $F_{En} = -10$. *Hence, considering portion isolated by section 3-3.*

$$\Sigma M_d = 0, \; \overset{+}{\curvearrowright}, \; 10 \times 1p = 10p \qquad \therefore \; Y_{nf} = -5 \qquad X_{nf} = -7.5 \qquad F_{nf} = -9.01$$

Bar nF: *Portion to right of 4-4,* $\Sigma F_y = 0 \qquad \therefore \; Y_{nF} = +38.3$

Bar md: *Portion to right of 1-1,* $\Sigma F_y = 0 \qquad \therefore \; Y_{md} = +6.6$

Example 4.5 *Determine the bar forces in all members of this truss.*

Portion to left of 1-1,

$$\Sigma M_D = 0, \; \overset{+}{\curvearrowright}$$
$$50 \times 3p = 150p$$
$$60 \times 1p = -60p$$
$$\overline{\hspace{2cm}}$$
$$\frac{90p}{50} = \frac{90 \times 30}{50} = 54 \qquad \therefore \; X_{bd} = +54$$

Discussion:

In the solution of this problem, it is possible to start out and apply the method of joints successfully at joints A, B, G, and F. However, if one attempts to apply this same procedure at any one of the remaining joints, he finds it impossible since there are more than two unknown bar forces at each of these joints. It is therefore desirable to resort to the method of sections. In this problem, the bar force in member bd is found by considering the portion to the left of section 1-1. The method of joints can then be applied at joint b and then successively at each of the remaining joints.

It should be noted that this is a compound truss. In such trusses it is usually impossible to solve for all the bar forces by using simply the method of joints. As illustrated in this problem, it is usually necessary to make at least one application of the method of sections.

Example 4.6   *Determine the bar forces in all members of this truss.*

Discussion:

In the solution of this example, it is possible to start at one end of the truss and work through to the other end, using only the method of joints to compute the bar forces. This is a simple truss, and it is always possible to find all the bar forces in such a truss in this manner once the reactions have been computed.

It also should be noted that the vertical components of the bar forces in the diagonals can also be easily obtained by using $\Sigma F_y = 0$ on the portions either to the right or to the left of the indicated vertical sections through the panels. The force in the verticals can then be obtained from $\Sigma F_y = 0$ at the joints, and the force in the chords from $\Sigma F_x = 0$ at the joints, working across from end to end of the truss.

4.7   Discussion of Method of Joints and Method of Sections.
The examples in the previous article illustrate that isolations of portions of the truss using both the method of joints and the method of sections must be employed in the stress analysis of trusses. Experience in such computations will teach the student how to combine these two methods most effectively. It is the purpose of this particular article to summarize and clarify the important points concerning them.

In the previous discussion of the method of joints, it is pointed out that this procedure enables one to determine immediately all the unknown bar forces acting on an isolated joint, provided that there are not more than two unknown forces and that these two unknown forces have different lines of action. It sometimes happens that there is only one unknown bar force acting on an isolated joint. In such a case, one of the two available equilibrium equations may be used to solve for the one unknown force, and the other may be used as a check that must be satisfied by all the forces acting on this joint. If there are more than two unknown forces acting on an isolated joint, it is usually impossible to obtain an immediate solution for any of the unknowns from the two equations of equilibrium that are available at that joint. In such cases, it is necessary to isolate additional joints and write two additional equations for each joint. In this manner, it is sometimes possible to obtain n independent equations, involving n unknown bar forces. Then these n equations can be solved simultaneously for the n unknowns.

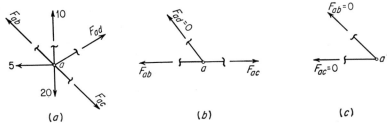

Figure 4.6   Special cases

There is one important case where there are more than two unknown bar forces, acting on an isolated joint but so arranged that it is possible to obtain the value of one of them immediately. If all the unknown forces except one have the same line of action, then the force in that one particular bar may be determined immediately. Such a case is shown in sketch a of Fig. 4.6. If the x axis is taken as being parallel to the line bac and the y axis perpendicular to this line, then the y component of the unknown force F_{ad} may be determined immediately from the equation $\Sigma F_y = 0$. No immediate solution may be obtained from $\Sigma F_x = 0$ at such a joint since this equation involves both the unknowns F_{ab} and F_{ac}. A special case of this type is shown in sketch b of Fig. 4.6, where the joint is acted upon by only the three unknown bar forces. If F_{ab} and F_{ac} have the same line of action, then it is apparent that the only remaining force at the joint, F_{ad}, must be zero. It is also of interest to consider the case shown in sketch c of Fig. 4.6. In this case, the joint is acted upon by only two forces, which do not have the same line of action; therefore, in order to satisfy $\Sigma F_x = 0$ and $\Sigma F_y = 0$ for such a joint, both F_{ab} and F_{ac} must be equal to zero.

It is also interesting to note that, once the reactions have been determined on a *simple* truss, then all the bar forces can be determined by using only the method of joints and never resorting to the method of sections. It is apparent that this is so, since there are only two unknown bar forces acting on the joint that was located *last* in arranging the layout of the bars of the truss. After these two bar forces have been determined by isolating this joint, then it will be found that the joints at the far ends of these two members are acted upon by only two unknown bar forces. Thus, by isolating the joints in the reverse order from that in which they were established in laying out the truss, the method of joints may be used to determine all the bar forces. This is the explanation of why it is possible to solve Example 4.6 in this manner. It should be noted, however, that in many cases of simple trusses the calculation of all the bar forces may be expedited by combining the use of both the method of sections and the method of joints, as illustrated by some of the examples in Art. 4.11.

When applying the method of sections, if the isolated portion of the truss is acted upon by three unknown bar forces that are neither parallel nor concurrent, then all three unknown forces may be determined from the three equilibrium equations available for the isolated portion. It is presumed, of course, that the reactions acting on any such portion have been determined previously. Of course, if there are only one or two unknown bar forces, these may be determined by using a like number of the available equations. The remainder of the equations that must be satisfied by the system of forces acting on the isolated portion may then be used simply as a check on the calculations up to this point.

It is sometimes possible to find some of the unknown forces by the method of sections even when there are more than three unknowns acting on the isolated portion. For example, suppose that the lines of action of all but one of the unknown forces intersect at a point a. Then, the stress in this one remaining bar can be determined from the equation $\Sigma M_a = 0$, that is, by summing up the moments of the forces about point a. Another similar case would be one where all the unknown bar forces except one are parallel. The stress in this remaining bar can then be determined by summing up all the force components that are perpendicular to the direction of the other unknown bar forces. In each of the above cases, the remaining two equilibrium equations for the isolated portion will involve more unknowns than there are equations, and hence no immediate solution for these remaining unknowns is possible.

In applying either the method of joints or the method of sections, it is important to realize that it makes no difference how many bars have been cut in which the bar forces are *known*. Only the number of unknown bar forces is important.

4.8 Statical Stability and Statical Determinacy of Truss Structures. Up to this point the emphasis has been placed on the methods of computing the bar forces in trusses. For this purpose, all the examples that have been used have been statically determinate and

stable.   With these ideas as a background, it is now possible to discuss
the question of statical stability and determinancy of trusses from a
general standpoint.

In discussing the arrangement of the members of a simple truss, it
was shown that a rigid truss is formed by using three bars to connect
three joints together in the form of a triangle and then using two bars to
connect each additional joint to the framework already constructed.
Thus, to form a rigid simple truss of n joints, it is necessary to use the
three bars of the original triangle plus two additional bars for each of the
remaining $(n - 3)$ joints.   If b denotes the total number of bars required,
then

$$b = 3 + 2(n - 3) = 2n - 3$$

This is the minimum number of bars that can be used to form a rigid
simple truss.   To use more is unnecessary, and to use fewer results in a
nonrigid or unstable truss.   If a simple truss having n joints and $(2n - 3)$
bars is supported in a manner that is equivalent to three links that are
neither parallel nor concurrent, then the structure is stable under a
general condition of loading and the reactions are statically determinate.
In the previous article, it is pointed out that, once the reactions are
found, all the bar forces of a simple truss can be computed by the method
of joints.

It may be concluded, therefore, that a stable simple truss having three
independent reaction elements and $(2n - 3)$ bars is statically determinate
with respect to both reactions and bar forces.   If there are more than
three reaction elements, the structure is statically indeterminate with
respect to its reactions; if there are more than $(2n - 3)$ bars but only
three reaction elements, it is indeterminate with respect to the bar
forces; and if there is an excess of both bars and reaction elements, the
structure is indeterminate with respect to both reactions and bar forces.

The same discussion and conclusions apply equally well to a compound
truss.   Suppose a compound truss is formed by connecting two simple
trusses together by means of three additional bars that are neither parallel nor concurrent.   If the two simple trusses have n_1 and n_2 joints,
respectively, the total number of bars b in the compound truss is

$$b = (2n_1 - 3) + (2n_2 - 3) + 3 = 2(n_1 + n_2) - 3$$

or if n denotes the total number of joints in the compound truss, i.e.,
if $n = n_1 + n_2$, then

$$b = 2n - 3$$

Thus, the minimum number of bars that can be used to form a rigid compound truss is the same as in the case of a simple truss.   If the remainder
of the discussion were carried out in a similar manner for a compound

truss, it would be found that the conclusions of the previous paragraph apply equally well to both simple and compound trusses.

It is desirable to discuss this question of determinacy and stability from a more general standpoint. Suppose a truss structure has r independent reaction elements, b bars, and n joints. If the truss as a whole is in equilibrium, then every isolated portion must likewise be in equilibrium. To isolate an entire bar or some portion of it would produce no new information since the equilibrium conditions of the bars were considered during the establishing of the definition of the term bar force. However, it is possible to isolate each of the n joints in turn and to write for each of these joints two new and independent equations of static equilibrium, $\Sigma F_x = 0$ and $\Sigma F_y = 0$. In this manner, a total of $2n$ independent equations would be obtained, involving as unknowns the r reaction elements and the b bar forces, a total of $(r + b)$ unknowns. These $2n$ equations must be satisfied simultaneously by the $(r + b)$ unknowns. By comparing the number of unknowns with the number of independent equations, it is possible to decide whether a truss structure is unstable, statically determinate, or indeterminate. The reasoning involved is similar to that used in Art. 2.5. **If $r + b$ is less than $2n$ there are not enough unknowns available to satisfy the $2n$ equations simultaneously, and therefore the structure is said to be statically unstable. If $r + b$ is equal to $2n$, the unknowns can then be obtained from the simultaneous solution of the $2n$ equations, and therefore the structure is said to be statically determinate. If $r + b$ is greater than $2n$, there are too many unknowns to be determined from these $2n$ equations alone, and therefore the structure is said to be statically indeterminate. The criterion establishes the combined degree of indeterminancy with respect to both reactions and bar forces, provided that the structure is neither statically nor geometrically unstable.** It is apparent that these conclusions agree with the foregoing discussion of simple and compound trusses.

At first glance, it might seem that the total number of independent equations of static equilibrium in a truss structure should include not only the $2n$ equations noted in the previous paragraph but also the three equations $\Sigma F_x = 0$, $\Sigma F_y = 0$, and $\Sigma M = 0$ applied to the entire structure as a free body. However, the following demonstration will prove that this offhand opinion is not so and that there are only $2n$ independent equations: Consider any truss as a free body acted upon by its reactions and applied loads such as the truss shown in Fig. 4.7a. Suppose that the system of forces shown in Fig. 4.7b is superimposed on the system in Fig. 4.7a; the combination of these two loading systems will then be as shown in Fig. 4.7c. The load system in b is a special system consisting of several pairs of equal and opposite forces, one pair for each member of the truss. For any particular member, both forces of its pair act along the member, one acting on the joint at one end of the member and the other on the joint at the other end.   Each of the forces is numerically equal to *the bar force in that member produced by the forces in system a* and acts in a sense that is the same as the action of this bar force on the joint.   Each pair of forces is in equilibrium, of course, and hence all the pairs acting together form a system that is in equilibrium.

Considering now the combined system in *c*, it is found that the forces acting at each joint of the truss are the same forces that would be acting on that joint if, under the loading of *a*, it were isolated by itself as a free body.   If, however, the applied forces, reactions, and bar forces satisfy simultaneously the $2n$ equations of statics obtained by isolating the n joints and writing $\Sigma F_x = 0$ and $\Sigma F_y = 0$ for each joint, the forces acting on *each* joint in *c* form a concurrent system of forces that are in equilibrium.   Since at each joint the forces are in equilibrium, the combined system

Figure 4.7   Equilibrium considerations

in *c* of all joints is in equilibrium and satisfies the equations $\Sigma F_x = 0$, $\Sigma F_y = 0$, and $\Sigma M = 0$ for the entire truss.   Since the combined system in *c* is in equilibrium and the portion of this system shown in sketch *b* is also in equilibrium by itself, then the remaining portion of the system as shown in sketch *a* must be in equilibrium and therefore must satisfy the equations $\Sigma F_x = 0$, $\Sigma F_y = 0$, and $\Sigma M = 0$ for the entire truss.   It may be concluded, therefore, that, if the reactions, bar forces, and applied loads satisfy the $2n$ equations of equilibrium obtained by isolating the joints of the truss, then the reactions and applied loads will automatically satisfy the three equations of equilibrium for the truss as a whole and that thus there are only $2n$ independent equations of static equilibrium involved in a truss.

It should be noted that comparing the count of the unknowns and the independent equations establishes a criterion which is necessary but not always sufficient to decide whether a truss is stable or not.   If $b + r$ is less than $2n$, then this comparison is sufficient for deciding that the truss is statically unstable.   If, however, $b + r$ is equal to or greater than $2n$, it does not automatically follow that the truss is stable.   This statement may be verified by considering the examples shown in Fig. 4.8.   In all four of these cases, the structures are unstable, whereas the count by itself indicates that *a* and *b* are statically determinate and *c* and *d* are indeterminate to the first degree.   *a* and *d* are unstable under a general condition of loading because in each case the reactions are equivalent to parallel links.   *b* and *c* are unstable, not because of the arrangement of the reactions, but because of the arrangement of the bars.   In *b*, for example, the reactions are statically determinate, but the truss is unstable and would collapse because there is nothing to carry the shear in the second panel from the right end.

These and other considerations lead to the conclusion that, even though the count indicates that the structure is either statically determinate or indeterminate, for it to be stable also, it is necessary that the following conditions shall likewise be satisfied: (1) The reactions must be equivalent to three or more links that are neither parallel nor concurrent.   (2) The bars of the truss must also be arranged in an adequate manner.   It is sometimes

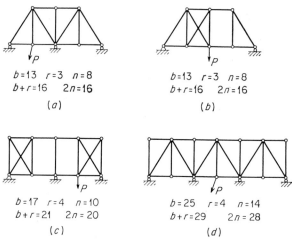

$b=13$ $r=3$ $n=8$
$b+r=16$ $2n=16$
(a)

$b=13$ $r=3$ $n=8$
$b+r=16$ $2n=16$
(b)

$b=17$ $r=4$ $n=10$
$b+r=21$ $2n=20$
(c)

$b=25$ $r=4$ $n=14$
$b+r=29$ $2n=28$
(d)

Figure 4.8   Unstable structures

difficult to determine whether or not the arrangement of the bars is adequate.   In such cases, if the arrangement is inadequate it will become apparent; for when a stress analysis is attempted, it will yield results that are inconsistent, infinite, or indeterminate.

4.9   Examples Illustrating the Determination of Stability and Determinancy.   It is easy to investigate the stability and determinancy of a truss structure that is formed by supporting in some manner a truss that is in itself a rigid body.   The truss itself may be merely a simple or compound truss or, in some cases, a simple or compound truss modified by adding more than the necessary number of bars.   In either case, the bars, reactions, and joints can be counted and the criteria of the last article applied to decide whether the structure is unstable, statically determinate, or statically indeterminate.   This count, of course, enables one to classify the structure with respect to both bar forces and reactions.   If the count shows that the structure is statically determinate or indeterminate, the question of stability must still be decided, for the count by itself is not sufficient to prove that the structure is stable.

It is also easy to classify this type of structure with respect to its reactions only. If there are less than three independent reaction elements, the structure is statically unstable under a general condition of loading regardless of how the bars of the truss are arranged. If there are three or more independent reaction elements and they are arranged so as to be equivalent to three or more links that are neither parallel nor concurrent, the structure is stable with respect to its reactions. For a

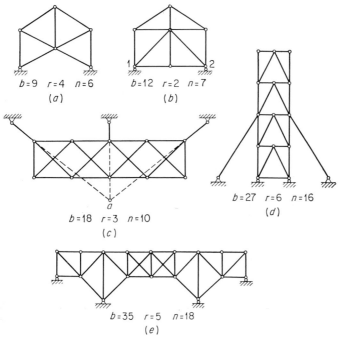

$b=9$ $r=4$ $n=6$
(a)

$b=12$ $r=2$ $n=7$
(b)

$b=18$ $r=3$ $n=10$
(c)

$b=27$ $r=6$ $n=16$
(d)

$b=35$ $r=5$ $n=18$
(e)

Figure 4.9   Examples for classification

stable structure, if there are exactly three reaction elements, these elements are statically determinate; if there are more than three reaction elements, the structure is statically indeterminate with respect to its reactions alone to a degree that is equal to the number of reaction elements in excess of three. Structures in this general category are shown in Fig. 4.9.

The count of the bars, joints, and reaction elements is shown in each of the sketches in Fig. 4.9. Considering only the reactions, structure a is stable and statically indeterminate to the first degree. Since $b + r = 13$ and $2n = 12$, it is also indeterminate to the first degree, considering both reactions and bar forces. The count of structure b indicates that it is statically determinate since $b + r$ and $2n$ are both equal to 14. A consideration of the reactions, however, discloses that this structure is actually unstable.   Likewise, the count indicates that structure c is statically indeterminate to the first degree, but consideration of the reactions shows that it is unstable.   Both the count and the consideration of the reactions indicate that structure d is indeterminate to the first degree.   With respect to the reactions only, structure e is indeterminate to the second degree, but a count of both bars and reactions discloses that it is actually indeterminate to the fourth degree.

There is another important type of truss structure that is built up out of more than just one rigid truss.   In this type, the structure is composed of several rigid trusses connected together in some manner and then the whole assemblage mounted on a certain number of supports.   In such cases, the supports are usually arranged so as to provide more than three independent reaction elements.   The connections between the several rigid trusses are, however, not completely rigid, so that certain equations of condition (or construction) are introduced so as to reduce the degree of indeterminancy or perhaps even to make the reactions statically determinate.   This type of structure is the hardest to analyze from a stability or determinancy standpoint.   However, some of the most important trussed structures—for example, cantilever and three-hinged arch bridges —belong in this category, and therefore it is important for the student to master the methods of investigating this type.   Structures of this general type are illustrated in Fig. 4.10.

The stability and determinancy of structures of the type shown in Fig. 4.10 may be investigated by comparing the count of the bars and reaction elements with the count of the joints.   With this criterion, it will be concluded that structures a, b, d, e, and f are statically determinate and structure c is indeterminate to the first degree.   In structures of this type, it is also important to consider whether or not the structure is statically determinate with respect to its reactions alone.   This may be done by comparing the count of the unknown reaction elements with the number of available equations in the same manner as discussed previously in Arts. 2.5 and 2.6.   In these cases, the available equations include the three equations of static equilibrium for the structure as a whole plus any equations of condition which may be introduced by the manner in which the several rigid trusses are connected together.

If two trusses are hinged together at a common joint, such as the joints marked a in Figs. 4.10a to e, one equation of condition is introduced, viz., that the bending moment about that point must be zero since the hinge cannot transmit a couple from one truss to the other.   If two trusses are connected together by a link or roller, such as the link marked l in structure d, two equations of condition are introduced since then both the direction and point of application of the interacting force are known. This means, therefore, (1) that the bending moment about $either$ end of the link must be zero, or in other words, (2) that the interacting force between the two trusses cannot have a component perpendicular to the link. If two trusses are connected together by two parallel bars, as is done in panels p of structures d and e, one equation of condition is

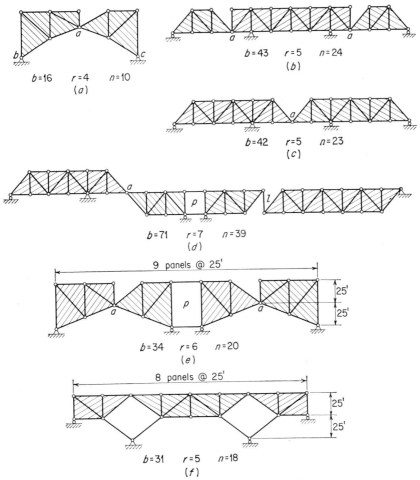

Figure 4.10   Examples for classification

introduced, viz., that the interaction between the two trusses cannot involve a force perpendicular to the two bars.   In the case of structures d and e, this means that the shear acting on panel p must be zero.

From this discussion, it is apparent that one equation has been introduced in structure a, two in b, one in c, four in d, and three in e.   It will be concluded, therefore, that, with respect to reactions only, structures a, b, d, and e are statically determinate and structure c is indeterminate to the first degree.   Structure f is a special type of structure, called a Wichert[1] truss in this country, that can be counted only by considering the bars, joints, and reactions.

There is no obvious instability in any of the structures of Fig. 4.10. If, however, one attempts to compute the reactions and bar forces for either structures e or f, the results will be inconsistent, infinite, or indeterminate; therefore, these structures are actually unstable.   In both

Howe Truss
(*a*)

Pratt Truss
(*b*)

Warren Truss
(*c*)

Warren Truss with verticals
(*d*)

K Truss
(*e*)

Sub-divided Warren Truss
(*f*)

Sub-divided Pratt Truss
or Baltimore Truss
(*g*)

Baltimore Truss with inclined
chord or Petit Truss
(*h*)

Figure 4.11   Conventional bridge trusses

cases, by changing only the geometry of the structure, it is possible to make the structure stable.   Structures e and f are therefore said to be *geometrically unstable*.   This type of instability may arise whenever equations of condition are introduced by the arrangement of the structure.   Sometimes the instability is obvious, but usually it does not become apparent until one attempts to compute the reactions, etc.[2]

4.10   Conventional Types of Bridge and Roof Trusses.   The members of a truss may be arranged in an almost unlimited number of ways, but the vast majority of trusses encountered in bridge or building work belong to one of the common types shown in Figs. 4.11 and 4.12.

[1] D. B. Steinman, "The Wichert Truss," D. Van Nostrand Company, Inc., New York, 1932.

[2] For a more complete discussion see W. M. Fife and J. B. Wilbur, "Theory of Statically Indeterminate Structures," McGraw-Hill Book Company, Inc., New York, 1937.

Since they are encountered so frequently, the student should be familiar with the names of these conventional types.

Trusses a, b, c, d, and e of Fig. 4.11 are simple trusses, while the remaining trusses are compound trusses built up out of the simple trusses (shaded). In order to achieve economical design of single-span steel-truss bridges, it is essential for the ratio of depth of truss to length of span to be between $\frac{1}{5}$ and $\frac{1}{10}$, for the diagonals to slope at approximately

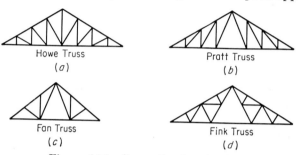

Howe Truss
(a)

Pratt Truss
(b)

Fan Truss
(c)

Fink Truss
(d)

Figure 4.12   Conventional roof trusses

45° to the horizontal, and for the panel lengths not to exceed 30 to 40 ft. Trusses a, b, c, and d can meet these requirements if the span is not too long. For long-span bridges, however, it becomes necessary to use one of the subdivided types such as f, g, or h.

All the roof trusses shown in Fig. 4.12 are simple trusses, with the exception of the Fink truss. This is a compound truss.

4.11   Illustrative Examples of Stress Analysis of Determinate Trusses.   The following examples illustrate the application of the previous discussions to the stress analysis of several conventional types of trusses. The analysis of such trusses is discussed further in Chap. 7.

Example 4.7   *Determine the bar forces in all members of this Pratt truss with a curved top chord.*

Discussion:

This Pratt truss is a simple truss and can therefore be analyzed by using simply the method of joints. This procedure, however, is not particularly efficient in a case where the two chords are not parallel. Probably the best procedure is first to find the horizontal components in the members of the curved chord. These may be computed by passing a vertical section through a panel and taking moments about the appropriate joint on the bottom chord. These computations are facilitated if the bending moments are known at the various joints along the bottom chord.

The bending moments at the bottom-chord joints may be computed very conveniently by drawing the shear and bending-moment diagrams as shown.   In this case where all the loads and reactions are vertical, the bending moment about any top-chord joint is the same as that about the bottom-chord joint directly under it.   Of course, if there are horizontal loads, this relationship is not necessarily true.

The horizontal components in the top chord being known, the remainder of the stress analysis can be accomplished by the method of joints.   It should also be noted that it i: easy to compute the vertical components in the diagonals once the shears in the panels and the vertical components in the top chords are known.

Example 4.8   Determine the bar forces in all members of this Fink roof truss.

$$14.3 \times \tfrac{82.5}{120} = 9.83$$

$$24 \times \tfrac{30}{120} = \underline{6}$$
$$\phantom{24 \times \tfrac{30}{120} = }15.83$$

$$16 \times \tfrac{33.54}{120} = 4.47$$

$$24 \times \tfrac{90}{120} = \underline{18}$$
$$\phantom{24 \times \tfrac{90}{120} = }22.47 \quad 24$$
$$\phantom{24 \times \tfrac{90}{120} = }15.83 \quad 14.3$$
$$\phantom{24 \times \tfrac{90}{120} = }38.30 \quad 38.3$$
$$\phantom{24 \times \tfrac{90}{120} = }\underline{\text{OK}}$$

$$F_{cg}: 22.47 \times \tfrac{60}{30} = 44.94$$

$$-(18 \times 30 + 3 \times 60)\tfrac{1}{30} = \underline{-24}$$
$$F_{cg} = \underline{+20.94}$$

Discussion:

Although this Fink truss is a compound truss, it can be analyzed by using only the method of joints. For example, after the reactions have been computed, the method of joints can be applied successively at joints i, H, and h. Since there are more than two unknown bar forces at each of joints g and G, it is not possible to consider these joints as the next step in the analysis. One can, however, determine the force in bar Ff by isolating joint F and the force in bar fG by isolating joint f. Then the stress analysis can be completed, still by means of the method of joints. This procedure is possible, however, only because joints E, F, and G and likewise joints E, f, and g lie on straight lines.

However, it is usually preferable to proceed as follows: After applying the method of joints at joints i, H, and h, the force in bar cg can be obtained by isolating the portion to the right of section 1-1 and taking moments about point E; the rest of the analysis can then be completed by the method of joints.

Note also that the stress analysis can be expedited by finding the forces in bars Cd, Cb, Gf, and Gh, using sections similar to section 2-2, and taking moments about points such as point E in the case of section 2-2.

The main point to remember is to consider the application of both the method of joints and the method of sections and combine the two approaches in such a way as to expedite the calculations.

Note that the geometry of the truss is rather complicated. This is often true in the case of roof trusses. In such cases it is often easier to accomplish the stress analysis of the truss by graphical methods.

Example 4.9   *Determine the forces in all members of this Howe truss.*

Index forces:

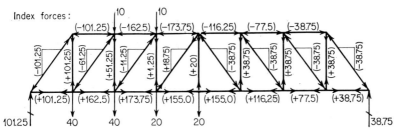

$$80 \times \frac{6.5}{8} = 65 \qquad\qquad 80 \times \frac{1.5}{8} = 15$$

$$40 \times \frac{4.5}{8} = 22.5 \qquad\qquad 40 \times \frac{3.5}{8} = 17.5$$

$$20 \times \frac{5.5}{8} = \underline{13.75} \qquad\qquad 20 \times \frac{2.5}{8} = \underline{6.25}$$

$$\underline{\underline{101.25}} \Updownarrow \qquad\qquad\qquad \underline{\underline{38.75}} \Updownarrow$$

$$\qquad\qquad\qquad\qquad\qquad\qquad 101.25$$

$$\qquad\qquad\qquad\qquad\qquad\qquad \underline{140.0} \qquad \therefore O.K.$$

Bar forces:

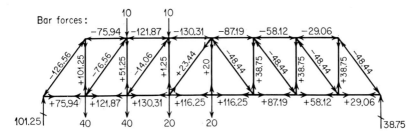

For verticals: bar force = 1 × (*index force*)
For diagonals: bar force = $^{50}/_{40}$ × (*index force*)
For chords: bar force = $^{30}/_{40}$ × (*index force*)

Check: $F_{ef} = 38.75 \times \, ^{120}/_{40} = \underline{\underline{+116.25}}$

Discussion:

After the reactions have been computed, it is possible to compute the vertical components in all the web members by working from one end of the truss to the other, using either the method of joints or the method of sections. Then it is possible to compute the horizontal components in the diagonals and apply the method of joints to obtain the chord forces. In this case, however, the computation of the chord forces depends only on the horizontal components in the various diagonals. Since all the diagonals have the same slope, the ratio between the vertical and horizontal components is the same for all of them—in this case as 40 is to 30. In applying $\Sigma F_x = 0$ at the various joints to obtain the chord forces, it is therefore permissible to use the values of vertical components temporarily in place of the horizontal components in the diagonals. In this manner, the values obtained for the chord forces are not equal to the true bar forces in the chords, but the ratio between these values and the true values is constant and equal to the ratio between the vertical and horizontal components in the diagonals.

These values of the chord forces which must be multiplied by a constant factor to obtain the true bar force are called **index forces** *for the chords. Likewise, the vertical components in the web members may be referred to as index forces for the webs. These index forces may be written down easily, as shown by the numbers in parentheses in the first force diagram. Then, the true bar forces may be obtained by multiplying the index forces by certain factors, as indicated in the second force diagram.*

The use of index forces is helpful in analyzing parallel-chord trusses that have equal panels and are acted upon by transverse loads. In other cases, the index-force method becomes involved and is usually inferior to the other methods already discussed.

4.12 Exceptional Cases. Occasionally one encounters certain trusses that cannot be classified as either simple or compound. Such a truss is shown in Fig. 4.13a. In these cases, it is usually difficult to tell by inspection whether the truss is rigid or not and whether it is statically determinate or indeterminate. In this particular case, a count of the structure shows that there are nine bars and six joints, which indicates that the structure is statically determinate. Whether or not the truss is stable is not apparent, but one way of finding out is to attempt a stress analysis and discover whether the results are consistent or not.

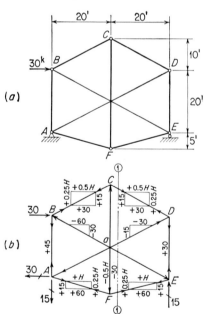

Figure 4.13 Complex truss

After computing the reactions, it is found that there is no joint at which there are only 2 unknown bar forces. Applying the method of joints will therefore not yield immediate solutions for the bar forces as in the case of simple trusses. It is also found that the method of sections likewise will not yield an immediate solution for any of the bar forces. Of course, it is possible to set up and solve 9 simultaneous equations involving the 9 unknown bar forces by using 9 of the 12 equations that result from applying the method of joints to the 6 joints of the structure.   If the 3 reactions have already been computed, the 3 remaining equations may be used for checking the results obtained for the 9 bar forces.

Setting up nine equations in this manner is a poor way to solve this problem, however.   Several other approaches are much superior, one of which is to proceed as follows: After computing the reactions, assume that the horizontal component of the bar force in member FE is a tension of H.   Then, from joint F, the horizontal component in FA must also be $+H$, and the bar force in FC is $-0.5H$.   By isolating joint C, it is then found that the horizontal and vertical components in both bars BC and CD are $+0.5H$ and $+0.25H$, respectively.   The forces in these five bars having been found in terms of H, it is now possible to pass section 1-1 through the truss, thus isolating the portion to the right of this section.   Summing up the moments about point a, an equation is obtained involving H as the only unknown.

$$\sum_{} \overset{R}{M_a} = 0, \; \text{\small ↶+}, \; 15H - (20)(0.5H) - (15)(20) = 0$$

whence $H = +60$.   With H known, all the other bar forces may be found by the method of joints as shown in Fig. 4.13b.   Since, in this manner, it is possible to make a consistent stress analysis of this truss under any condition of loading, it may be concluded that it is statically determinate and stable.

Trusses of this type, which cannot be classified as either simple or compound, may be called *complex* trusses.   Professor S. Timoshenko uses this terminology.[1]   In his excellent discussion of complex trusses, Timoshenko describes a general method of analysis of complex trusses called Henneberg's method.[2]

While the student should know how to recognize a complex truss and something about investigating its stability and stress analysis, he will not encounter this type often enough to warrant devoting more space to the subject here.   If additional information is required, the student is referred to Timoshenko's book.[3]   Several problems at the end of this chapter emphasize the fact that complex trusses may often be arranged so as to be geometrically unstable.   Cases of this type are not always obvious and may not become apparent until the stress analysis is attempted and is found to lead to inconsistent results.

4.13   Rigid Frames.   Before closing this chapter on truss structures, it is important to call to the attention of the student the difference between an ideal truss and a so-called "rigid frame."   The members of a rigid frame are usually connected together by moment-resisting (rigid) joints instead of being hinged together as in an ideal truss.   **Thus, a rigid frame may be defined as a structure composed of a number of members all lying in one plane and connected together so as to form a rigid framework by joints, some or all of which are moment-resisting (rigid) instead of hinged.**

[1] S. Timoshenko and D. H. Young, "Engineering Mechanics," vol. I, "Statics," McGraw-Hill Book Company, Inc., New York, 1956.

[2] This method was developed by L. Henneberg in his "Statik der Starren Systeme," Darmstadt, 1886.

[3] Timoshenko and Young, *op. cit.*

A moment-resisting joint is capable of transmitting both a force and a couple from one member to the other members connected by the joint. Such a joint can be formed by riveting or welding all the members to gusset plates. The detail of such joints is such that the angles between the ends of the various members at a joint remain essentially unchanged as the frame deforms under load. For this reason, moment-resisting joints are usually referred to as rigid joints.

By a strict interpretation of these definitions, a modern truss with riveted or welded joints should actually be classified as a rigid frame.

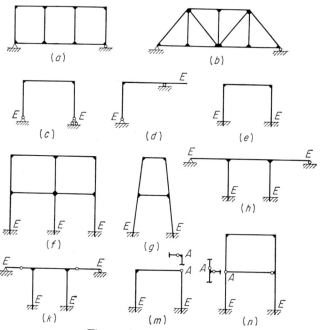

Figure 4.14   Rigid frames

However, since a satisfactory stress analysis may usually be obtained by assuming that such a truss acts as if it were pin-jointed, such structures are called trusses. The term rigid frame is reserved to designate structures of the type shown in all of Fig. 4.14 except sketch *b*. When rigid frames are represented by line diagrams as is done in this figure, moment-resisting joints are designated by indicating little fillets between the members meeting at a joint. Any pin joints are represented in the usual manner.

The stability and determinancy of rigid frames may be investigated by methods similar to those used for trusses. For this purpose, a criterion may be established comparing the number of unknown internal-force components and reaction elements with the number of independent equations of static equilibrium available for their solution. As in the case of trusses, the number of unknowns and equations may be expressed in terms of the number of members, joints, and reaction elements.

The total number of independent unknowns is equal to the sum of the number of unknown reaction elements plus the number of independent unknown internal-force components in the members. In a frame with rigid joints, the action of a joint on a member may consist of a couple as well as a force. Likewise, this force may have both axial and transverse components. As a result, the cross sections of a member may be subjected to an axial force, shear, and bending moment. However, if the axial force, shear, and bending moment are known at one end of a member, then similar quantities may be found for any other cross section of the member. There are therefore only three independent internal-force components for each member of the frame. If the number of reaction elements is r and the number of members is b, the total number of independent unknowns in a rigid frame is equal to $3b + r$.

If a rigid joint is isolated as a free body, it will be acted upon by a system of forces and couples. For equilibrium of such a joint, this system, therefore, must satisfy three equations of static equilibrium, $\Sigma F_x = 0$, $\Sigma F_y = 0$, and $\Sigma M = 0$. If the entire frame is in equilibrium, then each of its joints must be in equilibrium. If there are n rigid joints in the frame, each of these joints can be isolated as a free body and a total of $3n$ equations of static equilibrium obtained. As in the discussion of trusses, it may be shown that the three equations of equilibrium of the entire structure are not independent of these equations, and therefore it may be concluded that there are only $3n$ equations of static equilibrium for the entire rigid frame.

Occasionally hinges or some other special conditions of construction are introduced into the structure. **If in this manner s special equations of condition are introduced, the total number of equations available for the solution of the unknowns will equal $3n + s$. The criterion for stability and determinancy of the rigid frame is obtained by comparing the number of unknowns, $3b + r$, with the number of independent equations, $3n + s$. As before, it may, therefore, be concluded that**

> If $3n + s > 3b + r$, the frame is *unstable*
> If $3n + s = 3b + r$, the frame is *statically determinate*
> If $3n + s < 3b + r$, the frame is *statically indeterminate*

If the criterion indicates that the frame is statically determinate or indeterminate, it should be remembered from the similar discussion in Art. 4.8 that the count alone does not prove absolutely

that the structure is stable—it may still be statically or geometrically unstable.

This criterion establishes the combined degree of indeterminancy with respect to both reactions and internal-force components. The degree of indeterminancy with respect to reactions only may be established in the same manner as discussed in Art. 4.9 for truss structures and also in Arts. 2.5 and 2.9.

Table 4.1 shows the application of the above criterion to the frames in Fig. 4.14:

Table 4.1

Frame	n	s	b	r	$3n + s$	$3b + r$	Classification
a	8	0	10	3	24	33	Indeterminate—9th degree
b	8	0	13	3	24	42	Indeterminate—18th degree
c	4	0	3	3	12	12	Determinate
d	4	0	3	3	12	12	Determinate
e	4	0	3	6	12	15	Indeterminate—3d degree
f	9	0	10	9	27	39	Indeterminate—12th degree
g	6	0	6	6	18	24	Indeterminate—6th degree
h	6	0	5	9	18	24	Indeterminate—6th degree
k	6	2	5	9	20	24	Indeterminate—4th degree
m	4	1	3	6	13	15	Indeterminate—2d degree
n	6	3	6	6	21	24	Indeterminate—3d degree

In applying this criterion, any extremity of the frame, such as those marked E in Fig. 4.14, should be counted as a rigid joint even though just one member is connected to it. Sometimes the count of the s special equations of condition is rather difficult to make. It is quite obvious in structure k of Fig. 4.14 that the insertion of the two hinges has introduced two equations of condition. The insertion of the hinge joint A in structure m introduces one equation of condition, but the insertion of a similar joint A as shown in structure n introduces two equations of condition. In each case, the validity of these counts is more apparent if one considers the auxiliary sketches of the joints shown in each case. The auxiliary sketches show the manner in which the same structural action may be obtained at these joints by insertion of hinges in the ends of the members meeting at the joint. These alternative arrangements require one hinge for structure m and two hinges for the joint A in structure n. To generalize, it may be stated that the number of special condition equations introduced by the insertion of a hinge joint in a rigid frame is equal to the number of bars meeting at that joint minus one. If the s special equations are counted in this manner, the criterion yields the correct results.

After reading this last paragraph, the reader will no doubt appreciate the truth of the statement that it is almost impossible to count some structures properly without first knowing the answer. Because of the difficulties encountered in counting some structures, the authors feel that, while criteria such as the above are sometimes very useful, **the stress analyst should rely on a more fundamental approach to determine the degree of indeterminancy of an indeterminate structure. The most fundamental approach is to remove supports and/or to cut members until the structure has been reduced to a statically determinate and stable structure. The number of restraints that must be removed to accomplish this result is equal to the degree of indeterminancy of the actual structure.**

4.14 Problems for Solution

Problem 4.1 Classify the trusses of Fig. 4.15 as being simple, compound, or complex.

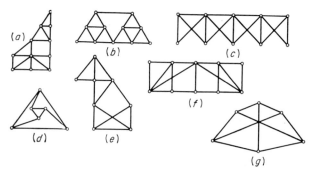

Figure 4.15 Problem 4.1

Problem 4.2 Classify the truss structures of Fig. 4.16 as being statically determinate or indeterminate, stable or unstable. If the structure is indeterminate, state the degree of indeterminancy both with respect to reactions and bar forces and with respect to reactions only. If the structure is unstable, state the reason for the instability.

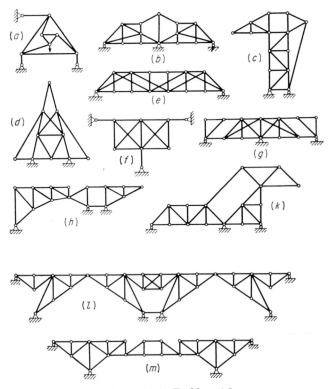

Figure 4.16   Problem 4.2

Problem 4.3   Compute the bar forces in the lettered bars of the trusses of Fig. 4.17 due to the loads shown.

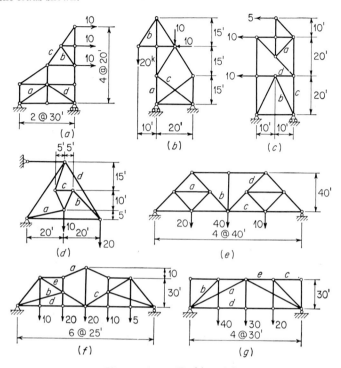

Figure 4.17   Problem 4.3

Problem 4.4   Compute all the bar forces in the trusses of Fig 4.18 due to the loads shown.

Figure 4.18   Problem 4.4

Figure 4.18 (*Continued*)

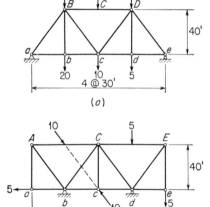

Figure 4.19   Problem 4.5

*Problem 4.5   Compute the bar forces in the structures of Fig. 4.19. (*Hint:* Remember that structures of this type may be geometrically unstable.)

*Problem 4.6   Compute the bar forces in the structures of Fig. 4.20. Also draw the shear and bending-moment curves for those members in which such stress conditions exist.

Figure 4.20   Problem 4.6

Problem 4.7   Compute the reactions for each of the structures shown in Fig. 4.21.

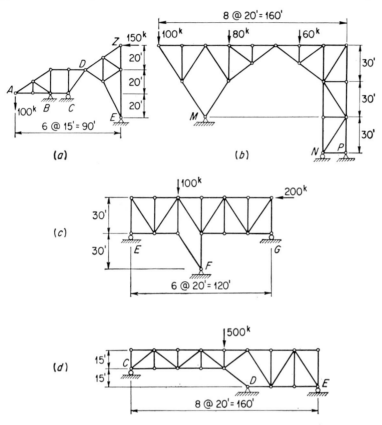

Figure 4.21   Problem 4.7

Problem 4.8   Compute the reactions for each of the structures shown in Fig. 4.22.

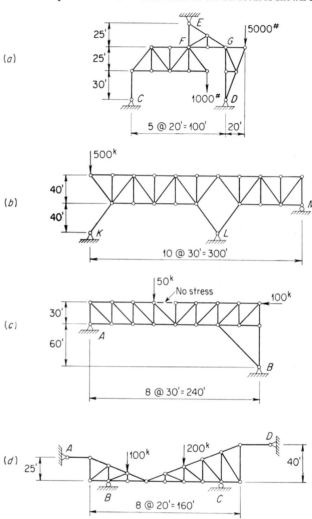

Figure 4.22   Problem 4.8

Problem 4.9 Compute the bar forces in the bars noted on each of the structures shown in Fig. 4.23.

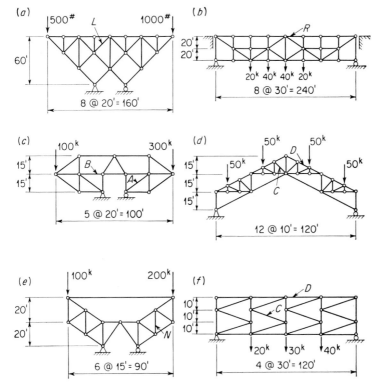

Figure 4.23 Problem 4.9

5

Graphic Statics

5.1 Introduction. Graphic statics is that branch of mechanics which deals with graphical rather than algebraic solutions of problems of statics. In this country, there seems to be an aversion toward graphical solutions among students and engineers. There are some problems, however, where the graphical solution is distinctly superior to the algebraic approach. There are other problems where just the reverse is true. In the middle ground between these two extreme situations, which method the engineer decides to use usually depends on his personal preference and background.

Among the problems that may be solved advantageously by graphical methods are the following: (1) determination of the bar forces in a truss that has a complex configuration and that is to be analyzed for a limited number of loading conditions; (2) cases where the true resultant deflection is required for every joint of a truss.

The student will find not only that a knowledge of graphical methods is useful in the solution of problems such as these but also that there are certain educational advantages which result from a study of the basic principles of graphical methods. He will find that these ideas aid him in visualizing and representing physical phenomena and often assist him in thinking about the algebraic solution of certain problems.

In this book, the discussion of graphic statics will be limited to the solution of two-dimensional, or planar, structures. Graphical methods can be extended, of course, to the more general three-dimensional problems, but in most cases the complexities introduced by the third dimension are greater for the graphical methods than for the algebraic methods.

5.2 Definitions. Before the fundamental principles of graphic statics are discussed, it is first necessary to emphasize certain ideas and definitions concerning forces and force systems. A *force* may be defined as any action which tends to change the state of motion (or rest) of the body to which it is applied. The forces acting on a body may be classified as either outer forces or inner forces (that is, the resultant effects of the stresses on internal sections exposed by cuts used to isolate the body under consideration). The outer forces may be further subdivided into the loads (active forces) applied to the structure from without and the reactions (reactive forces or couples) balancing or restraining the effects of the loads.

A force may be completely identified by the following specifications: (1) its point of application, (2) its direction, (3) its magnitude. According to this terminology, the "direction of a force" is intended to define the slope of its line of action while the "magnitude" indicates not only its numerical size but also the sense in which the force acts along this line of action, i.e., whether toward or away from a body.   A force is therefore a vector quantity since it has both magnitude and direction.   Hence, a force may be represented graphically by a line drawn toward or from the point of application and having a length that indicates the numerical size of the force to a certain scale.   The slope of this line indicates the direction of the force and an arrowhead the sense in which the force acts along this line.   A 3,000-lb force is represented in this manner by the vector $\overline{AB}$ in Fig. 5.1.   When this vector notation is used, the order of the letters indicates the sense of the force.   Thus, $\overline{AB}$ means that the force acts from A toward B.

Figure 5.1   Force vector

The use of the term "point of application" of a force implies that it is possible to concentrate a force at a point.   Physically, of course, this is impossible since a finite load applied at a point, i.e., applied to a zero area, would develop infinite contact stress intensities in the material.   No material can withstand such stresses, since it will deform at the point of contact until a small finite contact area is developed over which the load is distributed at finite stress intensities.   However, as far as the equilibrium condition of the body as a whole is concerned, it is legitimate to replace the actual load distributed over a small area by the equivalent total load concentrated at a point.

As previously explained in Art. 2.3, it is usually permissible to assume structures as being rigid (nondeformable) bodies in investigating their equilibrium conditions.   Thus, in most problems of graphic statics, it will be assumed that the structure is a rigid body and hence that the geometry after the application of the loads is essentially the same as before.

5.3   Composition and Resolution of Forces.   It is sometimes desirable to replace two forces by a single force that exerts the same effect on the equilibrium of the body being considered.   This single force that would have the same effect in producing motion is called the *resultant* of these forces.   It may be demonstrated that the magnitude and direction of the resultant of two concurrent forces may be obtained by drawing the diagonal of a parallelogram which has been constructed with the vectors representing these two forces drawn as sides.   Thus, to determine the magnitude and direction of the resultant of the forces F_1 and F_2 shown in Fig. 5.2a, a parallelogram is constructed as shown in Fig. 5.2b.   This

Figure 5.2   Composition of forces

parallelogram is constructed on the basis of two sides OA and OB obtained by drawing through point O two vectors $\overline{OA}$ and $\overline{OB}$ representing the forces F_1 and F_2, respectively. The magnitude and direction of the resultant R_{12} is given by the vector $\overline{OC}$, which is the diagonal of this parallelogram.

From Fig. 5.2d, it is apparent that the same results would be obtained from a parallelogram constructed by drawing vectors $\overline{AO}$ and $\overline{BO}$ both running into point O rather than away from this point. Likewise, from Fig. 5.2c, it is apparent that the same results could also be obtained by drawing either of the vector triangles OAC or OBC instead of the parallelogram. In constructing these triangles, either force may be drawn first and then the other force laid out from the end of the first vector. The resultant is then obtained in magnitude and direction from the closing vector of the triangle drawn from the beginning of the first vector to the end of the second.

The magnitude and direction of the resultant R_{12} having been determined in one of these ways, its point of application may be considered to be located at any point along its line of action. The line of action of the resultant must pass through the point of intersection of the two forces F_1 and F_2, or through point O' in Fig. 5.2a. If this were not so, the resultant would not exert the same effect as the two forces that it replaces since the moment of the resultant about an axis through any point in the plane would not be the same as the sum of the moments of the two forces about that axis. For example, the moments of both F_1 and F_2 about an axis through O' are zero, but the moment of the resultant R_{12} will also be zero only if the line of action of R_{12} also passes through point O'.

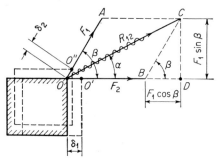

Figure 5.3   Parallelogram of forces

The validity of this parallelogram construction for determining the magnitude and direction of the resultant of two concurrent forces may be demonstrated in the following manner: Consider the two forces F_1 and F_2 acting at point O on the body shown in Fig. 5.3. The resultant R_{12} of these forces also acts at point O along some line of action specified by the unknown angle α. The unknown magnitude and direction of this resultant may be determined in the following manner: If this body is moved so that point O is given some arbitrary movement δ, the forces F_1 and F_2 will perform a certain amount of work. If the resultant R_{12} is to exert the same effect as the two forces F_1 and F_2, then it must perform the same amount of work during the movement δ. Suppose that the body is given an arbitrary translation so that point O moves to point O'. Upon equating the work done by F_1 and F_2 to the work done by R_{12}, Eq. (a) is obtained,

$$(R_{12} \cos \alpha)(\delta_1) = (F_2)(\delta_1) + (F_1 \cos \beta)(\delta_1)$$

or
$$R_{12} = \frac{F_2 + F_1 \cos \beta}{\cos \alpha} \qquad (a)$$

In the same manner, translating the body so that point O moves to O'',

$$[R_{12} \cos (\beta - \alpha)](\delta_2) = (F_1)(\delta_2) + (F_2 \cos \beta)(\delta_2)$$

$$R_{12} = \frac{F_1 + F_2 \cos \beta}{\cos (\beta - \alpha)} \qquad (b)$$

These two equations may now be solved for R_{12} and α. Equating the right-hand sides of these equations leads to the following expression for α:

$$\tan \alpha = \frac{F_1 \sin \beta}{F_2 + F_1 \cos \beta} \qquad (c)$$

Therefore, $\cos \alpha = \dfrac{F_2 + F_1 \cos \beta}{\sqrt{(F_1 \sin \beta)^2 + (F_2 + F_1 \cos \beta)^2}}$ (d)

Substituting in Eq. (a) from Eq. (d) leads to

$$R_{12} = \sqrt{(F_1 \sin \beta)^2 + (F_2 + F_1 \cos \beta)^2} \qquad (e)$$

By use of Eq. (c), the angle α may be laid off graphically as indicated in Fig. 5.3, while the magnitude of the vector R_{12} is shown by Eq. (e) to be given by the length of the hypotenuse of the right triangle ODC.   It is obvious, therefore, that the vector $\overline{OC}$ representing the resultant is likewise the diagonal of the parallelogram of forces $OACB$, which justifies the parallelogram construction described above.

This process of replacing forces F_1 and F_2 by a single resultant force R_{12} is known as the *composition of forces* F_1 and F_2.   The reverse of this process, that of replacing the effect of a single force R by two equivalent forces (called two *components*) F_1 and F_2, is called the *resolution of force* R.   In the latter process, the direction of the two components might be given and their magnitude obtained from the force triangle or parallelogram; or the direction and magnitude of one component might be given and the direction and magnitude of the other component determined in a similar manner.   The magnitude and direction of the two components F_1 and F_2 having been determined, they may both be applied at the point of application of the force R.   Of course, it is permissible to apply both the components F_1 and F_2 at any point along the line of action of the force R.

5.4   Resultant of Several Forces in a Plane—Force Polygon.   Consider a body subjected to a coplanar system of forces F_1, F_2, F_3, and F_4 as shown in Fig. 5.4a. This figure is simply a scaled diagram showing the point of application and line of action of the forces in their plane (or two-dimensional space) and is called the *space diagram*.   Suppose that it is required to find the resultant of these forces graphically. As described in the previous article, the resultant R_{12} of the forces F_1 and F_2 may be obtained in magnitude and direction from the force triangle 012.   The line of action of this resultant is drawn parallel to the vector $\overline{02}$ and through the intersection of the lines of action of the forces F_1 and F_2.   In the same manner, the resultant R_{123} of the forces R_{12} and F_3 may be obtained; and then the resultant R_{1234} of the forces R_{123} and F_4.   The last resultant R_{1234} is of course the resultant of all four forces F_1, F_2, F_3, and F_4.

The figure obtained by combining the force triangles 012, 023, and 034 and then omitting the dashed lines 02 and 03 is called the *force polygon* for the forces F_1, F_2, F_3, and F_4.   From this force polygon, the resultant R_{1234} of the entire system may be found directly without completing the intermediate force triangles.   The magnitude and direction of this resultant are given by the vector drawn from the initial to the final point of the force polygon—in this case by the vector $\overline{04}$.   To establish the line of action of this resultant in the space diagram, the lines of action of the intermediate resultants R_{12} and R_{123} must be established as described above.

This method of obtaining the magnitude, direction, and line of action of the resultant is applicable as long as the lines of action of the forces are not parallel and intersect within the limits of the drawing.   When this method is not applicable, it is necessary to resort to the use of a so-called "equilibrium (funicular) polygon," which will be described in Art. 5.7.

It should be noted that the order of drawing the forces in the force polygon is immaterial and that they are usually considered in a clockwise order simply as a matter of convenience.

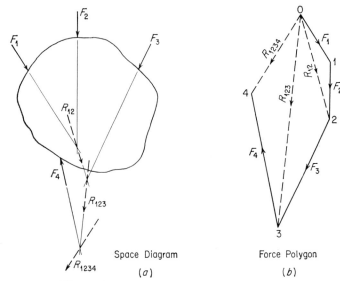

Space Diagram   Force Polygon
(a)   (b)

Figure 5.4   Resultant of planar force system

5.5   Equilibrium Conditions for Concurrent and Nonconcurrent Coplanar Force Systems.   Suppose that the force F_5 is added to the nonconcurrent force sys-

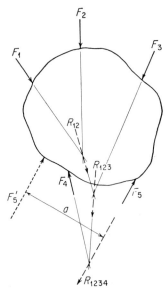

tem already shown in Fig. 5.4a.   The new system F_1, F_2, F_3, F_4, and F_5 is shown in Fig. 5.5.   Let the force F_5 have the same line of action as the resultant R_{1234}, and further let it be numerically equal to this resultant but acting in the opposite sense.   Then in this case it will be found that the force polygon for all five forces will close back on the original starting point O.   Closure of the force polygon indicates that the equations $\Sigma F_x = 0$ and $\Sigma F_y = 0$ are satisfied by the five forces themselves and that therefore their resultant effect cannot be a resultant force. The fact that, in the space diagram, F_5 and R_{1234} have the same lines of action and are also numerically equal, but opposite in sense, indicates that F_5 in effect holds the other four forces in equilibrium. In such a case, the force F_5 is called the *equilibrant* of the other four forces.

Suppose, however, that force F_5, instead of having the same line of action as R_{1234}, is displaced laterally a distance a as indicated by the dotted force F_5' in Fig. 5.5.   Now, although F_5' closes the force polygon, thus satisfying equations $\Sigma F_x = 0$ and

Figure 5.5   Planar force system equivalent to couple

$\Sigma F_y = 0$, in the space diagram the equal and opposite forces F_5' and R_{1234} are parallel, but their lines of action are displaced by the distance a.   Obviously, therefore, the resultant of the new system F_1, F_2, F_3, F_4, and F_5' is a couple equal in magnitude to $F_5'a$, and the system is not in equilibrium since $\Sigma M \neq 0$.

In the case of a nonconcurrent force system, it is therefore evident that closure of the force polygon is a necessary but not a sufficient condition to show that the system is in equilibrium. In addition to this condition, it is necessary to show in the space diagram that the system is not equivalent to a couple, i.e., that one force has the same line of action but is opposite in sense to the resultant of the remaining forces of the system.

Of course, if the force system is a concurrent system with the lines of action of all the forces intersecting in a common point, then it is impossible for the resultant effect of the system to be a couple. In such a case, closure of the force polygon indicating that the resultant effect of the system is not a resultant force is then sufficient to prove that this concurrent force system is in equilibrium.

5.6 Determination of Reactions by the Three-force Method. If only three nonparallel forces act on a body, it is easy to show that they must be concurrent in order to be in equilibrium. Consider any two of these three forces. The line of action of the resultant of these two forces must pass through their point of intersection. Then, in order for the remaining force to be the equilibrant of the other two, the line of action of this third force must coincide with that of the resultant of the other two. It may therefore be concluded that the lines of action of all three forces must intersect in a common point if the system is to be in equilibrium. This conclusion furnishes the basis for the so-called "three-force method" of determining the reactions of a statically determinate structure.

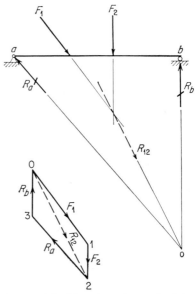

Consider, for example, the beam shown in Fig. 5.6. Suppose that it is desired to

Figure 5.6   Reactions determined by three-force method

find the reactions which are required to keep this structure in static equilibrium. First determine the magnitude and line of action of the resultant of the applied loads, using the force polygon and the space diagram. Then the structure may be considered to be acted upon by three forces—the resultant of the applied loads (R_{12} in this case) and the two reactions (R_a and R_b). For equilibrium of the structure, it is necessary for these three forces to be concurrent. In this case, the magnitude of both reactions and the direction of R_a are unknown, but the point of application of R_a and the line of action of R_b are both known. The line of action of R_b is known to be a vertical line passing through point b. Point o, the point of intersection of R_{12} and R_b, must therefore be the point of concurrency of the three forces. The line of action of R_a must therefore be along the line oa. Now, the directions of both reactions being known, their magnitudes may easily be determined since it is known that the vectors representing these reactions must close the force polygon. In this case, upon drawing a line through point 2 parallel to R_a and through point O, a line parallel to R_b establishes the intersection point 3, which determines the length of vectors $\overline{23}$ and $\overline{30}$ representing the reactions R_a and R_b, respectively. Of course, it is immaterial whether the force polygon is closed in this manner or by drawing the line parallel to R_a through point O and the line parallel to R_b through point 2.

It should be noted that this three-force method is not a completely general method of determining the reactions of a statically determinate structure. It may be used only when the resultant of the applied loads is a force the line of action of which intersects the known line of action of one of the reactions.

5.7 Funicular (Equilibrium) Polygon.   A method is discussed in Art. 5.4 by which the resultant of several coplanar forces may be determined.   This method fails when any point of intersection on the space diagram falls outside the paper and is not applicable to a system of parallel forces.   However, a general method using the *funicular (equilibrium) polygon* is applicable to any coplanar force system.

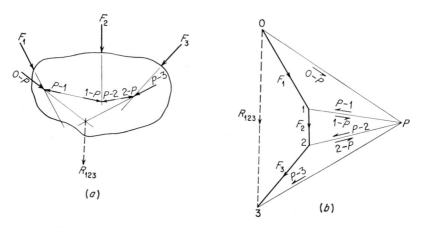

Figure 5.7   Resultant by use of force and funicular polygons

Suppose that the resultant of the forces F_1, F_2, and F_3 shown in Fig. 5.7a is required. The magnitude and direction of the resultant R_{123} is obtained from vector $\overline{O3}$ in the force polygon $O123$.   The line of action of this resultant on the space diagram may be determined as follows: Suppose, by using the force triangle $OP1$, that force F_1 is resolved into any two components $P1$ and OP at some point on its line of action. Suppose that the line of action of the component $P1$ is extended until it intersects the line of action of F_2.   At this point, resolve F_2 into components one of which, $1P$, is collinear with, but equal and opposite to, $P1$, and the other is equal to $P2$ as obtained from the force triangle $1P2$.   In the same manner, resolve F_3 into components $2P$ and $P3$ as shown.   Now the original force system of F_1, F_2, and F_3 has been replaced by six components, OP and $P1$, $1P$ and $P2$, and $2P$ and $P3$.   Of these six components, the pairs $P1$ and $1P$ and $P2$ and $2P$ are collinear but equal and opposite, and therefore each of these pairs is in equilibrium.   The resultant of the six components and therefore of the original force system is the resultant of the two remaining components OP and $P3$ and acts through their point of intersection.

The construction thus drawn between the lines of action of the forces in the space diagram is called the equilibrium, or funicular, polygon.   The sides of this polygon drawn between the forces are called *strings*.   The point P on the force polygon through which all the components are directed is called the *pole*.   The lines drawn from the vertices of the force polygon to the pole P are called *rays*.

In an actual problem, the line of action of the resultant is located by constructing the funicular polygon in a slightly different manner from that described above.   First a convenient pole P is selected, and rays are drawn from this pole to the vertexes of the force polygon. Then the strings of the funicular polygon are drawn on the space diagram parallel to the corresponding rays of the force polygon. Note that a string is drawn between the lines of action of two forces which are adjacent to each other in the force polygon and further that this string is drawn parallel to the ray directed through the intersection of these two adjacent force vectors. While it is not necessary to do so, usually the starting point for the funicular polygon is selected as some point on the line of action of the first force to have been laid out in the force polygon. Then, the intersection of the first and last string of the funicular polygon (such as the string between F_1 and R_{123} and that between F_3 and R_{123}, respectively) is a point on the line of action of the resultant of the system, which has been determined previously in magnitude and direction from the force polygon.

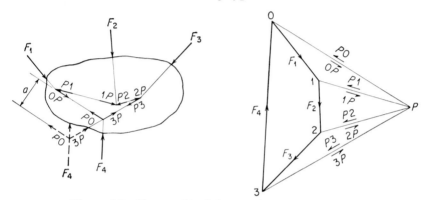

Figure 5.8   Closure of both force and funicular polygons

Suppose that a fourth force F_4 is added to the system in Fig. 5.7. Suppose further that F_4 is collinear with, but equal and opposite to, R_{123}. The new system will then be as shown in Fig. 5.8.

In such a case, the force polygon will close, indicating that $\Sigma F_x = 0$ and $\Sigma F_y = 0$. Likewise, when the funicular polygon is drawn, it is found that the first and last strings drawn from forces F_1 and F_4, respectively, are actually collinear. Of course, drawing the funicular polygon actually is just a means of replacing the four forces by the eight components shown. It is apparent that these eight components may be considered as four pairs, each of which is in equilibrium, and therefore the original force system must be in equilibrium.

Suppose that, instead of F_4 being collinear with R_{123}, its line of action is displaced to the dashed-line position, still being parallel and equal and opposite to R_{123}. Then, the force polygon will still close, but the first and last strings will no longer be collinear. They will now be parallel but displaced a distance a apart. In this case, the eight components represented by the funicular polygon will consist of three equal and opposite pairs in equilibrium, but the fourth pair OP and PO will be parallel, equal, and opposite and will be equivalent to a couple equal to $(OP)(a)$. The original force system will now be equivalent to a couple $(OP)(a)$ and will no longer be in equilibrium.

It may therefore be concluded that, for a system of nonconcurrent forces to be in equilibrium, it is necessary not only for the force polygon to be a closed figure but also for the funicular polygon to be a closed figure, i.e., the first and last strings of the funicular polygon must be coincident. If the

force polygon closes but the funicular polygon does not, the force system will be equivalent to a couple.

There is another principle associated with a funicular polygon which may often be used to advantage. **The strings of a funicular polygon may be considered to represent links connected together at the vertexes of the polygon by friction-less pins.** If one considers the fundamental principles involved in the construction of a funicular polygon, it is evident that **a linkage of this shape will support the sys-tem of loads applied to its joints. Of course, in cases where the funicular polygon is not a closed figure, it is also necessary to provide the proper reac-tions for the linkage acting along the directions of the first and last strings of the polygon.** The magnitudes of these two reactions are given by measuring the length of the first and last rays of the force polygon.

5.8 Use of Funicular Polygon to Determine Reactions. The use of the funicular polygon in determining the reactions of a statically determinate structure

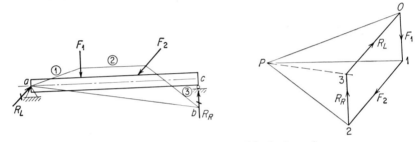

Figure 5.9 Reactions by use of funicular polygon

may be explained by considering the beam and loading shown in Fig. 5.9. In this case, the point of application and direction of the right reaction and the point of application of the left reaction are known, leaving as unknowns the magnitude of both reactions and the direction of the left one. These three unknowns may be found by knowing that both the force and funicular polygons must close if the combined system of loads and reactions is to be in equilibrium.

A portion of the force polygon may be drawn immediately, viz., vectors $\overline{01}$ and $\overline{12}$ representing the applied loads. Now select a pole P, and draw the rays to points O, 1, and 2. Draw a string parallel to ray PO between the unknown line of action of R_L and the force F_1. While the direction of R_L is unknown, it is known that point a is one point on its line of action and therefore this string may be drawn from point a to an intersection with F_1.* Likewise, draw successively the strings between F_1 and F_2 and then between F_2 and the known line of action of R_R. This last string intersects R_R at point b. The closing string of the funicular polygon will be the string ab. Now the corresponding ray may be drawn in the force polygon parallel to this closing string. This ray must go through the vertex that is the intersection of the vectors, representing R_R and R_L. Since string 3 was drawn between F_2 and R_R parallel to ray $P2$, one end of the vector representing R_R must be at point 2 on the force polygon. It is known further that this reaction is vertical. Through point 2, therefore, draw a vertical vector representing R_R. The other end of this vector must lie on the ray parallel to the closing string, and thus vertex 3 of the polygon is located. Vector $\overline{23}$ gives the magnitude of R_R, and vector $\overline{3O}$, the closing vector of the force polygon, gives the direction and magnitude of R_L.

The procedure is straightforward, but sometimes students become confused as to

* Why not start the funicular polygon with string 3 drawn parallel to ray $P2$ from point c to the line of action of force F_2?

whether to draw the vector for the reaction with the known direction through the first or last vertex of the force, i.e., in this case whether through point O or 2. Such confusion is not necessary if one remembers that a given string drawn between the lines of action of two forces is parallel to the ray which passes through the intersection of the two vectors representing these forces in the force polygon. In this case, string 1 is drawn parallel to ray PO and string 3 parallel to ray $P2$. This implies that one end of the vector representing R_L is at point O on the force polygon and one end of the vector for R_R at point 2.

This method of determining reactions is general and is not limited to special cases as is the three-force method.

5.9 Funicular Polygons Drawn through One, Two, or Three Specified Points. When one reconsiders the procedure for drawing a funicular polygon for a given set of forces, it is apparent that it is possible to draw an infinite number of funicular polygons for that particular set of forces, for any one of an infinite number of

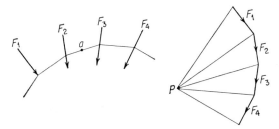

Figure 5.10   Funicular polygon through one specified point

points can be selected as the pole of the force polygon. Sometimes, however, it is necessary to draw the funicular polygon so that it will pass through certain specific points in the space diagram. Under such conditions, it becomes necessary to limit the selection of the pole to certain specific points.

First consider the case where it is necessary to pass the funicular polygon through *one* specific point in the space diagram, such as point a in Fig. 5.10. This may be done by drawing between forces F_2 and F_3 any desired string that also passes through point a. The ray corresponding to this string may now be drawn parallel to it and passing through the intersection of the vectors for F_2 and F_3 in the force polygon. The pole P may now be selected as any point along this ray and the remainder of the corresponding funicular polygon completed as shown. Obviously, any one of an infinite number of poles P can be selected in this manner, and hence an infinite number of polygons can be drawn passing through the single point a.

When it becomes necessary to pass the funicular polygon through two particular points such as a and b in Fig. 5.11, the procedure must be altered somewhat. Suppose temporarily that these forces are imagined to be applied to a structure supported by a hinge support at point a and a roller support supplying a vertical reaction at point b. Then, proceeding in the usual manner, these two imaginary reactions can be obtained, using the funicular polygon labeled with the strings 1, 2, 3, and 4 and the closing string ab'. This funicular polygon is drawn using the pole P. Of course, the value so determined for the reactions R_R and R_L will be the same regardless of what point is chosen for the pole P, and therefore the position of vertex v in the force polygon is unique. If the pole P has been selected as desired, the resulting funicular polygon will pass through points a and b and the closing string of this polygon will be the line ab. The corresponding ray for this string will be parallel to ab and will also pass through vertex v of the force polygon. This ray has been so drawn and labeled $5'$. Any point along this ray may now be selected as the pole P', which will result in a funicular polygon with strings 1′, 2′, 3′, 4′, and 5′, which pass through the two specified points a and b in the space diagram.   Again, it is apparent that any one of an infinite number of poles $P′$ can be selected in this manner and hence an infinite number of funicular polygons can be drawn passing through two specified points a and b.

Now consider a case where it is necessary to pass the funicular polygon through three specified points a, b, and c, as shown in Fig. 5.12.   As before, assume temporarily that these forces are acting on a structure supported by a hinge support at a and a roller support supplying a vertical reaction at c.   Continue as before, and determine these reactions R_L and R_R by drawing the funicular polygon with strings 1, 2, 3, 4, and 5 and

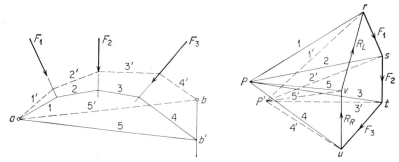

Figure 5.11   Funicular polygon through two specified points

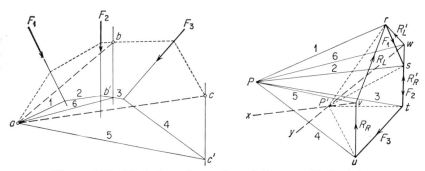

Figure 5.12   Funicular polygon through three specified points

thus locating vertex v in the force polygon.   As demonstrated in the preceding paragraph, the pole of a funicular polygon passing through points a and c must lie somewhere along the line vx parallel to line ac.   Now consider only the forces lying between points a and b, and assume these forces to be supported by a hinge support at a and a roller support supplying a vertical reaction at point b.   These reactions $R′_L$ and $R′_R$ may be determined by using the funicular polygon with strings 1, 2, 3, and 6 and thus locating vertex w in the force polygon.   Likewise, the pole of a funicular polygon passing through points a and b must lie somewhere along the line wy parallel to line ab. Hence, for the polygon to pass through all three points a, b, and c, the pole $P′$ must be located at the intersection of the lines vx and wy.   In this case, only one pole $P′$ may be located in this manner, and hence only one funicular polygon may be passed through three specified points.   Further, **a funicular polygon cannot be made to pass through more than three specified points.**

5.10   Graphical Determination of Shear and Bending Moment.   After finding the reactions of a beam graphically, shear and bending moment may also readily be found by graphical methods. Shear, being the transverse component of the resultant of the forces applied either to the left or to the right of a section, may easily be found from the force polygon. Graphical determination of bending moment, however, requires additional considerations beyond the techniques already discussed.

The bending moment at a section is equal to the moment of the resultant of the forces applied either to the left or to the right of the section. Of course, the magnitude and direction of such a resultant may be determined from the force polygon, while a point on its line of action is located by the intersection of the appropriate strings of the funicular polygon. By using this information and scaling the lever arm of the resultant, it is possible to compute the desired moment. It is simpler, however, to compute the moment by using the procedure developed by the following considerations:

Consider the force system F_1, F_2, and F_3 shown in Fig. 5.13, and suppose that it is desired to compute the sum of the moments of these three forces about point a. The

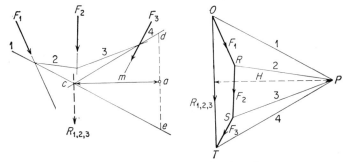

Figure 5.13 Graphical determination of moment

sum of the moments of these three forces is equal to the moment of their resultant about point a, which will be called M_a. Then,

$$M_a = (R_{123})(m) = (\overline{OT})(m) \qquad (a)$$

where $\overline{OT}$ is measured to the force scale and m to the distance scale. If the line de is drawn parallel to $\overline{OT}$, then the triangles OPT and cde are similar. Therefore, drawing H perpendicular to $\overline{OT}$,

$$\frac{de}{m} = \frac{\overline{OT}}{H} \qquad \text{or} \qquad (H)(de) = (\overline{OT})(m) \qquad (b)$$

Hence, $$M_a = (H)(de) \qquad (c)$$

where de is measured to the distance scale and H to the force scale. H is called the pole distance.

In general, determining the product of $(H)(de)$ furnishes a convenient way of evaluating the moment of the resultant (and hence of the three forces) about point a. The following procedure summarizes this graphical method of determining the moment of a system of forces about a given point a:

1. Construct the force polygon for this system. Select a pole P, and draw the corresponding funicular polygon.

2. Draw through point a in the space diagram a line parallel to the direction of the resultant of the system as determined in the force polygon.

2. Measure to the distance scale the intercept of this line between the strings of the funicular polygon, the intersection of which determines a point on the line of action of the resultant.

4. Also measure to the force scale the pole distance H that is the perpendicular distance from the pole P to the resultant vector in the force polygon.

5. The moment of the force system about point a is then equal to the product of the intercept, from step 3, and the pole distance, from step 4.

The following examples illustrate how conveniently this procedure may be applied to the computation of the bending moment at various points in a beam.

It is often necessary to consider cases where the load is distributed instead of concentrated. In such cases, the portion of the beam so loaded must be divided into a series of short sections. The total load acting on each section is then assumed to be concentrated at the center of gravity of the load for that section. The graphical solution for reactions, shear, and bending moment is then carried out as usual, considering the distributed load to be replaced by this series of concentrated loads. The values of the reactions found in this manner are not in error, but the values of shear and bending moment are exact only at the ends of the various short sections into which the distributed load is divided. The ordinates of the shear and bending-moment curves at intermediate points are not appreciably in error, however, provided that the lengths of the sections are reasonably small.

Example 5.1   *Draw the shear and bending moment diagrams for this beam.*

$M_c = 31.0 \times 2.30 = 71.3^{k'}$
$M_d = 31.0 \times 3.80 = 117.9$
$M_e = 31.0 \times 1.45 = 44.9$

Discussion:

In this example, all the loads are vertical and develop vertical reactions. As a result, at any point along the beam, the resultant of the loads either to the right or to the left of that section is a vertical force. The computation of shear and, particularly, bending moment is therefore considerably simplified. For example, in computing the bending moments at various points, the pole distance H will be constant for every point, and the intercepts measured in the funicular polygon will all be along vertical lines.

Example 5.2　　*Draw the shear and bending-moment diagrams for this beam.*

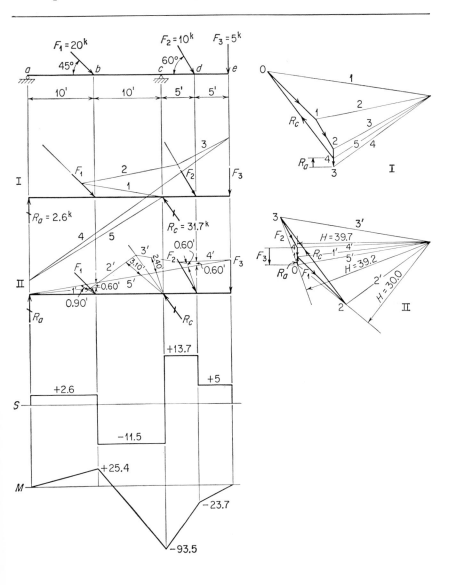

Computed by using forces on

Left   Right

$M_b = 39.7 \times 0.60 = 23.8$ or $30.0 \times 0.90 = 27.0$

$M_c = 30.0 \times 3.10 = 93.0$ or $39.2 \times 2.40 = 94.0$

$M_d = 39.2 \times 0.60 = 23.6$ or $39.7 \times 0.60 = 23.8$

Average $M_b = 25.4^{k'}$

Average $M_c = 93.5^{k'}$

Average $M_d = 23.7^{k'}$

Discussion:

In simple problems such as Example 5.1, the graphical method may be applied without difficulty. As soon as the loads are inclined or the beam is no longer supported in a simple end-supported manner, the method becomes considerably more complex.

In this case, after finding the reactions using force and funicular polygons I, it is necessary to redraw the force polygon so that the forces are laid out in the same order as they are encountered in traversing the member from one end to the other. After force polygon II and its corresponding funicular polygon have been laid out in this manner, it is possible to compute the shear and bending moment at all the various points along the beam. Normally, the second funicular polygon may be superimposed on the first. Here, however, two separate space diagrams have been drawn to avoid unnecessary confusion.

Note that the bending moments have been computed from the forces on each side of the section to obtain a check.

5.11 Bar Forces in Trusses—Maxwell Diagram—Bow's Notation. The graphical method of joints is a convenient method for determining the bar forces of certain statically determinate trusses. Assuming that the reactions have been determined previously by either graphical or algebraic methods, the bar forces can then be determined by drawing a series of force polygons, one for each joint. It will be found convenient, however, to combine all these polygons into one composite figure called a *Maxwell diagram* after its originator, Clerk Maxwell.

At any joint, the bar forces and external forces form a concurrent coplanar force system, which to be in equilibrium must produce a closed force polygon. Closure of the force polygon is equivalent to satisfying the two algebraic conditions $\Sigma F_x = 0$ and $\Sigma F_y = 0$. Since the directions of all forces acting on a joint are known, the *magnitude* of *two* unknown bar forces may be determined, therefore, by making the force polygon for the joint close. It is thus possible to determine all the bar forces in a *simple truss* by starting at a joint where there are only two unknown bar forces and then considering each of the other joints in turn, always working with a joint where there are not more than two unknowns.

In applying the graphical method of joints, the external and internal forces may be identified by using *Bow's notation*. To apply this notation, the spaces between external forces are designated by Roman numerals and those between bars by Arabic numerals, as illustrated in Fig. 5.14. Then, an external force may be identified by reading the numbers on each side of it in a clockwise order; for example, the force acting at joint B is called force I-II. Likewise, the internal force with which a member acts on a joint is identified by reading the numbers on each side of that member in a clockwise order about that joint; for example, member Bc acts on joint B with a force 32.

After the space diagram has been labeled according to Bow's notation, the reactions of a truss such as the one in Fig. 5.14 may be computed by either graphical or algebraic methods, whichever is more convenient. Then it is possible to isolate joint a where two bar forces are unknown and to determine these unknowns by drawing the force polygon shown.   The vectors of this polygon should be laid out in the clockwise order of the forces around the joint.   The ends of a vector should be identified by the same numbers that lie on each side of the corresponding force in the space diagram, arranged so that reading the number first at the rear and then at the front end of a vector places them in the same order as that in which they are encountered in going clockwise around the joint.   If this procedure is followed, then the numbers of the vertexes from start to finish of the force polygon read in the same order as that in which the numbers are encountered in going clockwise around the joint.   In this way, it is found from the force polygon for joint a that the forces with which bars aB and ab act on joint a are measured by the vectors $\overline{\text{I-1}}$ and $\overline{\text{I-VI}}$, respectively, which indicate that the character of force in aB is compression and that in ab is tension.

Joint a Joint b Joint B

Figure 5.14   Bow's notation

Having the force in ab, it is now possible to proceed to joint b and construct a force polygon from which the forces in bars Bb and bc may be determined.   Then proceeding to joint B, there are only two unknown bar forces, in bars Bc and BC, which may be determined from the force polygon for this joint.   Considering the remaining joints in turn enables one to complete the analysis of the truss.   Instead of constructing a separate polygon for each joint, however, it is more convenient to draw one Maxwell diagram that in effect combines all the separate joint polygons.

To construct a Maxwell diagram, first draw a force polygon for all the external forces, laying out the vectors in the same order as the forces are encountered in going clockwise around the structure.   If the reactions have been determined graphically and the resulting force polygon has not been laid out in this manner, then a new polygon must be drawn with the vectors so arranged.   The vertexes of this polygon should be labeled in the same manner as described above for the joint force polygon. The Maxwell diagram for the truss of Fig. 5.14 was started in this manner and is shown in Fig. 5.15.   Now consider a joint such as a where there are only two unknown bar forces, and note the numbers of the spaces surrounding this joint.   All but one, 1, have corresponding vertexes in the part of the Maxwell diagram drawn so far.   The missing vertex, number 1, may be located by drawing through the two adjacent vertexes, I and VI, lines parallel to the intervening bars, aB and ab, respectively. Now, considering joint b in the same way, vertex 2 is the only one missing and is located by drawing through vertexes 1 and V lines parallel to bars bB and bc, respectively.   The remaining missing vertexes 3, 4, 5, and 6 may be located in turn by considering successively joints B, C, c, and d (or D).   Note that, at the time when each of these joints is considered, there is only one missing vertex associated with that joint.

The construction of the Maxwell diagram having been completed, it is a simple matter to determine the magnitude and sense of the force with which a bar acts on a given joint.   *Read the numbers on each side of a bar in a clockwise order around a joint. The magnitude and sense with which that bar acts on that joint are given by the vector measured from the vertex of the first number to the vertex of the second number.*   The bar forces so determined in this example are recorded on the line diagram of the truss.

After comparing the Maxwell diagram with the force polygon for the separate joints, it is evident that the diagram is simply a composite figure in which all the joint

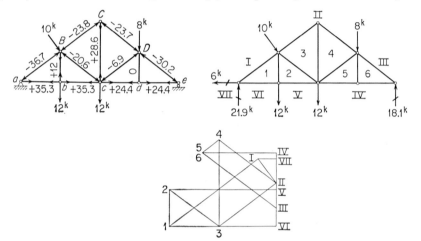

Figure 5.15   Maxwell diagram

polygons have been superimposed.   It is also evident that the use of the clockwise direction throughout this discussion is arbitrary: the whole system would have worked equally well if everything were reversed and taken in a counterclockwise order throughout.

5.12   Certain Ambiguous Cases—Fink Roof Truss.   The Maxwell diagram described in the previous article may be drawn without difficulty for any *simple truss*. When the ideas are applied to a *compound truss*, the diagram may be drawn up to a certain point; then one discovers that at each of the remaining joints there are more than two unknown bar forces and therefore more than one missing vertex.

Consider a compound truss such as the Fink roof truss shown in Fig. 5.16.   After finding the reactions, a force polygon for the external forces may be laid out and the Maxwell diagram started in the conventional manner by considering first joint a and then proceeding in turn to joints B and b.   Considering now either joint C or c, there are three unknown bar forces and therefore two unknown vertexes at either of these joints; it is thus impossible to continue with the Maxwell diagram.   Of course, it is possible to go across to joint i and work back successfully at joints h and H, but then the same dilemma is encountered at either of joints G or g.   One of the several alternative methods available to circumvent this difficulty is discussed below:

Suppose temporarily that we replace bars Cd and dD by the bar Dc as indicated by the dashed line.   We shall call the space enclosed by triangle cDE by number $6'$ and the space enclosed by triangle cCD by number $4'$.   Such a replacement does not alter the forces in bars aB, ab, bB, bc, bC, BC, DE, Ed, or cg of the original truss.　This is evident when one considers the computation of the forces in these members using the sections indicated.　The locations of vertexes 1, 2, and 3 of the Maxwell diagram, therefore, remain the same for either the original or the altered truss.　It is thus possible to locate vertex 4′ of the altered truss by considering joint C and then to proceed to joint D to locate vertex 6′.　The location of vertex 6′ so determined for the altered truss coincides with 6 for the original truss, since in either case the force in bars DE and dE is the same.　It is now possible to return to the original truss and, by considering in turn joints D and C, to locate the correct positions of vertexes 5 and 4, respectively.　Now it is easy to proceed in the conventional manner and locate the remaining vertexes 7 to 13.

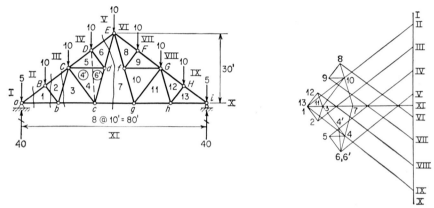

Figure 5.16　Analysis of Fink roof truss

5.13　Reactions and Bar Forces of Three-hinged Arches.　Once the reactions of a three-hinged arch have been determined, there is no difficulty encountered in drawing a Maxwell diagram to find the bar forces.　The reactions may be determined, of course, either analytically or graphically.　The graphical solution for the reactions of three-hinged arches requires some additional considerations, however.

One graphical method of finding the reactions utilizes an important characteristic of a three-hinged arch.　Consider the arch shown in Fig. 5.17.　The reactions of the structure may be computed by superimposing the separate effects of (1) the loads applied to the left half acting by themselves and (2) those applied to the right half. It is easy to find the separate effects, for in each case one half of the arch is not acted upon by any external loads.　In such cases, the reaction acting on the unloaded half must be directed through the center of the crown hinge at point b so that the bending moment about the hinge will be zero.　In both cases I and II, therefore, the graphical solution is the same as the case of an end-supported beam where the magnitude of both reactions but the direction of only one of them is unknown.　The reactions in cases I and II are obtained by selecting the poles P_1 and P_2 and drawing the funicular polygons shown.　If the two force polygons are plotted together as shown, it is then a simple matter to superimpose the two cases graphically and find the resultant reactions R_a and R_c developed by the combined system of loads.

A second graphical method of finding the reactions involves passing the funicular polygon of the external loads through the three hinges a, b, and c.　In Art. 5.7, it is pointed out that a system of external forces can be supported by a linkage system which has the same shape as the funicular polygon for those forces.　Considering one half of the arch at a time, the external loads acting on each half can be supported on a linkage with end reactions corresponding to a funicular polygon whose end strings pass through the hinges at the support and crown.   Since the action of the left half on the right half must be equal and opposite to the action of the right on the left, the end strings at the crown hinge of the funicular polygon of each half must be collinear. This means that the two separate polygons must be capable of being combined into

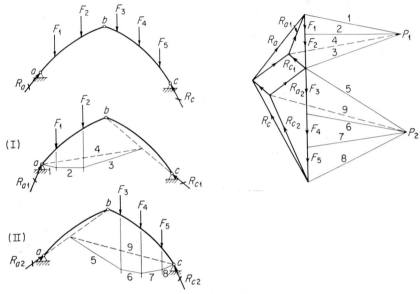

Figure 5.17   Three-hinged arch

one continuous polygon for the entire arch, which passes through all three hinges a, b, and c.   If a pole is found so that the funicular polygon for all the external loads passes through these three points, the end reactions may then be obtained by measuring the first and last rays on the force polygon.

5.14   Problems for Solution

Problem 5.1   Find graphically the resultant of the forces shown in Fig. 5.18. Indicate its magnitude.   Show its direction by indicating its horizontal and vertical components.   Use scale 1 in. = 1 ton.

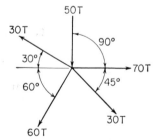

Figure 5.18   Problem 5.1

Problem 5.2 Find graphically the forces necessary to hold each of the frames of Fig. 5.19 in equilibrium. Indicate the magnitude of both the force and its horizontal and vertical components. Locate the line of action of the resultant force with reference to horizontal and vertical axes drawn through the center of each frame.

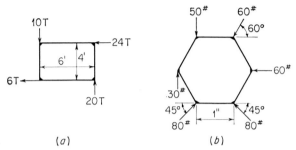

(a)   (b)

Figure 5.19   Problem 5.2

Problem 5.3 Find the resultant of the forces shown in Fig. 5.20 by use of the funicular polygon. Indicate its magnitude and direction, and locate the intersection of its line of action with the horizontal base line. Scales 1 in. = 5 ft, and 1 in. = 50 lb.

Figure 5.20   Problem 5.3

Problem 5.4 Find the horizontal and vertical components of the reactions of the structures of Fig. 5.21, using the three-force method.

Figure 5.21   Problem 5.4

Problem 5.5   Find the horizontal and vertical components of the reactions of the structures of Fig. 5.22, using the funicular polygon.

Figure 5.22   Problem 5.5

Problem 5.6   Find graphically the bar forces in the members of the Pratt roof truss of Fig. 5.23.

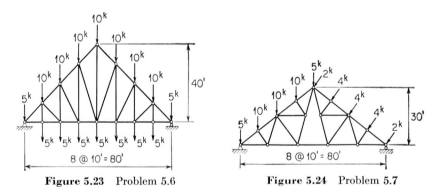

Figure 5.23   Problem 5.6   Figure 5.24   Problem 5.7

Problem 5.7   Find graphically the bar forces in the members of the Fink roof truss of Fig. 5.24.

Problem 5.8   Find the bar forces in the members of the truss of Fig. 5.25, using graphical methods.

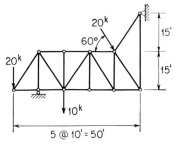

Figure 5.25   Problem 5.8

Problem 5.9   Draw the curves of shear and bending moment for the beams of Fig. 5.26, using graphical methods.

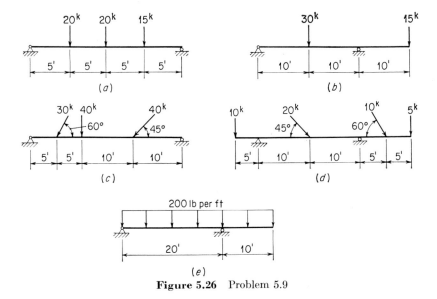

Figure 5.26   Problem 5.9

Problem 5.10   Draw the funicular polygon for the beam and loading of Fig. 5.27, so that it passes through the points of support and also through a point 20 ft below the center of the span.

Figure 5.27   Problem 5.10

Problem 5.11 A cable is suspended from two points at the same elevation and 20 ft apart. The cable supports nine weights of 100 lb each, spaced 2 ft apart, the distance between each support and the nearest weight being 2 ft. The lowest point on the cable is 5 ft below the line joining the supports. What is the length of the cable, and what is the maximum tension in it? Use graphical methods.

Problem 5.12 Find the reactions and bar forces of the trusses of Fig. 5.28, using graphical methods.

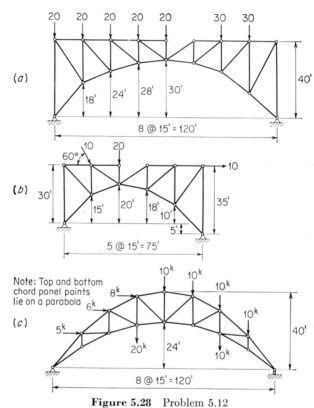

Figure 5.28 Problem 5.12

Problem 5.13 Using graphical methods, find the reactions and bar forces of the truss shown in Example 4.5.

6

Influence Lines

6.1 Introduction. Chapters 2 to 5 are devoted to a consideration of the basic ideas involved in the computation of reactions, shears, bending moments, and bar forces for statically determinate structures. Before any of these functions can be computed, it is of course necessary to establish the condition of loading for which the analysis is to be made. In Chap. 1, distinction is drawn between dead loads, such as the weight of the structure itself, which remain stationary, and live loads, which may vary in position on a structure.

When one is designing any specific part of a structure, it is necessary to proportion the part under consideration so that it has sufficient strength to withstand the greatest stress to which it may be subjected during the life of the structure. In order to design such a part, the greatest contribution of the live load to the total design stress is one of the items that must be determined. The stress produced in a given part by the live load varies with the position of the load on the structure. There is always one position of the live loads on a structure that will cause the maximum live stress in any particular part of the structure. The part of the structure and the type of stress involved may be, for example, the reaction at a support, the bending moment or shear at a section in a beam or girder, the tension or compression in a truss member, or the load carried by a particular rivet. The proper design of the various parts will, in general, depend on *different* live-load positions.

It should therefore be clear that it is essential for the structural analyst to understand clearly the methods by which the position of live load which causes the maximum stress at any point may be determined.

6.2 Illustration of Variation in Stress with Position of Load. Suppose that a downward load of unity is placed at point A on the beam AB of Fig. 6.1. By taking moments about B, the reaction R_{Ay} is found to act upward and to equal 1. At A' on the base line $A'B'$, A' being directly beneath A, let the distance $+1$ be plotted vertically. Let the applied unit load now travel to C; upon taking moments about B, R_{Ay} is found to equal $+\frac{9}{10}$. Plot this ordinate $+\frac{9}{10}$ at C' on the base line $A'B'$, C' being directly below the point of application of the unit load. Let the unit load now travel to D; R_{Ay} becomes $+\frac{8}{10}$; plot $+\frac{8}{10}$ vertically at D', which is directly below D.

Repeat the procedure for all positions of the unit load between A and B. The resultant reaction values, plotted in each instance from the base line $A'B'$, and directly below the particular load position, all lie on a straight line. This might have been foreseen, since, for the unit

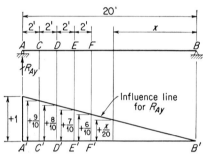

Figure 6.1   Simple influence line

load at any section at distance x from B, R_{Ay} equals $+x/20$. The ordinate $+x/20$ is plotted at distance x from B', and the plot of $x/20$ against x is linear.

Because of the manner of plotting this curve from the base line $A'B'$, a number of important conclusions can be drawn.

1. The ordinate at any point on this curve equals the value of R_{Ay} if a unit load is applied at that section. (Note that all ordinates refer to the reaction at point A and that it is the position of the unit load causing this reaction which is the variable in constructing the curve.)

2. As the unit load travels from B to A, the reaction at A increases linearly. The maximum value of R_{Ay} is seen to occur when the load is applied at A.

3. Since all the ordinates to this curve are positive, it may be concluded that a unit load applied at any point along the span AB causes an upward reaction at A. Hence, if this structure were to be loaded with a uniform live load, the live load should extend over the entire span AB in order to give a maximum value to R_{Ay}.

6.3   The Influence Line—Definition.   The curve drawn in Fig. 6.1 is called an *influence line* because it shows the influence on a certain function of a unit load as it travels across the structure. In this particular case the function under consideration is the vertical reaction at A. The function may, however, be anything that varies as the load moves across the span, such as moment or shear at a given section in a girder or beam, or bar force in a particular truss member, or deflection of a given point on a structure.

An influence line may be defined as follows: **An influence line is a curve the ordinate to which at any point equals the value of some** particular function due to a unit load (say a 1-lb load) acting at that point.

Curve b of Fig. 6.2 shows the influence line for the moment at C, center of an end-supported beam. That this curve satisfies the definition of an influence line may be verified by checking the ordinate at any point. If, for example, a 1-lb load is applied at D, the moment at C equals $\frac{1}{4} \times 10 = +2.5$ ft-lb. This is the ordinate to the influence line at point D.

Figure 6.2   Influence lines for simple end-supported beam

Curve c of this figure shows the influence line for shear at D, the left quarter point. That this curve satisfies the definition of an influence line may also be seen by checking the ordinate at any point. If, for example, the unit load is applied just to the right of D, the shear at D equals $+\frac{3}{4}$ lb.

By definition, an influence line shows the effect of a unit load as it travels across the span. It should be apparent that such a curve is closely related to a live load moving across a bridge. The usefulness of influence lines is not, however, limited to bridge structures, since they are of importance in the determination of maximum stresses in any structure subject to the action of live loads. These live loads may be the movable loads in an office building, or the aerodynamic loads on the wing of an airplane, or the hydrostatic support caused by the displacement of waves on the hull of a ship.

6.4   Properties of the Influence Line.   Influence lines may be used for two very important purposes: (1) to determine what position of live loads will lead to a maximum value of the particular function for

which an influence line has been constructed; (2) to compute the value
of that function with the loads so placed or, in fact, for any loading
condition.

Since the ordinate to an influence line equals the value of a particular
function due to a unit load acting at the point where the ordinate is
measured, the following two theorems hold:

1. **To obtain the maximum value of a function due to a single
concentrated live load, the load should be placed at the point
where the ordinate to the influence line for that function is a
maximum.** It is obvious that if the maximum positive value of a function is desired, the load should be placed at the point where the ordinate
to the influence line has its maximum positive value, while, if the maximum negative value is to be obtained, the position of the load is determined by the maximum negative ordinate.

2. **The value of a function due to the action of a single concentrated live load equals the product of the magnitude of the
load and the ordinate to the influence line for that function,
measured at the point of application of the load.**[1] This follows
from the principle of superposition. Further, the total value of a function due to more than one concentrated load can be obtained by superimposing the separate effects of each concentrated load, as determined by
Theorem 2.

---

[1] In the above definition of an influence line, it is suggested that the function involved
be computed for a 1-lb load.   As a result, the ordinates of typical influence lines would
have the following units: reactive forces, pounds; shear and axial forces, pounds;
bending moments, foot-pounds; etc.   On this basis, to compute the effect of some
other concentrated load the influence-line ordinate involved should be multiplied
by the dimensionless magnitude of this load (i.e., by simply the *number* of 1-lb loads
which it represents).   For example, by using Fig. 6.2b, the bending moment at C
produced by a load of 750 lb at D may be found to be

$$(2.5 \text{ ft-lb})(750) = 1,875 \text{ ft-lb}$$

Some structural engineers prefer to define an influence line as showing functions
caused by a dimensionless load of unity.   On such a basis, the product just noted
would be obtained by multiplying by a dimensional number of 750 lb, or

$$(2.5 \text{ ft})(750 \text{ lb}) = 1,875 \text{ ft-lb}$$

Still other structural engineers prefer to define the ordinates of an influence line as
being the ratio of the function involved to the dimensional 1-lb load causing it, and
therefore say that the ordinates in Fig. 6.2b have units of foot-pounds per pound.   On
this basis, the product noted would again be obtained by multiplying by a dimensional
number of 750 lb, or

$$(2.5 \text{ ft-lb per lb})(750 \text{ lb}) = 1,875 \text{ ft-lb}$$

This latter approach has some merit although it will not be used here.   According to
this usage, the ordinates of influence lines are referred to as *influence coefficients*.

To illustrate the application of these two theorems, suppose that a concentrated live load of 10,000 lb is applied to the beam of Fig. 6.4a. If the influence line of Fig. 6.4c is used, the maximum positive shear that this load can cause at D occurs with the load just to the right of D and equals $10,000(+\frac{7}{10}) = +7,000$ lb. The maximum negative shear at the same section occurs with the load just to the left of D and equals $10,000(-\frac{3}{10}) = -3,000$ lb. From Fig. 6.4e, the maximum positive moment at D occurs with the load at D and equals

$$10,000(+2\frac{1}{10}) = +21,000 \text{ ft-lb}$$

From the definition of an influence line, the following theorem, dealing with uniformly distributed live loads, is apparent:

3. **To obtain the maximum value of a function due to a uniformly distributed live load, the load should be placed over all those portions of the structure for which the ordinates to the influence line for that function have the sign of the character of the function desired.**

To compute, from the influence line, the actual value of the function due to a uniformly distributed live load, the following theorem should be used:

4. **The value of a function due to a uniformly distributed live load is equal to the product of the intensity of the loading and the net area under that portion of the influence line, for the function under consideration, which corresponds to the portion of the structure loaded.**

That the foregoing theorem is correct may be seen from the following: Let AB be the influence line for a given function F, for a portion of a structure, as shown in Fig. 6.3, that is subjected to a uniformly distributed load of w lb per ft, applied continuously to the structure between two points M and N. That portion of the uniform load applied in distance dx may be treated as a concentrated load equal to $w\,dx$. By Theorem 2, the value of the function F due to this differential load is given by $dF = w\,dx\,y$. The total value of F due to the load between M

Figure 6.3   Portion of influence line

and N is obtained by integrating dF between $x = 0$ and $x = a$, or $F = \int_0^a wy\,dx = w \int_0^a y\,dx = w$ multiplied by the area under that portion of the influence line which corresponds to the portion of the structure loaded.

To illustrate the application of Theorems 3 and 4, suppose that a uniform live load of 1,000 lb per ft is applied to the beam of Fig. 6.4a. To obtain the maximum positive shear at D (Fig. 6.4c), the uniform load should extend from C to A and from D to B. The value of this maximum positive shear at D is given by

$$1,000[\tfrac{1}{2}(5)(+\tfrac{1}{2}) + \tfrac{1}{2}(7)(+\tfrac{7}{10})] = +3,700 \text{ lb}$$

For maximum negative shear at D, the structure should be loaded from A to D, leading to a resultant shear at D equal to

$$1,000[\tfrac{1}{2}(3)(-\tfrac{3}{10})] = -450 \text{ lb}$$

For maximum positive moment at D, refer to Fig. 6.4e. The structure should be loaded from A to B; the resultant moment equals

$$1,000[\tfrac{1}{2}(10)(+2\tfrac{1}{10})] = +10,500 \text{ ft-lb}$$

For maximum values of functions due to a concentrated live load and uniformly distributed live load acting simultaneously, the maximum function due to each acting separately should be computed by the methods already given and the results superimposed. For example, to obtain the maximum negative moment at A, in the beam of Fig. 6.4a, due to a uniform load of 1,000 lb per ft and a single concentrated load of 10,000 lb, it is found by reference to Fig. 6.4d that the uniform load should extend from C to A and the concentrated load should be placed at C. The maximum negative moment at A is then given by

$$1,000[\tfrac{1}{2}(5)(-5)] + 10,000(-5) = -62,500 \text{ ft-lb}$$

Suppose that a uniform load of 1,000 lb per ft extends over the entire length of the beam of Fig. 6.4a. Functions are then computed on the basis of the algebraic sum of the component areas that comprise the entire influence line. From Fig. 6.4e, the resultant moment at D would, for example, be given by

$$1,000[\tfrac{1}{2}(5)(-\tfrac{7}{2}) + \tfrac{1}{2}(10)(+2\tfrac{1}{10})] = +1,750 \text{ ft-lb}$$

6.5 Construction of Influence Lines for Beams. Consider the beam shown in Fig. 6.4a. To illustrate the method of constructing influence lines, an influence line for the shear just to the left of point A will first be constructed, as shown in Fig. 6.4b. When a unit load is applied at any position to the left of this section, the shear just to the left of A equals the unit load and is negative. Hence the influence line has the ordinate -1 from C to A. When a unit load is applied in any position between A and B, the shear just to the left of A is zero. Hence the ordinate to the influence line is zero in this portion of the beam. The influence line for the shear at D will now be constructed, as shown in Fig. 6.4c.   If a unit load is applied at C, the shear at D may be computed from the reaction at B and is seen to equal $+\frac{1}{2}$.   As the unit load travels from C to A, the reaction at B and hence the shear at D decrease to zero.   Hence the influence line for the shear at D varies from $+\frac{1}{2}$ at C to zero at A.   Actually, this variation between C and A is linear.   That

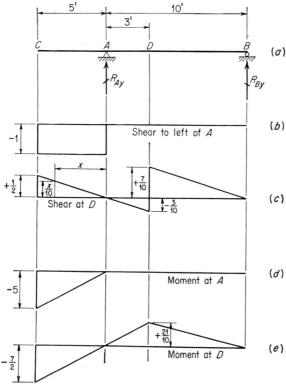

Figure 6.4   Influence lines for beam with overhang

the influence line between C and A is a straight line may be seen by either of the following two methods:

1. The unit load may be applied at any point between C and A and the shear at D computed.   When this value is plotted at the point of application of the load, it will be found to lie on a straight line.

2. If the distance from A to the load is denoted by x, the vertical reaction at B acts downward and has the value $x/10$.   The shear at D therefore equals $+x/10$.   The plot of $+x/10$ against x is a straight line.

As the unit load travels from A to a point just to the left of D, the reaction at B increases from zero to $+\frac{3}{10}$.   Hence the shear at D goes from zero to $-\frac{3}{10}$.   The ordinate to the influence line at a point just to the left of D is therefore $-\frac{3}{10}$.   That the influence line is a straight line varying from zero at A to $-\frac{3}{10}$ at D may be seen on the basis of either of the arguments which led to the conclusion that it was straight between C and A.

Now consider the unit load placed just to the right of D. If the shear at D is computed from the forces to the right of D, as has been done previously, it is necessary to consider two forces, the reaction at B and the unit load itself. If, on the other hand, the shear at D is computed from the forces to the left of D, it is necessary to consider only the reaction at A.

It is often preferable, in computing ordinates to influence lines, to work from the forces on the side of the section that is away from the unit load. For the case under consideration, $R_{Ay} = +\frac{7}{10}$, so that the shear at D is $+\frac{7}{10}$. This is the ordinate to the influence line just to the right of D. It is to be noted that as the unit load passes D, while moving from left to right, the shear at D increases suddenly from $-\frac{3}{10}$ to $+\frac{7}{10}$. As the unit load travels from just to the right of D to B, the reaction at A, hence the shear at D, decreases linearly from $+\frac{7}{10}$ to zero. Hence the influence line is a straight line running from $+\frac{7}{10}$ at D to zero at A.

The influence line for the moment at A will now be constructed, as shown in Fig. 6.4d. When a unit load is placed at C, the moment at A equals -5. As the load travels from C to A, the moment at A decreases linearly to zero. With the load at any position between A and B, the moment at A equals zero, as can be seen from a consideration of the forces to the left of A.

To construct the influence line for the moment at D, as shown in Fig. 6.4e, one may proceed as follows: Owing to a unit load at C, the moment at D equals $-\frac{1}{2}$, as may easily be computed from the reaction at B. As the load goes from C to A, the moment at D decreases linearly to zero. Hence the influence line is a straight line from $-\frac{1}{2}$ at C to zero at A. As the load goes from A to D, the reaction at B increases linearly from zero to $+\frac{3}{10}$; the moment at D, computed from this reaction, increases linearly from zero to $+\frac{3}{10} \times 7 = +2\frac{1}{10}$; hence the influence line is a straight line from zero at A to $+2\frac{1}{10}$ at D. As the load goes from D to B, the reaction at A decreases linearly from $+\frac{7}{10}$ to zero; the moment at D, computed from this reaction, decreases linearly from $+\frac{7}{10} \times 3 = 2\frac{1}{10}$ to zero at B.

6.6 Influence Lines for Girders with Floor Systems. The structural action of floor systems is discussed in Art. 3.9. The construction of influence lines for girders with floor systems may be illustrated by a consideration of Fig. 6.5. An influence line for the shear in panel BC will first be drawn, as shown in Fig. 6.5b. It should be noted that, since live loads can be applied to the girder only by the floor beams which are located at panel points A, B, . . . , G, the live shear has the same value at any section in a given panel of the girder.

When a unit load is placed at A, $R_{Gy} = 0$. The floor-beam reactions to the right of panel BC, that is, the forces applied to the girder by the floor beams at C, D, E, F, and G, are also zero. Hence, by computing the shear in panel BC from the forces acting on the girder to the right of the panel, the shear equals zero. When the unit load is placed at B, $R_{Gy} = +\frac{1}{6}$; the floor-beam reactions at C, D, . . . , G still equal zero; hence the shear in panel BC equals $-\frac{1}{6}$.

As the unit load travels along a stringer from one panel point to another, the influence line will be a straight line for the panel under

Figure 6.5   Influence lines for girder

consideration, provided that the stringers act as end-supported beams spanning the adjacent floor beams. That this is so may be seen from the following: As the unit load travels from one panel point to another, the reactions on the stringer, which are also the forces applied to the girder by the floor beams, vary linearly; hence any stress function for the girder, such as shear in a given panel, will also vary linearly. The influence line for shear in panel BC is therefore a straight line from zero at A to $-\frac{1}{6}$ at B.

When a unit load is placed at C, $R_{Ay} = +\frac{2}{3}$, while the floor-beam reactions at A and B are zero. Then the shear in panel BC equals $+\frac{2}{3}$, as is easily computed from the forces to the left of the panel. The influence line is a straight line from B to C.

The ordinates to the influence line at panel points D, E, F, and G may be computed by a procedure similar to that used in determining the ordinate at C, and the influence line will in each case be a straight line between panel points. It will be found that the influence line is a straight line from C to G.　These computations can be eliminated by the following reasoning: As the load travels from C to G, R_{Ay} decreases linearly from $+\frac{2}{3}$ to zero, as is easily seen from a consideration of the *external* forces acting on the structure; since the floor-beam reactions at A and B remain zero, the shear in panel BC decreases linearly from $+\frac{2}{3}$ to zero.

It should be pointed out that an influence line may always be constructed by computing the value of the function under consideration for successive positions of the unit load and taking care that one includes all points where the slope of the influence may change.　Panel points constitute such points; but as will be seen later, it is possible to arrange a structure so that other points may also be critical.　Experience in constructing influence lines makes it possible for one to recognize the fact that certain portions of the line are linear.　This leads to a saving in computations, but it is not a necessary procedure.

Figure 6.6　Effect of stringer arrangement

Consider now the influence line for the moment at panel point E of the girder of Fig. 6.5a, which is given in Fig. 6.5c.　As a unit load travels from A to E, R_{Gy} increases linearly from zero to $+\frac{2}{3}$, as may be seen from a consideration of the external forces, while the floorbeam reactions at F and G are zero.　Hence the moment at panel point E increases linearly from zero at A to a value equal to $+\frac{2}{3} \times 20 = +\frac{40}{3}$ at E, and the influence line is a straight line from zero at A to $+\frac{40}{3}$ at E.　As the unit load travels from E to G, R_{Ay} decreases linearly from $+\frac{1}{3}$ to zero; the floor-beam reactions at A, B, C, and D are zero; hence the influence line is a straight line from $+\frac{1}{3} \times 40 = +\frac{40}{3}$ at E to zero at G.

It is not necessary for the stringers in every panel to be simply supported by the adjacent floor beams.　Figure 6.6a illustrates a case where the stringers are cantilevered in panel BE and where the end stringer in panel EF cantilevers to point G.　The construction of an influence line for such a structure will be illustrated by considering the moment at panel point E in the girder, as shown in Fig. 6.6b.　As the unit load goes from A to C, consideration of the forces acting on the free body consisting of the girder plus stringer AC and the floor beams connecting stringer AC to the girder shows that R_{Fy} increases linearly from zero to $+\frac{1}{2}$.　Since the floor-beam reactions at E and F are zero, the moment in the girder at E increases linearly from zero at A to $+\frac{1}{2} \times 10 = +5$ at C.　With the unit load at D, $R_{Ay} = +\frac{1}{2}$; the floor-beam reactions at A and B are zero; hence the moment at E equals $+\frac{1}{2} \times 20 = +10$. As the unit load travels from D to G, R_{Ay} varies linearly from $+\frac{1}{2}$ to $-\frac{1}{6}$; the floor-beam reactions at A and B remain at zero; hence the moment at E varies linearly from $+10$ at D to $-\frac{1}{6} \times 20 = -3.33$ at G.

6.7   Interpretation of Influence Lines for Girders with Floor Systems. The four theorems of Art. 6.4 dealing with the use of influence lines are perfectly general and are applicable to influence lines for girders with floor systems. Suppose that live loads consisting of a uniform load of 1,000 lb per ft and a single concentrated load of 10,000 lb are applied to the structure of Fig. 6.5a. To obtain the maximum live shear in panel BC, refer to the influence line of Fig. 6.5b. It is first necessary to locate point a at which this influence line crosses the base line. Such a point is called a neutral point, since a load applied at this point has no effect on the function under consideration. This point may be located by similar triangles; its distance from B will be found to be 2 ft. The maximum positive live shear in panel BC occurs when the uniform load extends from the neutral point to G and when the concentrated load is at C; it is equal to

$$1,000[\tfrac{1}{2}(+\tfrac{2}{3})(48)] + 10,000(+\tfrac{2}{3}) = 22,667 \text{ lb}$$

Maximum negative live shear in this panel occurs when the uniform load extends from A to the neutral point and the concentrated load is at B; it has a value equal to

$$1,000[\tfrac{1}{2}(-\tfrac{1}{6})(12)] + 10,000(-\tfrac{1}{6}) = -2,667 \text{ lb}$$

In Fig. 6.5c, the maximum positive live moment at panel point E, due to the same live load, occurs with the uniform load extending over the entire span and with the concentrated load at E. Its value is equal to

$$1,000[\tfrac{1}{2}(+^{40}\!/_3)(60)] + 10,000(+^{40}\!/_3) = +533,333 \text{ ft-lb}$$

The foregoing method of computing maximum live shears and moments, based on locating neutral points and using exact areas under influence lines, is *exact*. The following *approximate* method is of importance, since it often involves less computation and is well suited to efficient organization of computations for complicated structures. In the approximate method, it is assumed that for uniform live load there is acting at each panel point either a full panel load or no panel load whatever, depending on whether the ordinate to the influence line indicates that a load at that panel point increases or decreases the value of the function for which a maximum value is desired.

A full panel load is the maximum possible load that can be applied to a girder by a floor beam. It can occur only when the stringers adjacent to the panel are fully loaded, and it is equal (for panels of equal length) to wl, where w is the intensity of the uniform load and l is the length of the panel.

Consider again the structure of Fig. 6.5a acted upon by live loads consisting of a uniform load of 1,000 lb per ft and a single concentrated load of 10,000 lb. For the uniform live load, the full panel load equals (1,000)(10) = 10,000 lb. To compute the maximum positive live shear in panel BC by the approximate method, this full panel load is placed at C, D, E, and F, since the influence line of Fig. 6.5b has positive ordinates at these panel points. No panel load will be placed at B, where the ordinate to the influence line is negative. The concentrated load will, as in the exact method, be placed at C. The resultant maximum positive live shear in panel BC is equal to

$$10,000(\tfrac{2}{3} + \tfrac{1}{2} + \tfrac{1}{3} + \tfrac{1}{6}) + 10,000(\tfrac{2}{3}) = 23,333 \text{ lb}$$

The corresponding value was 22,667 lb by the exact method, so that the result by the approximate method is seen to be slightly on the safe side, i.e., slightly larger than the exact value. The approximate method assumes a full panel load acting at C, which could not occur without completely loading stringer BC; loading stringer BC would cause a floorbeam reaction at B equal to half a full panel load, which by itself would cause negative shear in panel BC. Because the negative shear due to the partial panel load applied at B is neglected in the approximate method, the resultant positive shear computed is necessarily on the safe side. The approximate method of computing maximum values of functions never gives smaller values than does the exact method.

To find the maximum positive live moment at E for the same structure and loading by the approximate method, refer to the influence line of Fig. 6.5c. For the uniform load, a full panel load of 10,000 lb is applied at all intermediate panel points, since all the corresponding ordinates to the influence line are positive. The concentrated load is placed at E. The maximum positive live moment is given by

$$10,000(+1\tfrac{0}{3} + 2\tfrac{0}{3} + 3\tfrac{0}{3} + 4\tfrac{0}{3} + 2\tfrac{0}{3}) + 10,000(+4\tfrac{0}{3})$$
$$= +533,333 \text{ ft-lb}$$

This is the same value as that obtained by the exact method.

6.8 Series of Concentrated Live Loads—Use of Moment Diagram. The methods of using the influence line as previously presented apply to uniformly distributed live loads and to single concentrated live loads. They cannot, however, be used directly when the live load consists of a series of concentrated loads of given magnitude and spacing, such as are actually applied by the wheels of a locomotive or of a series of trucks. When there is more than one concentrated load, it is not possible, in general, to tell by inspection which of the concentrated loads should be placed at the maximum ordinate of the influence line in order to make the given function a maximum.

The method that should be followed for such a live load is essentially one of trial. In order to expedite the various trial solutions, it is desirable to organize such an analysis carefully, so as to minimize computations. For a series of concentrated loads, a moment diagram, such as is shown in Fig. 6.7, can be used to advantage. This particular moment diagram is computed for the seven concentrated loads spaced as shown. The diagram is practically self-explanatory. The numbers in the six bottom

Figure 6.7   Moment diagram

Figure 6.8   Use of moment diagram

rows may be explained by a single illustration: The number 1,900 under load 4 and in the horizontal line labeled Sum of moments about load 7 represents the moment about load 7 of loads 1 to 4; thus

$$10(40) + 20(30) + 20(25) + 20(20) = 1,900$$

To illustrate the use of the moment diagram, suppose that it is desired to compute the moment at load 3 in the beam of Fig. 6.8, due to the loading of Fig. 6.7 located as shown in Fig. 6.8. The moment about B of the applied loads is equal to 1,650 (the moment of loads 1 to 5 about load 6) plus 110 (the sum of the loads from 1 to 6), multiplied by 2 (the distance from load 6 to point B), whence $1,650 + 110(2) = 1,870$ kip-ft. Dividing this moment by the span of the beam, R_{Ay} is found to equal $1,870/50 = +37.4$ kips. Hence the moment at load 3, working from the forces to the left, is given by $+37.4(28) - 250 = +798$ kip-ft. It is to be noted that the moment of 250 kip-ft which was subtracted is the moment of loads 1 and 2 about load 3.

As a second example of the use of the moment diagram, the shear in panel BC of the girder of Fig. 6.9 will be computed for the loads shown acting, these loads being a part of the loading of Fig. 6.7. For the loads so placed, load 1 is not on the span. The girder reaction at A is given by

$$R_{Ay} = \frac{(1,650 - 350) + (110 - 10)3}{36} = +44.5 \text{ kips}$$

The sum of the floor-beam reactions at A and B is equal to

$$20 + \tfrac{5}{9}(20) = 31.1$$

Hence the shear in panel BC equals $+44.5 - 31.1 = +13.4$ kips.

In using the moment diagram it is usually convenient to reproduce it to scale on cardboard and place it in the proper position on a drawing of the structure to be analyzed, which is drawn to the same scale.

Figure 6.9   Use of moment diagram

6.9   Series of Concentrated Live Loads—Computation of Maximum Moment. The computation of maximum moment at a given section in a girder will be illustrated by computing the maximum moment at C of the girder of Fig. 6.10a, due to the live loading corresponding to the moment diagram of Fig. 6.7. The influence line for the moment at C is first constructed, as shown in Fig. 6.10b. The maximum moment at C will occur when one of the concentrated loads is at C; the first part of the problem consists in finding out which load should be at C in order to cause this maximum moment.

Before attempting this trial solution, the slope of each portion of the influence line, going from right to left, is first computed. For example, the portion of the influence line for the moment at C, which runs from F to C, has a slope of $+12\tfrac{}{3}0 = +\tfrac{2}{5}$.

Using the moment diagram of Fig. 6.7, place load 1 at C. This causes a certain moment at C, which, however, will not be computed at this stage of the analysis. Instead, the entire system of loads will be moved to the left until load 2 is at C, and computations will be carried out to determine whether the moment at C has been increased or decreased by this change in the position of the loads. To see whether the moment has become larger or smaller, it is convenient to divide the loads under consideration into three groups: (1) those loads which were on the structure before the loads were moved and which remain on the structure after the loads were moved; (2) those loads which were on the structure before the loads were moved but which have passed off the structure after the loads are moved; (3) those loads which were not on the structure before the loads were moved but which are on the structure after the loads are moved. For convenience we shall refer to these three load groups as load group 1, load group 2, and load group 3, respectively.

Figure 6.10   Girder influence lines

The following computations determine whether this load move has increased or decreased the moment at C. It should be noted that, if a load P moves a distance d and if the slope of the influence line is m, the corresponding change in moment equals Pdm.

Load 1 at section; move up load 2	Increase in moment	Decrease in moment
Load group 1—Loads 1 to 5	$80(10)(+\tfrac{2}{5}) = +320$	$10(10)(-\tfrac{3}{5}) = -60$
Load group 2—None	0	0
Load group 3—Load 6	$20(5)(+\tfrac{2}{5}) = \underline{+40}$	$\underline{0}$
All loads combined	$+360$	-60

The net change in moment is $+360 - 60 = +300$ kip-ft, so that a larger moment at C occurs with load 2 at the section (i.e., at C) than with load 1. However, it may be that a still larger moment occurs with load 3 at the section. The loads will now be moved to the left until load 3 is at C, and computations will be made to determine whether this new movement of loads has increased or decreased the moment at C.

Load 2 at section; move up load 3	Increase in moment	Decrease in moment
Load group 1—All loads	$100(5)(+\tfrac{2}{5}) = +200$	$30(5)(-\tfrac{3}{5}) = -90$
Load group 2—None	0	0
Load group 3—None	0	0
All loads combined	$+200$	-90

Since 200 is greater than 90, the moment has again increased. We shall now find out whether there will be a still further increase if load 4 is moved to the section.

Load 3 at section; move up load 4	Increase in moment	Decrease in moment
Load group 1—All loads	$80(5)(+\tfrac{2}{5}) = +160$	$50(5)(-\tfrac{3}{5}) = -150$
Load group 2—None	0	0
Load group 3—None	0	0
All loads combined	$+160$	-150

Again, the movement has increased. We shall now move up load 5.

Load 4 at section; move up load 5	Increase in moment	Decrease in moment
Load group 1—Loads 2 to 7	$60(10)(+\tfrac{2}{5}) = +240$	$60(10)(-\tfrac{3}{5}) = -360$
Load group 2—Load 1	0	0
Load group 3—None	0	0
All loads combined	$+240$	-360

Note that, although load 1 was considered as on the structure with load 4 at the section, it caused no moment at C, so that no change occurred when it passed off the structure. Since 240 is less than 360, moving up load 5 caused a decrease in the moment at C. Hence the maximum moment at C occurs with load 4 at C. With some experience in moving up loads, one might have foreseen that the maximum moment at C would not occur with load 1 at the section and that it probably would not occur with load 2 at the section. This would have eliminated a portion of the foregoing computations.

With the position of loads causing maximum moment at C known, the value of this moment may now be computed, either from the ordinates of the influence line directly or by using the moment diagram. By the latter procedure,

$$R_{Ay} = \frac{2,200 + 130(10)}{50} = +70 \text{ kips}$$

The moment of the floor-beam reactions at A and B about C is equal to the moment of loads 1, 2, and 3 about load 4, which is 500 kip-ft. Hence the maximum positive live moment at C equals

$$+70(20) - 500 = +900 \text{ kip-ft}$$

6.10 Series of Concentrated Live Loads—Computation of Maximum Shear. The foregoing method of moving up loads, based on the use of the influence line, is perfectly general and may be used for any influence line. As a second illustration of its application, the maximum positive shear in panel BC of the structure of Fig. 6.10a, due to the live loading of Fig. 6.7, will be computed. The solution might start by placing load 1 at C (the maximum positive ordinate to the influence line) and moving up load 2 to find out whether the shear in panel BC increases or decreases. This step is scarcely necessary, however, since an examination of the loading and the influence line of Fig. 6.10c will lead to the conclusion, without computations, that this movement will increase the shear in panel BC.

Load 2 at section; move up load 3	Increase in shear	Decrease in shear
Load group 1—All loads	$100(5)(+\frac{1}{50}) + 10*(5)(+\frac{1}{50}) = +11.0$	$20(5)(-\frac{4}{50}) = -8.0$
Load group 2—None	0	0
Load group 3—None	0	0
All loads combined	$+11.0$	-8.0

* This term is for load 1. The negative shear due to this load has decreased, leading to an increase in the positive shear in panel BC.

This shows an increase in the positive shear in panel BC. Hence we shall move load 4 up to the section.

Load 3 at section; move up load 4	Increase in shear	Decrease in shear
Load group 1—All loads	$80(5)(+\frac{1}{50}) + 10(5)(+\frac{1}{50}) = +9 0$	$40(5)(-\frac{4}{50}) = -16.0$
Load group 2—None	0	0
Load group 3—None	0	0
All loads combined	$+9.0$	-16.0

This shows a decrease in the positive shear in panel BC. Hence the maximum shear in panel BC occurs when load 3 is at C. The value of this maximum shear may be obtained as follows, using the moment diagram of Fig. 6.7:

$$R_{Ay} = \frac{2,200 + 130(5)}{50} = +57.0 \text{ kips}$$

The sum of the floor-beam reactions at A and B equals

$$10 + 20\!\!\!/_2 = 20 \text{ kips}$$

Hence the maximum positive live shear in panel BC equals

$$+57.0 - 20.0 = +37.0 \text{ kips}$$

6.11 Absolute Maximum Live Shear. The methods which have been given for the computation of maximum shear due to live loads assume that the section or panel in which the shear is to be computed is known. It is often desirable to compute the absolute maximum live shear in a member, i.e., the maximum live shear that can occur at any section in the member. For a simple end-supported beam or girder, absolute maximum live shear will occur at a section immediately adjacent to one of the end reactions. If the beam or girder is not a simple end-supported member, the absolute maximum live shear will occur on one side of one of the reactions. The true value of absolute maximum live shear can be determined only by computing the maximum live shear at each such section.

6.12 Absolute Maximum Live Moment. Similarly, the methods which have been given for the computation of maximum moment due to live loads assume that the section at which maximum live moment is to be computed is known. It is often necessary to compute the absolute maximum live moment for a beam or girder. For a simple end-supported beam, this occurs at mid-span for either a uniform live load or a single concentrated live load. For a simple end-supported

Figure 6.11 Position for absolute maximum moment

girder with a floor system, absolute maximum live moment occurs at the panel point nearest the center of the span. For a girder wholly or partly cantilevered, absolute maximum live moment is likely to occur at a reaction. If the section where absolute maximum live moment occurs cannot be definitely identified by inspection, it is necessary to compare maximum moments computed for various sections where absolute maximum live moment is likely to occur.

A special case of importance consists in determining the absolute maximum live moment due to the action of a series of concentrated live loads on an end-supported beam, as shown in Fig. 6.11. The moment curve for a series of concentrated loads is a series of straight lines intersecting at the positions of the loads, so that absolute maximum live moment must occur directly beneath one of the loads. Two questions must be answered: (1) Under which load does absolute maximum live moment occur? (2) What is the position of this load when absolute maximum live moment occurs?

The answer to the first question must often be determined by trial, but the second question is subject to direct analysis. Assume that in Fig. 6.11 the absolute maximum live moment will occur under load B. Let the distance from the center of the span to load B be denoted by x and the distance from load B to the resultant R of all the loads A, B, C, and D be denoted by d. We wish to determine the value of x that will make the moment at load B a maximum. The value of R_{My} may be determined by taking moments about N and considering the resultant force R rather than the actual loads A, B, C, and D. Thus

$$R_{My} = \frac{R\left(\dfrac{L}{2} + x - d\right)}{L} = \frac{R}{2} + \frac{Rx}{L} - \frac{Rd}{L}$$

Denoting by M_B the moment under load B,

$$M_B = R_{My}\left(\frac{L}{2} - x\right) - Aa = \left(\frac{R}{2} + \frac{Rx}{L} - \frac{Rd}{L}\right)\left(\frac{L}{2} - x\right) - Aa$$

$$= \frac{RL}{4} - \frac{Rd}{2} - \frac{Rx^2}{L} + \frac{Rxd}{L} - Aa$$

For a maximum value of M_B,

$$\frac{dM_B}{dx} = -\frac{2Rx}{L} + \frac{Rd}{L} = 0$$

whence $x = d/2$.

We may therefore conclude that **the maximum moment directly beneath one of a series of concentrated live loads that are applied to a simple end-supported beam occurs when the center of the span is halfway between that particular load and the resultant of all the loads on the span.**

If there are only two concentrated loads to consider, the absolute maximum live moment will occur under the heavier of the two loads. Such a case is illustrated in Fig. 6.12, where the distance from the 10-kip load to the resultant R of the two loads equals $(5 \times 12)/15 = 4$ ft. For absolute maximum moment, the 10-kip load is placed 2 ft from the center of the span, and thus the resultant R is 2 ft on the other side of the span center. At this point one should check to see whether or not both loads are on the span. If not, the absolute maximum moment occurs at mid-span when the heavy load is at the center of the span. For this case, both loads are on the span. The absolute maximum live moment occurs directly beneath the 10-kip load and is given by

$$M = \frac{15(12 - 2)^2}{24} = +62.5 \text{ kip-ft}$$

If there are more than two concentrated loads, it may not be possible to tell by inspection under which load the absolute maximum live moment will occur. It will usually occur under a large load near the center of the group of loads. The maximum moment that can occur under each of the loads may be determined by the foregoing method, and the largest of these moments will be the absolute maximum live moment.

6.13 Influence Lines for Trusses—General. Influence lines may be constructed for the bar forces in truss members and are important in determining the loca-

Figure 6.12 Absolute maximum moment for two loads

tion of live loads leading to maximum bar forces in truss members, as well as for computing the actual values of these maximum bar forces. The same general procedure as that used for constructing influence lines for beams and girders is applicable to trusses. It is always possible to compute the ordinate to the influence line for a unit load at each panel point of the truss. Usually the stringers act as end-supported beams between the floor beams, so that the influence line is a straight line between panel points. As was the case with beams and girders, it is often possible to reduce the amount of computation by recognizing the fact that the influence line is a straight line for several successive panels.

Once the influence line has been constructed for the force in a given truss member, the interpretation of the curve with respect to loading criteria and stress analysis is identical with that for beams and girders.

Influence lines for trusses are drawn to correspond to a unit load traveling across the *loaded chord*, i.e., the chord containing the panel points at which the live load is applied.

6.14 Influence Lines for a Pratt Truss. The construction and use of influence lines for trusses will be illustrated by a consideration of the Pratt truss of Fig. 6.13a. To construct the influence line for a chord member, such as bar L_2L_3, take moments about U_2 of the forces acting on one side of section A-A. With the unit load to the left of the section, the tension in L_2L_3 equals R_{6y} multiplied by 120 and divided by the truss height of 40 ft and hence is directly proportional to R_{6y}. Since R_{6y} varies linearly as a unit load travels from L_0 to L_2, the influence line is a straight line from zero at L_0 to $+\frac{1}{3}(^{120}\!/_{40}) = +1$ at L_2. Had this linearity not been recognized, the value of the ordinate to the influence line at L_1 might have been computed independently and would have been found to equal $+\frac{1}{6}(^{120}\!/_{40}) = +\frac{1}{2}$. With the unit load at L_2 or at any point to the right of section A-A, the tension in L_2L_3 equals R_{0y} multiplied by 60 and divided by 40. Since R_{0y} varies linearly as a unit load travels

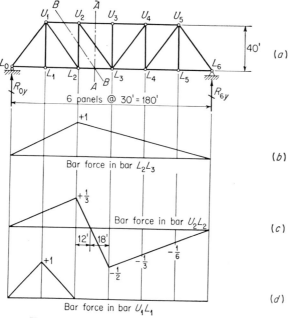

Figure 6.13 Influence lines for Pratt truss

from L_2 to L_6, the influence line is a straight line from $+\frac{2}{3}(^{60}\!/_{40}) = +1$ at L_2 to zero at L_6. This influence line is shown in Fig. 6.13b, where tension is plotted above the base line.

The construction of an influence line for bar force in a web member will be illustrated by Fig. 6.13c, where the vertical bar U_2L_2 is considered. When a unit load is to the left of section B-B, the tension in this member equals the reaction R_{6y}. Hence the influence line is a straight line from zero at L_0 to $+\frac{1}{3}$ at L_2. When the unit load is to the right of section B-B, the compression in U_2L_2 equals the reaction R_{06}. Hence the influence line is a straight line from $-\frac{1}{2}$ at L_3 to zero at L_6, negative values being plotted below the base line and indicating compression. Between panel points L_2 and L_3, the influence line is a straight line, assuming that the stringers are constructed so that they act as end-supported beams between the panel points L_2 and L_3.

For both the bars that have been considered, the influence lines extend over the entire length of the truss. Such bars are called *primary* truss members. Consider now the vertical member U_1L_1, the influence line for which is shown in Fig. 6.13d. Upon applying the method of joints to L_1, it is seen that the force in this bar is zero if the unit load is applied to any panel point other than L_1, in which case it equals $+1$. Such a member of the unit load, which is stressed for certain positions only, is called a *secondary* truss member.

To obtain maximum live bar forces in truss members by use of the influence line, no new principles are involved. For example, suppose that it is desired to determine the maximum compression in the vertical U_2L_2 due to a uniform live load of 2,000 lb per ft and a single concentrated live load of 15,000 lb.

By the exact method, the neutral point of the influence line of Fig. 6.13c is determined by similar triangles as being located 12 ft to the right of L_2. For maximum compression in U_2L_2, the uniform load should extend from the neutral point to L_6, while the concentrated load should be placed at L_3. The value of this maximum compression is given by

$$2,000(\tfrac{1}{2})(108)(-\tfrac{1}{2}) + 15,000(-\tfrac{1}{2}) = -61,500 \text{ lb}$$

By the approximate method, the panel loads for the uniform load equal $2,000 \times 30 = 60,000$ lb and are placed at L_3, L_4, and L_5. The concentrated load is placed at L_3. The maximum live compression is given by

$$60,000(-\tfrac{1}{2} - \tfrac{1}{3} - \tfrac{1}{6}) + 15,000(-\tfrac{1}{2}) = -67,500 \text{ lb}$$

6.15 Influence Lines for Truss with K Diagonals. For simple cases, such as that of the Pratt truss of Art. 6.14, it is relatively simple to eliminate as many computations as possible in the construction of influence lines by recognizing the fact that certain portions of the influence line are linear over several successive panels. For more complicated trusses, it is often necessary either (1) to compute ordinates for each successive panel point or (2) first to construct influence lines for members other than that under consideration and use the data thus obtained in constructing the influence line actually desired. This latter procedure may be illustrated by considering the diagonal U_2M_3 of the truss of Fig. 6.14a, which has K-type diagonals and for which the top-chord panel points lie on a parabola. This truss is actually statically indeterminate to the first degree. However, the indeterminacy is confined to the two center panels, and the three panels on each end are statically determinate.

A consideration of joint M_3 shows that the horizontal components of the bar forces in bars U_2M_3 and L_2M_3 are always equal in magnitude but opposite in character. Since the slopes of these two bars are the same, the vertical components of these bar forces are likewise equal in magnitude and opposite in character; thus they act in the same direction when holding in equilibrium the vertical forces applied to that portion of the structure on one side of section A-A. The top chord U_2U_3 has a vertical

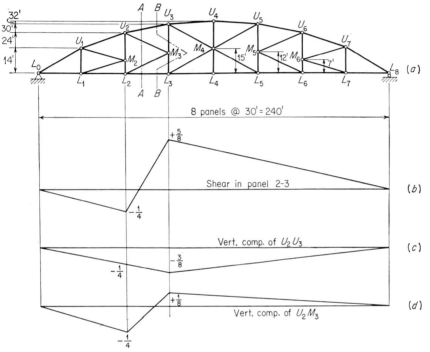

Figure 6.14   Influence lines for truss with K diagonals

component that must also be considered in the foregoing condition of equilibrium.

The influence line for the total shear in panel 2-3 is first drawn, as shown in Fig. 6.14b. Next, the influence line for the vertical component of the bar force in bar U_2U_3 is constructed, with the force in that member determined by taking moments about L_3 of the forces acting on one side of section B-B. This influence line is found to be a triangle with its apex at panel point 3, where the ordinate is equal to $-(\tfrac{3}{8})(^{150}\!\!/_{30})(\tfrac{6}{30}) = -\tfrac{3}{8}$.

Upon applying $\Sigma F_y = 0$ to that portion of the truss to the left of section A-A, the tensile vertical component of the bar force in U_2M_3 equals half the sum of the positive shear in panel 2-3 and the tensile vertical component in U_2U_3. Thus each ordinate to the influence line for the vertical component of bar force in U_2M_3 equals half the algebraic sum of the ordinates, at the same section, to the influence lines of Figs. 6.14b and c. Since these two influence lines change directions at L_2 and L_3 only, the influence line for the vertical component of bar force in U_2M_3 will change direction at those panel points only. The critical ordinates, i.e., the ordinates where the direction of the resultant influence line changes, will be as follows:

At L_2, $[-\frac{1}{4} + (-\frac{1}{4})]\frac{1}{2} = -\frac{1}{4}$ At L_3, $[+\frac{5}{8} + (-\frac{3}{8})]\frac{1}{2} = +\frac{1}{8}$

The resultant influence line for the vertical component of the bar force in bar U_2M_3 is shown in Fig. 6.14d.

6.16   Maximum Force in Truss Member Due to Series of Concentrated Live Loads.   Once the influence line has been constructed

Figure 6.15   Portion of influence line in Fig. 6.13b

for the bar force in a truss member, the position in which a series of concentrated live loads should be placed to make a given character of force in that member have a maximum value may be determined by moving up loads in the manner already described for girders.   To illustrate, the position of the loads of Fig. 6.7 that gives maximum tension in bar L_2L_3 of the truss of Fig. 6.13a will be determined.   The necessary portion of the influence line for this member (see Fig. 6.13b for the complete influence line) is reproduced in Fig. 6.15.

The computations are as follows (load 1 at L_2 does not give maximum, by inspection):

Load 2 at L_2; move up load 3	Increase in tension	Decrease in tension
Load group 1—All loads	$100(5)(+\frac{1}{120}) = +5\frac{0}{12}$	$30(5)(-\frac{1}{60}) = -\frac{5}{2}$
Load 3 at L_2; move up load 4		
Load group 1—All loads	$80(5)(+\frac{1}{120}) = +1\frac{0}{3}$	$50(5)(-\frac{1}{60}) = -2\frac{5}{6}$

Therefore, maximum tension in L_2L_3 occurs with load 3 at L_2.   To compute the value of this maximum tension, two different procedures are suggested.

Method 1 (based on moment diagram of Fig. 6.7):

$$R_{0y} = \frac{2,200 + 130(95)}{180} = 80.8 \text{ kips}$$

Hence the bar force in L_2L_3 is given by

$$\frac{+80.8(60) - 250}{40} = 115.0 \text{ kips}$$

Method 2 (based on computing ordinates to the influence line at each panel point):

Panel point	Floor-beam reaction		Influence-line ordinate	Increment of force in L_2L_3
1	$10(\frac{3}{6}) + 20(\frac{1}{6})$	$= + 8.3$	$+\frac{1}{2}$	$+ 4.2$
2	$10(\frac{3}{6}) + 20(\frac{5}{6} + \frac{5}{6} + \frac{5}{6} + \frac{3}{6} + \frac{2}{6} + \frac{1}{6})$	$= +78.3$	$+1$	$+78.3$
3	$20(\frac{1}{6} + \frac{3}{6} + \frac{4}{6} + \frac{5}{6})$	$= +43.3$	$+\frac{3}{4}$	$+32.5$
		Total stress in $L_2L_3 = \Sigma = $		$+115.0$ kips

6.17 Influence Tables. It is often advantageous to express influence data in the form of influence tables rather than in the form of curves. The influence table (Table 6.1) refers to the truss of Fig. 6.13a. It gives the force in each bar of the truss due to a unit load at each panel point. Forces in bars L_2L_3, U_2L_2, and U_1L_1 were taken directly from Figs. 6.13b, c, and d, respectively. Forces for other bars may be checked by the student.

In utilizing an influence table to compute maximum live bar forces by

Table 6.1 Influence Table for Truss of Fig. 6.13a

Bar	Bar force due to unit load at						
	L_0	L_1	L_2	L_3	L_4	L_5	L_6
L_0L_1	0.000	+0.625	+0.500	+0.375	+0.250	+0.125	0.000
L_1L_2	0.000	+0.625	+0.500	+0.375	+0.250	+0.125	0.000
L_2L_3	0.000	+0.500	+1.000	+0.750	+0.500	+0.250	0.000
L_0U_1	0.000	−1.041	−0.833	−0.625	−0.417	−0.208	0.000
U_1U_2	0.000	−0.500	−1.000	−0.750	−0.500	−0.250	0.000
U_2U_3	0.000	−0.375	−0.750	−1.125	−0.750	−0.375	0.000
U_1L_2	0.000	−0.208	+0.833	+0.625	+0.417	+0.208	0.000
U_2L_3	0.000	−0.208	−0.417	+0.625	+0.417	+0.208	0.000
U_1L_1	0.000	+1.000	0.000	0.000	0.000	0.000	0.000
U_2L_2	0.000	+0.167	+0.333	−0.500	−0.333	−0.167	0.000
U_3L_3	0.000	0.000	0.000	0.000	0.000	0.000	0.000

the approximate method, it is convenient to prepare a second table that is a summary of the influence table, as illustrated by Table 6.2.

In the summary of the influence table, the sum of the positive ordinates for a member is obtained by adding up, for that member, all the positive values from the influence table. The product of this sum and the panel load for uniform live load equals the maximum tension in that member due to uniform live load.

The sum of the negative ordinates for a member is obtained by adding up, for that member, all the negative ordinates from the influence table.

Table 6.2   Summary of Influence Table for Truss of Fig. 6.13a

Bar	Sum of ordinates			Max ordinates		Loaded length for	
	Positive	Negative	All	Positive	Negative	Tension	Compression
L_0L_1	+1.875	0.000	+1.875	+0.625	0.000	180	0
L_1L_2	+1.875	0.000	+1.875	+0.625	0.000	180	0
L_2L_3	+3.000	0.000	+3.000	+1.000	0.000	180	0
L_0U_1	0.000	−3.124	−3.124	0.000	−1.041	0	180
U_1U_2	0.000	−3.000	−3.000	0.000	−1.000	0	180
U_2U_3	0.000	−3.375	−3.375	0.000	−1.125	0	180
U_1L_2	+2.083	−0.208	+1.875	+0.833	−0.208	144	36
U_2L_3	+1.250	−0.625	+0.625	+0.625	−0.417	108	72
U_1L_1	+1.000	0.000	+1.000	+1.000	0.000	60	0
U_2L_2	+0.500	−1.000	−0.500	+0.333	−0.500	72	108
U_3L_3	0.000	0.000	0.000	0.000	0.000	0	0

The product of this sum and the panel load for uniform live load equals the maximum compression in that member due to uniform live load.

The sum of all the ordinates for a member is obtained by adding algebraically, for that member, the sum of the positive ordinates and the sum of the negative ordinates. If the dead panel loads are equal, the product of this sum and the dead panel load equals the dead bar force for any member except the verticals. For verticals, this product must be corrected for that portion of the dead load applied at the top-chord panel point.

The maximum positive ordinate for a member is obtained by choosing, for that member, the maximum positive value from the influence table. The product of this value and the concentrated live load equals the maximum tension in that member due to the concentrated live load.

The maximum negative ordinate for a member is obtained by choosing, for that member, the maximum negative value from the influence table. The product of this value and the concentrated live load equals the maximum compression in that member due to the concentrated live load.

The procedure for determining the total dead plus live bar force in any member from the summary of the influence table will be illustrated by considering bar U_2L_3 and the following loads:

Dead load = 2,000 lb per ft   Uniform live load = 1,000 lb per ft
Concentrated live load = 10,000 lb

	Max tension, kips	Max compression, kips
Dead	60(+0.625) = +37.5	+37.5
Live:		
Uniform	30(+1.250) = +37.5	30(−0.625) = −18.8
Concentrated	10(+0.625) = + 6.3	10(−0.417) = − 4.2
Total dead plus live bar force	+81.3	+14.5

Hence there is no stress reversal in this case.

6.18 Loaded Length. The loaded length is the length of that portion of a structure loaded with uniform live load to produce maximum live stress of a given character. This loaded length may be determined from the influence line for the member under consideration. For example, consider the girder of Fig. 6.5. The loaded length for positive moment at E is 60 ft. The loaded length for positive shear in panel BC is 48 ft; for negative shear in the same panel it is 12 ft. Loaded length is the controlling parameter in many formulas for impact.

When equivalent live loads are used in place of a series of concentrated live loads, the concentrated live load is not physically dissociated from the uniform live load. Hence it is correct to use the same loaded length for the concentrated live load that is used for the uniform live load, i.e., the impact factor for both components of the equivalent live load is based on the loaded length corresponding to the uniform load.

In computing loaded lengths, it is often permissible to estimate the location of the neutral point to the nearest half panel. This saves computations and does not introduce important errors into total computed stresses (dead + live + impact).

If desired, two columns may be added to the influence-table summary (Table 6.2) in which loaded lengths for tension and compression are given. The inclusion of these data in the summary of the influence table is helpful for computing impact bar forces in the various members.

6.19 Alternative Approach for Determination of Influence Lines. An alternative approach to the construction of influence lines may be made by introducing an imaginary deformation into the truss member or girder section under consideration. This method is of more interest than use in connection with statically determinate structures, but it is of importance in constructing influence lines for statically indeterminate structures, by both analytical and structural-model procedures.[1]

The method will be illustrated by a consideration of the truss of Fig. 6.16a, in which it is desired to construct the influence line for member L_2L_3. Suppose that a turnbuckle is imagined as inserted in member L_2L_3. If this turnbuckle were turned so that bar L_2L_3 were shortened by a small amount Δ, the structure would take the shape indicated by the

Figure 6.16   Alternative method for obtaining influence lines

dashed position of the truss. Since the truss is statically determinate, no elastic restraint would be encountered as the turnbuckle is turned; and if there were no loads on the structure, there would be no stress in any of the members. Suppose, however, that a unit load is imagined as being applied at any particular panel point such as L_1. Let F be the tension in L_2L_3 due to this unit load. Then, when the turnbuckle is taken up, it would be necessary to do work on the structure, to an amount equal to $+F(\Delta)$, since the turnbuckle would exert a tensile force equal to $+F$ on bar L_2L_3 at each end of the turnbuckle, and the total distance traveled by the two forces F, as shown in Fig. 6.16b, would equal Δ. The unit load at L_1 would move vertically through a distance δ_1 and while so moving would do work on the structure equal to $(-1)(\delta_1)$. The negative sign is introduced because the movement δ_1 is in a direction opposite to that of the unit load.

The stresses in the structure will not change during this deformation, so that the elastic strain energy stored in the members of the truss due to the fact that they are stressed will remain constant. Since the strain energy remains constant, there has been no net work done on the truss during the deformation, when all the forces are considered. Expressed

---

[1] This method of obtaining influence lines is called Müller-Breslau's principle and is discussed further in Art. 14.3.

in symbols,

$$+F(\Delta) - (1)(\delta_1) = 0$$

where

$$F = +\frac{\delta_1}{\Delta}$$

Had the unit load been placed at any other panel point L_n, similar considerations would lead to the conclusion that

$$F = +\frac{\delta_n}{\Delta}$$

But F is the bar force in bar L_2L_3 due to a unit load at L_n; hence it is the ordinate at panel point L_n to the influence line for the bar force in bar L_2L_3. The value of Δ is independent of the panel point considered. We may therefore conclude that the bottom chord of the truss as shown by the dotted lines of Fig. 6.16a has the *shape* of the influence line for tension in L_2L_3. The *scale* of the influence line is determined by dividing the

Figure 6.17   Influence line for force in truss diagonal

deflections δ_n by the imposed deformation Δ. If Δ is made equal to unity, the values δ_n are themselves numerically equal to the ordinates to the influence line.

To use fully this method of constructing influence lines requires either a model of the structure or a knowledge of the methods for computing deflections. However, even without computing deflections, it is often possible to visualize the shape that a structure would take and thus arrive at the shape of the influence line. In this manner, the critical points at which influence-line ordinates must be computed may be located. The position of live loads to cause maximum live stresses can often be told from the shape of the influence line, without actually computing the values of the critical ordinates.

For example, the dotted lines in Fig. 6.17 show the position the truss would take if the diagonal U_2L_3 were shortened. Since the bottom chord would change slope only at L_2 and L_3, ordinates to the influence line for force in U_2L_3 need be computed at these two panel points only. It may be concluded, moreover, without actually computing these ordinates, that by the approximate method the maximum live tension in U_2L_3 will occur with panel loads for uniform live load at L_3, L_4, and L_5 and with the concentrated live load at L_3. The actual value of this maximum live bar force can be computed by the equations of statics, with the loads in the foregoing positions.

6.20   Problems for Solution

*Problem 6.1   Referring to Fig. 6.18, construct the influence lines for (a) shear at a; (b) moment at a; (c) reaction at b.

Figure 6.18   Problems 6.1 and 6.2

*Problem 6.2   Referring to Fig. 6.18 and using a live load consisting of a uniform load of 500 lb per ft and a concentrated load of 5,000 lb, compute (a) the maximum upward reaction at b; (b) the maximum positive and negative moments at a; (c) the maximum positive and negative shears at a section just to the right of the support at b. (d) If the dead load is 1,000 lb per ft, compute, from the influence line, the maximum moment at a due to dead plus live load.

Problem 6.3   For the structure of Fig. 6.19, construct influence lines for (a) shear in panel AB; (b) moment at panel point C.

Figure 6.19   Problems 6.3 and 6.4

Problem 6.4   Compute, by both the exact and the approximate methods, the maximum live shear in panel AB and the maximum live moment at panel point C of the structure of Fig. 6.19, due to a uniform live load of 1,200 lb per ft and a single concentrated live load of 18,000 lb.

*Problem 6.5   For the structure of Fig. 6.20, construct influence lines for (a) shear in panel DE; (b) moment at panel point E.

Figure 6.20   Problems 6.5 and 6.6

Figure 6.21   Problems 6.7 to 6.10

Problem 6.6   Compute, by the approximate method, the maximum live shear in panel DE and the maximum live moment at panel point E of Fig. 6.20, due to the live load of Prob. 6.4.

Problem 6.7   Construct a moment diagram for the loading of Fig. 6.21.

Problem 6.8   Using the moment diagram for the loading of Fig. 6.21 and the structure of Fig. 6.19, determine (a) the left girder reaction when load 3 is at C; (b) the left girder reaction when load 5 is at C; (c) the shear in panel AB when load 3 is at E; (d) the moment at panel point D when load 2 is at D.

*Problem 6.9   For the loading of Fig. 6.21, compute the maximum live moment at panel point B of the girder of Fig. 6.10a.

*Problem 6.10   For the loading of Fig. 6.21, compute the maximum positive shear in panel CD of the girder of Fig. 6.10a.

Problem 6.11   Compute the absolute maximum shear in the beam of Fig. 6.4a, due to a live load of 1,000 lb per ft, plus a single concentrated live load of 5,000 lb.

*Problem 6.12   Compute the absolute maximum moment due to two concentrated live loads of 10 kips each, spaced at 10 ft and acting on an end-supported beam with a span of 20 ft.

Problem 6.13   Compute the absolute maximum moment due to four concentrated live loads of 12 kips each, spaced at 6 ft each and acting on an end-supported beam with a span of 25 ft.

*Problem 6.14   Compute the maximum live bar force in bars a and b of the truss of Fig. 6.22, due to a uniform live load of 750 lb per ft.   Consider both tension and compression.

Figure 6.22   Problem 6.14   **Figure 6.23**   Problems 6.15, 6.17, and 6.18

*Problem 6.15   The top-chord panel points of the truss of Fig. 6.23 lie on a parabola.   Draw influence lines for (a) horizontal component of the force in bar a; (b) force in bar b; (c) force in bar c; (d) force in bar d.

Problem 6.16   Construct an influence line for the force in bar U_2M_2 of the truss of Fig. 6.14a.

Problem 6.17   Compute the maximum bar force in bar a of the truss in Fig. 6.23, due to the loading of Fig. 6.21.

Problem 6.18   Prepare an influence-table summary of bars a, b, c, and d of the truss of Fig. 6.23.   Include loaded lengths in the summary.

Problem 6.19   For each of the beams shown in Fig. 6.24, construct the influence line for the shear in panel C-D and for the bending moment at panel point D.

Figure 6.24   Problem 6.19

Problem 6.20   For each of the bars noted on the trusses shown in Fig. 6.25, construct the influence line for the corresponding bar force.

(*a*)

(*b*)

Figure 6.25   Problem 6.20

7

Bridge and Roof Trusses

7.1 Introduction. Loadings for trusses are discussed in Chap. 1; stress analysis for trusses is treated in Chaps. 4 and 5, by mathematical and graphical procedures, respectively; influence lines for trusses and the determination of maximum live bar forces are considered in Chap. 6. In this chapter, we shall bring together the ideas contained in the earlier chapters and apply these concepts to the broader aspects of truss analysis. In addition to considering the general analysis of a typical roof truss and a typical bridge truss, we shall consider some further specific matters of

Figure 7.1 Truss bridge

importance, such as stress reversal and the effect of counters. Attention will then be given to the effect of skewing a bridge with respect to its abutments. Finally, a brief consideration will be given to movable bridges.

The trusses considered will be analyzed as planar structures, but it should be understood that actually they are portions of three-dimensional frameworks. To see why this procedure is permissible, refer to the deck bridge of Fig. 7.1, in which only the lateral loads P_1, P_2, . . . , P_5 will be assumed as acting, these loads lying in the plane of the top-chord lateral system. Suppose that a horizontal plane is passed through the structure at some elevation between the top and bottom chords. Considering the isolated part of the structure above this plane, it will be

221

seen that the horizontal components of the bar forces in the sway-bracing diagonals at the ends of the structure must hold the top-chord lateral system, acted upon by the lateral loads, in equilibrium.[1] These horizontal components provide the end reactions on the top-chord lateral system, which may therefore be analyzed as a planar truss. The vertical components of the bar forces in the sway-bracing diagonals must be held in equilibrium by the bar forces in the end verticals of the main vertical trusses. Thus the sway bracing in each end acts as a planar truss that transfers a reaction on the top-chord lateral system to the foundation.

Next, consider the same structure, with only the vertical loads P_1', P_2', . . . , P_5' assumed to be acting, these loads lying in the plane of the rear vertical truss. Suppose that a vertical plane, parallel to the main vertical trusses, is passed through the structure between these trusses. The sway-bracing diagonals at each end will be the only members cut that are capable of carrying vertical components. If the diagonals a are capable of carrying compression, they will be stressed and this will affect the bar forces in the end verticals of the rear vertical truss. This effect is of secondary importance, however, so that it is permissible and on the safe side to analyze the rear vertical truss as a planar truss acted upon by the loads P_1', P_2', . . . , P_5'.

If additional sway bracing is introduced at intermediate panel points, the situation becomes more complicated. As the panel points of the loaded vertical truss deflect vertically, the sway bracing at each intermediate panel point acts in a manner such that the corresponding panel point on the unloaded vertical truss must also undergo a certain amount of vertical movement. This produces what are called *participating stresses* in the unloaded vertical truss. However, if both vertical trusses have the same loading, there would, because of symmetry, be no participating stresses of this type. In an actual bridge, the vertical loads on the two main vertical trusses will not always be the same, but they are usually so nearly the same for the maximum loading conditions which control the design that the bar forces in the diagonals of sway bracing at intermediate panel points may be assumed as zero. Each main vertical truss can then be analyzed separately as a planar structure.

7.2   General Analysis of a Roof Truss. The general analysis of a roof truss includes not only the computation of bar forces in each member due to the various types of load that must be supported by the truss, but the combination, for each truss member, of the bar forces due to each type of loading, in a manner such that the maximum bar force that can

---

[1] This statement is not completely correct, because under an unsymmetrical system of lateral loads, the horizontal components of the bar forces in the diagonals of the main trusses would likewise assist in furnishing the reactions to the top-chord lateral system.

result from the combined effects of the different types of loading is obtained. To illustrate this procedure, consider the wall-supported roof truss of Fig. 7.2, which will be taken as an intermediate truss of a series of trusses spaced at 20 ft center to center. It will be assumed that the framing of the roof is such that loads from the roof are applied to the truss at the top-chord panel points only. The roofing, including the purlins that support the roofing between trusses, will be assumed to weigh 4.3 lb per sq ft of roof area; the truss itself will be assumed to weigh 75 lb per horizontal foot, with the weight equally divided between the top- and bottom-chord panel points. The snow load will be taken as 20 lb per sq ft of projected horizontal area of the roof. The ice load will be taken as 10 lb per sq ft of projected horizontal area of the roof. Wind loads shall be in accordance with the recommendations of the ASCE report[1] discussed in Art. 1.11 and shall be based on a maximum wind velocity of 100 mph. The analysis will be

Figure 7.2   Roof truss

limited to the following combinations of loads: (1) dead plus snow over the entire roof, (2) dead plus wind plus snow on the leeward side,[2] (3) dead plus ice over the entire roof plus wind. It is to be noted that the wind can blow from either the right or the left.

The dead bar forces will first be computed. For the bottom chord, the dead panel loads are given by $75\!/\!2(10) = 375$ lb; for the top chord, the dead panel loads are given by $375 + 4.3(11.2)(20) = 1{,}345$ lb. These panel loads, together with the dead bar forces they produce, are shown in Fig. 7.3. Since the dead bar forces are symmetrical about the center line of the truss, only half the truss is shown. The computations leading to the determination of the dead bar forces are omitted, since they involve no new procedures.

[1] Wind Bracing in Steel Buildings, *Proc. ASCE*, March, 1936, p. 397.

[2] This combination of loads is considered in the present discussion because it is one frequently investigated. It corresponds to a reasonable condition if wind loads are computed by a formula such as that by Duchemin (see footnote, Art. 1.11), since the snow might be likely to be blown from the roof by the pressure on the windward slope but remain on the leeward slope where there is neither pressure nor suction. When the recommendations of the ASCE report are followed, however, this particular load combination does not appear to be so likely to occur, since one may encounter, as in this particular problem, suction on both slopes, with the greater suction on the leeward slope. With this condition of wind load, the snow, if it remained on the roof at all, would appear more likely to remain on the windward side. However, it is always possible that snow, having fallen previous to the action of the wind, would have crusted over in a manner such as to act as assumed for loading condition 2.

Loading condition 1 calls for snow over the entire roof; loading condition 2 calls for snow on the leeward side only.   We shall first compute the truss bar forces for snow on the leeward side only; because the truss is symmetrical, we may then determine the bar forces due to snow over the entire roof by the principle of superposition, thus avoiding a complete

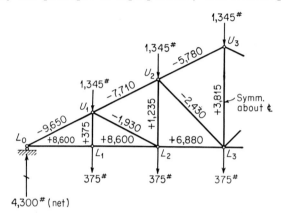

Figure 7.3   Bar forces due to dead load

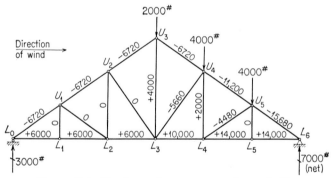

Figure 7.4   Bar forces due to snow on leeward side

second stress analysis.   The snow panel load is given by

$$20 \times 10 \times 20 = 4,000 \text{ lb}$$

With the snow on the leeward side only, the snow panel load at U_3 equals only half this value.   These panel loads, together with the bar forces they produce, are shown in Fig. 7.4.   Since this is an unsymmetrical loading condition, bar forces will be computed for the entire truss.

To obtain the bar forces due to full snow load, we may use the principle of superposition, as indicated by Fig. 7.5, since the bar forces due to loading a (as already computed in Fig. 7.4), superimposed upon the bar forces due to loading b (which can be obtained from Fig. 7.4 by symmetry), equal the bar forces due to loading c, which corresponds to full snow load.   For example, the bar force in bar L_0U_1 due to full snow load equals

$$-6,720 - 15,680 = -22,400$$

for bar U_2L_3, it equals $0 - 5,660 = -5,660$; etc.   Since this is a symmetrical loading condition, only half the truss is shown.   The bar forces in Fig. 7.6 could, of course, have been obtained by a separate stress analysis for the full snow-load condition.

Figure 7.5   Superposition of loadings

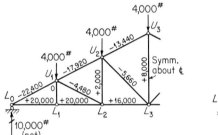

Figure 7.6   Bar forces due to full snow load

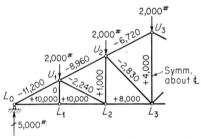

Figure 7.7   Bar forces due to full ice load

Loading condition 3 calls for ice over the entire roof.   Since the intensity of the ice load is half the intensity of the snow load, the bar forces due to full ice load may be obtained from Fig. 7.6 by direct proportion, equaling half the bar forces due to full snow load.   Bar forces due to full ice load are shown in Fig. 7.7.

For a wind velocity of 100 mph, by Eq. (1.3),

$$q = 0.002558(100)^2 = 25.6 \text{ lb per sq ft}$$

For the roof, $\tan \alpha = {}^{15}\!/_{30} = 0.5$, $\alpha = 26.6°$, whence, by Eq. (1.4), the windward slope is subjected to a suction of

$$p = [0.07(26.6) - 2.10](25.6) = 6.4 \text{ lb per sq ft}$$

The suction on the leeward slope equals $0.6(25.6) = 15.4$ lb per sq ft. Thus, for the windward side, the wind panel load equals

$$6.4(11.2)(20) = 1,435 \text{ lb}$$

For purposes of analysis it is more convenient to treat the vertical and horizontal components of the wind panel load, which equal 1,280 lb upward and 640 lb upwind, respectively. For the leeward side, the wind panel load equals 15.4(11.2)(20) = 3,450 lb. This panel load has an upward vertical component of 3,080 lb and a downwind horizontal component of 1,540 lb. Figure 7.8 shows the truss acted upon by the vertical and horizontal components of the wind panel loads and the bar forces for that condition of loading. The half panel loads at L_0 and L_6 were included in the analysis since the horizontal component of load applied at L_0 causes stresses in the truss. Since the wind loading is unsymmetrical, bar forces are computed for the entire truss.

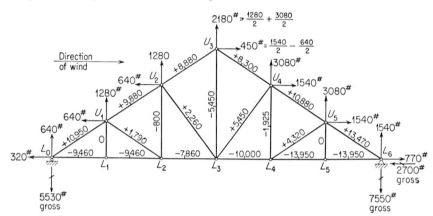

Figure 7.8   Bar forces due to wind load

In Table 7.1, we shall list the bar forces as given in Figs. 7.3, 7.4, and 7.6 to 7.8. Then we shall combine these bar forces to give the total bar force in each member corresponding to the three specified loading combinations. Finally we shall choose, for each member, the maximum bar force of each character which occurs in any of the three loading combinations, these maximum bar forces being those which would control the design of the members. The abbreviations used in the column headings are as follows: D = dead bar force; S = bar force due to snow load on both sides; S_L = bar force due to snow on the leeward side only; I = bar force due to ice on both sides; W = bar force due to wind. We shall list in the table only the bars in half the truss; but, in entering bar forces for the columns headed S_L and W, we shall enter first the bar force in the member itself, due to the loading under consideration, and second the bar force in the symmetrically placed member, due to the same loading.[1] This second entry covers the case which would exist were the direction of the wind to reverse, a condition for which the design must, of course,

[1] This procedure was not followed for the lower-chord members. Why?

Table 7.1   Bar-force Table for Roof Truss of Fig. 7.2

(All bar forces in lb)

Bar	D	S	S_L	I	W	(1) $D + S$	(2) $D + W + S_L$	(3) $D + W + I$	Max bar force	Load combinations
L_0L_1	+8,600	+20,000	+ 6,000 +14,000	+10,000	− 9,460 −13,950	+28,600	+ 5,140 + 8,650	+9,140 +4,650	+28,600	1
L_1L_2	+8,600	+20,000	+ 6,000 +14,000	+10,000	− 9,460 −13,950	+28,600	+ 5,140 + 8,650	+9,140 +4,650	+28,600	1
L_2L_3	+6,880	+16,000	+ 6,000 +10,000	+ 8,000	− 7,860 −10,100	+22,880	+ 5,020 + 6,780	+7,020 +4,780	+22,880	1
L_0U_1	−9,650	−22,400	− 6,720 −15,680	−11,200	+10,950 +13,470	−32,050	− 5,420 −11,860	−9,900 −7,380	−32,050	1
U_1U_2	−7,710	−17,920	− 6,720 −11,200	− 8,960	+ 9,880 +10,880	−25,630	− 4,550 − 8,030	−6,790 −5,790	−25,630	1
U_2U_3	−5,780	−13,440	− 6,720 − 6,720	− 6,720	+ 8,800 + 8,300	−19,220	− 3,700 − 4,200	−3,700 −4,200	−19,220	1
U_1L_2	−1,930	− 4,480	0 − 4,480	− 2,240	+ 1,790 + 4,320	− 6,410	− 140 − 2,090	−2,380 + 150	+ 150 − 6,410	3 1
U_2L_3	−2,430	− 5,660	0 − 5,660	− 2,830	+ 2,260 + 5,450	− 8,090	− 170 − 2,640	−3,000 + 190	+ 190 − 8,090	3 1
U_1L_1	+ 375	0	0 0	0	0 0	+ 375	+ 375	+ 375	+ 375	1, 2, 3
U_2L_2	+1,235	+ 2,000	0 + 2,000	+ 1,000	− 800 − 1,925	+ 3,235	+ 435 + 1,310	+1,435 + 310	+ 3,235	1
U_3L_3	+3,815	+ 8,000	+ 4,000	+ 4,000	− 5,450	+11,815	+ 2,365	+2,365	+11,815	1

provide. In carrying forward the totals that include either S_L or W, the sums corresponding to both entries are computed.

7.3 Permissible Stresses for Members Stressed by Wind. When members carry stresses due to wind loads, it is usual to permit somewhat higher stresses in design than would otherwise be the case. For example, some specifications state that members subject to stresses produced by a combination of wind and other loads may be proportioned for stress intensities $33\frac{1}{3}$ per cent greater than those such as specified in Art. 1.22, provided that the section thus required is not less than that required for the combination of other loads, without including wind. They state further that this increase of $33\frac{1}{3}$ per cent is also permissible for members subject only to stresses produced by wind loads.

Instead of designing members carrying wind loads on the basis of increased stresses equal to $\frac{4}{3}$ of the usual permissible stresses, it is obvious that the same results will be obtained by designing on the basis of the usual permissible stresses, but allowing for only $\frac{3}{4}$ of the computed total bar forces in such members, since $F/\frac{4}{3}f = \frac{3}{4}F/f$. Hence, in preparing a bar-force table such as Table 7.1, one might proceed by entering in the column headed Max bar force the largest of the following: $D + S$; $\frac{3}{4}(D + W + S_L)$; $\frac{3}{4}(D + W + I)$. The member would then be designed for this maximum bar force, with the usual permissible stresses.

7.4 General Analysis of a Bridge Truss. The general analysis of a bridge truss consists in computing the bar force in each member, due

Figure 7.9   Highway bridge truss

to each type of loading, and the combination, for each truss member, of these forces into the maximum total bar force that will control design. To illustrate this procedure, we shall consider the Warren type of highway truss of Fig. 7.9, which will be analyzed for dead, live, and impact loads. It will be assumed that the truss, including details and secondary bracing, weighs 0.500 kip per ft, with this dead weight divided equally between the top- and bottom-chord panel points. The weight per foot of that portion of the floor system carried by the truss will be taken as 0.800 kip,

Table 7.2   Influence Table for Truss of Fig. 7.9

Bar	Bar force due to unit load at								
	L_0	L_1	L_2	L_3	L_4	L_5	L_6	L_7	L_8
L_0L_2*	0	+0.875	+0.750	+0.625	+0.500	+0.375	+0.250	+0.125	0
L_2L_4	0	+0.625	+1.250	+1.875	+1.500	+1.125	+0.750	+0.375	0
L_0U_1	0	−1.238	−1.060	−0.885	−0.708	−0.530	−0.354	−0.177	0
U_1U_3	0	−0.750	−1.500	−1.250	−1.000	−0.750	−0.500	−0.250	0
U_3U_4	0	−0.500	−1.000	−1.500	−2.000	−1.500	−1.000	−0.500	0
U_1L_2	0	−0.177	+1.060	+0.885	+0.708	+0.530	+0.354	+0.177	0
L_2U_3	0	+0.177	+0.354	−0.885	−0.708	−0.530	−0.354	−0.177	0
U_3L_4	0	−0.177	−0.354	−0.530	+0.708	+0.530	+0.354	+0.177	0
U_1L_1	0	+1.000	0	0	0	0	0	0	0
U_2L_2	0	0	0	0	0	0	0	0	0
U_3L_3	0	0	0	+1.000	0	0	0	0	0
U_4L_4	0	0	0	0	0	0	0	0	0

* By the method of joints, the stress in L_0L_1 is equal to the stress in L_1L_2 as long as only vertical loads are applied at joint L_1. Hence to save space in this and the following tables, these two members will be treated as a single member.

acting at the bottom-chord panel points.   For live load, an equivalent live-load system will be used, consisting of a uniform load of 0.650 kip per ft and a single concentrated load of 20.0 kips.   Impact will be computed in accordance with Eq. (1.1).   Maximum live bar forces are to be computed by the approximate method.   For each member of the left half of the truss, the maximum total bar force of each character is to be obtained.

We shall first compute the ordinates to the influence line for each member of the left half of the truss, considering the effect of a unit load at each bottom-chord panel point of the entire truss.   These ordinates are summarized in the influence table (Table 7.2).   Since no unusual conditions are encountered in the computations of these values, the details of the computations will be omitted.

A summary of the influence table (Table 7.2) will next be prepared (Table 7.3).

Table 7.3   Summary of Influence Table for Truss of Fig. 7.9

Bar	Sum of ordinates			Maximum ordinates		Loaded length, ft, for	
	Positive	Negative	All	Positive	Negative	Tension	Compression
L_0L_2	+3.500	0	+3.500	+0.875	0	240	0
L_2L_4	+7.500	0	+7.500	+1.875	0	240	0
L_0U_1	0	−4.952	−4.952	0	−1.238	0	240
U_1U_3	0	−6.000	−6.000	0	−1.500	0	240
U_3U_4	0	−8.000	−8.000	0	−2.000	0	240
U_1L_2	+3.714	−0.177	+3.537	+1.060	−0.177	206	34
L_2U_3	+0.531	−2.654	−2.123	+0.354	−0.885	69	171
U_3L_4	+1.769	−1.061	+0.708	+0.708	−0.530	137	103
U_1L_1	+1.000	0	+1.000	+1.000	0	60	0
U_2L_2	0	0	0	0	0	0	0
U_3L_3	+1.000	0	+1.000	+1.000	0	60	0
U_4L_4	0	0	0	0	0	0	0

Preparatory to the construction of a bar-force table for the members under consideration, we shall compute the panel loads for dead and live load.   For dead load, the top-chord panel load equals 30(0.250) = 7.5 kips; the bottom-chord panel load equals 7.5 + 30(0.800) = 31.5 kips. For uniform live load, the panel load equals 30(0.650) = 19.5 kips; the concentrated live load, which is already expressed as a panel load, equals 20.0 kips.

In the stress table (Table 7.4), the dead bar forces are computed by the principle of superposition, as shown in Fig. 7.10.   The bar forces due to the loading of Fig. 7.10a are first computed.   This loading assumes that the total dead load is applied at the bottom chord, so that the dead panel load for bottom-chord panel points equals $31.5 + 7.5 = 39.0$. Since the influence table is based on the application of loads to the bottom-chord panel points, the bar forces for this condition of loading are obtained by multiplying, for each member, the sum of all the ordinates to the

Table 7.4 Bar-force Table for Truss of Fig. 7.9
(All stresses in kips)

Bar	$D =$ dead bar force	$L =$ live bar force			Impact fraction	$I =$ impact bar force	$L + I$	Total $= D + L + I$
		Uniform	Con-cen-trated	Total				
L_0L_2	$+136.5$ —	$+ 68.3$ —	$+17.5$ —	$+ 85.8$ —	0.137 —	$+11.8$ —	$+ 97.6$ —	$+234.1$ —
L_2L_4	$+292.5$ —	$+146.2$ —	$+37.5$ —	$+183.7$ —	0.137 —	$+25.2$ —	$+208.9$ —	$+501.4$ —
L_0U_1	— -193.0	— $- 96.5$	— -24.7	— -121.2	— 0.137	— -16.6	— -137.8	— -330.8
U_1U_3	— -234.0	— -117.0	— -30.0	— -147.0	— 0.137	— -20.2	— -167.2	— -401.2
U_3U_4	— -312.0	— -156.0	— -40.0	— -196.0	— 0.137	— -26.8	— -222.8	— -534.8
U_1L_2	$+138.0$ —	$+ 72.5$ $- 3.5$	$+21.2$ $- 3.5$	$+ 93.7$ $- 7.0$	0.151 0.300	$+14.2$ $- 2.1$	$+107.9$ $- 9.1$	$+245.9$ —
L_2U_3	— $- 83.0$	$+ 10.4$ $- 51.8$	$+ 7.1$ -17.7	$+ 17.5$ $- 69.5$	0.258 0.169	$+ 4.5$ -11.8	$+ 22.0$ $- 81.3$	— -164.3
U_3L_4	$+ 27.6$ —	$+ 34.5$ $- 20.7$	$+14.2$ -10.6	$+ 48.7$ $- 31.3$	0.191 0.219	$+ 9.3$ $- 6.9$	$+ 58.0$ $- 38.2$	$+ 85.6$ $- 10.6$
U_1L_1	$+ 31.5$ —	$+ 19.5$ —	$+20.0$ —	$+ 39.5$ —	0.270 —	$+10.7$ —	$+ 50.2$ —	$+ 81.7$ —
U_2L_2	— $- 7.5$	— —	— —	— —	— —	— —	— —	— $- 7.5$
U_3L_3	$+ 31.5$ —	$+ 19.5$ —	$+20.0$ —	$+ 39.5$ —	0.270 —	$+10.7$ —	$+ 50.2$ —	$+ 81.7$ —
U_4L_4	— $- 7.5$	— —	— —	— —	— —	— —	— —	— $- 7.5$

influence line by the total dead panel load of 39.0. The bar forces due to the loading of Fig. 7.10b are next computed, the value 7.5 being that of the top-chord dead panel load. This stress analysis is exceedingly simple, and results, as shown in the figure, in a bar force of -7.5 in all verticals and zero force in all other members. If the loadings of Figs. 7.10a and b are superimposed, the loading of Fig. 7.10c, which corresponds to the actual dead loading, is obtained. Hence the dead bar forces may be obtained by superimposing the bar forces computed for the loadings of Figs. 7.10a and b. To summarize, the dead bar forces for a given member may be computed as follows: (1) Multiply the *total* dead panel load by the sum of all the ordinates to the influence line. (2) To the bar force from step 1, subtract, *for the verticals only*, the magnitude of the top-chord dead panel load.

Had the dead load not been uniformly distributed, the bar forces corresponding to the loading of Fig. 7.10a would require recourse to the influence table, with bar forces obtained by summing the cross products of the individual panel loads and corresponding ordinates from the influence table. It is, of course, possible, and sometimes desirable, to obtain

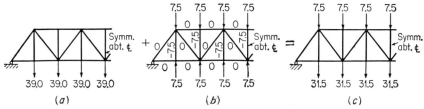

Figure 7.10   Computation of dead bar forces

dead bar forces by a separate analysis for dead loads, without making use of influence data.

Maximum tension and compression due to uniform live load are entered in the next column. These values are obtained by multiplying the uniform live panel load (19.5) by the sum of the positive and negative ordinates, respectively, to the influence line. Maximum tension and compression due to concentrated live load are entered in the following column. These values are obtained by multiplying the concentrated live panel load (20.0) by the maximum positive and negative ordinates, respectively, to the influence line. Total live bar force of each character is then obtained by summing the effects of the uniform and concentrated live loads.

Impact fractions, computed in accordance with Eq. (1.1), are then entered; these impact fractions multiplied by the *total* live bar forces give the impact bar forces, which are then added to the total live bar forces, leading to the total bar forces due to live load and impact. Total bar forces due to dead load plus live load plus impact are entered in the final column. It is to be noted that live and impact bar forces of both characters are carried forward in the bar-force table, until it is definitely ascertained that no stress reversal (see Art. 7.5) can occur. In the actual design of a truss, bar forces due to other causes, such as wind loads, would be considered, such forces being combined with dead, live, and impact bar forces in additional columns in the stress table. In this example, bar forces due to wind have been omitted because the analysis of lateral systems and portals has been reserved for discussion in a later chapter.

7.5   Stress Reversal.   In the highway truss analyzed in Art. 7.4, all the members were assumed to be capable of carrying either tension or compression, and the maximum bar force of each character was obtained. In preparing the bar-force table of Table 7.4, the total bar force due to dead plus live plus impact was obtained by simply adding the $L + I$ bar forces algebraically to the dead bar forces. In the case of only one member, U_3L_4, did the live plus impact total exceed the dead bar force, when the live plus impact total was of opposite character from the dead bar force.

For U_3L_4, the interpretation of this condition is as follows: Depending upon the position of the live load on the structure, the total bar force due to dead + live + impact may be either tension or compression. This alternation of stresses as live load travels across the span is called stress reversal. When members are subjected to stress reversal, it is usual to follow a more conservative design procedure than would result if the usual permissible stresses were used in conjunction with the $D + L + I$ totals of Table 7.4. For example, one specification states that "if the alternate stresses (stress reversals) occur in succession during one passage of the live load, each shall be increased by 50 per cent of the smaller. . . .   If the live-load and dead-load stresses are of opposite sign, only 70 per cent of the dead-load stress shall be considered as effective in counteracting the live-load stress." The following of such a specification results in a build-up of total bar force for which a member subject to stress reversal shall be designed. Since the usual stresses are used in conjunction with this increased total, a more conservative design results than would otherwise be the case.

To illustrate the application of the foregoing specification, consider U_3L_4:

Dead	$+27.6$	$0.7(+27.6) = +19.3$
Live + impact	$+58.0$	-38.2
	$+85.6$	-18.9
	$+ 9.5 = 18.9(0.50)$	$- 9.5 = 18.9(0.50)$
	$+95.1$ kips	-28.4 kips

The member should be designed to withstand both these bar forces.

7.6   Counters.   A member with a large slenderness ratio (length divided by radius of gyration) will buckle when subjected to relatively small compressive forces. Such a member can carry tension satisfactorily but can carry only a negligible amount of compression. The diagonals of a truss may be designed so that they act in such a manner, in which case they are called tension diagonals. If a truss were to carry dead loads only, as shown in Fig. 7.11a, single tension diagonals in each panel would be satisfactory, since their slopes could be chosen in a manner such that the dead shear in each panel would produce tension in the diagonals. When live loads are considered, it is always possible that, for some position of the live loads, the maximum shear in a given panel due to live loads plus impact, of a character opposite to that of the dead shear, may exceed the dead-load shear. This would tend to produce compression in the tension diagonal, a condition that must be avoided, unless a second tension diagonal, called a *counter*, is added to the panel, the counter having a slope opposite to that of the main tension diagonal. The counter

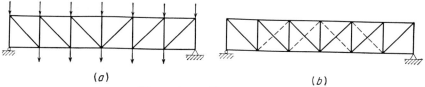

(a)   (b)

Figure 7.11 Use of counters

will have no stress due to dead loads only, since it buckles slightly under the action of the dead shear. When the shear in the panel changes sign owing to live loads and impact, however, the main tension diagonal buckles and has zero stress and the counter comes into action, carrying the resultant shear due to dead plus live plus impact as a tension member.

In designing a truss with tension diagonals, one should first determine the panels where counters are required. Counters are most likely to be necessary in the panels nearest the center of the truss, since the dead shear in such panels is smaller than in the end panels, while the live shear of opposite character to that of the dead shear is larger than in the end panels and hence more likely to exceed the dead shear. A typical truss with counters is shown in Fig. 7.11b, in which the counters are indicated by the dotted diagonals of the four panels nearest the center of the truss.

To illustrate the determination of maximum bar forces in a member of a truss with counters, consider the computation of the maximum compression in member U_3L_3 of the structure of Fig. 7.12a. An influence line can be constructed that will show how the bar force in U_3L_3 will vary as a unit load moved across the span. Such an influence line cannot be used to determine how to place live loads for maximum compression in U_3L_3, however, for the following reason: The computation of each ordinate will depend on whether the main diagonal or the counter is in action in each of the two center panels. This condition will vary for different positions of the unit load. For example, with the unit load at L_2, L_2U_3

and L_3U_4 will be in action and U_2L_3 and U_3L_4 will have zero stress, while with the unit load at L_3, U_2L_3 and L_3U_4 will be in action and L_2U_3 and U_3L_4 will have zero stress. Hence, in effect, *the different ordinates to the influence line will correspond to the action of different structures, and under such circumstances the principle of superposition does not hold.* The maximum compression in U_3L_3 due to dead plus live plus impact loads depends

Figure 7.12 Analysis of truss with counters

on which diagonals are in action under the *total* loading leading to that maximum compression.

To simplify this illustration, let us assume that the dead panel loads are applied to the bottom chord only and equal 30.0 kips, that the uniform live panel is 20.0 kips and the concentrated live load is 25.0 kips, and that impact is to be neglected.

The four possible ways in which the diagonals of the two center panels can act are shown in Figs. 7.12b to e. If they act as shown in Fig. 7.12b,

U_3L_3 cannot be stressed, as may be seen by applying the method of joints to joint U_3. If they act as shown in Fig. 7.12c, the live load cannot be placed so as to produce compression in U_3L_3, as may be seen by applying the method of joints to L_3. Even under dead loads this represents an impossible condition, since it is necessary for L_2U_3 and U_3L_4 to carry compression. If the diagonals act as shown in Fig. 7.12d, the live loads will be placed as shown to produce maximum compression in U_3L_3. This is a possible condition since U_2L_3 and U_3L_4 are both in tension, and leads to a resultant compression of -3.3 kips in U_3L_3. If the diagonals act as shown in Fig. 7.12e, there results the same compression of -3.3 kips in U_3L_3, this also being a possible condition, since L_2U_3 and L_3U_4 are both in tension.

Hence we may conclude that the maximum compression which can occur in U_3L_3 is -3.3 kips.

When a truss has counters, the determination of maximum bar forces in members influenced by the action of the counters must be approached by trial. Each position of live load that may reasonably lead to the maximum bar force desired must be investigated. If diagonals capable of carrying tension only have been assumed to be in action, the results of any investigation are invalidated unless the computed bar forces in such members indicate that they actually carry tension.

7.7 Movable Bridges—General. When the topography of a bridge site is such that it is desirable to have the roadway close to the surface of the body of water crossed by the bridge, the vertical under-clearance requirements of the navigation passing beneath the bridge may require a movable bridge. A movable bridge is one that may be moved to permit the passage of navigation. The three most important types of movable bridges are (1) bascule bridges, (2) vertical-lift bridges, and (3) horizontal-swing bridges. The type to be used depends largely upon the horizontal and vertical clearance requirements of the navigation. Whether a low-level movable bridge or a high-level fixed bridge should be used in a given site can usually be determined only by a careful economic study.

7.8 Bascule Bridges. A bascule bridge may prove economical where horizontal navigation requirements do not necessitate too long a span and where a high vertical clearance is required. A typical bascule bridge is shown in Fig. 7.13. Motive power drives a pinion at D, which engages the rack E, thus opening or closing the span. The required motive power is reduced by the action of the counterweight C.

The dead-load bar forces in a bascule span change as the bridge is opened or closed, and it is possible that the dead bar forces in certain members during such an operation may exceed the total bar forces with the bridge closed and subjected to traffic.

To find the maximum dead bar forces that occur while the span is being raised or lowered,[1] let F_H be the dead bar force in any member, with the span horizontal, and F_V be the dead bar force in the same member after the span is vertical (i.e., after having rotated through 90° from its closed position), both these values being easily computed by the usual methods of analysis. With the bridge partly opened and the bottom chord making

Figure 7.13 Bascule bridge

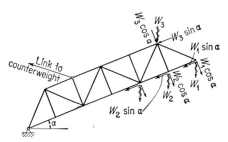

Figure 7.14 Bascule bridge, partially open

an angle α with the horizontal, as shown in Fig. 7.14, each dead panel load may be resolved into two components, one perpendicular and one parallel to the bottom chord. The components of dead load that are perpendicular to the bottom chord will cause bar forces equal to $F_H \cos \alpha$, while the components of dead load that are parallel to the bottom chord will cause bar forces equal to $F_V \sin \alpha$. Hence, for any angle α, the total dead bar force F_D in any member is given by

$$F_D = F_V \sin \alpha + F_H \cos \alpha \qquad (a)$$

Placing the derivative of F_D with respect to α equal to zero,

$$\frac{dF_D}{d\alpha} = F_V \cos \alpha - F_H \sin \alpha = 0$$

---

[1] See O. E. Hovey, "Movable Bridges," vol. I, p. 219, John Wiley & Sons, Inc., New York, 1926.

whence $\tan \alpha = F_V/F_H$.   Substituting this value of α into Eq. (a),

$$\text{Max } F_D = F_V \frac{F_V}{\sqrt{F_V'^2 + F_H'^2}} + F_H \frac{F_H}{\sqrt{F_V'^2 + F_H'^2}} = \sqrt{F_V'^2 + F_H'^2} \quad (7.1)$$

With the bridge closed, the dead-load reaction at the free end will be zero, since the counterweight holds the dead loads in equilibrium, but live loads produce reactions at each end, in the same manner as for an end-supported span.

7.9 Vertical-lift Bridges.   When the horizontal-clearance require-ment is greater than the vertical-clearance requirement for navigation, a vertical-lift bridge is likely to prove economical.   A typical vertical-lift bridge is shown in Fig. 7.15.   The span AB is raised or lowered

Figure 7.15   Vertical-lift bridge

vertically by cables running over sheaves at D that are supported at the tower tops.   The motive power required for this motion is reduced by the counterweights C.   These counterweights are usually designed to balance the entire dead load of the movable span, so that the dead-load reactions are taken by the cables.   Live loads on the movable span pro-duce reactions on the piers at A and B, however.

7.10 Horizontal-swing Bridges.   Horizontal-swing bridges give unlimited vertical clearance, but the center pier constitutes an obstruc-tion to traffic.   A large horizontal area is required for this type of movable bridge.   Horizontal-swing bridges may be of either the center-bearing type, as shown in Fig. 7.16a, or the rim-bearing type, as shown in Fig. 7.16b.   In either case, the bridge is opened by swinging it horizontally about the vertical center line.   When the bridge is open, the two spans cantilever from the center pier and are statically determinate.   When the bridge is closed, the trusses are continuous and hence statically inde-terminate.   Stress analysis for the closed condition depends on principles discussed in the portion of this book dealing with statically indeterminate structures.

When a swing bridge is closed, the dead reactions developed at the outer ends of the structure depend on the design. If these ends just touched their supports, any live load on one span would cause uplift at the far end of the other span. This condition is usually avoided by lifting the ends a slight amount when they are closed. The desired dead-load reaction can be computed so that it will exceed the maximum live-load reaction of opposite character.

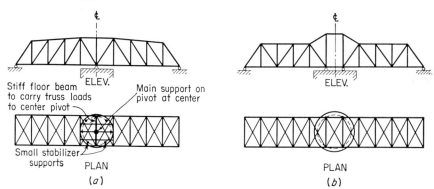

Figure 7.16   Horizontal-swing bridges

7.11   Skew Bridges. If the abutments are not perpendicular to the longitudinal axis of a bridge, the bridge is said to be skewed. Figure 7.17b shows the plan view of such a structure. In order to keep the connections from becoming complicated, the floor beams are usually kept perpendicular to the main trusses. This is likely to make the main trusses unsymmetrical. The two end posts of a truss should have the same slope so that the end portals will lie in a plane. This may lead to an inclined hanger as shown by bar a, Fig. 7.17a.

Figure 7.17   Skew bridge

When analyzing bar forces in the members of a truss of a skewed bridge, one may proceed by the same general approach followed for a bridge that is perpendicular to the abutments. However, in dealing with live loads, one should take into consideration the irregularity of the floor system. This will alter the details of the computation of live panel loads, which may not be the same for all panel points.

7.12   Problems for Solution

Problem 7.1   For the roof truss and loadings of Art. 7.2:

(a) Compute the maximum bar force of each character for each member of the left half of the truss, due to dead plus wind loads combined.

(b) Comparing the bar forces computed in part a with the maximum bar forces given in the bar-force table of Table 7.1, for what members if any would the loading condition of part a control design? (*Note:* In part b do not consider permissible increases in stress intensities for members stressed by wind.)

(c) Is it necessary for this truss to be anchored at its supports to prevent uplift? If so, determine the uplift force for which each anchorage should be designed, allowing a factor of safety of 50 per cent in this force.

*Problem 7.2   The roof truss of Fig. 7.18 is an intermediate truss of a series of trusses spaced on 15-ft centers. The dead loads acting on this truss are as shown in the figure. The snow load is 20 lb per sq ft horizontal projected area. Wind loads are to be computed by the Duchemin formula and based on a wind-pressure intensity of 20 lb per sq ft on a vertical surface. Compute the maximum bar force of each character in each member due to each of the following load combinations: (1) dead plus snow, (2) dead plus wind (note that wind may blow from either direction). What bar force will control the design of each member?

Figure 7.18   Problem 7.2

*Problem 7.3   The dead panel loads in kips are shown on the bridge truss of Fig. 7.19. The truss is subjected to a uniform live load of 1.0 kip per ft and a concentrated live load of 15.0 kips. Impact is to be computed in accordance with Eq. (1.1). Prepare a bar-force table for the members of the left half of this truss, in which the following columns are included: dead, uniform live, concentrated live, total live, impact, live plus impact, total dead plus live plus impact. For live bar forces, use the approximate method of analysis. Give bar forces of both characters where they exist. Combine dead bar forces with live plus impact bar forces (a) by algebraic addition; (b) in accordance with the specifications of Art. 7.5 for members subject to stress reversal.

Figure 7.19   Problems 7.3 and 7.4

*Problem 7.4   Assuming that the diagonals of the truss of Fig. 7.19 can carry tension only, at what panels are counters necessary?

Problem 7.5   The loads shown acting on the truss of Fig. 7.20 are the dead panel loads in kips. The diagonals of this truss can carry tension only. The truss is acted on by the following live load: uniform, 0.700 kip per ft; concentrated, 20.0 kips. Impact is to be computed in accordance with Eq. (1.1).

Figure 7.20   Problem 7.5

Compute the maximum bar force due to dead plus live plus impact in (a) L_3U_4; (b) U_3U_4.

*Problem 7.6   Figure 7.21 shows a bascule span acted upon by its dead panel loads in kips.

(a) Compute the dead bar forces, including the tension in the link to the counterweight, with the span in the closed position as shown.

(b) Compute the maximum dead bar force that will occur as the span is raised through an angle of 90°, for all members except L_0U_1.

(c) Is the method of analysis used in part b applicable to the determination of the maximum dead bar force in L_0U_1?

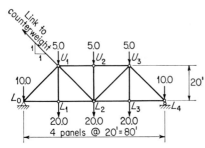

Figure 7.21   Problem 7.6

Problem 7.7   Figure 7.22 shows a horizontal-swing bridge truss acted upon by its dead panel loads in kips. Dashed-line members carry tension only.

(a) Compute the dead bar forces when the bridge is swung into its open position.

(b) When the bridge is closed, each end of the structure is raised 1 in. above the elevation it has when the bridge is open. If a force of 10 kips applied upward at L_0 when the bridge is open would raise L_0 by 1 in. and lower L_9 by $\frac{1}{4}$ in., compute the dead reaction at L_0 and L_9 with the bridge in the closed position.

(c) Compute the dead bar forces in the truss with the bridge in the closed position, based on the dead reactions corresponding to part b.

Figure 7.22   Problem 7.7

Problem 7.8   For the single-track railroad skew bridge for which the plan view is shown in Fig. 7.23, the weight of the track and ties is 500 lb per ft of track; the weight of each stringer, including details, is 125 lb per ft; the weight of each floor beam, including details, is 175 lb per ft.

(a) Compute those portions of the dead panel loads acting on girder AB that are applied by the floor beams to the girder at panel points C, D, E, and F.

(b) If the track is subjected to a uniform live load of 5,000 lb per ft, extending over the entire structure, what are the live panel loads acting on the girder AB that are applied by the floor beams to the girder at panel points C, D, E, and F?

Figure 7.23   Problem 7.8

8

Long-span Structures

8.1 Introduction. As the span of a structure becomes larger, the bending moments to which the structure is subjected increase rapidly if simple end-supported structures are used. Even if the load per foot to be carried by the structure did not increase with the span, the moment due to distributed loads would vary with the square of the span. Actually, the dead weight increases with the span, so that the bending moment increases at a rate greater than the square of the span. Since the chord stresses in trusses depend on bending moments to be carried by the truss, these considerations are of importance in the design of trusses as well as in the design of beams and girders.

For an economical structure, it is desirable, for the case of long spans, to adopt some means of construction that will reduce the bending moments to values less than would occur for simple end-supported structures. There are a number of methods by which this can be accomplished. In this chapter, some of these methods will be illustrated by considering the analysis of several types of long-span structures.

8.2 Cantilever Structures— General. In a cantilever structure, bending moments are reduced by shortening the span in which positive bending occurs, by supporting an end-supported beam, of a length shorter than the total span, on cantilevered arms that act in negative

Figure 8.1 Cantilever construction

bending. The structure of Fig. 8.1 shows cantilever construction and is statically determinate. The maximum moment in beam BC equals

$$\tfrac{1}{8}w\left(\frac{2L}{3}\right)^2 = \frac{wL^2}{18}$$

241

The maximum moment in the cantilever arm AB occurs at A and equals

$$-\frac{w}{2}\left(\frac{2L}{3}\right)\left(\frac{L}{6}\right) - w\left(\frac{L}{6}\right)\left(\frac{L}{12}\right) = \frac{-5wL^2}{72}$$

Had a simple span of length L been used, the maximum moment would have been $+wL^2/8$. Hence, in this particular case, the reduction in maximum moment resulting from cantilever construction is from $wL^2/8$ to $5wL^2/72$, or about 45 per cent. It should be pointed out that maximum moment is not the only criterion by which the relative merit of alternative types of construction should be judged, but it is an important factor in determining the desirability of using a particular type of structure for a given span. Moments and shears along the entire length of

Figure 8.2   Typical cantilever girder bridge

the structure, computed for all types of loads including live loads, must be considered in the actual design.

To obtain the fixity of supports at A and D for the cantilevers AB and CD of Fig. 8.1 would be difficult under many conditions. The same principle of cantilever construction is present, however, in the structure of Fig. 8.2, where this difficulty has been eliminated. The moments in this structure, between A and D, are identical with the moments in the structure of Fig. 8.1. The moments at A and D, however, are resisted by the flanking spans AE and DF. The moment at A, for example, is held in equilibrium by the reaction at E and the load applied between E and A.

8.3   Statical Condition of Cantilever Structures.   For a cantilever structure to be statically determinate with respect to its outer forces, there must be as many independent equations available for the determination of these outer forces as there are independent reactions for the structure. Except for a simple cantilever beam, there are always more than three independent reactions for a cantilever structure, but there are only three independent equations of statics that can be applied to the entire structure. To make a cantilever structure statically determinate, it is therefore necessary to introduce certain construction features that make it possible to apply the equations of statics to certain portions of the structure, thus obtaining additional independent equations of condition.   Some of these construction features are inherent to cantilever construction; others must be specially provided.

Such construction features are illustrated by the structure of Fig. 8.3. The hinge at a constitutes one such construction feature, since $\Sigma M_a = 0$ may be applied to those forces acting on that portion of the structure lying on *either* side of joint a.   The hinge at b is similar in its effect, since it permits one to apply $\Sigma M_b = 0$ to those forces acting on that portion of the structure lying on either side of joint b.

The hinge at c permits the application of $\Sigma M_c = 0$ to those forces acting on that portion of the structure lying on either side of joint c.

Figure 8.3   Cantilever truss bridge

Instead of utilizing the hinge at c in this manner, the following alternative interpretation is usually advantageous: Because there are hinges at both b and c, the hanger bc carries axial force only and hence has no component of force perpendicular to bc, that is, bc is a link.   One may therefore conclude that, if a section is taken through bc, the sum of the forces perpendicular to bc which act on either side of the section equals zero.   For the case under consideration, this means that the equation $\Sigma F_x = 0$ may be applied to those forces acting on that portion of the structure lying on one side of section A-A.

The omission of the diagonal in panel $defg$ constitutes another construction feature that permits an additional independent equation of statics with respect to external forces, since, as a result, no shear can be carried by this panel.   Hence the equation $\Sigma F_y = 0$ may be applied to the forces acting on one side of section B-B.

There are, therefore, the following seven independent equations available for determining the reactions of this structure:

(1) $\Sigma M = 0$ for all forces acting on the structure
(2) $\Sigma F_x = 0$ for all forces acting on the structure
(3) $\Sigma F_y = 0$ for all forces acting on the structure
(4) $\Sigma M_a = 0$ for all forces acting on one side of hinge a
(5) $\Sigma M_b = 0$ for all forces acting on one side of hinge b
(6) $\Sigma F_x = 0$ for all forces acting on one side of section A-A
(7) $\Sigma F_y = 0$ for all forces acting on one side of section B-B

There are also seven independent reactions, R_{hy}, R_{iy}, R_{ix}, R_{fy}, R_{fx}, R_{gy}, and R_{jy}. Therefore this structure is statically determinate with respect to its outer forces. That the structure is also statically determinate with respect to both outer and inner forces may be verified from the fact that the total number of bars (75) plus the total number of reactions (7) equals twice the number of joints $(2 \times 41) = 82$.

8.4 Stress Analysis for Cantilever Trusses. To determine the reactions for the structure of Fig. 8.3 due to the load acting as shown, one may proceed as follows: Assume all reactions to act in the directions shown in the figure.

Apply $\Sigma F_x = 0$ to that portion of structure to left of section A-A; this
shows that $R_{ix} = 0$

Apply $\Sigma F_x = 0$ to entire structure; this shows that $R_{fx} = 0$

Apply $\Sigma M_b = 0$ to that portion of structure to left of hinge b:

$$+R_{hy}(6)(30) + R_{iy}(2)(30) = 0 \qquad R_{iy} = -3R_{hy}$$

Apply $\Sigma M_a = 0$ to that portion of structure to left of hinge a:

$$-(100)(3)(30) + R_{hy}(12)(30) + (-3R_{hy})(8)(30) = 0 \qquad R_{hy} = -25$$
$$R_{iy} = -3(-25) = +75$$

Apply $\Sigma F_y = 0$ to that portion of structure to left of section B-B:

$$-25 + 75 - 100 + R_{fy} = 0 \qquad R_{fy} = +50$$

Apply $\Sigma F_y = 0$ to that portion of structure to right of section B-B:

$$+R_{gy} + R_{jy} = 0 \qquad R_{gy} = -R_{jy}$$

Finally, applying $\Sigma M_a = 0$ to that portion of structure to right of hinge a:

$$-50(3)(30) - (-R_{jy})(4)(30) - R_{jy}(9)(30) = 0$$
$$R_{jy} = -30 \qquad R_{gy} = +30$$

The available equations can often be applied in different sequences; but if the structure is stable, the same results will be obtained, regardless of the sequence followed.

Once the reactions are known, the bar forces can be computed by the usual methods of analysis for statically determinate trusses. Since the analysis can be carried out for a unit load at any panel point, the construction of influence lines for reactions or bar forces involves no special difficulties, although it is often advantageous first to construct influence lines for reactions or bar forces other than the one under consideration and use the data thus obtained in constructing the influence line actually desired.

The foregoing procedure is illustrated by constructing the influence line for bar a of the structure of Fig. 8.4a. The influence line for the force in

bar *FE* will first be constructed, with the force computed by taking
moments about *D* of the forces acting on that part of the structure between
D and section *M-M*. The influence line for the force in bar *a* is then
drawn, with the force computed by taking moments about *G* of the forces
acting on that part of the structure between sections *M-M* and *N-N*. The
forces entering into the resultant equations consist of the force in the
hanger *FE*, the applied unit load, and the force in bar *a* itself.

Figure 8.4   Typical bar-force influence lines

8.5   Continuous Structures.   The reduction in maximum moment
that results from the shortening of the span effective in producing positive
bending in cantilever construction may be obtained in a somewhat similar
manner by continuity in a structure, although continuous structures are
usually statically indeterminate.   The fixed end beam shown in Fig. 8.5*a*
will deflect under a uniformly distributed load as shown by the dotted line
ABCD.   At points *B* and *C*, the bending changes from one character to
another, so that the curvature of the deflected beam reverses.   At such
points (called *points of inflection*) the bending moment is zero, so that the
curve of moments for the beam *AD* is just as it would be if there were
hinges at these inflection points.   Because of construction difficulties in
developing the fixed end moments at *A* and *D* for long-span structures,
partial restraint against changes of slope at these points may be obtained
by the addition of flanking spans, as shown in Fig. 8.5*b*.   The location of

the points of inflection B' and C' will depend on the span ratio a.   The
continuous truss shown in Fig. 8.5c derives the same advantages from
continuity as does the continuous beam of Fig. 8.5b.   With five independent reactions, this continuous truss is statically indeterminate to the

Figure 8.5   Continuous structures

Figure 8.6   Wichert truss

second degree, and its analysis depends on methods that take into consideration the elastic properties of the structure.

It is possible, however, by omitting certain bars, to make a continuous
truss statically determinate.   This is accomplished in the Wichert[1] truss,
invented and patented by E. M. Wichert of Pittsburgh, Pa., by omitting

[1] See D. B. Steinman, "The Wichert Truss," D. Van Nostrand Company, Inc.,
New York, 1932.

the vertical members over intermediate points of support. Such a structure is shown in Fig. 8.6. This structure has 40 bars and 4 reactions, or a total of 44 unknowns; there are 22 joints, hence 44 equations of statics available for the determination of inner and outer forces; the structure therefore has the correct count for statical determination and is actually statically determinate unless certain slopes are given to bars a and b, in which case it is possible for the structure to become geometrically unstable, a condition that can be recognized by inconsistent results from the application of the equations of statics.

For the structure of Fig. 8.6, acted upon by the load shown, the application of $\Sigma F_x = 0$ to the entire structure shows that $R_{Bx} = 0$. To determine the vertical reactions, one may proceed as follows: Taking moments about D of the forces to the right of section $N\text{-}N$ and assuming all vertical reactions to act upward,

$$-R_{Cy}(5)(30) + X_b(50) = 0 \qquad X_b = +3R_{Cy}$$
$$Y_b = +\tfrac{2}{3}X_b = +2R_{Cy}$$

Taking moments about D of the forces to the left of section $M\text{-}M$,

$$+R_{Ay}(5)(30) - 100(3)(30) - X_a(50) = 0 \qquad X_a = +3R_{Ay} - 180$$
$$Y_a = +\tfrac{2}{3}X_a = +2R_{Ay} - 120$$

Applying $\Sigma F_y = 0$ at joint B,

$$+R_{By} + 2R_{Cy} + 2R_{Ay} - 120 = 0$$
whence $\qquad\qquad R_{By} = 120 - 2R_{Ay} - 2R_{Cy}$

Since the foregoing equation expresses the center reaction in terms of the two end reactions, these end reactions may now be determined by applying $\Sigma M = 0$ and $\Sigma F_y = 0$ to the entire structure. For $\Sigma M_A = 0$,

$$+100(2)(30) - (120 - 2R_{Ay} - 2R_{Cy})(5)(30) - R_{Cy}(10)(30) = 0$$

For $\Sigma F_y = 0$,

$$R_{Ay} - 100 + (120 - 2R_{Ay} - 2R_{Cy}) + R_{Cy} = 0$$

The solution of these two equations leads to $R_{Ay} = +40$ and $R_{Cy} = -20$, whence $R_{By} = 120 - 2(+40) - 2(-20) = +80$.

With the reactions known, the bar-force analysis presents no further difficulty. Since an analysis can be carried out in the foregoing manner for a unit load at any panel point, influence lines for reactions and bar forces can be constructed.

8.6 Arches—General. Another method of reducing maximum moments in long-span structures consists in adopting a structural layout in which applied vertical loads produce horizontal reactions that act in a manner such that the moments due to these horizontal reactions tend to reduce the moments that would otherwise exist. Figure 8.7 shows an arch, which is a structure that develops horizontal *thrust* reactions under the action of vertical loads. This particular arch is of the two-hinged type. The vertical reactions on this structure may be determined by statics by taking moments about an end hinge of all the forces acting on the arch; for the load P acting as shown, they have the values given on the figure. The relation between the horizontal reactions R_{Ax} and R_{Bx} can be determined by statics ($\Sigma F_x = 0$), but the actual values of these reactions can be obtained only on the basis of an elastic analysis, since

Figure 8.7   Two-hinged arch

Figure 8.8   Curved beam

Figure 8.9   Three-hinged arch

with four independent reactions this two-hinged arch is statically indeterminate to the first degree.

If the hinge at one end were replaced with a roller, as shown in Fig. 8.8, the structure would be, not an arch, but a statically determinate curved beam, and the bending moment at the point of application of the load would equal $P(1 - k)kL$. For the two-hinged arch of Fig. 8.7, however, this moment is reduced by the moment $R_{Ax}b$.

An arch may be made statically determinate by building in a third hinge at some internal point, such as at the crown, in addition to the end hinges. Such a structure is shown in Fig. 8.9 and is called a three-hinged arch. This structure has four independent reactions; three equations of statics can be applied to the structure as a whole, and one equation of condition can be obtained by taking moments about the hinge at C of the forces acting on *either* side of the hinge. Thus, taking moments about A

of all the forces acting on the structure leads to

$$R_{By} = +100(^{20}\!/_{100}) = +20$$

Similarly, taking moments about hinge B, $R_{Ay} = +100(^{80}\!/_{100}) = +80$. Now, taking moments about the hinge C of the forces acting on that portion of the structure to the right of the hinge,

$$+R_{Bx}(30) - 20(50) = 0 \qquad R_{Bx} = +33.3$$

Applying $\Sigma F_x = 0$ to the entire structure, $R_{Ax} = +33.3$.

The moment at the point of application of the load is given by

$$M_D = +80(20) - 33.3(25) = +767 \text{ kip-ft}$$

For a simple end-supported beam of the same span and loading, the moment at the load would equal $+80(20) = +1,600$ kip-ft. Hence the arch construction has reduced this moment by 52 per cent. The arch ribs must, however, carry compression that is not present in the end-supported beam. For example, the compression at the crown C in the arch of Fig. 8.9, where the rib is horizontal, equals the horizontal reaction and therefore has a value of -33.3 kips for the load considered. It is, however, usually more economical to carry loads by uniform axial stress than by bending stresses, although, if the axial stress is compression, one must provide stability against elastic buckling.

8.7 Analysis of Three-hinged Trussed Arch. The arch ribs AC and BC of the structure of Fig. 8.9 may be replaced by trusses, as shown

Figure 8.10 Three-hinged trussed arch

in Fig. 8.10. Since there are four reactions on this structure, it would be statically indeterminate were it not for the hinge at e, which is effective since the bar EF, shown dotted, is connected at its ends in such a manner that it can carry no axial force.

The reactions for this structure may be computed as follows: Taking moments about a of all the forces acting on the structure,

$$+100(30) + 200(2)(30) + 300(6)(30) - R_{iy}(8)(30) = 0$$
$$R_{iy} = +287.5 \text{ kips}$$

Taking $\Sigma F_y = 0$, for all forces acting on the structure,

$$+R_{ay} - 100 - 200 - 300 + 287.5 = 0 \qquad R_{ay} = +312.5 \text{ kips}$$

To obtain R_{ix}, apply $\Sigma M = 0$ about the hinge at e, considering the forces acting on the part of the structure to the right of the hinge.

$$+300(2)(30) + R_{ix}(48) - 287.5(4)(30) = 0 \qquad R_{ix} = +344 \text{ kips}$$

Since $\Sigma F_x = 0$ for the entire structure, R_{ax} also equals $+344$ kips. R_{ax} might have been computed by taking moments about the hinge at e of the forces to the left of the hinge, leading to

$$+312.5(4)(30) - R_{ax}(48) - 100(3)(30) - 200(2)(30) = 0$$
$$R_{ax} = +344 \text{ kips}$$

In computing bar forces, the effect of the horizontal reactions must not be overlooked. To compute the force in FG, for example, taking moments about f of the forces to the right of section M-M,

$$+300(30) + 344(45) - 287.5(90) - F_{FG}(15) = 0 \qquad F_{FG} = -93 \text{ kips}$$

If there is no load between the center hinge and one end of the truss, the resultant reaction at that end of the truss must have a direction such that it passes through the center hinge, because the moment about the hinge of the forces acting on that side of the hinge must equal zero. Thus, if we consider the action of a unit vertical load at B on the structure of Fig. 8.10, $R_{iy} = +\frac{1}{8}$; since the resultant reaction at i lies along the dotted line drawn through i and e, we conclude immediately that

$$R_{ix} = +\frac{1}{8}(1\frac{0}{4}) = +\frac{5}{16}$$

This fact is often convenient in analysis, particularly in constructing influence lines.

If the three-hinged arch of Fig. 8.10 were subjected to equal vertical panel loads at each top-chord panel point (or at each bottom-chord panel point), the following stress condition would result: (1) The force in each top chord would be zero. (2) The force in each diagonal would be zero. (3) The force in each vertical would equal the top-chord panel load. (4) The horizontal component of force in each bottom chord would be the same and equal to the horizontal reactions. These facts may be verified by the student and would be useful, for example, in computing dead bar forces for a uniformly distributed dead load. Such conditions exist because the bottom-chord panel points of this structure lie on a parabola. If a funicular polygon were drawn for the loads under consideration, so that it passed through the three hinges, the polygon would coincide with the location of the bottom chords.

8.8   Influence Lines for Three-hinged Trussed Arch.   Influence lines for a three-hinged trussed arch may be constructed by considering successive positions of the unit load, but a method similar to the following will often prove advantageous: We shall construct the influence line for bar FG of the structure of Fig. 8.10.   We shall first construct the influence line for that portion of the force in bar FG due to the unit load and the vertical reactions only.   Since these reactions have the same values they would have for an end-supported beam, the influence line for this portion of the force is a triangle with its maximum value occurring when the load is directly over the center of moments f, where the ordinate equals $-\tfrac{5}{8}(\tfrac{90}{15}) = -3.75$, as shown in Fig. 8.11a.   We shall next construct an influence line for $R_{ax} = R_{ix}$.   As the unit load travels from A to E, R_{iy}, hence R_{ix} (which equals $\tfrac{5}{2}R_{iy}$) increases linearly.   With the load at E, R_{ix} equals $\tfrac{5}{2}(+\tfrac{1}{2}) = +1.25$.   Hence the influence line for R_{ix} is a straight line from zero at A to $+1.25$ at E.   By similar reasoning, considering the reactions at a, the influence line for $R_{ax} = R_{ix}$ is a straight line from $+1.25$ at E to zero at I.   The

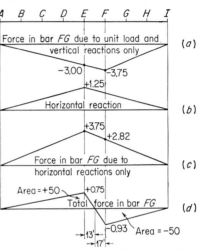

Figure 8.11   Influence lines for arch in Fig. 8.10

influence line for the magnitude of this horizontal reaction is shown in Fig. 8.11b.   The force in bar FG due to the horizontal reactions equals

$$+R_{ix}(\tfrac{45}{15}) = +3R_{ix}$$

Hence, the influence line for this portion of the force in bar FG is a triangle with its apex at E, where the ordinate equals $+3(+1.25) = +3.75$, as shown in Fig. 8.11c.   The influence line for the total force in bar FG is now obtained by superimposing the influence lines of Figs. 8.11a and c, leading to the influence line of Fig. 8.11d.

It will be noted that the net area under this influence line is zero, as should be the case, since a uniform load extending over the entire structure would cause no force in the top chords.

8.9   Three-hinged Trussed Arches with Supports at Different Elevations.   The points of support of a three-hinged trussed arch may be at different elevations, as shown in Fig. 8.12.   The vertical reactions will then differ from the values they would have for an end-supported truss, since, when moments are taken about one point of support, the horizontal reaction at the far end enters into the equation. The reactions can, however, be obtained by statics. Referring to Fig. 8.12a and taking moments about a of all the forces acting on the structure,

$$+100(60) - R_{ix}(20) - R_{iy}(240) = 0$$

whence

$$R_{ix} = +300 - 12R_{iy}$$

Now, taking moments about the hinge at e of the forces acting to the right of the hinge,

$$+R_{ix}(38) - R_{iy}(120) = 0$$
$$R_{iy} = +{}^{38}\!\!/_{120}R_{ix} = +{}^{38}\!\!/_{120}(+300 - 12R_{iy})$$

whence

$$R_{iy} = +19.8 \text{ kips} \quad \text{and} \quad R_{ix} = +300 - 12(19.8) = +62.5 \text{ kips}$$

The foregoing solution required the solution of two simultaneous equations, which might have been avoided by taking the reactions as shown in

Figure 8.12 Supports at different elevations

Fig. 8.12b, where R'_{ix} is taken as acting along a line passing through the two points of support and R'_{iy}, while a vertical reaction, differs from R_{iy}, since R'_{ix} has a vertical component. Taking moments about a,

$$+100(60) - R'_{iy}(240) = 0 \qquad R'_{iy} = +25.0$$

Taking moments about e and considering R'_{ix} to act at point o,

$$+ \frac{12.00}{12.04} R'_{ix}(48) - 25.0(120) = 0$$

whence $R'_{ix} = +62.7$ kips.   Hence the actual horizontal reaction at i is given by

$$R_{ix} = +62.7 \left(\frac{12.00}{12.04} \right) = +62.5 \text{ kips}$$

while the actual vertical reaction at i is given by

$$R_{iy} = +25.0 - \frac{1}{12.04} (62.7) = +19.8 \text{ kips}$$

For the particular case under consideration, since there are no loads applied to the right of the hinge at e, we might have concluded immediately that the resultant reaction at i passed through e, whence

$$R_{ix} = {}^{120}\!\!/_{38} R_{iy} = +3.16 R_{iy}$$

Then, taking moments about a,

$$+100(60) - 3.16 R_{iy}(20) - R_{iy}(240) = 0$$

whence

$$R_{iy} = +19.8 \text{ kips} \quad \text{and} \quad R_{ix} = +3.16(+19.8) = +62.5 \text{ kips}$$

8.10   Suspension Bridges.   An important method of reducing bending moments in long-span structures consists in providing partial

Figure 8.13   Suspension bridge

support at points along the span by means of a system of cables, as in a suspension bridge.   Referring to Fig. 8.13, a suspension bridge is usually erected in a manner such that all the dead load is carried by the cable. When live load is applied to such a structure, tension in the hangers transfers a large portion of the live load to the cable.   Hence, the stiffening truss AB is subjected to no dead moments, and the live moments it must carry are substantially reduced.   For long-span structures, this is of particular importance, since so much of the load is carried by the cable in tension, which is a highly efficient manner of carrying loads.

A suspension bridge such as that of Fig. 8.13 is statically indeterminate. By the introduction of certain features of construction, it may, however, be made statically determinate.   The analysis of statically determinate suspension bridges is treated in Art. 10.10.

8.11 Problems for Solution

*Problem 8.1   (a) Construct an influence line for the vertical reaction at A of the structure of Fig. 8.2, taking $a = L/2$.

(b) How does the maximum reaction at A due to a uniform live load of 1,000 lb per ft compare with the maximum pier load that would result at A if EA, AD, and DF were simple end-supported spans?

*Problem 8.2   Referring to the cantilever bridge of Fig. 8.3, construct an influence line for (a) the force in the hanger bc; (b) the vertical reaction at i; (c) the bar force in the top chord de. (d) Compute the maximum force in bar de due to the following loading: dead load, 2,000 lb per ft; uniform live load, 1,000 lb per ft; concentrated live load, 10,000 lb.

Problem 8.3   Determine the forces in all the bars of the Wichert truss of Fig. 8.6 due to a load of 100 kips acting at D.

*Problem 8.4   Construct an influence line for the reaction at A of the Wichert truss of Fig. 8.6.

Problem 8.5   A three-span Wichert truss is the same on each side of an axis of symmetry as that portion of Fig. 8.6 to the left of U_8L_8, except for the fact that the pier symmetrical to B has a roller support. Compute all the reactions on this structure due to a uniform load of w lb per ft extending over the entire structure, applied to the top-chord panel points.

Problem 8.6   Compute the shear and axial force at point D of the structure of Fig. 8.9 due to the load shown, assuming that the slope of the arch rib at D is 30° from the horizontal.

Problem 8.7   Compute the bar forces in all the members of the three-hinged arch of Fig. 8.10 due to a uniform load of 1,000 lb per ft applied along the entire length of the structure. Panel loads are to be applied at the top-chord panel points.

*Problem 8.8   Construct an influence line for the force in bar bc of the structure of Fig. 8.10.

Problem 8.9   What is the maximum force in bar Bc of the structure of Fig. 8.10 due to the following loading: dead load, 1,000 lb per ft; uniform live load, 500 lb per ft; concentrated live load, 5,000 lb?

*Problem 8.10   Solve Prob. 8.8, using Fig. 8.12a.

*Problem 8.11   Solve Prob. 8.9, using Fig. 8.12a.

Problem 8.12   Construct the reaction influence lines for each of the structures shown in Fig. 8.14.

Figure 8.14   Problem 8.12

9

Three-dimensional Frameworks

9.1 Introduction. Although most engineering structures are three-dimensional, it is often permissible to break a three-dimensional structure down into component planar structures and to analyze each planar structure for loads lying in its plane. Consider, for example, a typical through-parallel-chord truss highway bridge. Such a structure is three-dimensional, but it can be broken down into six component structures, each of which is planar, the two main vertical trusses, the top-chord lateral system, the bottom-chord lateral system, and the two end portals. Often a given member must be considered as part of more than one component planar structure: a bottom chord of a vertical truss, for example, is also likely to be a chord of the bottom-chord lateral system. This introduces no difficulty, since for such members the stresses can be computed for each component planar structure in which it participates and these two contributions superimposed to give the total stress in the member.

In some three-dimensional structures, however, the stresses are interrelated between members not lying in a plane, in a manner such that the analysis cannot be carried out on the basis of component planar structures. For such structures, a special consideration of the analysis of three-dimensional structures is necessary.

Structures that may fall into this latter classification include towers, guyed masts, derricks, framing for domes, and framing for aircraft, to mention only a few. Such structures may be either statically determinate or statically indeterminate. In this chapter, consideration will be given to statically determinate three-dimensional structures, but the methods for analyzing statically indeterminate structures, given elsewhere in this book, are applicable in principle to statically indeterminate three-dimensional structures.

In this treatment of three-dimensional structures, analysis will be made with reference to three coordinate axes. OX and OY will be used as in the case of planar structures, i.e., with OX horizontal and OY vertical; the third axis OZ is horizontal and perpendicular to the plane XOY. It should be pointed out that the basic approach to the analysis of three-dimensional structures is the same as for planar structures. Any equation of statics may be applied to the structure as a whole or to any portion of the structure. There are, however, more equations of statics available, since forces may be summed up along a new coordinate axis and moments may be taken about two new coordinate axes.

9.2 Statical Condition. It is usually assumed that the members of a three-dimensional framework are pin-connected in a manner such that the members carry axial force only.[1] Hence there is only one independent component of bar force for each member of the framework. Although each member can have three components of bar force, one parallel to each of the three coordinate axes, the relations between these three components can be computed from the projections of the member. At a point of support of a space framework, it is possible to have three independent components of force reactions, although the structure may be designed at a point of support so that one or more of these reaction components equal zero. In Fig. 9.1a, the hinge support shown, which is actually a universal joint, can develop three independent reactions, R_{ox}, R_{oy}, and R_{oz}. Suppose that the hinge is replaced with a roller, as shown in Fig. 9.1b. Since this resists horizontal movement in the Z direction only, the reactions R_{oy} and R_{oz} can be developed, but R_{ox} equals zero. If the roller is replaced by a spherical ball, there can be no horizontal reaction whatever and only the vertical reaction R_{oy} can be developed. This condition is shown in Fig. 9.1c. Sometimes it may be convenient to represent these three typical supports by an equivalent number of *links*. For example, the *universal-joint support* shown in Fig. 9.1a is equivalent to three concurrent but nonplanar links such as shown isometrically in Fig. 9.1d; the *roller support* in Fig. 9.1b, to the two concurrent links in the plane YOZ as shown in Fig. 9.1e; and the *ball support* in Fig. 9.1c, to the one link in the OY direction as shown in Fig. 9.1f.

To represent these three types of support in plan view, heavy dotted lines will be drawn along the lines of action where horizontal reactions can exist. This is illustrated in Fig. 9.2, where (a) represents a hinge-type support in which horizontal reactions can be developed in both the X and Z direction; (b) represents a roller-type support, with the roller so placed that a horizontal reaction can be developed in the Z direction only; (c) represents a roller-type support, with the roller so placed that a hori-

[1] Such a ball joint will be represented by small open circles in the line-diagram representation of space frameworks.

zontal reaction can be developed in the X direction only; and (d) represents a ball-type support, in which there can be no horizontal reaction.

Thus the total number of independent unknown stress elements present in the analysis of a three-dimensional framework equals the number of bars plus the number of independent reaction components (or links),

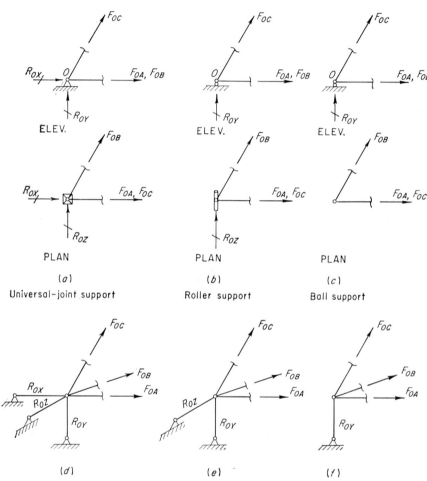

Figure 9.1   Typical supports of space frameworks

there being one, two, or three of the latter at each point of support, depending on the type of construction used at the reaction point.

For a three-dimensional framework, six independent equations of statics may be written regarding the equilibrium of the external loads and reactions acting on the entire structure.   If $OX, OY,$ and OZ represent the three coordinate axes, these equations are $\Sigma F_x = 0$,

$\Sigma F_y = 0$, $\Sigma F_z = 0$, $\Sigma M_x = 0$, $\Sigma M_y = 0$, and $\Sigma M_z = 0$. ΣM_x denotes the sum of the moments about the OX axis of all the forces acting on the structure, etc.

It may therefore be concluded that a necessary (although not sufficient) condition for statical determination of a three-dimensional framework with respect to its outer forces is that the total number of independent reaction components shall equal six.

PLAN　　　PLAN　　　PLAN　　　PLAN
(a)　　　(b)　　　(c)　　　(d)

Figure 9.2　Indication of horizontal reaction components

If we now consider **both the internal and external forces, three independent equations of statics** can be written **for each joint,** viz., $\Sigma F_x = 0$, $\Sigma F_y = 0$, and $\Sigma F_z = 0$. Equations of statics applied to the structure as a whole will not furnish further independent equations. **It may therefore be concluded that a necessary (although not sufficient) condition for statical determination of a three-dimensional framework with respect to both inner and outer forces is that the total number of bars plus the total number of independent reaction components shall equal three times the number of joints.**

The application of these principles may be illustrated by considering Fig. 9.3a. Considering first only the external forces, if the horizontal reactions are arranged as shown in the plan view, there

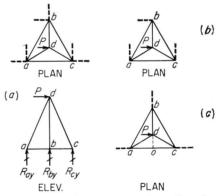

Figure 9.3　Arrangement of reactions for stability

is a total of 9 independent reaction components, so that the structure is statically indeterminate to the $9 - 6 =$ third degree. If rollers are substituted for hinges, so that the horizontal reactions act as shown in Fig. 9.3b, the number of independent reactions is six and the structure is statically determinate. Suppose, however, that the rollers are placed so that the horizontal reactions have the directions indicated in Fig. 9.3c. Then, while the numerical count indicates that this structure is statically determinate with respect to its outer forces, it is actually unstable. The Z reaction at b, for example, will apparently have two values, depending on whether it is determined by applying $\Sigma F_z = 0$ to the entire structure (in which case it equals zero) or whether it is computed by applying the equation $\Sigma M_y = 0$ about a vertical axis through a (in which case it must have a value). This shows that the numerical count, while a necessary condition for statical determination, is not a sufficient criterion. **The reactions must be placed so that they can resist translation along and rotation about each of the three coordinate axes, if a three-dimensional structure is to be stable.** The reactions shown in Fig. 9.3c all pass through point o; they cannot resist rotation about a vertical axis passing through that point.

Considering now both internal and external forces, in Fig. 9.3a, there are present 15 independent unknowns: 6 bar forces and 9 reaction components. There are 4 joints and hence $4 \times 3 = 12$ independent equations of statics. Therefore the structure is statically indeterminate to the $15 - 12 =$ third degree. With the horizontal reactions arranged as shown in Fig. 9.3b, there are only 12 independent unknowns: 6 bar forces and 6 reactions. There are still 12 independent equations of statics. Hence the structure is statically determinate with respect to both inner and outer forces.

Figure 9.4 Determination of reactions

9.3 Determination of Reactions. If a three-dimensional framework is statically determinate with respect to its outer forces and if it is supported at only three points, its reactions can be readily determined by applying the equations of statics to the structure as a whole. When there are more than three points of support, it is usually necessary to determine some or all of the bar forces before the reactions can be evaluated. In this article, consideration will be given to structures where the reactions can be determined directly.

In Fig. 9.4, the vertical reactions will first be determined. If moments are taken about a horizontal axis passing through any two points of support, the vertical reaction at the third point of support will be the only unknown occurring in the resulting equation. Upon applying $\Sigma M_x = 0$ about ac as an axis, R_{by} is the only external force that could have a moment; hence, $R_{by} = 0$. Upon applying $\Sigma M_z = 0$ about the line of

action of R_{az},

$$+10{,}000(20) - R_{cy}(20) = 0$$

from which $R_{cy} = +10{,}000$ lb.   Applying $\Sigma F_y = 0$ to the entire structure,

$$R_{ay} + 10{,}000 = 0$$

from which $R_{ay} = -10{,}000$ lb.

To determine the horizontal reactions, if $\Sigma M_y = 0$ is applied about a vertical axis passing through the intersection of the lines of action of any two horizontal reactions, the third horizontal reaction will be the only unknown occurring in the resulting equation.   Taking moments, for example, about a vertical axis through point o and assuming R_{cz} to act toward the rear of the structure,

$$-10{,}000(5) - R_{cz}(20) = 0 \qquad R_{cz} = -2{,}500 \text{ lb}$$

Now, applying $\Sigma F_z = 0$ to the entire structure and assuming R_{az} to act toward the rear of the structure,

$$R_{az} - 2{,}500 = 0 \qquad R_{az} = +2{,}500 \text{ lb}$$

Finally, applying $\Sigma F_x = 0$ to the entire structure and assuming R_{bx} to act to the left,

$$+10{,}000 - R_{bx} = 0 \qquad R_{bx} = +10{,}000 \text{ lb}$$

As was the case with planar structures, the particular equations of statics used and the order in which they are applied may be varied in accordance with the ingenuity of the analyst.

9.4 Determination of Bar Forces.   A bar of a three-dimensional framework may have projections on each of three coordinate axes.   This is illustrated in Fig. 9.5, where the bar ab has the projections ax, ay, and az in the directions of the OX, OY, and OZ axes, respectively.   In terms of these projected lengths, the length of the bar ab is given by

Figure 9.5 Projections of bar

$$ab = [(ax)^2 + (ay)^2 + (az)^2]^{1/2}$$

Since the force F_{ab} is axial, the components of F_{ab} parallel to the coordinate axes are

$$X_{ab} = F_{ab}\frac{ax}{ab} \qquad Y_{ab} = F_{ab}\frac{ay}{ab} \qquad Z_{ab} = F_{ab}\frac{az}{ab}$$

By combining these relations, it is easy to express one component of force in terms of either of the other force components.   For example, $X_{ab} = Y_{ab}(ax/ay)$, etc.

At any joint where the converging bars do not lie in a plane, three equations of statics are available for bar-force determination. Hence, if not more than three bars with unknown forces meet at such a joint, these bar forces may be determined. This general method of procedure, which is the method of joints expanded to three dimensions, may be illustrated by its application to joint d of the structure of Fig. 9.4.[1] The following table of dimensions will first be prepared:

Table 9.1

Member	Length	Projections		
		X	Y	Z
ad	22.9	10	20	5
bd	20.6	0	20	5
cd	22.9	10	20	5
ab	14.14	10	0	10
bc	14.14	10	0	10
ac	20.0	20	0	0

At joint d, assuming all bars to be in tension, the following equations may be written:

$$\Sigma F_x = 0 \qquad +10{,}000 - X_{ad} + X_{cd} = 0$$
$$\Sigma F_y = 0 \qquad -Y_{ad} - Y_{bd} - Y_{cd} = 0$$
$$\Sigma F_z = 0 \qquad +Z_{ad} - Z_{bd} + Z_{cd} = 0$$

The nine components of bar force involved in these three equations may be expressed in terms of the three independent bar forces F_{ad}, F_{bd}, and F_{cd} as follows:

$$+10{,}000 - \frac{10}{22.9} F_{ad} + \frac{10}{22.9} F_{cd} = 0$$

$$-\frac{20}{22.9} F_{ad} - \frac{20}{20.6} F_{bd} - \frac{20}{22.9} F_{cd} = 0$$

$$+\frac{5}{22.9} F_{ad} - \frac{5}{20.6} F_{bd} + \frac{5}{22.9} F_{cd} = 0$$

The simultaneous solution of these three equations leads to

$$F_{ad} = +11{,}450 \text{ lb} \qquad F_{bd} = 0 \qquad F_{cd} = -11{,}450 \text{ lb}$$

In this particular structure, the vertical reactions can first be determined, as is shown in Art. 9.3, and the forces in bars ad, bd, and cd can be computed more easily by taking advantage of that fact. At joint a,

---

[1] The student should note that this particular application is given solely for the purpose of illustrating a procedure of general importance. The solution of this joint could be substantially simplified by the application of Theorem I, Art. 9.6.

for example, the vertical reaction acts downward and equals 10,000 lb. Applying $\Sigma F_y = 0$ at joint a,

$$-10,000 + Y_{ad} = 0 \qquad Y_{ad} = +10,000$$

$$F_{ad} = +10,000 \left(\frac{22.9}{20.0}\right) = +11,450^*$$

F_{bd} and F_{cd} can be similarly obtained from $\Sigma F_y = 0$ at joints b and c, respectively.   However, it is important for the general approach based on writing three simultaneous equations at joint d to be understood, since in more complicated three-dimensional structures it may be the only procedure that can be used.

The analysis of the bars connecting the points of support of Fig. 9.4 will now be carried out, advantage being taken of the fact that the hori-

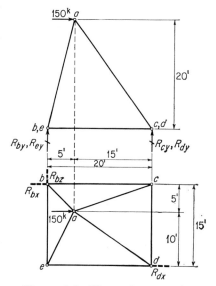

Figure 9.6 Bar-force calculation by method of joints

Figure 9.7 Illustrative example

zontal reactions are determined in Art. 9.3.   The values of these reactions are shown in Fig. 9.6.   As an illustration, joint a will be considered and the equation $\Sigma F_z = 0$ written.   Noting that $Z_{ad} = +11,450(5/22.9)$,

$$+2,500 + 11,450 \left(\frac{5}{22.9}\right) + F_{ab}\left(\frac{10}{14.14}\right) = 0 \qquad F_{ab} = -7,070 \text{ lb}$$

The force in bar ac can now be found by a similar procedure, by applying $\Sigma F_x = 0$ to joint a. F_{bc} can be obtained by applying $\Sigma F_z = 0$ at joint c.

9.5   Case Where Reactions Cannot Be Computed without Considering Bar Forces.   The structure of Fig. 9.7 is statically determinate with respect to its inner and outer forces combined.   Since there are only three horizontal reactions, these may be determined by a

* Note that this equation may be written directly as

$$-10,000 + \frac{20.0}{22.9} F_{ad} = 0 \qquad F_{ad} = +11,450$$

consideration of the external forces only but the vertical reactions cannot be computed without taking the bar forces into consideration. If the forces in ab, ac, ad, and ae can be computed, then the vertical reactions may be obtained from the vertical components of these bar forces.

At joint a, 4 unknown bar forces are present, so that, with only 3 equations of statics available, a direct solution for these bar forces cannot be made. A stress analysis of this structure, on the basis of statics only, should be possible, however, since with 5 joints there are 15 independent equations of statics, and there are only 15 independent unknown forces— 8 bars, 4 vertical reactions, and 3 horizontal reactions.

Table 9.2

Bar	Projection			Length
	X	Y	Z	
ab	5	20	5	21.2
ac	15	20	5	25.5
ad	15	20	10	26.9
ae	5	20	10	22.9
bc	20	0	0	20.0
cd	0	0	15	15.0
de ⌐	20	0	0	20.0
eb	0	0	15	15.0

For this structure, however, the equations of statics are simultaneous in character. A convenient approach under this condition is to adopt, as a temporary unknown, one of the bar forces. Other bar forces and reactions can then be expressed in terms of this temporary unknown, and eventually one of the equations of statics will permit its evaluation. To illustrate this procedure, take F_{cd} as the temporary unknown. At joint c, apply $\Sigma F_z = 0$.

$$F_{cd} + \frac{5}{25.5} F_{ac} = 0 \qquad F_{ac} = -5.10 F_{cd}$$

At joint d, apply $\Sigma F_z = 0$.

$$F_{cd} + \frac{10}{26.9} F_{ad} = 0 \qquad F_{ad} = -2.69 F_{cd}$$

Assume that the vertical reactions at c and d act up. Then at joint c, applying $\Sigma F_y = 0$,

$$R_{cy} + \frac{20}{25.5} F_{ac} = 0$$

$$R_{cy} = -0.784 F_{ac} = -0.784(-5.10 F_{cd}) = +4.00 F_{cd}$$

At joint d, applying $\Sigma F_y = 0$,

$$R_{dy} + \frac{20}{26.9} F_{ad} = 0$$

$$R_{dy} = -0.744 F_{ad} = -0.744(-2.69 F_{cd}) = +2.00 F_{cd}$$

Now, taking moments about be of all the forces acting on the structure

$$+150(20) - R_{cy}(20) - R_{dy}(20) = 0$$

whence

$$+150(20) - 4.00 F_{cd}(20) - 2.00 F_{cd}(20) = 0_d \qquad F_{cd} = +25 \text{ kips}$$

Since R_{cy}, R_{dy}, F_{ac}, and F_{ad} have already been expressed in terms of F_{cd}, they may now be evaluated. With these forces known, the remainder of the structure can be analyzed without difficulty.

9.6 Special Theorems. While three-dimensional frameworks can be analyzed by the methods that have been presented, the following theorems are of importance because they often result in an appreciable saving in computations:

I. If all the bars meeting at a joint, with the exception of one bar n, lie in a plane, the component normal to that plane of the force in bar n is equal to the component normal to that plane of any external load or loads applied at that joint. That this theorem is correct may be seen from a consideration of the static equilibrium of the joint, summing up all the forces normal to the plane that contains all bars except n. In the structure of Fig. 9.4, for example, suppose that this theorem is applied to joint d. Bars ad and dc lie in the plane adc; the component of bar force in bar bd, normal to plane adc, must equal the component of the applied load normal to the same plane. For this particular case, the applied load also lies in the plane adc and hence has no component normal to that plane. We can conclude, then, that the bar force in bar bd is zero. Recognition of this fact would simplify the analysis of joint d carried out in Art. 9.4 by means of three simultaneous equations, since only two equations would be necessary.

On the basis of Theorem I, two corollary theorems may be stated:

II. If all the bars meeting at a joint, with the exception of one bar n, lie in a plane and if no external load is applied at that joint, the force in bar n is zero.

III. If all but two bars at a joint have no bar force and these two are not collinear, and if no external load acts at that joint, the bar force in each of these two bars is zero.

9.7 Application of Special Theorems—Schwedler Dome. The importance of these three theorems in the analysis of three-dimensional frameworks may be illustrated by considering the Schwedler dome shown in Fig. 9.8, acted upon by a vertical load P applied at joint A. The bars shown by dotted lines in the plan view have no bar force, as may be concluded from the foregoing theorems, applied as follows:

At joint F, bars EF, KF, and LF all lie in a plane, but AF does not. Since no load is applied at joint F, the force in bar AF is zero, in accordance with Theorem II. A similar consideration of joints E, D, C, and B leads to the conclusion that bars EF, DE, CD, and BC, respectively, all have zero bar force.

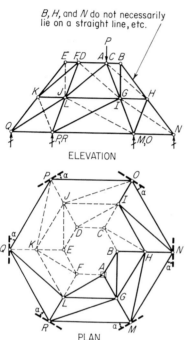

Considering joint F again, since the bar forces in FA and FE are zero, bars KF and LF comprise two bars meeting at a joint where no load is applied. Hence the bar forces in KF and LF are zero, on the basis of Theorem III. A similar consideration of joints E, D, and C leads to the conclusion that bars KE and JE, JD and ID, and IC and HC, respectively, all have zero force.

Now, considering joint K, since KE and KF have zero force, bar KL is a single bar lying outside the plane of bars JK, PK, and QK. Hence bar KL has zero force. In a similar manner, a consideration of joints J and I shows that bars JK and IJ have zero force.

Considering joint K again, since bars JK, EK, FK, and LK have zero force, bars QK and PK comprise two bars meeting at a joint where no external load is applied. The forces in these two bars are therefore zero. A similar consideration of joint J shows that bars PJ and OJ also have zero force.

Hence, when this framed dome is acted upon by a vertical load at A, only the bars shown by solid lines in the plan view of Fig. 9.8 carry force. To complete the analysis of this structure, the method of joints may now be applied successively to joints A, B, L, G, H, and I, and the bar forces in all the bars except those of the base ring thus determined. The vertical reactions can then be determined by applying $\Sigma F_y = 0$ at each point of support.

To determine the horizontal reactions and the bar forces in the base-ring bars, all of which lie in a plane, it is necessary to take the force in one of the base-ring

The figure caption reads:

Figure 9.8   Schwedler dome

bars as a temporary unknown. Suppose F_{RM} is taken as the temporary unknown.
At joint R, the application of $\Sigma F_x = 0$ and $\Sigma F_z = 0$ permits one to express F_{QR}
and the horizontal reaction at R in terms of F_{RM}. (Note that joint R is also acted
upon by the X and Z components of bar force in bars LR and GR.) Proceeding
clockwise around the base ring and successively writing similar equations at
joints Q, P, O, and N enable one to express the bar forces in all the base-ring bars,
and all the horizontal reactions except that at M, in terms of F_{RM}. If the equations $\Sigma F_x = 0$ and $\Sigma F_z = 0$ are now applied at
joint M, the values of F_{RM} and the horizontal
reaction at M may be obtained. Since all the
other bar forces and horizontal reactions have
been previously expressed in terms of F_{RM}, their
values may now be determined.

It is possible for a Schwedler dome to be
geometrically unstable, even though the statical
count holds, if the angles between the horizontal
reactions and the base-ring bars have certain
values.[1]

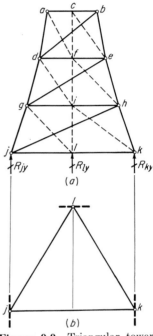

9.8 Towers. Unless the legs of a
framed tower have a constant batter
throughout their length, the structure
should be analyzed on the basis of three-
dimensional considerations. Figure 9.9a
shows the side elevation of a tower of
triangular cross section, in which the batter
of the legs is not constant. Figure 9.9b
shows the arrangement of horizontal reactions. This structure is statically determinate, as may be verified, and it may be
analyzed panel by panel, beginning with the

Figure 9.9 Triangular tower

top panel and working down. Whenever, as in this case, adjacent legs of
the top panel lie in a plane, the bar force in any of the top ring bars may
be computed most easily by utilizing the three theorems of Art. 9.6. For
example, F_{ab} may be computed by noting that its component normal to
the face $acfd$ must balance the component of the external load at joint a,
which is also normal to this plane. Once the top ring bar forces are
known, the forces in the legs and diagonals of the top panel may be computed. The forces in these bars together with any external loads at
joints d, e, and f comprise the loading on the second panel which may now
be analyzed similarly, etc.

If, however, adjacent legs of a panel do not lie in a plane, a more general
approach must be used to obtain the ring bar forces. Starting as before

[1] C. M. Spofford, "Theory of Structures," 4th ed., chap. 16, Space Frameworks,
McGraw-Hill Book Company, Inc., New York, 1939.

with the top panel, the bar force in any top ring bar may be taken as a temporary unknown. If F_{ab} is chosen for this purpose, application of the method of joints at joint b permits one to express F_{bc} in terms of F_{ab}. Similar treatment at c gives F_{ca} in terms of F_{ab}. Finally, F_{ab} may be evaluated by applying the method of joints at joint a.

It is customary to have secondary bracing members in each horizontal plane where the batter of the tower legs changes and often at panel points where no change in batter occurs. In a tower with a rectangular cross section, for example, this bracing may consist of horizontal diagonals connecting diagonally opposite panel points. The presence of such members may make a tower statically indeterminate. It is common practice, however, to assume for the purpose of analyzing the main members of the tower that the bar forces in these secondary bracing members are zero, thus permitting such analyses to be carried out by the principles of statics.

9.9 Tower with Straight Legs. If the batter of the tower legs is constant over the entire height, the tower may be analyzed on the basis of component planar trusses. Such a structure is shown

Figure 9.10   Rectangular tower with straight legs

in Fig. 9.10. A load P, applied at any joint, may be resolved into three components: C_1, parallel to the tower leg; C_2, horizontal and lying in the plane of one adjacent face of the tower; and C_3, horizontal and lying in the plane of the other adjacent face of the tower.

It is easy to show by the theorems of Art. 9.6 that C_1 causes bar forces in the bars of leg GC only, C_2 causes forces in the bars of tower side $CDGH$ only, and C_3 causes forces in the bars of tower side $ACEG$ only.

Thus the bar forces due to each of the components C_1, C_2, and C_3 can be obtained by carrying out a separate planar analysis, and the total force in any bar due to load P can be obtained by superposition of the effects of

its three components.   Since each panel load can be handled in the foregoing manner, this constitutes a general procedure for analysis.

If all the faces of such a tower are identical, influence data can be prepared, giving the bar forces in each bar of one of the faces due to (1) a unit
horizontal load, applied successively at each joint of that face; and (2) a
unit load parallel to the tower leg, applied successively at each joint of
that face.   Such influence data, prepared for one face of the tower, will be
applicable to all faces of the tower.
By resolving panel loads into components as previously outlined and by
using these influence data, stresses in
any member, due to any condition of
external loading, may be obtained by
superposition.

9.10   General Theory for Three-dimensional Frameworks.

Many
space frameworks used in conventional
structures may be analyzed by the
application of the methods and procedures discussed above.   In order to
handle with facility some of the problems regarding the more unconven-
tional frameworks, however, it is
necessary to study the statical stability and statical determinancy of space
frameworks in a more rigorous manner,[1] similar to that used in Chap. 4

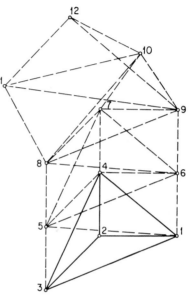

Figure 9.11   Simple space framework

for trusses (or planar frameworks).   A brief outline of such a treatment
follows.

Arrangement of Members of Simple Space Framework.   A group of
points which do not lie in a plane could be connected together by a rigid
and noncollapsible space framework by constructing this framework in
the following manner.   (See Art. 4.3 for definitions of the adjectives
"rigid" and "noncollapsible.")   First form a tetrahedronal nucleus by
using six bars to connect together four points which do not lie in a plane,
as shown by the solid lines connecting joints 1, 2, 3, and 4 in Fig. 9.11.
Joint 5 could then be rigidly connected to this nucleus by bars from joints
1, 3, and 4 as indicated by the dashed lines.   Joints 6 to 12 could be connected in sequence as shown, using *three bars which do not lie in a plane* to
connect each new joint to the framework previously formed.

[1] For an excellent discussion of statically determinate space frameworks, the reader
is referred to S. P. Timoshenko and D. H. Young, "Theory of Structures," chap. 4,
pp. 163–212, McGraw-Hill Book Company, Inc., New York, 1945.

Using the same terminology as for trusses, a space framework formed in the manner just described is called a **simple space framework.** The number of bars b required to form such a framework of n joints is obviously $3(n - 4) + 6$, or $b = 3n - 6$.

Formation of Compound Space Frameworks. Several simple space frameworks may be connected together to form a so-called **compound space framework,** as illustrated in Fig. 9.12, by using *six bars the axes of which do not intersect a single straight line.* In Fig. 9.12, the two simple space frameworks are shaded, and the six connecting bars are shown by the dashed lines. Note that the total number of bars used in such a case is

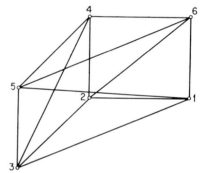

Figure 9.12 Compound space framework

Figure 9.13 Complex space framework

$(3n_1 - 6) + (3n_2 - 6) + 6$, or $b = 3(n_1 + n_2) - 6$, or $b = 3n - 6$, where n_1 and n_2 represent the number of joints in the individual simple space frameworks and n represents the total number of joints in the entire structure.

Complex Space Frameworks. Many practical space frameworks cannot be classified as either *simple* or *compound* and are therefore categorized as being **complex space frameworks.** An illustration of such a framework is shown in Fig. 9.13. Note that this framework would be a simple space framework if a member 1-4 were substituted for member 2-6. As before, the number of bars required to construct a rigid and noncollapsible complex space framework is given by $b = 3n - 6$.[1]

[1] As was also emphasized in Chap. 4, such a criterion is a *necessary but not sufficient* condition that the framework is rigid and noncollapsible. Though the number of bars may be adequate, if they are not properly arranged the space framework may be *geometrically unstable.*

Supports for Space Frameworks.   If a rigid noncollapsible space framework is supported such that the **reaction components are equivalent to six links the lines of action of which do not intersect a single straight line,** the structure will be **stable** and these six reaction components are **statically determinate** from the six equations of statics noted in Art. 9.2 and applied to the structure as a whole.   Such an arrangement is shown in Fig. 9.14 by the links shown by the heavy black lines and numbered 1 to 6.

Obviously if link 6 had a line of action coinciding with line *aa*, the structure would be supported in an unstable fashion since there would be

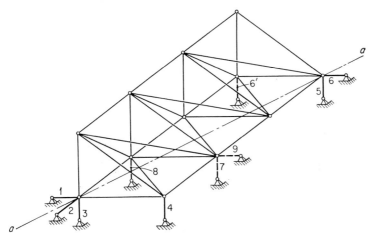

Figure 9.14   Arrangement of reactions

no reaction capable of resisting rotation of the structure about an axis coinciding with axis of link 3.   This would likewise be true if link 6 were replaced by the vertical link 6'.   Note that in either of these situations the axes of the six links involved intersect a vertical line coinciding with link 3 since links 4, 5, and 6' which are parallel to link 3 intersect this vertical line at infinity.   Of course if additional links such as 7, 8, and 9 were added to the original set—links 1 to 6—the structure would be stable but the reactions would be statically indeterminate, in this case to the third degree.

In many practical space frameworks, there are more than six reaction components provided.   Often in such cases, if there are r reaction components, $(r - 6)$ bars have been omitted from the $(3n - 6)$ required for a rigid and noncollapsible framework; and as a result,

$$b = (3n - 6) - (r - 6)$$

or $(b + r) = 3n$.   In other words, the omission of the $(r - 6)$ bars is equivalent to introducing $(r - 6)$ equations of condition (or construction). When this is done properly so that geometric instability is avoided, the structure is stable and statically determinate. Sometimes the reactions can be determined directly from the combination of the equations of condition and the equations of statics for the structure as a whole. Oftentimes, however, the reactions cannot be obtained without first determining some of the bar forces as illustrated above in Art. 9.5.

These and similar considerations lead to the following conclusions regarding the stability of a space framework structure and the combined statical determinancy of it with respect to both reaction components and bar forces. For a space framework, a total of $3n$ independent equations of statics are available by isolating each joint and writing the three equations—$\Sigma F_x = 0$, $\Sigma F_y = 0$, and $\Sigma F_z = 0$. Involved among these equations are a total of $(b + r)$ unknowns, that is, b bar forces and r reaction components. Comparison of the number of unknowns with the number of equations indicates that

If $(b + r) < 3n$, the structure is *unstable*
If $(b + r) = 3n$, the structure is *statically determinate*
If $(b + r) > 3n$, the structure is *statically indeterminate*

If this criterion indicates that the frame is statically determinate or indeterminate, it should be remembered that the count alone does not prove it is also stable—it may still be statically or geometrically unstable if the bars or reaction components are improperly arranged.

Stress Analysis of Statically Determinate Space Frameworks. The stress analysis of many space frameworks can be carried out by using a combination of the method of joints and the method of sections as discussed previously in Chap. 4 for trusses (or planar frameworks). The additional geometry of the three-dimensional structure impedes the rate of progress with such computations very considerably, of course.

Consider, for example, the case of a *simple* space framework which is supported in a statically determinate fashion. In such a case, the reactions may be determined from a consideration of the equilibrium of the entire structure. Once the reactions are known, the definition of the external forces acting on the structure is complete. Then one may isolate the last joint established in the pseudo-construction of the simple space framework (such as joint 12 in Fig. 9.11). At this joint, there are only three unknown bar forces, which can then be determined from the three equilibrium equations for this joint. If one works backward through the structure considering the joints in the reverse order—11, 10, 9, etc.—there will be only three unknown bar forces at each joint. Thus, the entire solution for the bar forces can be completed simply by successive application of the method of joints.

In the case of a *compound* space framework, even after the reactions have been determined, one can proceed just so far using the method of joints before finding that a joint cannot be isolated where there are only three unknown bar forces. At such a point in the solution, the method of sections must be applied to obtain some of the bar forces. In the case of *complex* space frameworks, even after the reactions have been determined, one finally reaches a point in the solution where neither the method of joints nor the method of sections will lead to a direct solution. In such a case, one must resort to a procedure such as described in Art. 4.12 for planar frameworks or to Henneberg's method (see reference cited in Art. 4.12).

In recent years, some extremely complicated space frameworks have been involved in radar transmitters and receivers. Such structures involve vast numbers of joints and bars, and sometimes cumbersome geometry. Often, deflection limitations and vibrational characteristics rather than strength requirements control the design. Modern digital computers have been used extensively in the analysis of such structures, utilizing displacement matrix methods such as described briefly in Chap. 15.

9.11 Problems for Solution

Problem 9.1   Show that the tower of Fig. 9.10 is statically determinate.

*Problem 9.2   Find the reactions on the structure of Fig. 9.15 due to the load of 1,000 lb acting as shown.

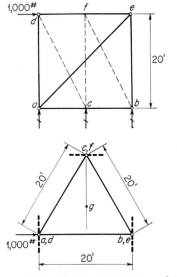

Figure 9.15   Problems 9.2, 9.3, and 9.4

*Problem 9.3   Find the bar forces in the structure of Fig. 9.15 due to the load of 1,000 lb acting as shown.

*Problem 9.4   Find the reactions and bar forces of the structure of Fig. 9.15 if the load of 1,000 lb is applied at joint d but with a direction such that it passes through point g, which lies at the center of the equilateral triangle def.

*Problem 9.5   (*a*) Show that the structure of Fig. 9.16 is statically indeterminate to the first degree.

(*b*) Find the reactions on the structure of Fig. 9.16 and the bar forces in all the bars, for the load of 10,000 lb acting as shown, assuming that bar ef is in compression and has a force equal to half the applied load.

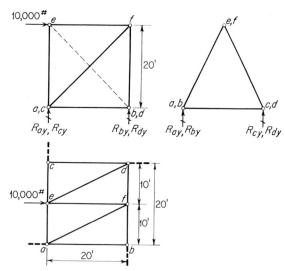

Figure 9.16   Problem 9.5

Problem 9.6   If the angle α between the horizontal reaction and the base-ring bar has the same value at each point of support of a Schwedler dome, as shown in Fig. 9.8, prove that, under the action of any vertical load on the dome, the algebraic sum of the horizontal reactions is zero.

*Problem 9.7   A tower similar to that of Fig. 9.9 has 10 panels with a height of 10 ft each; $ab = bc = ca = 10$ ft; $de = ef = fd = 12$ ft; at the tower base, $jk = kl = lj = 40$ ft.   At joint a, the following external loads are applied: a horizontal load of 10,000 lb, acting to the right, in a direction parallel to the OX axis; a horizontal load of 5,000 lb, acting to the rear, in a direction parallel to the OZ axis; and a vertical load of 20,000 lb, acting downward.

(*a*) What are the bar forces in bars ab, bc, and ca?

(*b*) What are the resultant X, Y, and Z components of the forces applied at joints d, e, and f by the legs and diagonals of the top panel?

(*c*) What are the reactions on the tower?

Problem 9.8   The tower of Prob. 9.7 weighs 50,000 lb.   The maximum wind load acting on the tower exerts a lateral pressure equal to 400 lb per ft of tower height. Against what uplift must a point of tower support be designed if the specifications state that the tower supports shall be designed for 150 per cent of the maximum net uplift?

Problem 9.9   Compute the reactions and bar forces for each of the space frameworks shown in Fig. 9.17.

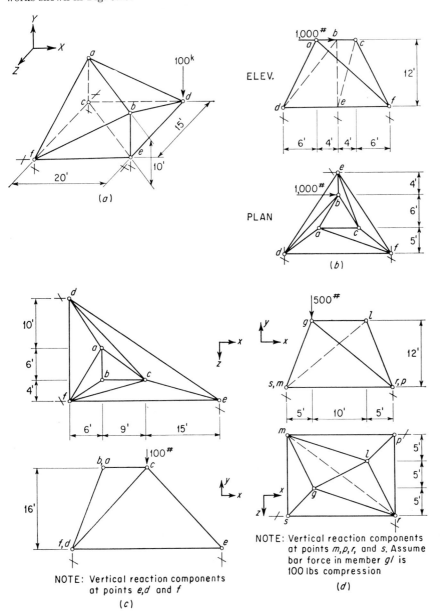

Figure 9.17   Problem 9.9

10
Cables

10.1 Introduction. Cables are used in many important types of engineering structures. They form the main load-carrying elements for suspension bridges and cable-car systems. They are used extensively for permanent guys on structures such as derricks and radio towers. They are also used for temporary guys during erection. Although exact cable analyses may require mathematical procedures beyond the scope of this book, a knowledge of certain fundamental relationships for cables is important in structural engineering.

When a cable supports a load that is uniform per unit length of the cable itself, such as its own weight, it takes the form of a catenary; but unless the sag of the cable is large in proportion to its length, the shape taken may often be assumed to be parabolic, the analysis being thus greatly simplified.

10.2 General Cable Theorem. Consider the general case of a cable supported at two points a and b, which are not necessarily at the same elevation, and acted upon by any system of vertical loads P_1, P_2, . . . , P_n as shown in Fig. 10.1a. The cable is assumed to be perfectly flexible, so that the bending moment at any point on the cable must be zero. Since all the loads are vertical, the horizontal component of cable tension, which will be denoted by H, has the same value at any point on the cable and the horizontal reactions are each equal to H.

Let ΣM_b = sum of moments about b of all loads P_1, P_2, . . . , P_n

ΣM_m = sum of moments about any point m on cable of those of loads P_1, P_2, . . . , P_n that act on cable to left of m

Taking moments about b, of all the forces acting on the cable,

$$+H(L \tan \gamma) + R_{ay}L - \Sigma M_b = 0$$

from which

$$R_{ay} = \frac{\Sigma M_b}{L} - H \tan \gamma \qquad (a)$$

276

Taking moments about m of those forces acting on that portion of the cable to the left of m,

$$+H(x \tan \gamma - y_m) + R_{ay}x - \Sigma M_m = 0$$

Substituting R_{ay} from Eq. (a) and simplifying,

$$Hy_m = \frac{x}{L} \Sigma M_b - \Sigma M_m \qquad (b)$$

In interpreting Eq. (b), it should be noted that y_m is the vertical distance from the cable at point m to the cable chord ab which joins the points of cable support. The right side of Eq. (b) may be seen to equal the bending moment that would occur at point m (see Fig. 10.1b) if the

Figure 10.1 Derivation of cable theorem

loads $P_1, P_2, \ldots, P_n$ were applied to an end-supported beam of span L and m were a point on this imaginary beam, located at distance x from the left support.

From Eq. (b), we may therefore state the following general cable theorem: **At any point on a cable acted upon by vertical loads, the product of the horizontal component of cable tension and the vertical distance from that point to the cable chord equals the bending moment which would occur at that section if the loads carried by the cable were acting on an end-supported beam of the same span as that of the cable.**

It is to be emphasized that this theorem is applicable to any set of vertical loads and holds true whether the cable chord is horizontal or inclined.

10.3 Application of General Cable Theorem. Suppose that the loading on a cable is defined and that the distance from the cable to the

cable chord is known at one point, as is the case in Fig. 10.2. Neglecting
the weight of the cable itself, the bending moment at point d on an imaginary beam of equal span is equal to

$$2,330(20) - 1,000(10) = 36,600 \text{ ft-lb}$$

Hence, by the general cable theorem, $10H = 36,600$, or $H = 3,660$ lb.
To determine the distance of any other point such as c from the cable
chord, the general cable theorem is applied at section c, leading to
$3,660y_c = 2,330(10)$, from which $y_c = 6.38$ ft.   The segment of the cable

between a and c lies along a straight
line, since the weight of the cable
has been neglected, and has a
length equal to

$$\sqrt{(10)^2 + (6.38)^2} = 11.85 \text{ ft}$$

Since the horizontal component of
cable tension equals 3,660 lb, the
actual cable tension between a and
c equals $3,660(11.85/10) = 4,340$ lb.
The left vertical reaction on the
cable equals the vertical component

Figure 10.2   Application of cable theorem

of cable tension in segment ac and is given by $3,660(6.38/10) = 2,330$ lb.
For this particular case, this value equals the left vertical reaction on the
imaginary end-supported beam.   Had the cable chord been inclined,
however, these two vertical reactions would have had different values.

10.4   Shape of Uniformly Loaded Cable.   The case of a loading
that is uniform per horizontal foot and applied over the entire span of the
cable is important not only because it is substantially the type of cable
loading occurring in suspension bridges, but because a cable carrying
only its dead weight can be treated approximately on the assumption
that the dead weight is uniform per horizontal foot.   In Fig. 10.3, the
general cable theorem leads to

$$Hy_m = \frac{wLx}{2} - \frac{wx^2}{2} \qquad (a)$$

Let the particular value of y_m at mid-span be denoted by h.   The distance
h is called the cable sag and is measured vertically in all cases.   For the
mid-span, where $x = L/2$ and $y_m = h$, the foregoing equation reduces to
$Hh = wL^2/8$, whence

$$H = \frac{wL^2}{8h} \qquad (10.1)$$

This relation for H is of primary importance.   Note that it holds whether
the cable chord is inclined or horizontal.   Substituting this value of H

into Eq. (a) and solving for y_m lead to

$$y_m = \frac{4hx}{L^2}(L - x) \tag{10.2}$$

Equation (10.2) defines the shape of the cable, located with respect to the cable chord and in terms of the cable sag.   It is often desirable to

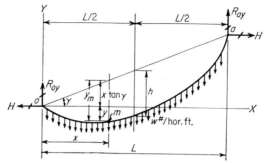

Figure 10.3   Cable carrying uniform load per horizontal foot

define the shape of the cable with respect to a horizontal axis.   If the origin o of the axes is taken at the left end of the cable, as shown in Fig. 10.3, the relation $y = +x \tan \gamma - y_m$ may be used.   Substituting y_m as expressed by Eq. (10.2) leads to

$$y = \frac{4hx}{L^2}(x - L) + x \tan \gamma \tag{10.3}$$

If the cable chord is horizontal, $\tan \gamma = 0$, whence

$$y = \frac{4hx}{L^2}(x - L) \tag{10.4}$$

Figure 10.4   Cable geometry

If the cable chord is horizontal and if it is desired to define the cable curve with respect to axes with their origin at c, the low point on the cable, which is at mid-span, reference to Fig. 10.4 shows that, since

$$x = \frac{L}{2} + x_c \quad \text{and} \quad y = -h + y_c$$

these relations may be substituted into Eq. (10.4), leading to

$$y_c = \frac{4h}{L^2}x_c^2 \tag{10.5}$$

10.5   Tension in Uniformly Loaded Cable.   The force at any point in a cable is axial.   For a uniformly loaded cable, the horizontal component of cable tension can be computed by means of Eq. (10.1).

Consider a differential element of cable of length ds and horizontal projection dx. Then T_x, the tension in the cable at any distance x from the origin, is given by $H\,ds/dx$. For the case of the inclined cable chord, as shown in Fig. 10.3, differentiation of Eq. (10.3) leads to

$$\frac{dy}{dx} = \frac{8hx}{L^2} - \frac{4h}{L} + \tan\gamma$$

$$= \frac{8\theta x}{L} - 4\theta + \tan\gamma$$

where $\theta = h/L$ and is called the sag ratio.

Further, since $ds = [1 + (dy/dx)^2]^{1/2}\,dx$, $T_x = H[1 + (dy/dx)^2]^{1/2}$, or

$$T_x = H\left(1 + \frac{64\theta^2 x^2}{L^2} + 16\theta^2 + \tan^2\gamma - \frac{64\theta^2 x}{L}\right.$$
$$\left. + \frac{16\theta x}{L}\tan\gamma - 8\theta\tan\gamma\right)^{1/2} \quad (a)$$

The maximum tension occurs at one end of the cable.

For $x = 0$: $T_{\max} = H(1 + 16\theta^2 + \tan^2\gamma - 8\theta\tan\gamma)^{1/2}$
For $x = L$: $T_{\max} = H(1 + 16\theta^2 + \tan^2\gamma + 8\theta\tan\gamma)^{1/2}$ (10.6)

If the cable chord is horizontal, $\tan\gamma = 0$, whence at either end of the cable

$$T_{\max} = H(1 + 16\theta^2)^{1/2} \qquad (10.7)$$

For the special case of the horizontal cable chord, Eq. (10.7) may also be derived as follows: The maximum cable tension occurs at the end of the cable and equals the resultant reaction on the cable. For this reaction, the horizontal component is H, while the vertical component equals half the total load on the cable, or $wL/2$, which may also be expressed as $4Hh/L = 4H\theta$, since $H = wL^2/8h$; hence

$$T_{\max} = (H^2 + R_y^2)^{1/2}$$
$$= (H^2 + 16H^2\theta^2)^{1/2}$$
$$= H(1 + 16\theta^2)^{1/2}$$

10.6   Illustrative Examples

Example 10.1 *A cable supporting a uniform load of 1 kip per horizontal foot is suspended between two points of equal elevation, which are 2,000 ft apart, with a sag ratio such that the horizontal component of cable tension is 2,500 kips. What is the maximum tension in the cable?*

Solution: *Since* $H = wL^2/8h$, $2,500 = 1(2,000)^2/8h$, $h = 200$ ft,

$$\theta = \frac{h}{L} = \frac{200}{2,000} = \frac{1}{10}$$

$$T_{max} = H(1 + 16\theta^2)^{1/2} = 2,500(1 + {}^{16}\!/_{100})^{1/2} = 2,690 \ kips$$

Example 10.2 *A cable supporting a uniform load of 100 lb per horizontal foot is suspended between two points 200 ft apart horizontally, with one point of support 50 ft higher than the other. The tension in the cable is adjusted until the sag at mid-span (i.e., the vertical distance from the cable to the cable chord at mid-span) equals 12.5 ft. What is the maximum tension in the cable?*

Solution: $H = \dfrac{wL^2}{8h} = \dfrac{100(200)^2}{8(12.5)} = 40,000\ lb$

$\theta = \dfrac{h}{L} = \dfrac{12.5}{200} = 0.0625 \qquad tan\ \gamma = \dfrac{50}{200} = 0.25$

The maximum cable tension occurs at the high point of support and is given by

$$T_{max} = H(1 + 16\theta^2 + tan^2\ \gamma + 8\theta\ tan\ \gamma)^{1/2}$$
$$= 40,000[1 + 16(0.0625)^2 + (0.25)^2 + 8(0.0625)(0.25)]^{1/2}$$
$$= 44,700\ lb$$

10.7   Length of Uniformly Loaded Cable. If s_o is the total length of a cable, then

$$s_o = \int_0^L ds = \int_0^L \left[1 + \left(\frac{dy}{dx}\right)^2 \right]^{1/2} dx \tag{a}$$

For the case of a horizontal cable chord, using Eq. (10.5), which is based on the origin being located at the low point on the cable, which is at mid-span,

$$\frac{dy}{dx} = \frac{8hx}{L^2}$$

whence

$$s_o = 2 \int_0^{L/2} \left(1 + \frac{64h^2x^2}{L^4} \right)^{1/2} dx \tag{b}$$

Integration of this relation leads to the following exact expression:

$$s_o = \frac{L}{2} (1 + 16\theta^2)^{1/2} + \frac{L}{8\theta} \ln\left[4\theta + (1 + 16\theta^2)^{1/2}\right] \tag{10.8}$$

The use of Eq. (10.8) requires the use of natural logarithms. A very useful approximate expression for determining cable length when the cable chord is horizontal may be obtained by expanding the term

$$\left(1 + \frac{64h^2x^2}{L^4} \right)^{1/2}$$

occurring in Eq. (b) into an infinite series by the binomial theorem and considering only the first few terms of the resultant series. This leads to

$$s_o = 2 \int_0^{L/2} \left[(1)^{1/2} + \frac{1}{2} (1)^{-1/2}(64) \frac{h^2x^2}{L^4} \right.$$
$$\left. + \frac{1}{2}\left(-\frac{1}{2}\right)\left(\frac{1}{2}\right) (1)^{-3/2}(64)^2 \frac{h^4x^4}{L^8} + \cdots \right] dx$$

which simplifies into

$$s_o = L\left(1 + \frac{8\theta^2}{3} - \frac{32\theta^4}{5} + \cdots\right) \qquad (10.9)$$

This equation converges rapidly, the first three terms giving sufficient accuracy for many purposes.

If the cable chord is inclined, an exact equation for s_o could be obtained by substituting dy/dx as obtained from Eq. (10.3) into Eq. (a). This leads, however, to an extremely cumbersome result. For many purposes the following approximate treatment gives results of sufficient accuracy.

Assume that the length of such a cable is the same as it would be for a cable with a horizontal cable chord, where the span equals the length of the inclined cable chord, that is, $L \sec \gamma$, and the sag equals $h \cos \gamma$, which is an approximate expression for the maximum perpendicular distance from the cable to the cable chord. With these assumptions,

$$\theta' = \frac{h \cos \gamma}{L \sec \gamma} = \frac{\theta}{\sec^2 \gamma}$$

Now, applying Eq. (10.9) to this hypothetical cable and using only the first two terms,

$$s_o = L \sec \gamma \left(1 + \frac{8}{3}\frac{\theta^2}{\sec^4 \gamma}\right)$$

$$= L\left(\sec \gamma + \frac{8}{3}\frac{\theta^2}{\sec^3 \gamma}\right) \qquad (10.10)$$

To find the approximate length of the cable of Example 10.1, Art. 10.6, use Eq. (10.9) ($\theta = \frac{1}{10}$).

$$s_o = 2,000\left[1 + \frac{8}{3}\left(\frac{1}{100}\right) - \frac{32}{5}\left(\frac{1}{10,000}\right)\right]$$
$$= 2,000(1.000 + 0.0267 - 0.0006) = 2,052 \text{ ft}$$

To find the approximate length of the cable of Example 10.2, Art. 10.6, use Eq. (10.10).

$$\theta = 0.0625 \qquad \sec^2 \gamma = 1 + \tan^2 \gamma = 1 + (0.25)^2 = 1.0625$$

$$\sec \gamma = 1.031$$

$$s_o = 200\left[1.031 + \frac{8}{3}\frac{(0.0625)^2}{(1.031)^3}\right] = 208 \text{ ft}$$

10.8 Elastic Stretch of Cables. When a cable supports a load, it undergoes an elastic stretch, which is often of importance in determining cable sags and also for other purposes. By the definition of the modulus of elasticity,

$$E = \frac{F/A}{\Delta L/L} \qquad \text{whence } \Delta L = \frac{FL}{AE}$$

An element of a cable of length ds is subject to a tension T_x. A convenient method of determining the elastic stretch of a cable consists in first determining T_{av}, which by definition will be taken as that average tension which if applied throughout the length of the cable will cause the same total elastic change of length as actually occurs. Stated mathematically,

$$\frac{T_{av}s_o}{AE} = \int_0^{s_o} \frac{T_x \, ds}{AE}$$

where A and E are assumed constant. Hence

$$T_{av} = \frac{1}{s_o} \int_0^{s_o} T_x \, ds = \frac{1}{s_o} \int_0^{s_o} H \frac{ds}{dx} \, ds = \frac{H}{s_o} \int_0^L \left[1 + \left(\frac{dy}{dx}\right)^2 \right] dx \quad (a)$$

Considering a loading that is uniform per horizontal foot, and an inclined cable chord, dy/dx may be obtained from Eq. (10.3), and equals $(8hx/L^2) - (4h/L) + \tan \gamma$. Substituting this value of dy/dx into Eq. (a) and integrating,

$$T_{av} = \frac{HL}{s_o} \left(1 + \frac{16}{3} \theta^2 + \tan^2 \gamma \right) \quad (b)$$

Using Eq. (10.10) to express s_o,

$$T_{av} = H \frac{1 + (16\theta^2/3) + \tan^2 \gamma}{\sec \gamma + \frac{8}{3}(\theta^2/\sec^3 \gamma)} \quad (10.11)$$

If the cable chord is horizontal, $\gamma = 0$, whence

$$T_{av} = H \frac{1 + (16\theta^2/3)}{1 + (8\theta^2/3)} \quad (10.12)$$

Suppose, for example, that it is required to find the elastic stretch of the cable of Example 10.1, Art. 10.6, for which s_o was found to equal 2,052 ft in Art. 10.7. Taking $E = 27,000,000$ psi and $A = 50$ sq in.,

$$T_{av} = 2,500 \frac{1 + \frac{16}{3}(\frac{1}{100})}{1 + \frac{8}{3}(\frac{1}{100})} = 2,570 \text{ kips}$$

$$\text{Elastic stretch} = \frac{T_{av}s_o}{AE} = \frac{2,570(2,052)}{\frac{50}{144}(27,000)(144)} = 3.91 \text{ ft}$$

To the nearest foot, the *unstressed* length of this cable would be

$$2,052 - 4 = 2,048 \text{ ft}$$

10.9 Guyed Structures. The application of the various relations for cables to guys can be shown by a consideration of the structure shown in Fig. 10.5. Suppose that a cable weighing 4.16 lb per ft is to be used as a guy and that it is required that this guy hold the mast BC vertically when the load of 100,000 lb is applied. Taking moments about C of the forces acting on the mast and noting that H, the horizontal component of cable tension, acts to the left on the mast,

$$100H = 100,000(10) \qquad H = 10,000 \text{ lb}$$

This value of H must be developed to hold the mast vertically; thus the cable sag must conform to the following value:

$$10,000 = \frac{wL^2}{8h} = \frac{5.00(150)^2}{8h}$$
$$h = 1.41 \text{ ft}$$

since, in this approximate solution, the cable is assumed to be parabolic and acted upon by a uniform load of

$$w = 4.16(180.2/150) = 5.00 \text{ lb per horizontal foot}$$

The maximum tension in the guy would occur at B and by using Eqs. (10.6) equals

$$T_{max} = 10,000 \left[1.000 + 16 \left(\frac{1.41}{150} \right)^2 + \left(\frac{100}{150} \right)^2 + 8 \left(\frac{1.41}{150} \right) \left(\frac{100}{150} \right) \right]^{1/2}$$
$$= 12,240 \text{ lb}$$

It should be noted that a close approximation to the foregoing solution can be obtained by considering the cable to act as a straight tie rod lying along the chord AB. The length of this chord is 180.2 ft; the tension would equal

Figure 10.5   Cable guy

$$10,000 \left(\frac{180.2}{150} \right) = 12,000 \text{ lb}$$

The only error introduced in this approximate solution arises from the fact that the slope of the cable at B is actually steeper than that of the chord. Unless the sag ratio of the cable is large, this difference in slope is not likely to be of importance.

It is usually necessary to have more than one guy on a mast or other guyed structure, in order that the mast may be held against overturning in more than one direction. Under these conditions, the guys are adjusted so that they have a certain initial tension; an initial tension equal to about half the maximum tension that will occur under load is commonly used. In Fig. 10.6, suppose that the sags of the guys AB and AC have been adjusted so that, with no horizontal load applied to the mast, the horizontal component of cable tension in each guy is 6,000 lb. Under these circumstances, the maximum initial stress in each guy, following the approximate method of analysis suggested in the discussion of Fig. 10.5, will equal $+6,000 \times 1.414 = +8,500$ lb.

When the load of 5,000 lb is applied at the top of the mast, a resultant horizontal force of 10,000 lb, acting to the left, must be applied at A by the two guys to maintain equilibrium. By an approximate method of analysis that leads to reasonably accurate results, it may be assumed that this load of 10,000 lb is applied by increasing the horizontal component of tension in guy AB by 5,000 lb and decreasing the horizontal component of tension in guy AC by the same amount, leading to $H_{AB} = +11,000$ lb and $H_{AC} = +1,000$ lb. The maximum guy tension is then equal to

Figure 10.6　Guyed mast

$$+11,000 \times 1.414 = +15,500 \text{ lb}$$

Actually, when the load of 5,000 lb is applied at the top of the mast, point A moves to the right. Guy AB permits this movement since it undergoes additional elastic stretch and since its sag decreases. The sag in guy AC increases, and the length of that guy shortens elastically. An exact analysis, taking into account elastic changes of length and sag changes, can be made, but it is relatively complicated. The foregoing approximate solution is more practical for usual design problems.

10.10 Statically Determinate Suspension Bridges. A suspension bridge is usually constructed in a manner such that the dead loads are carried entirely by the cables. A large portion of the dead load comes from the roadway and is uniform. It is commonly assumed that the entire dead load is uniform per horizontal foot. On the basis of this assumption, the cables are parabolic under dead load only. When live load is applied, with partial loadings so as to give maximum forces in members, the cables tend to change their shape. In order to prevent local changes of slope in the roadway, due to live load, from being too large, the floor beams of the floor system are usually framed into stiffening trusses, which in turn are supported by hangers running to the cables. These stiffening trusses distribute the live load to the various hangers, in a manner such that even under live loads the cable may be assumed to remain essentially parabolic. As long as the cable remains parabolic, it must be acted upon by a load that is uniform per horizontal foot. Since the hangers are equally spaced, this is equivalent to stating that the hanger tensions in a given span must be equal. In the "elastic" theory of suspension bridges, all the hangers in a given span are assumed to have equal tensions. That this assumption is not strictly correct may be shown by the more accurate and more complicated "deflection" theory of suspension bridges. However, unless a suspension bridge is long and flexible, the elastic theory may lead to results that are not greatly in error.

If the stiffening trusses of a suspension bridge are arranged and supported as shown in Fig. 10.7a, with a hinge at some intermediate point

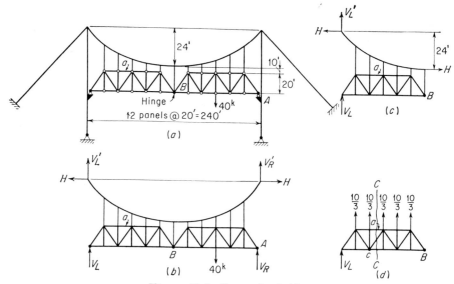

Figure 10.7 Suspension bridge

in the main-span stiffening truss, the structure is statically determinate, provided that it is assumed that all the hangers in a given span have equal tensions. The application of the various relations for cables to a statically determinate suspension bridge will be illustrated by an analysis of the structure shown in that figure.

Suppose this bridge is subjected to a live load of 40 kips acting as shown in the figure. Consider the equilibrium of all the forces acting on that portion of the structure shown in Fig. 10.7b. The horizontal components of cable reaction at each end of the cable are equal and have the same line of action. Taking moments about point A,

$$(V_L + V'_L)(240) - 40(60) = 0 \qquad V_L + V'_L = +10 \text{ (upward)}$$

Now consider the equilibrium of all the forces acting on that portion of the structure shown in Fig. 10.7c, taking moments of these forces about the hinge at B.

$$(V_L + V'_L = 10)(120) + H(30) - H(54) = 0 \qquad H = 50.0 \text{ kips}$$

The maximum cable tension in the main span occurs at the ends of the cable and by Eq. (10.7) equals $50.0(1 + {}^{16}\!\!/_{100})^{\frac{1}{2}} = 53.9$ kips.

Let X equal the tension in each hanger. The equivalent uniform load of the hangers equals $X/20$ kips per ft. To evaluate X, use the relation $H = wL^2/8h$, where $w = X/20$.

$$50.0 = \frac{X}{20} \frac{(240)^2}{8(24)} \qquad X = +\frac{10}{3} \text{ kips}$$

Once the hanger tensions have been determined, the forces in the bars of the stiffening truss are readily evaluated. For example, to find the force in bar a, first find V_L by taking moments about B of the forces acting on the portion of the structure shown in Fig. 10.7d.

$$+120V_L + {}^{10}\!\!/_3(20 + 40 + 60 + 80 + 100) = 0 \qquad V_L = -{}^{25}\!\!/_3 \text{ (down)}$$

Now taking moments about c of the forces acting on the portion of the structure to the left of section C-C (Fig. 10.7d),

$$-{}^{25}\!\!/_3(40) + {}^{10}\!\!/_3(20) + F_a(20) = 0 \qquad F_a = +13.33 \text{ kips}$$

For this particular structure, the side spans are not suspended. The cables of the side spans act as guys to the towers. The horizontal component of cable tension is the same for side and center spans, as can be seen by taking moments about the hinge at a tower base of the forces acting on a tower. V_L is assumed to act on the center line of the tower.

10.11   Problems for Solution

Problem 10.1   A cable with a span of 1,000 ft carries concentrated loads spaced at horizontal intervals of 200 ft. The magnitudes of these loads, from left to right, in kips, are 100, 50, 200, and 300. The right end of the cable is 100 ft higher than the left end. The maximum distance, measured vertically from the cable to the cable chord, is 50 ft. Neglecting the weight of the cable itself,

(a) What is the vertical distance from the cable chord to the point of application of each load?

(b) What is the length of the cable?

(c) What is the maximum tension in the cable?

*Problem 10.2   A side-span suspension-bridge cable has a span of 500 ft and a sag ratio of $\frac{1}{40}$. The slope of the cable chord is defined by $\tan \gamma = 0.7$. The load on the cable is 1,000 lb per horizontal foot; $E = 27,000,000$ psi; the area of the cable is 50 sq in.

(a) What is the maximum slope of the cable?

(b) What is the maximum tension in the cable?

(c) Compute, to the nearest foot, the length of this cable.

(d) Compute, to the nearest foot, the unstressed length of this cable.

Problem 10.3   Prepare a set of curves from which the ratio s_o/L can be read, for values of θ ranging from 0 to 0.25 and values of tan γ ranging from 0 to 1, for cables where the loading is uniform per horizontal foot.

Problem 10.4   A cable with a span of 1,000 ft and a horizontal cable chord carries 1,500 lb per horizontal foot.   The tension is adjusted until the maximum cable force is 2,000,000 lb.   The temperature is +50°F; E = 27,000 kips per sq in.; A = 40 sq in.

(a) What is the corresponding sag at mid-span?

(b) What is the unstressed length of this cable at +100°F?

Problem 10.5   The top of a derrick mast is guyed with 12 guys, spaced 30° apart as seen in plan view.   Each guy has a span of 400 ft and a vertical rise of 150 ft.   The guy cable weighs 5 lb per ft of cable; the sag of each guy is 4 ft.

(a) What compression is exerted on the derrick mast by the sum of the vertical cable reactions?

(b) What is the maximum force in each guy?

(c) The mast of the derrick is 150 ft high.   If the boom line exerts a horizontal force of 100,000 lb at the top of the mast, what is the approximate value of the maximum force occurring in any guy?   (Assume that each guy participates in resisting this force, in proportion to the cosine of the angle between the guy and the force, as seen in plan view.)

*Problem 10.6   A suspension bridge is similar to that shown in Fig. 10.7a, having 20 panels of 20 ft each and a cable sag ratio of $\frac{1}{10}$.   The stiffening truss is 20 ft deep.

(a) If a live load of 1,000 lb per ft acts over the entire bottom chord, compute the maximum cable tension in the suspended span and the maximum bottom-chord force in the stiffening truss.

(b) Construct influence lines for (1) horizontal component of cable tension; (2) hanger tension; (3) force in the stiffening-truss diagonal of the second panel from the left tower.

(c) The dead load on this structure is 5 kips per ft.   The live load consists of a uniform load of 2 kips per ft and a single concentrated load of 20 kips.   Neglecting impact, what cross-sectional area is required for each hanger, using an allowable stress of 50 kips per sq in. for cables in tension?

11

Approximate Analysis of Statically Indeterminate Structures

11.1 Introduction. From a broad viewpoint, the analysis of every structure is approximate, for it is necessary to make certain assumptions in order to carry out the analysis. For example, in computing the stresses in a pin-connected truss, it is assumed that the pins are frictionless, so that the truss members carry axial force only. It is, of course, impossible to build a pin connection that is frictionless, and as a result the stress analysis of a pin-connected truss is approximate. It may therefore be said that there is no such thing as an "exact" analysis.

However, if proper judgment is exercised in making the assumptions upon which the analysis of a given structure is based, the resultant errors will be small. A stress analysis based on the usual assumptions that underlie structural theory is often called "exact," although it may be seen that, strictly speaking, this term is not used correctly. It is, however, a convenient term to use, for it is desirable to distinguish between analyses based on the usual assumptions which are relatively exact and analyses based on further assumptions which introduce further errors and which are therefore frankly approximate.

When one speaks of an approximate analysis for a given structural problem, one does not necessarily refer to any particular set of assumptions and resultant approximations. The particular approximate method to be used under any given circumstances will depend on the time available for the analysis and the degree of accuracy considered necessary.

For structural types that occur commonly in structural analysis, one may take advantage of approximate methods of analysis worked out by others and investigated as to their accuracy so that they can be used with a fair degree of confidence. The approximate methods described in engi-

289

neering literature do not, however, cover all cases. A good stress analyst should be familiar enough with the action of statically indeterminate structures to be able to set up his own assumptions when he encounters circumstances not covered by the literature.

In this chapter, a number of approximate solutions for common types of statically indeterminate structures are given. A knowledge of these methods is of importance, but of perhaps greater importance is the fact that the procedures here outlined will serve as a basis for making intelligent assumptions that will permit simplified approximate analyses of other types of statically indeterminate structures.

Figure 11.1 Effect of elastic properties on stress analysis

11.2 Importance of Approximate Methods in Analyzing Statically Indeterminate Structures. The analysis of a statically determinate structure does not depend on the elastic properties of its members. Because of this, relatively simple "exact" stress analyses can be carried out for such structures.

In a statically indeterminate structure, however, stress analysis depends on the elastic properties of members. These elastic properties include modulus of elasticity, cross-sectional area, cross-sectional moment of inertia, and length of member. That this is so may be visualized by reference to Fig. 11.1. Suppose that the stiffness of beam AB is made very small in comparison with the stiffness of beam CD. This may be accomplished by making $E_1 I_1/L_1^3$ very small in comparison with $E_2 I_2/L_2^3$. Then beam CD will carry a greater portion of load P than will beam AB. Suppose further that the tension tie EF that connects the two beams is given a very small stiffness by making $E_3 A/h$ small. This might be accomplished by constructing the tie EF of rubber, which has a very low value of E. Under this condition the beam CD would carry still more of the load P.

If the quantities determining the stiffnesses of members in a statically indeterminate structure are known, a so-called "exact" analysis may be carried out that will yield results of the same order of accuracy as can be obtained for statically determinate structures. In actual practice, however, the following three factors may prevent an exact analysis:

1. The stress analyst may lack the knowledge necessary to carry out the statically indeterminate analysis.

2. The time required to carry out a statically indeterminate analysis

may be so great that an exact solution must be abandoned. In some cases, the need of meeting time schedules may be the controlling factor. In other instances, economic considerations may make it desirable to use an approximate method of analysis. It may be less expensive to use more material, as a result of basing design on approximate stresses and on a higher apparent factor of safety with respect to the computed stresses, than to save material by basing design on exact stresses and a lower apparent factor of safety. This attitude may sometimes be properly taken in designing relatively unimportant structures or secondary portions of important structures. The analyst will also be influenced in this connection by his judgment as to the magnitude of the errors likely to be introduced by the approximate method he proposes to use.

3. When the design of a statically indeterminate structure is first begun, the areas and moments of inertia of its members are not known. It is therefore necessary to carry out an approximate analysis for stresses in the structure, so as to obtain some idea as to the required sizes of these members. Once these tentative sizes have been assigned, an elastic analysis may be carried out. In general, the first elastic analysis will show that the actual stresses in the structure are not satisfactory, and it is only by successive designs that a satisfactory final result can be obtained. Approximate analyses of statically indeterminate structures are therefore important in preliminary design stages.

11.3 Number of Assumptions Required. It has previously been pointed out that, for an analysis of a structure to be possible on the basis of the equations of statics only, there must be available as many independent equations of statics as there are independent components of force in the structure. If there are n more independent components of force than there are independent equations of statics, the structure is statically indeterminate to the nth degree. It will then be necessary to make n independent assumptions, each of which supplies an independent equation or relation, in order that an approximate solution can be worked out on the basis of statics only.

If fewer than n assumptions are made, a solution based on statics only will not be possible. If more than n assumptions are made, the assumptions will not in general be consistent with each other and the application of the equations of statics will lead to inconsistent results, depending on which equations are used and the order in which they are used. The first step in the approximate analysis of a statically indeterminate structure is to find the degree to which the structure is indeterminate and hence the number of assumptions to be made.

11.4 Parallel-chord Trusses with Two Diagonals in Each Panel. Trusses of this type occur frequently in structural engineering, as, for example, in the top- and bottom-chord lateral systems of a bridge,

as described in Art. 1.21.   The approximate analysis of such a truss will
be illustrated by considering the truss of Fig. 11.2, in which it is assumed
that all members are capable of carrying either compression or tension.
It should first be noted that this truss is statically indeterminate to the
sixth degree; that this is true may readily be seen from the fact that, if
one diagonal were removed from each panel, the remaining members

Figure 11.2   Truss with double diagonal system

would form a statically determinate truss.   It is therefore necessary to
make six independent assumptions as to stress conditions.   *It will be
assumed that in each panel the shear is equally divided between the two
diagonals;* since there are six panels, this amounts to six independent
assumptions.   It is now easy to complete the analysis of the structure,
by using only relations of statics.   The solution is shown in Fig. 11.3,
the method of index force having been employed.   The shear in each
panel is first computed from the external forces.   As an illustration, the

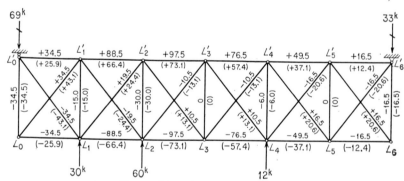

Figure 11.3   Illustrative example

shear in panel (1-2) is -39 kips.   This shear is equally divided between
L_1L_2' and $L_1'L_2$, so that the index forces in these two bars are $+19.5$ and
-19.5, respectively.   Index forces for all diagonals are determined in a
similar manner.[1]   From these index forces, the index forces in all other
members may be determined in the usual manner.   In Fig. 11.3 the
actual bar forces are given in parentheses for each member.

[1] See Example 4.9.

In trusses of this type, the diagonals are often designed as tension members only, by making their slenderness ratios (unsupported length divided by radius of gyration) large, since then, when a diagonal is subjected to compression, it will buckle slightly and carry only a negligible load. When the diagonals are designed in this manner, the total shear in each panel is carried in tension by a single diagonal. A consideration of the total shear on each panel enables one to tell which diagonal has a tendency to buckle and therefore carries no load. In Fig. 11.3, if it is assumed that the diagonals were designed so that they could carry tension only, all the diagonals that carried compression in the previous analysis would now have zero force. This, in effect, makes the truss statically determinate, and hence no difficulty is encountered in completing the analysis.

11.5 Multiple-system Trusses. Trusses with redundant web members can, under some circumstances, be analyzed approximately by

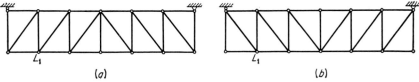

(a)   (b)

Figure 11.4 Component trusses of truss in Fig. 11.2

imagining that the indeterminate truss is equivalent to two or more statically determinate trusses superimposed on each other. The truss of Fig. 11.2, for example, might be built up by combining the two trusses shown in Fig. 11.4. For this particular type of truss, however, a vertical load applied at any panel point such as L_1 could be carried by either of the trusses shown in Fig. 11.4. Hence, it is not possible to assign such a load to one component truss only. Consider next the truss shown in Fig. 11.5a, which is statically indeterminate to the first degree. The truss might be built up by superimposing the two trusses shown in Figs. 11.5b and c. If a vertical load is applied at any panel point for this truss, it can be assumed to be carried by one component truss only. Suppose, for example, that a vertical load is applied at L_1, L_3, or L_5; it can then be assumed to be carried entirely by the truss of Fig. 11.5b, since the diagonals of that truss can hold the vertical load in equilibrium. Loads applied at these panel points on the truss of Fig. 11.5c could not be carried unless the bottom chords carried them in bending. Since the truss members are designed to carry axial force only, this is not possible. Similarly, vertical loads at L_2 or L_4 could be assumed to be carried entirely by the truss of Fig. 11.5a. The loads applied to the truss of Fig. 11.5a can therefore be assigned definitely to one or the other of the component trusses. Each of these component trusses is statically determinate and can easily be analyzed for the loading it is assumed to carry. Bar forces in the actual truss can then be determined by superimposing the bar forces from the two component trusses. The bar force in any diagonal is obtained from the component truss in which that diagonal occurs, but the bar force in any chord or end post is obtained by adding up the forces for that chord or end post, as obtained for each component truss.

Since the truss of Fig. 11.5a is statically indeterminate to the first degree, the approximate analysis here outlined is based on a single assumption that, in any *one* panel, the total external shear is divided between the two diagonals of that panel in the manner which would occur if the two component trusses could operate independently under the loadings applied at their respective panel points. This assumption

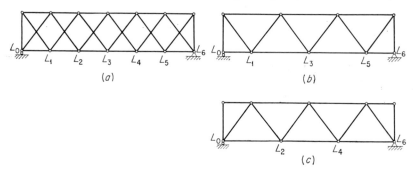

Figure 11.5   Multiple-system truss

having been made for the division of shears in *one* panel, the division of shears on the same basis in other panels follows directly from the equations of statics, so that no further assumptions are involved.

To illustrate this approximate method of analyzing trusses with multiple web systems, consider the truss shown in Fig. 11.6a. This truss may be considered as composed of three component trusses, as indicated by the full, dash, and dotted lines used in drawing the diagonals. The bar forces for each of the three component trusses are given in Figs. 11.6b to d. These component bar forces are then superimposed and the total bar forces written on Fig. 11.6a. For example, the total bar force in U_2L_3 is taken directly from Fig. 11.6b (+35.4), while the total bar force in U_2U_3 is obtained by adding up the bar forces for this member as obtained from the component trusses, $-50.00 - 38.9 - 55.5 = -144.4$.

The same approach may be followed if it is desired to construct influence lines for forces in bars of multiple-system trusses. In Figs. 11.7a and b, influence lines for bars U_2L_3 and U_2U_3 are drawn. Since U_2L_3 is a member of the component truss of Fig. 11.6b, the influence line is first drawn by considering that truss only. The ordinate at L_3 is the only significant ordinate to this influence line, however, since, when the unit load is at any other bottom-chord panel point, it is carried by one of the other component trusses, and the bar force in U_2L_3 is zero. Since the influence line is a straight line between panel points, the resultant influence line for this member is as shown by the heavy line in Fig. 11.7a. Bar U_2U_3 is a member of each of the three component trusses. Considering it in turn as a member of each of the trusses shown in Figs.

Figure 11.6   Illustrative example

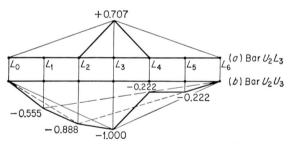

Figure 11.7   Influence lines for truss in Fig. 11.6

11.6b to d, the influence line as a member of each component truss is constructed; these three influence lines are shown by the full, dash, and dotted lines, respectively, in Fig. 11.7b. The ordinate at L_3 is the only one that has any significance for the influence line drawn on the basis of Fig. 11.6b; the ordinates at L_1 and L_4 are the only ones that have any significance for the influence line drawn on the basis of Fig. 11.6c; and the ordinates at L_2 and L_5 are the only ones that have any significance for the influence line drawn on the basis of Fig. 11.6d. These significant points are connected by the heavy solid line shown in Fig. 11.7b, giving the resultant influence line for force in bar U_2U_3.

11.6 Portals. Portal structures, similar to the end portals of the bridge described in Art. 1.21, have as their primary purpose the transfer of horizontal loads, applied at their tops, to their foundations. Clearance requirements usually lead to the use of statically indeterminate structural layout for portals, and approximate solutions are often used in their analyses. Consider the portal shown in Fig. 11.8a, all the members of which are capable of carrying bending and shear as well as axial force. The legs are hinged at their bases and rigidly connected to the cross girder at the top. This structure is statically indeterminate to the first degree;

Figure 11.8   Portal frame

hence, one assumption must be made. Solutions of this type of structure, based on elastic considerations, show that the total horizontal shear on the portal will be divided almost equally between the two legs; it will therefore be assumed that the horizontal reactions for the two legs are equal to each other and therefore equal to $P/2$.* The remainder of the analysis may now be carried out by statics. The vertical reaction on the right leg can be obtained by taking moments about the hinge at the base of the left leg. The vertical reaction on the left leg can then be found by applying $\Sigma F_y = 0$ to the entire structure. Once the reactions are known, the curves of bending moment and shear are easily computed, leading to values for bending moment as given in Fig. 11.8b. It is well to visualize the deformed shape of the portal under the action of the applied load. This is shown, to an exaggerated scale, in Fig. 11.8c.

Consider now a portal similar in some ways to that of Fig. 11.8a but with the bases of the legs fixed, as shown in Fig. 11.9a. This struc-

*This assumption is reasonable if the frame is symmetrical and the bending stiffnesses of the legs are equal. What would be a reasonable assumption if the stiffnesses of the legs are not equal?

ture is statically indeterminate to the third degree, so that three asumptions must be made. As was the case when the legs were hinged at their bases, it will again be assumed that the horizontal reactions for the two legs are equal and hence equal to $P/2$. Figure 11.9c shows the deformed shape of the portal under the action of the applied load. It will be noted that near the center of each leg there is a point of reversal of curvature. These are points of inflection, where the bending moment is changing sign and hence has zero value. It will therefore be assumed that there is a point of inflection at the center of each leg; this is structurally equivalent to assuming that hinges exist at points a and a', as shown in Fig.

Figure 11.9   Portal frame with fixed legs

11.9c. The vertical reactions on this portal equal the axial forces in the portal legs and may be determined by successively taking moments about a and a' of all the forces acting on that portion of the structure above a and a'. For example, taking moments about a,

$$+P\frac{h}{2} - R_{cy}b = 0 \qquad R_{cy} = +\frac{Ph}{2b}$$

The moment reaction at the base of each leg equals the shear at the point of inflection in the leg multiplied by the distance from the point of inflection to the base of the leg and therefore equals $(P/2)(h/2) = Ph/4$. Once the reactions are known, the curves of shear and bending moment for the members of the portal are easily determined by statics. The curves of bending moment for this structure and loading are given in Fig. 11.9b.

Portals for bridges are often arranged in a manner similar to that shown in Fig. 11.10a. In such a portal, the legs AB and CD are continuous from A to B and C to D, respectively, and are designed so as to be capable of carrying bending moment and shear as well as axial force.

The other members that comprise the truss at the top of the portal are considered as pin-connected and carrying axial force only. Such a structure is statically indeterminate to the third degree; the following three assumptions will be made:

1. The horizontal reactions are equal.
2. A point of inflection occurs midway between the base A of the leg AB and the end H of the knee brace for leg AB.
3. A point of inflection occurs midway between the base C of the leg CD and the end I of the knee brace for leg CD.

The horizontal reactions therefore each equal $P/2$. The moment at the base of each leg equals the shear in the leg multiplied by the distance

Figure 11.10   Bridge portal

from the point of inflection to the base of the leg and has a value of $(P/2)(10) = 5P$. Vertical reactions can be obtained by successively taking moments about the points of inflection a and a' of the forces acting on that portion of the structure above a and a'. These equations show the vertical reactions each equal to $9P/10$ and acting in the directions shown in the figure.

To find the forces in the bars connected to the legs, one may proceed as follows: Considering the leg AB as a rigid body and taking moments about B of the forces acting on the leg,

$$+ \frac{P}{2}(28) - 5P - X_{HF}(8) = 0 \qquad X_{HF} = + \frac{9P}{8}$$

$$\therefore Y_{HF} = + \frac{9P}{8}\left(\frac{4}{5}\right) = + \frac{9P}{10}$$

To find the force in bar BF, apply $\Sigma F_y = 0$ to all the forces acting on leg AB.

$$+Y_{BF} - \frac{9P}{10} + \frac{9P}{10} = 0 \quad \therefore Y_{BF} = 0 \quad \therefore X_{BF} = 0$$

To find the force in bar BE, apply $\Sigma F_x = 0$ to all the forces acting on leg AB.

$$+X_{BE} + 0 + \frac{9P}{8} + P - \frac{P}{2} = 0 \quad \therefore X_{BE} = -\frac{13P}{8}$$

With all the forces acting on leg AB known, as shown in Fig. 11.10b, the axial force on any section of the leg may be computed, and curves of shear and moment for the leg may be constructed. Leg CD can be analyzed in a similar manner. The remaining bar forces may then be computed without difficulty.

11.7 Mill Bents. Bents of mill buildings are often constructed as shown in Fig. 11.11. An approximate analysis of stresses in such a bent when it is acted on by lateral loads may be carried out on the basis of assumptions identical with those made for the portal of Fig. 11.10, viz., the horizontal reac-

Figure 11.11 Mill bent

tions at the bases of the legs are equal, and a point of inflection occurs in each leg at an elevation of 7.5 ft above the base of the leg. The application of the equations of statics to carry out the analysis after these assumptions have been made follows the same general procedure as that employed for the portal.

11.8 Towers with Straight Legs. If the legs of a statically determinate tower have a constant batter throughout their length, each face of the tower lies in a plane. For such a tower, stress analysis for lateral loads can be carried out by resolving all lateral loads into components lying in the planes of the faces of the tower that are adjacent to the joints where the lateral loads are applied. Each face of the tower may then be analyzed as a planar truss, acted upon by forces lying in the plane of that truss. Such an analysis leads directly to the forces in the web members of each face, while the forces in the legs are obtained by superimposing the bar forces resulting from the analyses of the adjacent faces.

The planar truss of each face, however, may be statically indeterminate. For such a tower, stress analysis may still be carried out on the basis of planar trusses, but it is necessary to make certain assumptions if the analysis is to be based on statics only. In Fig. 11.12a, let it be required to determine the bar forces in the diagonals of panel $abcd$. Passing section M-M through this panel, at the elevation of the intersection of the diagonals, take moments about o, which is at the intersection of the extended legs, of all the forces acting on that portion of the truss above section M-M. Since the legs extended pass through the origin of the moments, the moments of forces P_1, P_2, and P_3 are held in equilibrium by the moments of the horizontal components of the forces in the diagonals ad and bc, which act with the lever arm h.

If the diagonals can carry tension only, diagonal ad will have zero bar force, so that only one unknown appears in the foregoing equation, and the horizontal component of force in bar bc is obtained directly. If, however, the diagonals can carry compression as well as tension, it may be assumed that the horizontal components of force in the two diagonals are numerically equal but opposite in sign. This reduces the number of independent unknowns in the foregoing equation to one, and the horizontal components of the diagonal bar forces may thus be determined.

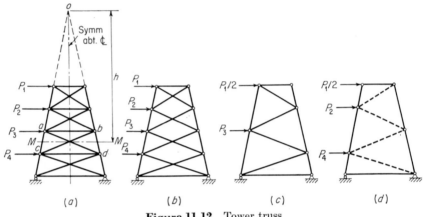

Figure 11.12   Tower truss

If the horizontal bars at the intermediate panel points are omitted, as shown in Fig. 11.12b, the tower truss may be considered as being composed of two component trusses as shown in Figs. 11.12c and d and each truss may be analyzed by statically determinate procedures for the loads assigned to it. Resultant forces in the actual truss may then be determined by superimposing the bar forces from the two component trusses.

It is therefore seen that the same general procedures as those used for the approximate analyses of end-supported indeterminate trusses may be applied in the approximate analyses of tower sides which are actually statically indeterminate planar cantilever trusses.

11.9   Stresses in Building Frames Due to Vertical Loads. A building frame consists primarily of girders, which carry vertical loads to columns, and of the columns themselves. While such a frame might be built like that shown in Fig. 11.13a, which is statically determinate, it would have little resistance against horizontal forces, such as wind loads, which it must also carry. It is therefore actually built as shown in Fig. 11.13b, in which the girders are rigidly connected to the columns so that all the members can carry bending moment, shear, and axial force. Such a frame is called a rigid frame; it is also referred to as a building bent. Because of the rigid construction, a building frame is highly indeterminate.   The degree to which it is indeterminate can be investigated by an examination of Fig. 11.13c.   Suppose that each girder is cut near mid-span as shown.   The resulting structure will be statically determinate, since each column, together with its girder stubs, acts as a cantilever.   To arrive at this condition, however, it is necessary to remove the bending moment, shear, and axial force in each girder where it is cut.   If n is the number of girders in the bent, it is necessary to remove $3n$ redundants to make the bent statically determinate; hence the bent is indeterminate to the $3n$th degree.   The bent of Fig. 11.13b

Figure 11.13   Building bent

Figure 11.14   Girder for building bent

is therefore statically indeterminate to the 18th degree.   A bent with 100 stories and 8 stacks of columns would include 700 girders and be statically indeterminate to the 2,100th degree.   It is therefore highly advantageous to have approximate methods available for the analysis of such structures.

Since a building frame of the type just considered is statically indeterminate to a degree equal to three times the number of girders, it will be necessary to make three stress assumptions for each girder in the bent if an analysis is to be carried out on the basis of statics only.   In Fig. 11.14a, if a girder is subjected to a load of w lb per ft, extending over the entire span, both of the joints A and B will rotate as shown in Fig. 11.14b, since, while they are partly restrained against rotation, the restraint is not complete.   Had the supports at A and B been completely fixed against rotation, as shown in Fig. 11.14c, it can easily be shown from a consideration of bending moments in a fixed-end beam that the points of inflection would be located at a distance of $0.21L$ from each end. If the supports at A and B were hinged, as shown in Fig. 11.14d, the points of zero moment would be at the end of the beam. For the actual case of partial fixity, the points of inflection may be assumed to lie somewhere between the two extremes of $0.21L$ and $0.00L$ from the ends of the beam. If they are assumed to be located at one-tenth of the span length from each end joint, a reasonable approximation has been made.

Figure 11.15 Assumptions regarding girders

Figure 11.16 Girder bending moments

Solutions of building bents based on elastic action show that under vertical loads the axial force in the girders is usually very small.

The following three assumptions will therefore be made for **each girder**, in analyzing a building bent acted upon by vertical loads:

1. The axial force in the girder is zero.

2. A point of inflection occurs at the one-tenth point measured along the span from the left support.

3. A point of inflection occurs at the one-tenth point measured along the span from the right support.

This is equivalent to assuming that the bent acts structurally in the same manner as does the statically determinate bent of Fig. 11.15. Girders may then be analyzed by statics, as will be illustrated by considering Fig. 11.16. The maximum positive moment occurs at span center and is given by

$$M = +\tfrac{1}{8}(1.0)(16)^2 = +32.0 \text{ kip-ft}$$

The maximum negative moment occurs at either end of the span and is given by

$$M = -8.0(2) - 1.0(2)(1) = -18.0 \text{ kip-ft}$$

The maximum shear occurs at each end of the span and is given by

$$S = 8.0(1) + 2.0(1) = 10 \text{ kips}$$

Since the end shears acting on the girders are equal to the vertical forces applied to the columns by the girders, the axial forces in the columns are easily found by summing up the girder shears from the top of the column down to the column section under consideration.

To produce maximum compression in a column, bays on both sides of the column are loaded. For interior columns, moments applied at a given floor by the two girders oppose each other; hence the column moments are small and are often neglected in design. For exterior columns, however, girders apply moments to only one side of the columns; hence the column moments are larger and must be considered in design. In computing column moments, however, assumption 1 is invalid. Girder moments should be divided between columns in proportion to their stiffnesses.

11.10 Stresses in Building Frames Due to Lateral Loads— General. In Art. 11.9, it is pointed out that approximate methods of

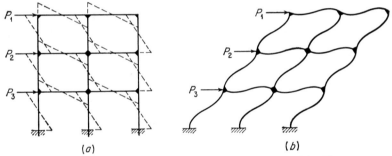

(a)   (b)

Figure 11.17   Building frame subjected to lateral loading

analyzing bents are of importance because of the fact that such structures are highly indeterminate. It is shown that the degree of statical indetermination for a bent such as that of Fig. 11.17a equals three times the number of girders in the bent. The number of assumptions that must be made to permit an analysis by statics depends on the structure itself so that for this bent one must make three times as many assumptions as there are girders, regardless of the type of loading considered. The assumptions made in analyzing building bents acted upon by vertical loads will not, however, be suitable for lateral-load analysis, for the structural action of bents is entirely different when lateral loads are considered. This may be seen by a consideration of Fig. 11.17b, which illustrates, to an exaggerated scale, the shape that a building frame takes under the action of lateral loads. It will be noted that, while points of inflection occur in the members, they do not occur in the same manner as under the action of vertical loads. Actually, when a building bent is acted upon by lateral loads, there will be, as shown in Fig. 11.17*b*, a point of inflection near the center of each girder and each column. The assumption that points of inflection occur at the mid-points of all members is therefore a reasonable one and is often among those made to carry out by statics an approximate analysis of building bents under lateral loads. The moment curves for the structure of Fig. 11.17 are of the type shown by the dotted lines of Fig. 11.17*a*.

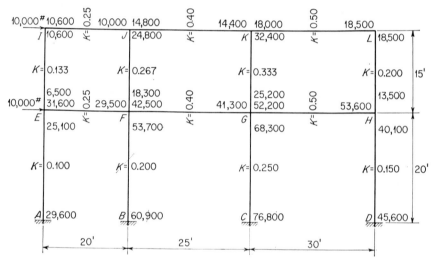

Figure 11.18   "Exact" solution for end moments caused by lateral loading

In this treatment, three approximate methods for analyzing building frames acted upon by lateral loads will be given. These methods are (1) the portal method, (2) the cantilever method, (3) the factor method.

In order that the relative accuracies of these methods may be considered, all three methods are applied to the same bent. This bent and its loading are shown in Fig. 11.18. It is possible to make a so-called "exact" solution for this bent and loading, using, for example, the "slope-deflection" method of analyzing statically indeterminate rigid frames, as treated in Chap. 13. Such a solution is of interest for the comparison of the results of the approximate methods and has led to the values of end moments in foot-pounds in the girders and columns of the bent of Fig. 11.18 that are shown by the numbers at the ends of the members.

For the slope-deflection solution and also for the factor-method solution, it is necessary to know the relative stiffness of each member. Relative stiffness is denoted by K and for a given member is obtained by dividing its moment of inertia by its length.   Values of K are shown for each member of the bent of Fig. 11.18.

11.11   The Portal Method.   In the portal method, the following assumptions are made:

1. There is a point of inflection at the center of each girder.
2. There is a point of inflection at the center of each column.
3. The total horizontal shear on each story is divided between the columns of that story in a manner such that each interior column carries twice as much shear as each exterior column.

This last assumption is arrived at by considering each story to be made up of a series of portals, as shown in Fig. 11.19.   Thus, while an exterior column corresponds to a single portal leg, an interior column corresponds to two portal legs, so that it becomes reasonable to assume interior columns to carry twice the shear of exterior columns.

Figure 11.19   Series of portals equivalent to building frame

If there are m columns in a story, assumption 3 is equivalent to making $(m - 1)$ assumptions per story, regarding column-shear relations.

With reference to the bent of Fig. 11.18, application of the portal methods results in making the following number of assumptions:

Inflection points in girders	$2 \times 3 = 6$
Inflection points in columns	$4 \times 2 = 8$
Column shear relations	$2 \times 3 = \underline{6}$
Total	20

Since there are six girders in this bent, the structure is indeterminate to the eighteenth degree.   Hence, the portal method makes more assumptions than are necessary.   However, it so happens that the additional assumptions are consistent with the necessary assumptions, and no inconsistency of stresses, as computed by statics, results.

To illustrate the application of the portal method, it will now be applied to the bent of Fig. 11.18.   The following discussion refers to Fig. 11.20, where the results of the portal-method analysis are given.

Column Shears.   In accordance with assumption 3, let x = shear in each exterior column of a given story; then $2x$ = shear in each interior column of the same story.   For the first story,

$$x + 2x + 2x + x = 6x = 10,000 + 10,000 = 20,000$$
$$x = 3,333 \qquad 2x = 6,667$$

For the second story, $6x = 10,000; x = 1,667; 2x = 3,333.$

Column Moments. In accordance with assumption 2, the moment at the center of each column is zero. Hence, each end moment for a given column equals the shear on that column multiplied by half the length of that column. For example, M_{AE}, the moment at the A end of column AE, equals $3,333 \times 10 = 33,333$ ft-lb; $M_{FJ} = 3,333 \times 7.5 = 25,000$ ft-lb; etc.

Girder Moments. Reference to Fig. 11.17b, which shows the type of deformation occurring in a building frame acted upon by lateral forces,

Figure 11.20   Solution for end moments by portal method

(a)   (b)   (c)

Figure 11.21   Free-body sketches for portions of bent shown in Fig. 11.20

indicates that girder and column moments act in opposite directions on a joint. This fact is further clarified in Fig. 11.21a, from which the following equation may be written: $M_{c1} + M_{c2} = M_{g1} + M_{g2}$. Hence we conclude that for any joint the sum of the column end moments equals the sum of the girder end moments. This relation may be used to determine girder end moments, since the column end moments have already been evaluated. At joint E, for example,

$$M_{EF} = 33,333 + 12,500 = 45,833 \text{ ft-lb}$$

Since by assumption 1 there is a point of inflection at the center of girder EF, M_{FE} also equals 45,833 ft-lb. Equating girder moments to column moments at joint F gives $M_{FG} + 45,833 = 66,667 + 25,000$, whence M_{FG} also equals 45,833 ft-lb. Continuing across the girders of the first floor in this manner, all the end moments in the girders of the first floor equal 45,833 ft-lb. Girder end moments in the roof may be determined in a similar manner; each will be found to equal 12,500 ft-lb.

Girder Shears. In Fig. 11.21b, if $\Sigma M = 0$ is written for the forces acting on a girder, taking moments about one end of the girder, $SL = 2M$, whence $S = 2M/L$. Hence the shear in girder EF is given by

$$S_{EF} = \frac{2 \times 45,833}{20} = 4,583 \text{ lb} \qquad S_{IJ} = \frac{2 \times 12,500}{20} = 1,250 \text{ lb} \qquad \text{etc.}$$

Column Axial Forces. In Fig. 11.21c, the axial forces in the columns may be obtained by summing up, from the top of the column, the shears applied to the column by the girders. Thus

$$F_{EI} = +1,250 \text{ lb} \qquad F_{AE} = +1,250 + 4,583 = +5,833 \text{ lb} \qquad \text{etc.}$$

Girder axial forces, while not usually important in design, may be obtained in a similar manner, by summing up, from one end of the girder, the shears applied to the girder by the columns; one would, of course, include the effects of the lateral loads themselves in such a summation.

11.12 The Cantilever Method. In the cantilever method, the following assumptions are made:

1. There is a point of inflection at the center of each girder.
2. There is a point of inflection at the center of each column.
3. The intensity of axial stress in each column of a story is proportional to the horizontal distance of that column from the center of gravity of all the columns of the story under consideration.

This last assumption is arrived at by considering that the column axial stress intensities can be obtained by a method analogous to that used for determining the distribution of normal stress intensities on a transverse section of a cantilever beam.

If there are m columns in a story, assumption 3 is equivalent to making $(m - 1)$ assumptions regarding column axial-stress relations, for each story. Hence, as with the portal method, the cantilever method makes more assumptions than are necessary, but again the additional assumptions prove to be consistent with the necessary assumptions.

To illustrate the application of the cantilever method, it will now be applied to the building frame of Fig. 11.18. The following discussion refers to Fig. 11.22b, where the results of the cantilever-method analysis are given.

Figure 11.22 Solution for end moments by cantilever method

Column Axial Forces. Assuming that all columns have the same cross-sectional area, the center of gravity of the columns in each story is found by the following equation:

$$x = \frac{20 + 45 + 75}{4} = 35.0 \text{ ft from } AEI$$

For the first story, refer to Fig. 11.22a. If the axial force in AE is denoted by $+F_{AE}$, then, by assumption 3, the axial forces in BF, CG, and DH will be $+{}^{15}\!/_{35}F_{AE}$, $-{}^{10}\!/_{35}F_{AE}$, and $-{}^{40}\!/_{35}F_{AE}$, respectively. Taking moments about a, the point of inflection in column DH, of all the forces acting on that part of the bent lying above the horizontal plane passing through the points of inflection of the columns of the first story,

$$+10,000(25) + 10,000(10) - F_{AE}(75) - {}^{15}\!/_{35}F_{AE}(55)$$
$$+ {}^{10}\!/_{35}F_{AE}(30) = 0$$

whence $F_{AE} = +3,890$; $F_{BF} = +{}^{15}\!/_{35}(+3,890) = +1,670$; etc.

For the second story, the column axial forces are in the same ratio to each other as they are in the first story. They would be evaluated in a similar manner, taking moments about the point of inflection in HL of all the forces acting on that portion of the bent lying above a horizontal plane passing through the points of inflection of the columns of the second story. Column axial forces are shown at the center of each column of Fig. 11.22b.

Girder Shears. The girder shears may be obtained from the column axial forces at the various joints. For example, at joint E,

$$S_{EF} = +833 - 3,890 = -3,057$$

at joint F, $S_{FG} = -3,057 + 358 - 1,670 = -4,369$; etc. Girder shears are shown at the center of each girder of Fig. 11.22b.

Girder Moment. Since the moment at the center of each girder is zero, the moment at each end of a given girder equals the shear in that girder multiplied by half of the length of that girder. For example,

$$M_{EF} = 3,057 \times 10 = 30,570 \text{ ft-lb} \quad M_{KJ} = 1,191 \times 12.5 = 14,880 \text{ ft-lb}$$

etc.

Column Moments. Column moments are determined by beginning at the top of each column stack and working progressively toward its base, as shown in the following illustration: At joint J, the column moment equals the sum of the girder moments, whence

$$M_{JF} = 8,330 + 14,880 = 23,210 \text{ ft-lb}$$

Since there is a point of inflection at the center of FJ, M_{FJ} also equals 23,210 ft-lb. At joint F, $M_{FB} + 23,210 = 30,570 + 54,600$, whence $M_{FB} = 61,960$ ft-lb. M_{BF} also equals 61,960 ft-lb, since a point of inflection is assumed midway between B and F.

11.13 The Factor Method.[1] The factor method of analyzing building frames acted upon by lateral loads is more accurate than either the portal or the cantilever method. Whereas the portal and cantilever methods depend on certain stress assumptions that make possible a stress analysis based on the equations of statics, the factor method depends on certain assumptions regarding the elastic action of the structure which

[1] J. B. Wilbur, A New Method for Analyzing Stresses Due to Lateral Loads on Building Frames, *Boston Soc. Civ. Engrs.*, vol. 21, no. 1, January, 1934.

make possible an approximate slope-deflection analysis of the bent. While based upon the slope-deflection method of analysis, it is possible to formulate a relatively simple set of rules by which the method can be applied without knowledge of the elastic principles upon which it is based.

Before applying the factor method, it is necessary to compute the value of $K = I/L$ for each girder and each column. It is not necessary to use absolute values of K, since the stresses depend upon the relative stiffnesses of the members of the bent. It is, however, necessary for the K values for the various members to be in the correct ratio to each other.

The factor method may be applied by carrying out the following six steps:

1. For each joint, compute the girder factor g by the following relation: $g = \Sigma K_c/\Sigma K$, where ΣK_c denotes the sum of the K values for the columns meeting at that joint and ΣK denotes the sum of the K values for all the members of that joint. Write each value of g thus obtained at the near end of each girder meeting at the joint where it is computed.

2. For each joint compute the column factor c by the following relation: $c = 1 - g$, where g is the girder factor for that joint as computed in step 1. Write each value of c thus obtained at the near end of each column meeting at the joint where it is computed. For the fixed column bases of the first story, take $c = 1$.

3. From steps 1 and 2, there is a number at each end of each member of the bent. To each of these numbers, add half of the number at the other end of the member.

4. Multiply each sum obtained from step 3 by the K value for the member in which the sum occurs. For columns, call this product the column moment factor C; for girders, call this product the girder moment factor G.

5. The column moment factors C from step 4 are actually the approximate relative values for column end moments for the story in which they occur. The sum of the column end moments in a given story may be shown by statics to equal the total horizontal shear on that story multiplied by the story height. Hence, the column moment factors C may be converted into column end moments, by direct proportion, for each story.

6. The girder moment factors G from step 4 are actually approximate relative values for girder end moments for each joint. The sum of the girder end moments at each joint is equal, by statics, to the sum of the column end moments at that joint, which can be obtained from step 5. Hence, the girder moment factors G may be converted to girder end moments, by direct proportion, for each joint.

The factor method will now be illustrated by applying it to the bent

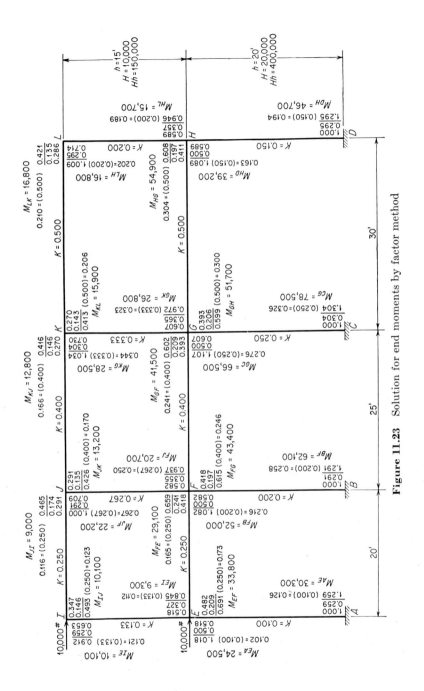

Figure 11.23 Solution for end moments by factor method

311

of Fig. 11.18. The following discussion refers to Fig. 11.23, where computations for the factor method and the results obtained by it are shown. Values of K are written on the various members as part of the given data. For each story, on the right side of the figure, values of H, the total horizontal shear on the story, and Hh, the product of H and the story height h, are first worked out. Illustrative details of the solution follow:

Step 1. Computation of Girder Factors

$$\text{For joint } E: g_E = \frac{0.133 + 0.100}{0.133 + 0.100 + 0.250} = 0.482$$

This number is written at the left end of girder EF.

$$\text{For joint } F: g_F = \frac{0.267 + 0.200}{0.267 + 0.200 + 0.250 + 0.400} = 0.418$$

This number is written at the left end of girder FG and at the right end of girder EF.

$$\text{For joint } I: g_I = \frac{0.133}{0.133 + 0.250} = 0.347$$

This number is written at the left end of girder IJ.

Girder factors for all other joints are computed in a similar manner and written at the near end of each girder meeting at the joint where the girder factor is computed.

Step 2. Computation of Column Factors

$$\text{For joint } E: c_E = 1 - g_E = 1.000 - 0.482 = 0.518$$

This number is written at the top of column AE and at the bottom of column EI.

$$\text{For joint } J: c_J = 1.000 - 0.291 = 0.709$$

This number is written at the top of column FJ.

$$\text{For joint } A: c_A = 1.000$$

since this is a fixed column base of the first story. This number is written at the bottom of column AE.

Column factors for all other joints are computed by similar procedures and written at the near end of each column meeting at the joint where the column factor is computed.

Step 3.   Increasing the Number at Each End of Each Member by Half of the Number at the Other End of That Member

For joint A: Member AE: $1.000 + 0.5(0.518) = 1.259$
For joint E: Member EI: $0.518 + 0.5(0.653) = 0.845$
          Member EF: $0.482 + 0.5(0.418) = 0.691$
          Member EA: $0.518 + 0.5(1.000) = 1.018$

Similar computations for all joints are made directly on Fig. 11.23.

Step 4.   Computation of Column Moment Factors and Girder Moment Factors

For joint A: Member AE: $C_{AE} = 1.259(0.100) = 0.126$
For joint E: Member EI: $C_{EI} = 0.845(0.133) = 0.112$
          Member EF: $G_{EF} = 0.691(0.250) = 0.173$
          Member EA: $C_{EA} = 1.018(0.100) = 0.102$

Similar computations for all joints are made directly on Fig. 11.23.

Step 5.   Determination of Column Moments

Since the column moment factors are relative values of column end moments for each story of the bent, this is another way of saying that

$$M_{AE} = AC_{AE} \qquad M_{EA} = AC_{EA} \qquad M_{BF} = AC_{BF} \qquad \text{etc.}$$

where M_{AE}, M_{EA}, M_{BF}, etc., are the actual moments at the ends of the columns and A has the same value for all the columns of a given story.

Figure 11.24   Isolated columns of a given story

The sum of the end moments may therefore be expressed by

Σ column end moments
$$= A(C_{AE} + C_{EA} + C_{BF} + C_{FB} + C_{CG} + C_{GC} + C_{DH} + C_{HD})$$
$$= A\Sigma C \text{ for story} \qquad\qquad (a)$$

Consider the static equilibrium of all the forces acting on all the columns of a given story. Refer to Fig. 11.24, and take moments about the base of the right-hand column at point a.

$$(S_1 + S_2 + S_3 + S_4)h$$
$$= M_1 + M_2 + M_3 + M_4 + M_5 + M_6 + M_7 + M_8$$

The sum $S_1 + S_2 + S_3 + S_4$ equals H, the total horizontal shear on the story. The sum $M_1 + M_2 + \cdots + M_8$ equals the sum of the column end moments for the story. Hence

$$\Sigma \text{ column end moments} = Hh \tag{b}$$

From Eqs. (a) and (b),

$$A = \frac{Hh}{\Sigma C \text{ for story}} \tag{c}$$

For each story, A may be determined by Eq. (c). The end moment for each column of that story may then be obtained by multiplying the respective column moment factor by A.

This procedure is illustrated by its application to the first story of the bent of Fig. 11.23.

$$A_1 = \frac{400,000}{0.126 + 0.102 + 0.258 + 0.216 + 0.326 + 0.276 + 0.194 + 0.163}$$
$$= 241,000$$
$$M_{AE} = 0.126(241,000) = 30,300 \text{ ft-lb}$$
$$M_{EA} = 0.102(241,000) = 24,500 \text{ ft-lb}$$
$$M_{BF} = 0.258(241,000) = 62,100 \text{ ft-lb}$$

Moments in the other column ends for the first story are similarly obtained, by using $A_1 = 241,000$. Moments in the column ends of the second story are obtained from A_2, which is computed by applying Eq. (c) to the second story, leading to $A_2 = 83,000$.

Step 6. *Determination of Girder Moments*

Since the girder moment factors are relative values of girder end moments for a given joint, this is another way of saying, with reference to Fig. 11.25, that $M_{AB} = B_A G_{AB}$ and $M_{AC} = B_A G_{AC}$, where B_A has the same value in each of the foregoing relations. Moreover, since at any joint the sum of the girder moments equals the sum of the column moments, B_A may be evaluated from the following relation:

$$B_A G_{AB} + B_A G_{AC} = M_{AE} + M_{AD}$$

whence, at any joint N,

$$B_N = \frac{\text{sum of column moments at joint } N}{\text{sum of girder moment factors at joint } N} \tag{d}$$

For each joint, B_N may be evaluated by Eq. (d). The end moment for each girder at that joint may then be obtained by multiplying the respective girder moment factor by B_N. This procedure is illustrated by its application to joint F of the bent of Fig. 11.23.

$$B_F = \frac{52,000 + 20,700}{0.165 + 0.246} = 176,500$$

$$M_{FE} = 0.165(176,500) = 29,100 \text{ ft-lb}$$
$$M_{FG} = 0.246(176,500) = 43,400 \text{ ft-lb}$$

It will be noted that the application of this procedure for step 6 to exterior joints of a bent results in discovery that girder end moments at these joints equal the sum of the column end moments, as they should by

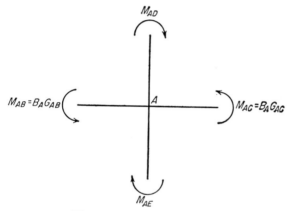

Figure 11.25 Isolated joint

statics. Thus girder end moments at exterior columns may be obtained directly from column end moments by statics, and the computation of girder moment factors at these joints is not necessary.

The shears and axial forces in the columns and girders may be computed by the equations of statics, once the end moments are known.

11.14 Problems for Solution

*Problem 11.1   Owing to a uniform live load of 500 lb per ft, compute the maximum bar force of each character in the following bars of the truss of Fig. 11.2: (a) L_3L_4; (b) $L_3'L_4$. (Diagonals can carry compression.)

*Problem 11.2   Owing to a uniform live load of 1,000 lb per ft and a single concentrated live load of 10,000 lb, compute the maximum bar force in the following bars of the truss of Fig. 11.6a: (a) U_5U_6; (b) L_4U_6; (c) U_0L_0.

Problem 11.3   The portal of Fig. 11.8a is acted upon by a uniformly distributed wind load of 200 lb per ft along the entire length of the left column. If $h = 40$ ft and $b = 30$ ft, construct the moment curves for all the members of the portal.

Problem 11.4   Solve Prob. 11.3, using the portal of Fig. 11.9a.

Problem 11.5   Solve Prob. 11.3, using the portal of Fig. 11.10a, with dimensions as shown on the figure.

*Problem 11.6   For the mill bent of Fig. 11.11,

(a) Draw the shear and moment curves for the left supporting column.

(b) What are the forces applied to the roof truss by the columns and knee braces?

Problem 11.7   A tower of rectangular cross section, with sides similar to that of Fig. 11.12a, has five vertical panels, the height of each being 10 ft.   The width of each side of the tower is 15 ft at the base and 7.5 ft at the top.   Each panel point on the left side of one face of the tower is subjected to a horizontal panel load of 1,000 lb, acting to the right and lying in the plane of the face under consideration.   Determine the bar forces in all the members of this tower face, assuming that the diagonals of each panel have equal bar forces but of opposite character.

Problem 11.8   A building bent has three equal bays of 20 ft each and three stories of 12 ft each.   The columns of the first story are fixed at their bases.   For each girder the dead load is 500 lb per ft and the live load is 300 lb per ft.   Determine (a) the maximum positive girder moment occurring in the bent; (b) the maximum negative girder moment occurring in the bent; (c) the maximum girder shear occurring in the bent; (d) the maximum exterior column compression occurring in the bent; (e) the maximum interior column compression occurring in the bent; (f) the maximum exterior column moment occurring in the bent; (g) the maximum interior column moment occurring in the bent.

*Problem 11.9   The building bent of Prob. 11.8 is acted upon by a horizontal force of 5,000 lb applied at each girder elevation on the left exterior columns.   Determine the bending moment at each end of each member by the portal method.

*Problem 11.10   Solve Prob. 11.9 by the cantilever method.

*Problem 11.11   Solve Prob. 11.9 by the factor method, if the moment of inertia of each girder is three times as great as the moment of inertia of each column.

Problem 11.12   Compute the bar force in member *R* of the portal frame shown in Fig. 11.26.   Make any assumptions that you consider reasonable and necessary.

Figure 11.26   Problem 11.12

Problem 11.13   Calculate the force in bar A of the structure shown in Fig. 11.27. Make any reasonable assumptions that are necessary.

Figure 11.27   Problem 11.13

Problem 11.14   All truss members of the structure shown in Fig. 11.28 are capable of carrying both tension and compression.   The points of inflection are 4 ft above the base of each column.   Calculate the axial force in member P.

Figure 11.28   Problem 11.14

Problem 11.15   Use the cantilever method to determine the shears and end moments in the girders of the building frame shown in Fig. 11.29.   Areas of columns are shown at the top of the figure.

Figure 11.29   Problem 11.15

12

Deflections of Structures

12.1 Introduction. Engineering structures are constructed from materials that deform slightly when subjected to stress or a change in temperature. As a result of this deformation, points on the structure undergo certain movements called deflections. Provided that the elastic limit of the material is not exceeded, this deformation and the resulting deflection disappear when the stress is removed and the temperature returns to its original value. This type of deformation or deflection is called *elastic* and may be caused either by loads acting on the structure or by a change in temperature.

Sometimes, the deflection of the structure is the result of settlement of the supports, play in pin joints, shrinkage of concrete, or some other such cause. In such cases, the cause of the deflection remains in action permanently, and therefore the resulting deflections never disappear. This type of deflection may be called *nonelastic* to distinguish it from the elastic type mentioned above. In either type, it should be noted, at this time, that deformation and deflection may occur with or without stress in the structure. This will be discussed in detail later.

The structural engineer often finds it necessary to compute deflections. For example, in the erection of cantilever or continuous bridges or in designing the lifting devices for swing bridges, it is imperative to compute the deflection of various points on the structure. In certain cases, computations must be made to see that the deflection of a structure does not exceed certain specified limits. For example, the deflection of the floor of a building must be limited to minimize the cracking of plaster ceilings, and the deflection of a shaft must be limited to ensure the proper functioning of its bearings. Deflections must also be computed in order to analyze the vibration and dynamic response characteristics of a structure. Perhaps the most important reason for the structural engineer's interest in deflection computations is that the stress analysis of statically indeterminate structures is based largely on an evaluation of their deflection under load.

Numerous methods have been presented in the literature for computing deflections. Of the various methods the following are considered the most fundamental and useful and will therefore be discussed in this chapter:

1. Methods to compute one particular deflection component at a time:
   a. Method of virtual work (applicable to any type of structure)
   b. Castigliano's second theorem (applicable to any type of structure)
2. Methods to compute several deflection components simultaneously:
   a. Williot-Mohr method (applicable to trusses only)
   b. Bar-chain method (applicable to trusses only)
   c. Moment-area method (elastic-load method or conjugate-beam method) (applicable to beams and frames)

12.2 Nature of the Deflection Problem. The computation of the deflection of a structure is essentially a problem in geometry or trigonometry. Of course, it is first necessary to define the deformation of the particles or elements of the structure, but once this is done the deflections may be computed by using geometrical or trigonometrical principles.

This is particularly evident in the case of a simple truss, which is usually composed of triangles. The configuration of these triangles may be determined if the lengths of their three sides are known. Thus, if the lengths of the members before and after deformation are known, the position of the joints before and after may be calculated by trigonometry. From the difference of the two positions of any joint, its deflection may then readily be determined. This procedure, though simple in theory, is a laborious one and therefore not suitable for practical application.

In the case of a truss, it is also possible to solve the deflection problem graphically simply by superimposing the layouts of the deformed and undeformed truss. This procedure is obvious and simple in theory, but in order to achieve any accuracy such a large scale would have to be used that it would be physically impossible for a draftsman to make the drawing.

The so-called "method of rotation" is another means of computing truss deflections that is simple in theory but impractical in application. This method gives us some useful ideas concerning the kinematics of truss deflection, however. In applying this method, the deflection of any joint of a simple truss due to a change in length of any one member may be determined by investigating the resulting rotation of one portion of the truss with respect to the other, the latter being assumed as fixed in position. By considering the effect of each member separately and summing up the results, the total deflection of any joint due to the change in length of all members may be determined.

To illustrate this procedure, consider first the effect of a change in length of the upper chord U_2U_3 of the truss of Fig. 12.1. Since all deformations are small, it is permissible to assume that the rotations of members are so small that

$$\alpha = \sin \alpha = \tan \alpha$$

It is further permissible to consider that the arc, along which a point actually travels as a body is rotated through a small angle, coincides with its tangent for all practical purposes. To consider the effect of the change in length of U_2U_3 on the deflections, first remove the pin at joint U_3 and then allow this change in length, ΔL, to take place. If the left-hand portion of the truss is considered to be held fixed in position, it then is necessary to rotate member U_2U_3 about U_2 and the dotted portion of the truss about L_3 until the points U_3 coincide again. During these rotations, point U_3 on member

Figure 12.1 Truss deflection caused by change in length of a chord bar

Figure 12.2 Truss deflection caused by change in length of a diagonal bar

U_2U_3 may be considered to move vertically, and on the dotted portion horizontally. In such a case, the intersection of these two paths will fall along the original position of U_2U_3, and the final position of U_3 is located as shown. Then,

$$\delta = \alpha b = \frac{\Delta L}{a} b = \frac{b}{a} \Delta L$$

Now if the supports do not settle, joint L_6 must not actually move vertically; so the entire truss must be rotated clockwise about L_0 until L_6 is back on its support. The dashed line joining L_0 and L_6 will therefore correspond to the line of zero deflection, and the downward vertical deflection of joint L_3 will be, by proportion,

$$\delta_{L_3} = \frac{L - b}{L} \delta = \frac{L - b}{L} \frac{b}{a} \Delta L$$

In a similar manner, the deflection caused by the change in length of a typical diagonal may be evaluated by proceeding as indicated in Fig. 12.2. These considerations demonstrate the impracticality of this method, but the ideas involved are directly applicable to the Williot-Mohr method, which is discussed in Art. 12.12.

While the various methods discussed above are impractical, it is important to recognize their existence, for it gives us confidence to know that the deflection problem can be solved using simple "everyday" ideas. Further, it is now obvious that some refinement must be introduced in theory to reduce the labor in the practical solution of such problems.

12.3 Principle of Virtual Displacements. Perhaps the most general, direct, and foolproof method for computing the deflections of structures is the *method of virtual work*. This method is based on an application of the *principle of virtual displacements*, which was originally formulated by John Bernoulli in 1717.   This principle may be developed by the following considerations:

Consider a truly rigid body which is in static equilibrium under a system of forces Q.   In this sense, a rigid body is intended to mean an undeformable body in which there can be no relative movement of any of its particles.   Suppose first that, as shown in Fig. 12.3, this rigid body is translated without rotation a small amount by some other cause which is separate from and independent of the Q-force system. Upon selecting an origin o and two coordinate reference axes x and y, this translation may be defined by δ_o, the actual translation of the origin o, or by the two components δ_{ox} and δ_{oy}, in the x and y directions, both assumed to be plus when in the sense shown.   Since the body is rigid, every point on the body will be translated through exactly the same distance as point o.

All the Q forces may be resolved into x and y components, designated as Q_{nx} and Q_{ny} for any particular force Q_n and assumed to be plus when in the same sense as the plus sense of the corresponding coordinates.   Since these Q forces are

Figure 12.3   Virtual translation of rigid body

in static equilibrium, the following equations are satisfied by the components of these forces:

$$\Sigma Q_{nx} = 0 \qquad \Sigma Q_{ny} = 0 \qquad \Sigma(Q_{nx}y_n - Q_{ny}x_n) = 0 \qquad (a)$$

Consider now the work W_Q done by only these Q forces as they "ride along" when the rigid body is translated a small amount δ_o by some *other* cause.   Since this translation is small, all the Q forces may be assumed to maintain the same position and direction relative to the body and to each other and, hence, to remain in equilibrium during the translation.   Then, we may write that

$$W_Q = \Sigma(Q_{nx}\delta_{ox} + Q_{ny}\delta_{oy}) = \delta_{ox}\Sigma Q_{nx} + \delta_{oy}\Sigma Q_{ny}$$

and, therefore, in view of Eqs. (a), the total work done by the Q forces in such a case is equal to zero.

In a similar manner, we may consider the work done by the Q forces during a small rotation α_o of the rigid body about point o.   During a small angular rotation, a point may be assumed to move along the normal to the radius drawn from the center of rotation to that point, i.e., along the tangent rather than the arc.   Hence, the x and y components of the displacement of any point n may be computed to be as shown in Fig. 12.4.   Since the angular rotation is small, the Q forces again may be assumed to remain in equilibrium.   Then, we may write that

$$W_Q = \Sigma(Q_{nx}\alpha_o y_n - Q_{ny}\alpha_o x_n) = \alpha_o\Sigma(Q_{nx}y_n - Q_{ny}x_n)$$

and, therefore, in view of Eqs. (a), the total work done by the Q forces during the rotation of a rigid body is also equal to zero.

Figure 12.4   Virtual rotation of rigid body

After a little thought, it is evident that *any* small displacement of a rigid body may be broken down into a translation of a given point on the body plus a rotation of the rigid body about that point. Since, in the case of either translation or rotation, the work done by the Q system (which is a system in equilibrium) has been shown to equal zero, the following principle is obviously true in the general case where a rigid body may be given *any* type of small displacement:

Bernoulli's principle of virtual displacements: **If a system of forces Q acting on a rigid body is in equilibrium and remains in equilibrium as the body is given any small virtual displacement, the virtual work done by the Q-force system is equal to zero.**

In this statement, the term **virtual** has been used to indicate that the action producing the displacement is separate from and independent of the Q-force system. The work done by the Q-force system as it "rides along" during such a **virtual displacement** would be called **virtual work.**

12.4   Fundamentals of Method of Virtual Work. The principle of virtual displacements may now be used to develop the basis for the method of virtual work for computing the deflection of structures. This method is applicable to any type of structure—beam, truss, or frame; planar or space frameworks. For simplicity, however, consider any planar structure such as that shown in Fig. 12.5. Suppose that this structure is in static equilibrium under the external loads and reactions of the Q-force system shown.

Since the body as a whole is in equilibrium, any particular particle such as the crosshatched one may be isolated and will also be in equilibrium under the internal Q stresses developed by the external Q forces. If this particle and its adjoining particles are isolated, it will be acted upon by internal Q stresses on any internal boundaries with adjacent particles but by external Q forces on any external boundaries. On the adjacent internal boundaries of any two adjoining particles, the internal stresses will be numerically equal but act in opposite directions.

Now suppose that the body is subjected to a small change in shape caused by some source *other* than the Q-force system. Such a change in shape would give the Q-force system a ride and would be called a *virtual change in shape* or a *virtual deformation*. Owing to this change in shape,

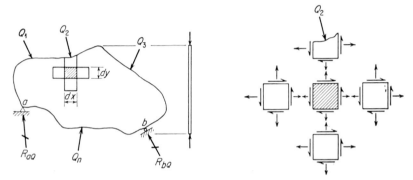

Figure 12.5 Planar structure in equilibrium under Q-force system

any particle such as the crosshatched one might be deformed as well as translated and rotated as a rigid particle. Hence, the boundaries of such a particle may be displaced, and therefore the Q stresses acting on such boundaries would move and, hence, do virtual work. Let the virtual work done by the Q stresses on the boundaries of the differential particle be designated by dW_s. Part of this virtual work will be done because of the movements of the boundaries of the particle caused by the deformation of the particle itself; this part will be called dW_d. The remaining part of dW_s will be the virtual work done by the Q stresses during the remaining part of the displacement of the boundaries and will be equal to $dW_s - dW_d$. However, this remaining displacement is caused by the translation and rotation of the particle as a *rigid body*, and according to the principle of virtual displacements, the virtual work done in such a case is equal to zero. Hence,

$$dW_s - dW_d = 0 \quad \text{or} \quad dW_s = dW_d$$

If the virtual work done by the Q stresses on all particles of the body is now added up, this equation becomes

$$W_s = W_d \qquad (12.1)$$

To evaluate first W_s, we recognize that this term represents the total virtual work done by the Q stresses and forces on all the boundaries of all particles. However, for every *internal* boundary of a particle, there is an adjoining particle whose adjacent boundary is actually the same line on the body as a whole, and therefore these adjacent boundaries are displaced exactly the same amount. Since the forces acting on the two adjacent internal boundaries are numerically equal but opposite in direction, the total virtual work done on the pair of adjoining internal boundaries is zero. Hence, since all the internal boundaries occur in pairs of adjoining boundaries, there is no net virtual work done by the forces on all the *internal* boundaries. W_s, therefore, consists only of the work done by the *external* Q forces on the *external* boundaries of the particles. Equation (12.1) may therefore be interpreted in the following manner:

Law of Virtual Work. **If a deformable body is in equilibrium under a Q-force system and remains in equilibrium while it is subjected to a small virtual deformation, the external virtual work done by the external Q forces acting on the body is equal to the internal virtual work of deformation done by the internal Q stresses.**

This law of virtual work is the basis of the method of virtual work used to compute deflections. Before such computations can be made, suitable expressions must be developed so that the external virtual work and internal virtual work of deformation may be evaluated. In addition, certain "tricks" must be used in selecting a suitable Q system so that the desired deflection components may be computed. All this will be explained in the following articles.

It is important to emphasize the assumptions and limitations of this development in order to appreciate the flexibility and generality of the method of virtual work.

1. The only requirement of the external Q forces and the internal Q stresses is that they shall form a system of forces which are in equilibrium and remain in equilibrium throughout the virtual deformation. This requirement will not be satisfied if the virtual deformation has varied the geometry of the structure appreciably.

2. The relations that have been derived are independent of the cause or type of deformation—they are true whether the deformation is due to loads, temperature, errors in lengths of members, or other causes or whether the material follows Hooke's law or not.

3. In addition to being small so that the geometry of the structure is not altered appreciably, the deformations must be **compatible;** that is, the

elements of the structure must deform so as to fit together after deformation and to satisfy the conditions of restraint at the supports.

12.5 Expressions for External and Internal Virtual Work. It is easy to evaluate W_s, the external virtual work done by a system of Q forces acting on any structure. Let δ denote the displacement of the point of application of a Q force during the virtual deformation of the structure. This displacement δ is to be measured along the same direction as the line of action of its corresponding Q force. The virtual work done by the force Q_1 will then be Q_1 times δ_1, and therefore the total external virtual work done by all the Q forces including both loads and reactions will be

$$W_s = Q_1\delta_1 + Q_2\delta_2 + Q_3\delta_3 + \cdots$$

This expression may be represented as follows:

$$W_s = \Sigma Q\delta \qquad (12.2)$$

which simply means that the product of Q times δ must be evaluated for each Q force and summed up for all the Q forces, including both loads and reactions. Note that having assumed the work to be positive in this formula implies that δ should be considered plus when in the same sense as its corresponding Q force.

Figure 12.6   Axial change of length

It is also relatively easy to evaluate W_d, the internal virtual work of deformation. In this instance, however, expressions for W_d must be developed for different types of deformation, i.e., for axial change in length, shear deformation, bending deformation, etc. Consider first the simple case of a little element having an undeformed length of s and a cross-sectional area of a, as shown in Fig. 12.6. Suppose that the Q stress intensities σ_Q are uniformly distributed over the cross section a so that the axial force is $(\sigma_Q)(a)$. If the virtual deformation of this element is simply a uniform axial strain e, the axial change in length Δs will be equal to $(e)(s)$. The internal virtual work of deformation done by the Q stresses in this case will simply be

$$W_d = \sigma_Q a\,\Delta s = \sigma_Q aes \qquad (12.3)$$

This expression may now be used to evaluate the internal virtual work of deformation for a beam or a member of a truss or frame.

Consider the case of a member deformed by a two-dimensional system of P loads, or by a change in temperature. Suppose that the centroidal axis of the member is straight and that all the cross sections of the member have axes of symmetry lying in the plane of the P loads. The resultant of all the internal P stresses, then, will also lie in this same plane.   The axial force F_P at any cross section will produce an axial strain that is uniform for all the fibers at this section.   Suppose that the strain produced by the change in temperature is also uniform at this cross section. Let e_o denote the uniform axial strain at any particular cross section produced by these two effects.   The P-load system may also produce a shear and bending moment at this cross section.   Because of these two effects, a longitudinal element such as that of Fig. 12.7 will be subjected to shear and normal stresses as shown.   More detailed analysis reveals that, unless a member is very deep in comparison with its length, the effect of the shear stress is small in comparison with the deflection caused by the

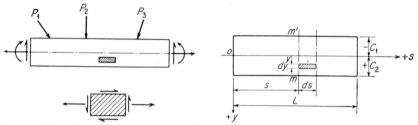

Figure 12.7   Shear and bending by P loads

Figure 12.8   Coordinate axes

elongation and contraction of these elements under the longitudinal normal stresses.   In this book, therefore, the effect of shearing stresses will be neglected.

Neglecting the effect of shear deformation, it is then easy to evaluate the virtual work of deformation done simply as a result of the elongation and contraction of the longitudinal elements.   Suppose that the Q-force system lies in the same plane as the P forces of Fig. 12.7 and exerts some axial force, shear, and bending moment on the cross sections of the member.   We now want to develop an expression for the internal virtual work of deformation done by the resulting Q stresses as the member is subjected to virtual deformation of the type described in the previous paragraph. We select the orthogonal axes at o—s, y, and z—so that the s axis coincides with the centroidal axis of the member and the z axis is normal to the plane of the paper.   If we now consider a longitudinal element located at the position (s,y), in this member, as shown in Fig. 12.8, it is apparent that, under the conditions described, this element is precisely similar to the one shown in Fig. 12.6.   The virtual work for a longitudinal element may therefore be evaluated by means of Eq. (12.3).   Doing this for all the elements of the member and summing them up will give us the virtual work of deformation for the entire member.

Assuming that the normal stresses may be found by elementary beam theory, let

M_P = bending moment on section mm' due to P loads (which cause virtual deformation)

M_Q = bending moment on section mm' due to Q loads

F_P = axial force on section mm' due to P loads

F_Q = axial force on section mm' due to Q loads

σ_P = normal stress at point (s,y) due to P loads = $(F_P/A) + (M_P y/I)$

σ_P' = normal stress at point (s,y) due to $F_P = F_P/A$

σ_P'' = normal stress at point (s,y) due to $M_P = M_P y/I$

σ_Q = normal stress at point (s,y) due to Q loads = $(F_Q/A) + (M_Q y/I)$

e = axial strain of a longitudinal element at a point (s,y) due to P loads and temperature change

e_o = axial strain of a longitudinal element at a point on the centroidal axis due to P loads and temperature change

I = moment of inertia of cross section mm' about oz axis

A = cross-sectional area of cross section mm'

E = modulus of elasticity of the material

b = width of cross section mm' at fiber y

Considering now the longitudinal element of the member at point (s,y), the length of which is ds, the width b, and the depth dy, then

$$e = e_o + \frac{\sigma_P''}{E} = e_o + \frac{M_P y}{EI}$$

and the virtual work of deformation for this element is

$$(\sigma_Q b \, dy)(e \, ds) = \left(\frac{F_Q}{A} + \frac{M_Q y}{I}\right)(b \, dy)\left(e_o + \frac{M_P y}{EI}\right) ds$$

The total virtual work of deformation for the entire member is therefore

$$W_d = \int_0^L \int_{-C_1}^{+C_2} \left(\frac{F_Q}{A} + \frac{M_Q y}{I}\right)(b \, dy)\left(e_o + \frac{M_P y}{EI}\right) ds$$

$$= \int_0^L \int_{-C_1}^{+C_2} \left(\frac{F_Q e_o}{A} + \frac{M_Q e_o}{I} y + \frac{F_Q M_P}{EIA} y + \frac{M_Q M_P}{EI^2} y^2\right) b \, dy \, ds$$

Noting that

$$\int_{-C_1}^{C_2} b \, dy = A \qquad \int_{-C_1}^{C_2} yb \, dy = 0 \qquad \int_{-C_1}^{C_2} y^2 b \, dy = I$$

this expression simplifies to

$$W_d = \int_0^L F_Q e_o \, ds + \int_0^L \frac{M_Q M_P}{EI} ds \qquad (12.4)$$

This expression may now be applied and further simplified for the common types of members encountered in planar structures, such as beams and members of trusses and frames.

12.6 Deflection of Trusses, Using Method of Virtual Work.
An expression for the law of virtual work as applied specifically to trusses

may be obtained by substituting in Eq. (12.1) from Eqs. (12.2) and (12.4). Consider first the case of an ideal pin-jointed truss where both the deforming P loads and the Q loads are applied only at the joints of the truss. In such a case, the individual members will be subjected only to axial forces with no shear or bending moment involved, and the second term in Eq. (12.4) will disappear. Furthermore, F_Q will be constant throughout the length of a given member and, since

$$\int_0^L e_o \, ds = \text{axial change in length of a member} = \Delta L$$

the virtual work of deformation for one particular truss member becomes

$$W_d = F_Q \int_0^L e_o \, ds = F_Q \, \Delta L$$

Summing such products up for all the members of the truss, the internal virtual work of deformation for the entire truss may be represented as

$$W_d = \Sigma F_Q \, \Delta L$$

and, therefore, the law of virtual work as applied to an ideal pin-jointed truss becomes

$$\Sigma Q \delta = \Sigma F_Q \, \Delta L \qquad (12.5)$$

Suitable expressions for ΔL may easily be developed, depending on whether the change in length is produced by the P loads, by a change in temperature, or by some other cause. For a prismatic member having a constant cross-sectional area A and a constant modulus of elasticity E:
If the deformation is due to joint loads P on the truss,

$$\Delta L = (e_o)(L) = \left(\frac{\sigma_P'}{E}\right)(L) = \left(\frac{F_P}{A}\right)\left(\frac{L}{E}\right) = \frac{F_P L}{A E} \qquad (12.5a)$$

If the deformation is due to a uniform change in temperature t,

$$\Delta L = (e_o)(L) = (\alpha_t t)(L) = \alpha_t t L \qquad (12.5b)$$

If the deformation is caused by both these effects acting simultaneously,

$$\Delta L = \frac{F_P L}{A E} + \alpha_t t L \qquad (12.5c)$$

where, in addition to the notation introduced previously,
  F_P = bar force in member due to deforming loads P
  F_Q = bar force in member due to loads Q
  α_t = coefficient of thermal expansion of material
  L = length of member
Equation (12.5) is the basis for the method of virtual work for computing the deflection of ideal pin-jointed trusses, but as yet we do not know how to use it to do this job for us. Suppose, for example, that we wish to compute the vertical component of the deflection of joint c caused by the P loads shown in Fig. 12.9a. Suppose that we select as the Q-load

system a unit vertical load at joint c together with its reactions. If we imagine that we first apply this Q system to the structure, then when we apply the actual deforming loads P, the Q loads will be given a ride and will do a certain amount of external virtual work. According to the law of virtual work, the internal Q stresses will do an equal amount of internal virtual work as the members change length owing to the F_P stresses. Applying Eq. (12.5),

$$(1)(\delta^{\downarrow}_c) + W_R = \sum F_Q \frac{F_P L}{A E}$$

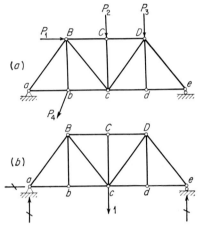

where W_R represents the virtual work done by the Q reactions if the support points move and could be evaluated numerically if such movements were known. If the supports are unyielding, $W_R = 0$ and

$$(1)(\delta^{\downarrow}_c) = \sum F_Q F_P \frac{L}{A E}$$

Figure 12.9 Application of method of virtual work to pin-jointed truss

The bar forces F_Q and F_P due to the Q- and P-load systems, respectively, may easily be computed. These data combined with the given values of L, A, and E give us enough information to evaluate the right-hand side of the above equation and, therefore, to solve for the unknown value of δ_c.

Figure 12.10 shows how to select suitable Q systems for use in the computation of other deflection components that may be required. Note that the "trick" is simply to select the Q-force system in such a way that the desired deflection is the only unknown δ appearing on the left-hand side of the equation. Some students worry about the deflection produced by the Q system. We do not care what this is. We want to find the deflection produced by the given cause of deformation. The Q system is purely a system that rides along and does virtual work and, thereby, enables us to compute the desired deflection. Note also that in these computations we never have to worry about or compute the *real* work done by the P loads as they deflect the structure.

The following illustrative examples show how to organize these computations in certain typical problems. In using the law of virtual work, it is particularly important to note the sign convention involved. In setting up the formulas for external and internal virtual work done by the Q system, it was assumed that the work was positive. This implies first that δ is to be considered positive when it is in the same direction as its corresponding Q force. Furthermore, this implies that both F_Q and ΔL are to be considered positive when in the same sense. If F_Q is considered plus when tension, then ΔL is plus when an elongation and, therefore, F_P is plus when tension and t plus when an increase in temperature.

After studying the following examples, it will be evident that there are two principal sources of difficulties—units and signs. The novice will probably have less difficulty with units if force units are assigned to the

Figure 12.10 Typical Q-force systems used in truss-deflection problems

Q force and stresses, although some authorities treat these forces as dimensionless. Ordinarily it is advisable to use the same length units throughout a problem; however, in some cases it is desirable to mix such units in order to obtain more convenient numbers. For instance, in these examples A and E are used in inch units, while L is used in feet. What is done in this respect is largely a matter of personal preference, but everyone should follow one rule: Be sure the units are consistent. As for signs, no difficulty should be encountered if one is careful and follows the convention noted above. Be sure to check the signs of all products, however. Note also that F_Q and F_P are *actual* bar forces, not the horizontal or vertical components.

Example 12.1   (a) *Compute the vertical component of deflection of joint c, due to the* 100^k *load shown.* $E = 30 \times 10^3$ *kips per sq in.*

(b) *Compute the vertical component of deflection of joint c, due to a decrease of temperature of $50°F$ in the bottom chord only.* $\alpha_t = 1/150{,}000$ *per °F.*

(a)
$$\sum Q\delta = \sum F_Q \,\Delta L = \sum F_Q F_P \frac{L}{AE}$$

$$(1^k)(\delta_c^\downarrow) = \frac{1}{E} \sum F_Q F_P \frac{L}{A}$$

$$= \frac{+325.01^{k^2/''^2}}{30 \times 10^{3 \; k/''^2}}$$

$$\therefore \; \delta_c = \underline{+0.01083 \, ft} \qquad \therefore \; down$$

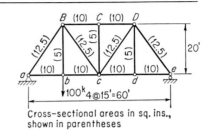

Cross-sectional areas in sq. ins., shown in parentheses

(b)
$$\Sigma Q\delta = \Sigma F_Q \,\Delta L = \Sigma F_Q \alpha_t t L$$

$$(1^k)(\delta_c^\downarrow) = \alpha_t \Sigma F_Q t L$$

$$= \left(\frac{1}{150{,}000} \; per \; °F \right) (-1{,}125^{k°F'})$$

$$\therefore \; \delta_c = \underline{-0.0075 \, ft} \qquad \therefore \; up$$

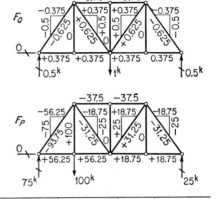

Bar	L	A	$\dfrac{L}{A}$	F_Q	F_P	$F_Q F_P \dfrac{L}{A}$	t	$F_Q t L$
Units	$'$	$''^2$	$'/''^2$	k	k	$k^2/''^2$	$°F$	$k°F'$
ab	15	10	1.5	+0.375	+ 56.25	+ 31.64	−50	− 281.25
bc	15	10	1.5	+0.375	+ 56.25	+ 31.64	−50	− 281.25
cd	15	10	1.5	+0.375	+ 18.75	+ 10.55	−50	− 281.25
de	15	10	1.5	+0.375	+ 18.75	+ 10.55	−50	− 281.25
BC	15	10	1.5	−0.75	− 37.5	+ 42.19	0	0
CD	15	10	1.5	−0.75	− 37.5	+ 42.19	0	0
aB	25	12.5	2	−0.625	− 93.75	+117.19	0	0
Bc	25	12.5	2	+0.625	− 31.25	− 39.06	0	0
cD	25	12.5	2	+0.625	+ 31.25	+ 39.06	0	0
De	25	12.5	2	−0.625	− 31.25	+ 39.06	0	0
bB	20	5	4	0	+100	0	0	0
cC	20	5	4	0	0	0	0	0
dD	20	5	4	0	0	0	0	0
Σ						+325.01		−1,125

Example 12.2 *Compute the horizontal component of the deflection of joint E, due to the load shown.* $E = 30 \times 10^3$ *kips per sq in.*

Cross-sectional areas in sq. ins., shown in parentheses

$$\sum Q\delta = \sum F_Q \, \Delta L = \sum F_Q F_P \frac{L}{AE}$$

$$(1^k)(\overrightarrow{\delta_E}) = \frac{1}{E}\sum F_Q F_P \frac{L}{A} = \frac{+56.25^{k^2 /''^2}}{30 \times 10^{3\ k /''^2}}$$

$$\therefore \ \delta_E = \underline{+0.001875\ ft} \qquad \therefore \ \text{to right}$$

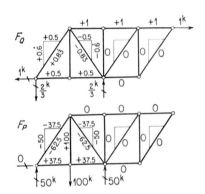

Bar	L	A	$\dfrac{L}{A}$	F_Q	F_P	$F_Q F_P \dfrac{L}{A}$
Units	$'$	$''^2$	$'/''^2$	k	k	$k^2/''^2$
ab	15	10	1.5	$+0.5$	$+37.5$	$+\ 28.13$
bc	15	10	1.5	$+0\ 5$	$+37.5$	$+\ 28.13$
aB	25	12.5	2	$+0.83$	-62.5	-104.17
Bc	25	12.5	2	-0.83	-62.5	$+104.17$
Σ						$+\ 56.25$

Discussion:

Note that any bar in which either F_Q or F_P is zero may be omitted from the tabulation since the product of $F_Q F_P (L/A)$ would be zero for such a bar.

Example 12.3 *For the truss in Example 12.2, compute the horizontal component of the deflection of joint E, due to the following movements of the supports:*

> At a, horizontal = 0.5″ to left
> At a, vertical   = 0.75″ down
> At c, vertical   = 0.25″ down

Use the stress analysis for the Q system from the previous problem. In this example, the deflection is caused simply by support movements. There are no changes in length of the members, that is, $\Delta L = 0$ for all members.

$$\Sigma Q\delta = \Sigma F_Q \, \Delta L = 0$$

$$(1^k)(\overrightarrow{\delta_E}) + (1^k)(0.5'') + (\tfrac{2}{3}^k)(0.75'') - (\tfrac{2}{3}^k)(0.25'') = 0$$

$$\therefore \ \delta_E = -0.5 - 0.5 + 0.167 = \underline{-0.833\ in.} \qquad \therefore \ \text{to left}$$

Discussion:

In evaluating the external virtual work done by the Q reactions, be careful to include the proper sign for the work. Any particular reaction does plus or minus virtual work depending on whether its point of application moves in the same or the opposite sense as the reaction, respectively.

Deflections due to support settlement may also be evaluated simply by a consideration of the kinematics of the problem. In sketch a, the solid line shows the outline of the truss in its original position. The truss may then be translated as a rigid body until the support

(a)　　　　　　　　　　　　　　　(b)

at a is in its final position—the translated position is shown by the dashed line. The truss must then be rotated counterclockwise about a until the support at c is in its proper position. The final position of the truss is shown by the dotted line. In these sketches, the movements have been exaggerated tremendously to clarify the mechanics of the problem. The horizontal movement of point E may therefore be computed as

Due to translation	$0.5''$ to left
Due to rotation about a	$\dfrac{0.5''}{30'} \times 20' = 0.\dot{3}''$ to left
Total horizontal movement of point E	$0.5'' + 0.\dot{3}'' = 0.8\dot{3}''$ to left

The computation of the movement during rotation requires some explanation, and it likewise illustrates the application of a useful theorem. Consider the movement of a point m as a rigid body is rotated about some center O through some small angle α. In sketch b, this angle has been exaggerated tremendously so that the geometry is clearer. Actually, the angle α is so small that the angle (in radians), its sine, and its tangent are all essentially equal to each other. This means that it is legitimate to consider that m moves to its rotated position m' along the tangent shown rather than along the actual arc. Suppose that it is desired to obtain the component of the displacement mm' along some given direction through m such as XX. Drop a perpendicular OA from point O to this direction XX. From the sketch it is apparent that triangles mm'm'' and OmA are similar. Then,

$$\frac{\delta_v}{\delta} = \frac{d}{R} \qquad \delta_v = \frac{\delta}{R}\,d = \alpha d$$

since α ≈ δ/R. Therefore, the following theorem may be stated:

If a rigid body is rotated about some center O through some small angle α, the component of the displacement of a point m along some direction XX through that point is equal to the angle α times the perpendicular distance from O to the line XX.

Applied to the above truss,

$$\alpha = \frac{0.5''}{30'}$$

Therefore, the horizontal movement of E during rotation about O is

$$\frac{0.5''}{30'}\,(20') = 0.\dot{3}''$$

Example 12.4 *Compute the relative deflections of joints b and D along the line joining them, due to the following causes:*

(a) *The loads shown.* $E = 30 \times 10^3$ *kips per sq in.*

(b) *An increase in temperature of 80°F in the top chord; a decrease of 20°F in the bottom chord.* $\alpha_t = 1/150{,}000$ *per °F.*

Cross-sectional areas in sq. ins. shown in parentheses

(a)

(b)

$$(a) \quad \sum Q\delta = \sum F_Q \, \Delta L = \sum F_Q F_P \frac{L}{AE}$$

$$(1^k)(\delta_b^{\nearrow}) + (1^k)(\delta_D^{\swarrow}) = \frac{1}{E}\sum F_Q F_P \frac{L}{A}$$

$$(1^k)(\delta_{b-D}^{\swarrow}) = \frac{55.0^{k^2\prime/\prime\prime^2}}{30 \times 10^{3\,k/\prime\prime^2}}$$

$$\therefore \; \delta_{b-D} = \underline{+0.00183 \; ft} \qquad \therefore \; together$$

$$(b) \quad \Sigma Q\delta = \Sigma F_Q \, \Delta L = \Sigma F_Q \alpha_t t L = \alpha_t \Sigma F_Q t L$$

$$(1^k)(\delta_{b-D}^{\swarrow})$$

$$= \left(\frac{1}{150{,}000} \; per \; °F\right)(-747.2^{k°F\prime})$$

$$\therefore \; \delta_{b-D} = \underline{-0.00499 \; ft} \qquad \therefore \; apart$$

Bar	L	A	$\dfrac{L}{A}$	F_Q	F_P	$F_Q F_P \dfrac{L}{A}$	t	$F_Q t L$
Units	$\prime$	$\prime\prime^2$	$\prime/\prime\prime^2$	k	k	$k^2{}\prime/\prime\prime^2$	°F	$k°F\prime$
bc	15	5	3	-0.416	$+67.5$	-84.5	-20	$+125$
cd	15	5	3	-0.416	$+67.5$	-84.5	-20	$+125$
CD	15	5	3	-0.831	-78.75	$+197.0$	$+80$	-997.2
bC	25	2.5	10	-0.695	-18.75	$+130$	0	0
Cd	25	2.5	10	$+0.695$	$+18.75$	$+130$	0	0
dD	20	5	4	-0.555	$+105$	-233	0	0
Σ						$+55.0$		-747.2

Discussion:

Many students are confused about temperature or settlement deflection problems dealing with statically determinate trusses. They "feel" that stresses must be developed in the members in such cases. However, no reactions can be developed on a statically deter-

*minate truss unless there are loads acting on the structure.   This can be proved by apply-
ing equations of statics.   If there are no reactions or external loads, then there can be no
internal bar forces.   From a physical standpoint, the deformation of such trusses that
is the result of support settlements or changes in length due to temperature may take place
without encountering resistance, and therefore no reactions and bar forces can be developed.*

All the trusses discussed so far have been ideal pin-connected trusses
acted upon by Q or P loads, which were always applied at the joints.   If a
pin-connected truss is deformed by P loads, some of which are applied to
certain members between the joints, such members are subjected to M_P
bending moments.   If, however, only joint deflections are desired, the
Q system consists simply of certain joint loads, which cause no M_Q bending
moments.   The second term on the right side of Eq. (12.4) disappears,
therefore, and the law of virtual work for such a case is the same as
Eq. (12.5).   The same thing is likewise true in the cases where, in order to
compute the deflection desired, it is necessary to apply Q loads between
the joints but the P loads causing deformation are applied only at the
joints so that there are no M_P bending moments.

The case of a pin-connected truss having both P and Q loads applied
between the joints is handled like that of a rigid frame structure, which is
discussed in the next article.   The case of riveted trusses is also discussed
there.

**12.7   Deflection of Beams and Frames, Using Method of
Virtual Work.**   An expression for the law of virtual work as applied to
beams or frames may likewise be ob-
tained by substituting in Eq. (12.1)
from Eqs. (12.2) and (12.4).   Consider first the case of a beam deformed
by transverse loads.   In such a case,
if the reactions have no axial components, the cross sections of the beam
are subjected only to shear and bend-

Figure 12.11   Deflection of beams

ing moment with no axial force.   The first term of Eq. (12.4) will disappear, and the law of virtual work as applied to this case will be simply

$$\sum Q\delta = \int M_Q M_P \frac{ds}{EI} \qquad (12.6)$$

Remember that the effect of shearing deformation has been neglected in
the development of Eq. (12.4).   Such a case is shown in Fig. 12.11.   To
find the vertical, horizontal, or, in fact, any component of the deflection
of a point on such a beam, a unit load is applied in the appropriate direction.   This unit load together with its reactions constitutes the Q system,
which rides along during the deformation of the beam.   The solution of a
beam-deflection problem is basically similar to the solution of a truss-

deflection problem but differs in the detail of evaluating the right-hand side of Eq. (12.6).

Before the integration of the right-hand side can be accomplished, both M_Q and M_P must first be expressed as functions of s. It is usually necessary to separate the integration for the entire beam into the sum of several integrals, one for each of several portions of the beam. The integration must be broken at points where there is a change in the functions representing M_Q, M_P, or I in terms of s. The integration process can often be simplified by selecting different origins for the measurement of s for these various portions of the beam. The technique of organizing such computations will be illustrated in the following examples.

Note particularly the sign convention used for the various terms in Eq. (12.6). Any suitable convention may be used for M_Q and M_P as long as the same convention is used for both. Usually, the ordinary beam convention is the most satisfactory. δ is, of course, plus when in the same sense as its corresponding Q force.

Often it is necessary to find the change in slope of some cross section of a beam. To do this, select as the Q system a distributed load, such as that shown in Fig. 12.12, and its reactions. This load is distributed across the cross section in a manner such as to be equivalent to a unit couple. Let the intensity of this load at a distance y from the centroidal axis be q_y. Considering only the effect of bending deformation, a cross section that was plane before bending remains plane and normal to the elastic curve after bending. If a cross section is rotated through a small angle α, a point at distance y from the centroidal axis would move $(\alpha)(y)$. Then, the external virtual work done by the distributed q load during the rotation of the cross section caused by the P system would be

Figure 12.12 Q system used to obtain change of slope of cross section

$$\int (q_y b \, dy)(\alpha y) = \alpha \int q_y b y \, dy = (1)(\alpha)$$

since the moment of the q load about the centroidal axis $= \int q_y b y \, dy = 1$. Having recognized that the external virtual work done by such a distributed q load is simply its resultant unit couple times α, we may henceforth consider that we apply a unit couple to the cross section and not trouble about showing the distributed load in detail. Applying Eq. (12.6) in this case, therefore, yields the following:

$$(1)(\alpha_a^{\curvearrowright}) + W_R = \int M_Q M_P \frac{ds}{EI}$$

From this point on, the rest of the solution is similar to that for a vertical deflection.

Example 12.5   *Compute the vertical deflection at A, due to load P applied at point B.*

$$\sum Q\delta = \int M_Q M_P \frac{ds}{EI}$$

$$(1^k)(\delta_A\downarrow) = \int_A^B M_Q M_P \frac{dx}{EI}$$

$$+ \int_B^C M_Q M_P \frac{dx}{EI}$$

From A to B,

$$0 < x < a \qquad M_Q = -x \qquad M_P = 0$$

From B to C,

$$0 < x < (L - a)$$

$$M_Q = -(a + x) \qquad M_P = -Px$$

$$(1^k)(\delta_A\downarrow) = 0 + \frac{1}{EI}\int_0^{L-a} [-(a+x)]$$

$$[-Px]\,dx$$

$$= \frac{P}{EI}\left[\frac{ax^2}{2} + \frac{x^3}{3}\right]_0^{L-a}$$

$$= \frac{P}{EI}\left[\frac{a(L-a)^2}{2} + \frac{(L-a)^3}{3}\right]$$

$$\delta_A^{\downarrow} = \frac{P}{6EI}(L-a)^2(2L+a)$$

Example 12.6   *Compute the vertical deflection of a, due to the load shown.*

$$E = 30 \times 10^3 \text{ kips per sq in.} \qquad I = 200 \text{ in.}^4$$

$$\sum Q\delta = \int M_Q M_P \frac{ds}{EI}$$

$$(1^k)(\delta_a^{\downarrow}) = \int_a^b M_Q M_P \frac{dx}{EI} + \int_b^c + \int_d^c$$

From a to b,

$$M_P = 0$$

From b to c,

$$0 < x < 10 \qquad M_Q = \frac{x}{4} - 5 \qquad M_P = 5x$$

From d to c,

$$0 < x < 10 \qquad M_Q = -\frac{x}{4} \qquad M_P = 5x$$

$$(1^k)(\delta_a^{\downarrow}) = \frac{1}{EI}\left[0 + \int_0^{10}\left(\frac{x}{4} - 5\right)(5x)\,dx + \int_0^{10}\left(\frac{-x}{4}\right)(5x)\,dx\right]$$

$$= \frac{1}{EI}\left\{\left[\frac{5}{12}x^3 - \frac{25}{2}x^2\right]_0^{10} + \left[-\frac{5}{12}x^3\right]_0^{10}\right\} = -\frac{1,250^{k'^3}}{EI}$$

$$\therefore \delta_a = \frac{-1,250^{k'^3}}{(30 \times 10^3 \times 144)^{k/'^2}\left(\dfrac{200}{144 \times 144}\right)^{'^4}} = \underline{-0.030 \text{ ft}} \qquad \therefore up$$

Discussion:

The origin for measuring x in any given portion may be selected at will, but note that the same origin must be used for x in the expressions for both M_Q and M_P for a given portion. An origin should be selected that minimizes the number of terms in the expressions for M_Q and M_P and that also reduces the labor in substituting the limits of integration.

Example 12.7 *Compute the change in slope of the cross section at point a caused by the load shown.* $E = 30 \times 10^3$ *kips per sq in.* $I_1 = 150$ *in.*[4] $I_2 = 200$ *in.*[4]

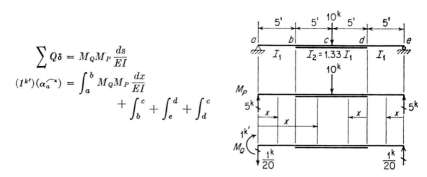

$$\sum Q\delta = M_Q M_P \frac{ds}{EI}$$

$$(1^{k'})(\alpha_a^{\curvearrowright}) = \int_a^b M_Q M_P \frac{dx}{EI}$$

$$+ \int_b^c + \int_e^d + \int_d^c$$

From a to b,

$$0 < x < 5 \qquad I_1 \qquad M_Q = 1 - \frac{x}{20} \qquad M_P = 5x$$

From b to c,

$$5 < x < 10 \qquad 1.33I_1 \qquad M_Q = 1 - \frac{x}{20} \qquad M_P = 5x$$

From e to d,

$$0 < x < 5 \qquad I_1 \qquad M_Q = \frac{x}{20} \qquad M_P = 5x$$

From d to c,

$$0 < x < 5 \qquad 1.33I_1 \qquad M_Q = \frac{1}{4} + \frac{x}{20} \qquad M_P = 25 + 5x$$

$$(1^{k'})(\alpha_a^{\curvearrowright}) = \frac{1}{EI_1}\left[\int_0^5 \left(1 - \frac{x}{20}\right)(5x)\,dx + \int_5^{10}\left(1 - \frac{x}{20}\right)(5x)\frac{dx}{1.33} \right.$$
$$+ \int_0^5 \left(\frac{x}{20}\right)(5x)\,dx + \int_0^5 \left(\frac{1}{4} + \frac{x}{20}\right)(25 + 5x)\frac{dx}{1.33}\right] = \frac{1}{EI_1}\left\{\left[\frac{5x^2}{2} - \frac{x^3}{12}\right]_0^5\right.$$
$$+ \frac{1}{1.33}\left[\frac{5x^2}{2} - \frac{x^3}{12}\right]_5^{10} + \left[\frac{x^3}{12}\right]_0^5 + \frac{1}{1.33}\left[\frac{25x}{4} + \frac{5}{4}x^2 + \frac{x^3}{12}\right]_0^5\right\}$$
$$= \frac{1}{EI_1}\left\{\frac{5}{2}(25) + \frac{1}{1.33}\left[\frac{5}{2}(100 - 25) - \left(\frac{1,000 - 125}{12}\right)\right]\right.$$
$$\left. + \frac{1}{1.33}\left[\frac{25}{4}(5) + \frac{5}{4}(25) + \frac{125}{12}\right]\right\}$$
$$= \frac{1}{EI_1}\left[62.5 + \frac{1}{1.33}(187.5 - 62.5 + 62.5)\right] = \frac{1}{EI}(62.5 + 140.6) = \frac{203.1^{k^2\prime^3}}{EI_1}$$

$$\therefore \; \alpha_a = \frac{(203.1)^{k/^2}}{(30 \times 10^3 \times 144)^{k/^2} \left(\dfrac{150}{144 \times 144}\right)^{/^4}} = \underline{+0.0065 \; radian} \qquad \therefore \; clockwise$$

Discussion:

The selection of the origins for measuring x is not necessarily the best in this solution but was intended to illustrate several of the possible ways of handling the problem. Whenever cancellations are made before integration or before substitution of limits, be very sure that the cancellation is legitimate—check to see that both the terms and the limits are the same.

Example 12.8   *Compute the change in slope of the cross section of point B. E and I constant.*

$$\sum Q\delta = \int M_Q M_P \frac{ds}{EI}$$

$$(1^{k'})(\alpha_B^\curvearrowleft) = \int_A^B M_Q M_P \frac{dx}{EI}$$

From A to B, $0 < x < L$

$$M_Q = \frac{x}{L} \qquad M_P = \frac{wL}{2} x - \frac{wx^2}{2}$$

$$(1^{k'})(\alpha_B^\curvearrowleft) = \int_0^L \left(\frac{x}{L}\right)\left(\frac{wLx}{2} - \frac{wx^2}{2}\right)\frac{dx}{EI}$$

$$= \frac{w}{EI}\left[\frac{x^3}{6} - \frac{x^4}{8L}\right]_0^L = \frac{wL^3}{24EI}$$

$$\therefore \; \alpha_B = \frac{wL^3}{24EI} \qquad \therefore \; counterclockwise$$

Consider now the more general case of a beam or rigid frame where the cross sections of the members are subjected to an axial force as well as shear and bending moment. Several cases of this type are shown in Fig. 12.13. The deflection of such structures may also be caused by temperature changes as well as by the axial forces and bending moments developed by the P loads. As a result, both terms in Eq. (12.4) must be considered in evaluating the internal virtual work. The law of virtual work as applied to such cases may be expressed as follows:

Figure 12.13   Structures subjected to both axial change in length and flexure

$$\sum Q\delta = \int F_Q e_0 \, ds + \int M_Q M_P \frac{ds}{EI} \qquad (12.7)$$

where the axial strain e_0, including the effect of both axial force and

temperature, is

$$e_0 = \alpha_t t + \frac{F_P}{AE}$$

Usually the entire structure may be split up into several portions over each of which F_Q, F_P, A, and t are constant. Likewise, to evaluate the second term on the right side of Eq. (12.7), the integration may be split up into several parts, each of which covers a portion over which the functions representing M_Q, M_P, and I remain of the same form. The portions used in evaluating the first term in Eq. (12.7) are not necessarily the same

Figure 12.14 Q system for obtaining relative deflections

portions as those used to evaluate the second term. In any event, Eq. (12.7) may be represented more conveniently in the following form:

$$\sum Q\delta = \sum F_Q\,\Delta L + \sum \int M_Q M_P \frac{ds}{EI} \qquad (12.8)$$

where

$$\Delta L = \int e_0\,ds = \alpha_t t L + \frac{F_P L}{AE}$$

The summation signs on the right side of Eq. (12.8) indicate that such terms must be summed up for all the separate portions of all members of the structure.

The application of Eq. (12.8) to a specific problem involves the techniques already illustrated in Examples 12.1 to 12.8. Example 12.9 will show how to arrange the computations. Most beam or frame deflection problems involve finding some component of the deflection of a point or the change in slope of a cross section. Sometimes, however, it is necessary to find the relative deflections of two adjacent cross sections such as a and a' in Fig. 12.14. The relative horizontal, vertical, or angular displacements at points a and a' may be found by selecting the Q systems shown in sketch A, B, or C, respectively.

Example 12.9   *Compute the change in slope of the cross section on the left side of the hinge at c, due to the load shown.*

$$\sum Q\delta = \sum F_Q F_P \frac{L}{AE}$$

$$+ \sum \int M_Q M_P \frac{ds}{EI}$$

$$(1^{k'})(\alpha\overset{\frown}{_{CL}}) = \int_A^B M_Q M_P \frac{dy}{EI}$$

$$+ \int_B^C M_Q M_P \frac{dx}{EI}$$

$$+ \int_E^D + \int_D^C + \sum F_Q F_P \frac{L}{AE}$$

Note: $F_Q F_P \dfrac{L}{AE}$ *may be evaluated for same*

portions AB, BC, ED, and DC. Dashed line indicates lower fibers for applying beam convention to signs of M_Q and M_P.

Const. E,I,A
$E = 30 \times 10^{3\,k/\square"}$
$I = 2,500^{"4}$
$A = 20^{"2}$

From A to B,

$$L = 10' \qquad 0 \to y \to 10$$

$$F_Q = +\frac{1}{16} \qquad M_Q = -\frac{y}{20}$$

$$F_P = -60 \qquad M_P = -48y$$

From B to C,

$$L = 8' \qquad 0 \to x \to 8$$

$$F_Q = -\frac{1}{20} \qquad M_Q = -\frac{1}{2} - \frac{x}{16}$$

$$F_P = -48 \qquad M_P = -480 + 60x$$

From E to D,

$$L = 10 \qquad 0 \to y \to 10$$

$$F_Q = -\frac{1}{16} \qquad M_Q = -\frac{y}{20}$$

$$F_P = -60 \qquad M_P = -48y$$

From D to C,

$$L = 8 \qquad 0 \to x \to 8$$

$$F_Q = -\frac{1}{20} \qquad M_Q = -\frac{1}{2} + \frac{x}{16}$$

$$F_P = -48 \qquad M_P = -480 + 60x$$

M_P, F_P

M_Q, F_Q

$$(1^{k'})(\alpha\overset{\frown}{_{CL}}) =$$

$$\frac{1}{EI}\left[2\int_0^{10}\left(\frac{-y}{20}\right)(-48y)\,dy + \int_0^8\left(-\frac{1}{2} - \frac{x}{16}\right)(-480 + 60x)\,dx \right.$$

$$\left. + \int_0^8\left(-\frac{1}{2} + \frac{x}{16}\right)(-480 + 60x)\,dx \right] + \frac{2}{AE}\left(-\frac{1}{20}\right)(-48)(8)$$

$$= \frac{1}{EI}\left[(1.6y^3)\Big|_0^{10} + 2(240x - 15x^2)\Big|_0^8 \right] + \frac{38.4}{AE}$$

$$(1^{k'})(\alpha_{CL}^{\curvearrowright}) = \frac{3{,}520}{EI} + \frac{38.4}{AE} = \frac{(3{,}520)^{k^{2'^3}}}{(30 \times 10^3 \times \cancel{144})^{k/'^2}\left(\dfrac{2{,}500}{144 \times \cancel{144}}\right)^{'^4}}$$

$$+ \frac{(38.4)^{k^{2'}}}{(30 \times 10^3 \times \cancel{144})^{k/'^2}\left(\dfrac{20}{\cancel{144}}\right)^{'^2}}$$

$$\therefore \alpha_{CL} = +0.00676 + 0.000064 = \underline{+0.006824 \; radian} \qquad \therefore \; clockwise$$

Discussion:

In problems involving both bending and axial deformation, be particularly careful of units. Note that the contribution of the axial-deformation term is only about 1 per cent of that due to bending deformation. This is more or less typical of the relative size of these two effects in frame-deflection problems. It is therefore usually permissible to neglect the effect of axial deformation in such cases.

A truss with riveted joints is essentially a rigid frame. In the discussion in Art. 4.2, it will be recalled that the members of such trusses are subjected to shear and bending moment as well as axial forces even when the loads are applied at the joints. However, as far as the stresses and strains in the members are concerned, a given riveted truss may be considered to be equivalent to a corresponding pin-connected truss, as shown in Fig. 12.15. This equivalent truss, however, is loaded not only with the given joint loads but also by couples on the ends of each bar, which are equal to the moments at the ends of the corresponding members of the riveted truss. More detailed analysis shows that, in most cases, these end couples by themselves produce very small bar forces in the members. In other words, the bar forces in the equivalent pin-connected truss are produced almost entirely by the joint loads. In the previous article, it is pointed out that the joint deflections of a pin-connected truss are a function only of the axial change in length of the members and do not depend on the bending deformation of such members. The deflection of the joints of the equivalent pin-connected truss under both the joint loads and the end couples is therefore essentially the same as that of an ideal pin-connected truss acted upon by only the joint loads. Hence, a riveted truss is assumed to be an ideal pin-connected truss when the deflection of the joints is computed. It should be realized, of course, that the bending of the members of riveted trusses does affect the deflection of points other than the joints.

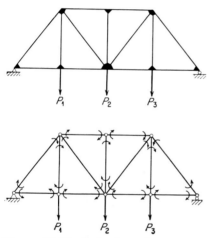

Figure 12.15 Deflections of truss with rigid joints

At no place in the previous discussion has the case of a beam or a frame with a curved axis and varying cross sections been considered. The detailed consideration of such structures is beyond the scope of this book.

If the curvature and variation of the cross sections are not great, the normal stresses in such structures may be assumed to be distributed linearly, and the deflection of the structure may therefore be computed by applying Eq. (12.7). In such cases, the integrals on the right-hand side of this equation can seldom be evaluated exactly, and their values must be approximated by a summation process. For this purpose, the axis of the structure is divided into a number of short portions of equal length Δs. The values of F_Q, e_o, M_Q, M_P, and I are computed for the cross section at the center of each of these short portions. The products of $F_Q e_o \Delta s$ and $M_Q M_P \Delta s / EI$ may then be evaluated for each portion. The sum of these products for all the portions approximates the value of the right-hand side of Eq. (12.7). The accuracy of this summation process increases as the length of the individual portions is decreased.

12.8 Development of Moment-area Theorems. The moment-area theorems may often be used more conveniently than the method of virtual work in the computation of slopes and deflections of beams and frames, particularly when the deformation is caused by concentrated rather than distributed loads. These theorems are based on a consideration of the geometry of the elastic curve of the beam and the relation between the rate of change of slope and the bending moment at a point on the elastic curve.

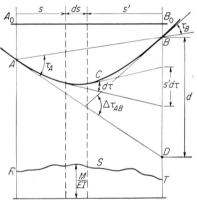

Figure 12.16 Derivation of moment-area theorems

Referring to Fig. 12.16, consider a portion ACB of the elastic curve of a beam that was *initially straight* and in the position A_oB_o in its unstressed condition. Draw the tangents to the elastic curve at points A and B. The tangent at A intersects the vertical through B at D. The angle $\Delta\tau_{AB}$ is the change in slope between the tangents at points A and B. Recognize that the deflection and curvature have been exaggerated tremendously in this sketch. Actually, the inclination of any tangent to the elastic curve is so small that an angle such as τ_A is approximately equal to its sine and its tangent, and its cosine is approximately equal to unity.

Consider a differential element of this curve having a horizontal projection ds, and draw the tangents to the elastic curve at each end of this element. The change in slope between these tangents is the angle $d\tau$, and its value may be obtained by considering Fig. 12.17.

$$d\tau = \frac{(\sigma_c \, ds)/E}{c} = \frac{Mc}{EI}\frac{ds}{c} = \frac{M}{EI} \, ds$$

It is then evident that the total change in slope between the tangents at A and B is the sum of all the angles $d\tau$ for all the elements ds along the elastic curve ACB, or

$$\Delta\tau_{AB} = \int_A^B d\tau = \int_A^B \frac{M}{EI} ds \qquad (12.9)$$

Let RST be the bending-moment curve for the portion AB, every ordinate of which has been divided by the EI of the beam at that point. Such a curve is called the M/EI curve. It is evident that the integral in Eq. (12.9) may be interpreted as the area under the M/EI curve between A and B. Hence, from Eq. (12.9), the *first moment-area theorem* may be stated:

The change in slope of the tangents of the elastic curve between two points A and B is equal to the area under the M/EI curve between these two points.[*]

In view of the fact that the deformation and slopes are actually small, it is evident from Fig. 12.16 that the intercept on the line BD (drawn normal to the unstrained position of the beam) between the tangents at the ends of the element ds may be written as $s' \, d\tau$, and consequently

$$d = \int_A^B s' \, d\tau = \int_A^B \frac{M}{EI} s' \, ds \qquad (12.10)$$

Figure 12.17 Differential change in slope

The last integral may be interpreted as the static moment, about an axis through point B, of the area under the M/EI curve between points A and B. Hence, from Eq. (12.10), the *second moment-area theorem* may be stated:

The deflection of point B on the elastic curve from the tangent to this curve at point A is equal to the static moment about an axis through B of the area under the M/EI curve between points A and B.[*]

Note that this deflection is measured in a direction normal to the original position of the beam.

The two theorems may be used directly to find the slopes and deflections of beams simply by drawing the moment curve for the loads causing deformation and then computing the area and static moments of all or part of the corresponding M/EI curve. This procedure is illustrated in

---

[*] Provided that within the portion AB of the beam no discontinuities (such as hinges) have been inserted.

Examples 12.10 to 12.12.   It will become apparent from these examples that these computations may be facilitated by introducing some new ideas.   The analogy based on these ideas is discussed in the next article and will be called the *elastic-load method*.

These theorems may be extended without difficulty to members that were not initially straight.   The consideration of such cases is beyond the scope of this book.

Example 12.10   *Using the moment-area theorems, compute the deflection at points b and c and the slope of the elastic curve at point b.   E and I are constant.*

Applying second moment-area theorem,

$$\delta_b = \left(\frac{180}{EI}\right)\left(\frac{6}{2}\right)(4) = \frac{2,160}{EI} \ (down)$$

$$\delta_c = \left(\frac{180}{EI}\right)\left(\frac{6}{2}\right)(4+6) = \frac{5,400}{EI} \ (down)$$

Applying first moment-area theorem,

$$\Delta_\tau = \left(\frac{180}{EI}\right)\left(\frac{6}{2}\right) = \frac{540}{EI}$$

$$\therefore \ \tau_b = \frac{540}{EI}$$

A sign convention could be formulated for the application of the moment-area theorems.   This has not been done here for fear that it might be confused with the convention proposed in the next article for the elastic-load method.   When applying the moment-area theorems, signs may be handled as shown in Examples 12.10 to 12.12.   In these examples, the elastic curve is first sketched roughly showing the proper curvature as indicated by the signs of the bending-moment diagram.   In the computation of a deflection (or angle) shown on this sketch, the contribution of a particular portion of the M/EI diagram (regardless of the sign of M in that portion) is considered as plus or minus, depending on whether it tended to increase or decrease, respectively, the magnitude of that deflection as shown on the assumed sketch. Thus, a positive final result confirms the sense shown for the deflection.

Example 12.11 *Using the moment-area theorems, compute the slope of the elastic curve at points a and m and the deflection at m.*

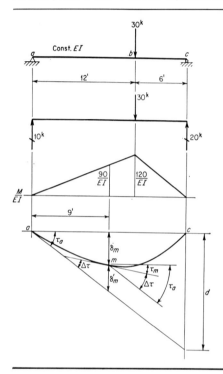

Since slopes are small, $\tan \tau_a = \tau_a$.

$$\therefore \tau_a = \frac{d}{18}$$

Applying second moment-area theorem,

$$d = \left(\frac{120}{EI}\right)\left[\left(\frac{12}{2}\right)(6+4) + \left(\frac{6}{2}\right)(4)\right]$$

$$= \frac{8,640}{EI} \qquad \therefore \tau_a = \frac{480}{EI}$$

From sketch of elastic curve, $\tau_m = \tau_a - \Delta\tau$. *But by first moment-area theorem,*

$$\Delta\tau = \left(\frac{90}{EI}\right)\left(\frac{9}{2}\right) = \frac{405}{EI}$$

$$\therefore \tau_m = \frac{480 - 405}{EI} = \frac{75}{EI}$$

Also, from sketch, $\delta_m = 9\tau_a - \delta'_m$. *Applying second moment-area theorem*

$$\delta'_m = \left(\frac{90}{EI}\right)\left(\frac{9}{2}\right)(3) = \frac{1,215}{EI}$$

$$\therefore \delta_m = (9)\left(\frac{480}{EI}\right) - \frac{1,215}{EI} = \frac{3,105}{EI}$$

Example 12.12 *Using the moment-area theorems, compute the deflections at points b and e and the slope at point c. Constant E and I.*

$$\tau_d = \frac{d_1}{20},$$

$$d_1 = \frac{1}{EI}\left[(37.5)\left(\frac{20}{2}\right)(10)\right.$$

$$-\left.(25)\left(\frac{10}{2}\right)\left(10 + \frac{2}{3} \times 10\right)\right] = \frac{5,000}{3EI}$$

$$\therefore \tau_d = \frac{250}{3EI}$$

$$\delta_b = 10\tau_d + \delta_b',$$

$$\delta_b' = \frac{1}{EI}\left[(25)\left(\frac{10}{2}\right)\left(\frac{20}{3}\right)\right.$$

$$-\left.(37.5)\left(\frac{10}{2}\right)\left(\frac{10}{3}\right)\right] = \frac{625}{3EI}$$

$$\therefore \delta_b = \frac{2,500}{3EI} + \frac{625}{3EI} = \frac{3,125}{3EI} \text{ (down)}$$

$$\delta_e = 5\tau_d - \delta_e',$$

$$\delta_e' = \frac{1}{EI}\left[(25)\left(\frac{5}{2}\right)\left(\frac{10}{3}\right)\right] = \frac{625}{3EI}$$

$$\therefore \delta_e = \frac{1,250}{3EI} - \frac{625}{3EI} = \frac{625}{3EI} \text{ (up)}$$

$$\tau_c = \tau_d + \Delta\tau,$$

$$\Delta\tau = \frac{(25 + 12.5)(5)}{2EI} - \frac{(18.75)(5)}{2EI} = \frac{93.75}{2EI}$$

$$\therefore \tau_c = \frac{250}{3EI} + \frac{93.75}{2EI} = \frac{781.25}{6EI}$$

Discussion:

Note that it becomes more difficult to handle signs properly when a beam is bent by both plus and minus bending moment. To minimize these difficulties, it is advisable to sketch the elastic curve as accurately as possible. The curvature can be sketched correctly by simply following the bending-moment diagram—plus bending moment makes the elastic curve concave upward and minus bending moment makes it concave downward. It will be found advantageous to handle these more difficult problems by the elastic-load method, for thereby the sign difficulty may be handled more or less automatically.

Note also that, in a portion such as bd where a straight-line portion of the moment curve goes from plus to minus, it is often advantageous for computation purposes to replace the actual moment curve by the dashed lines shown. In this case, the plus and minus triangles under the actual moment curve are replaced by the plus triangle with an altitude of 37.5 and a base of 10 and the minus triangle with an altitude of 25 and also a base of 10. A little thought will verify that this procedure is legitimate for the computation of the net area or of the net static moment of the area about any vertical axis.

12.9   Elastic-load Method.   The ideas involved in the elastic-load method may be developed by considering the elastic curve ACB of a member AB, which was originally straight and has been bent as shown in Fig. 12.18.   Let RST be the M/EI curve.   Applying the second moment-area theorem,

$$d = \int_A^B s' \frac{M}{EI}\, ds$$

Then,

$$\tau_A = \frac{d}{L} = \frac{1}{L} \int_A^B s' \frac{M}{EI}\, ds$$

This equation simply states that τ_A is equal to the static moment, about an axis through B of the area under the M/EI curve between A and B,

(a)

(b)

(c)

Figure 12.18   Development of elastic-load method

divided by L.   It is interesting to note, however, that the form of this computation for τ_A seems very familiar to us.   Suppose that we imagine that the M/EI diagram, RST, represents a distributed vertical load applied to a simple beam supported at points A and B, as shown by the dashed lines in Fig. 12.18b.   Then the computation for the vertical reaction at point A would involve taking moments about an axis through point B (normal to the plane of the paper), and as a matter of fact, this vertical reaction at point A would be exactly equal to the value of τ_A as computed above.

This analogy may be carried still further if we consider the form of the computation for τ_m and δ_m.   Note that τ_m gives the slope of the tangent with reference to the direction of the chord AB of the elastic curve and that δ_m gives the deflection of point m from the same chord AB. Consider first τ_m; then

$$\tau_m = \tau_A - \Delta\tau$$

But, according to the first moment-area theorem, $\Delta\tau = \int_A^m M/EI\, ds$, and hence

$$\tau_m = \tau_A - \int_A^m \frac{M}{EI}\, ds$$

Continuing to consider the M/EI diagram as the loading and τ_A as the reaction at point A on the imaginary beam, we see from this equation that τ_m is equal to the reaction τ_A minus the load applied between A and m. In other words, τ_m may be interpreted as being the shear of point m of this imaginary beam. Likewise,

$$\delta_m = (a)(\tau_A) - \delta'_m$$

But, from the second moment-area theorem, $\delta'_m = \int_A^m s''(M/EI)\,ds$, and hence

$$\delta_m = (\tau_A)(a) - \int_A^m s'' \frac{M}{EI}\,ds$$

To continue the analogy, from this equation it is apparent that δ_m may be interpreted as the bending moment at point m of the imaginary beam.

From these considerations, it may be concluded that the elastic curve of a beam AB is exactly the same as the bending-moment curve for an imaginary simple end-supported beam of the same span AB, which is loaded with a distributed transverse load equal to the M/EI diagram of actual beam AB. Further, the slope of the tangent to the elastic curve at any point is equal to the corresponding ordinate of the shear diagram for the imaginary beam AB loaded with the M/EI diagram. When used in this manner, the M/EI diagram is referred to as the "elastic load," and therefore this procedure for computing the deflection and slope of a beam is called the *elastic-load method*. The shears and bending moments produced by the *elastic load* acting on the imaginary beam are often referred to as the *elastic shears* and the *elastic moments*, respectively.

By using this analogy, the problem of computing deflections and slopes of a beam is reduced to a procedure well known to a structural engineer. All he has to do is to compute the reactions, shear, and bending moment on an imaginary end-supported beam loaded with a distributed transverse load. The following examples illustrate the convenience of the elastic-load method.

The example used in developing these ideas has unyielding supports at points A and B. As a result, these points do not deflect, and therefore the chord of the elastic curve joining points A and B remains horizontal and coincident with the undeformed position of the axis of the beam. The slope τ_m and the deflection δ_m give, therefore, the true slope and deflection with reference to the original position of the beam. The elastic-load method may be applied, of course, to any portion AB of a beam whether the chord AB of the elastic curve remains fixed in position or not. Remember, however, that the shear and bending moment obtained by the elastic-load method give the slope and deflection *measured with reference to the chord AB*. If the chord has moved, the quantities so obtained do not give the true slope and deflection measured with reference to the original position of the beam until they are corrected for the effect of the chord movement.

In the general case where the chord may or may not move, the procedure of applying the elastic-load method may be summarized in the following statement:

The slopes and deflections of an elastic curve measured with reference to one of its chords AB are equal, respectively, to the (elastic) shears and (elastic) moments of an imaginary end-supported beam of span AB loaded with a distributed (elastic) load consisting of the M/EI diagram for that portion AB.*

In order to take full advantage of the elastic-load method, **it is desirable to follow the same sign convention and principles as those used in drawing regular load, shear, and bending-moment curves.** Since upward loads are considered as positive in such computations, plus M/EI ordinates indicate upward loads. Plotting the shear and bending-moment curves for the imaginary beam according to the usual beam convention, plus bending moment would be plotted above the axis and minus values below. Plus bending moment on the imaginary beam therefore indicates deflections above the chord, and minus values indicate deflections below the chord. Likewise, plus shear on the imaginary beam indicates that the elastic curve slopes upward, proceeding from left to right, and minus shear that it slopes downward.

* Provided that within the portion AB of the beam no discontinuities (such as hinges) have been inserted.

Example 12.13 *Compute the slopes and deflections of this beam, using the elastic-load method.*

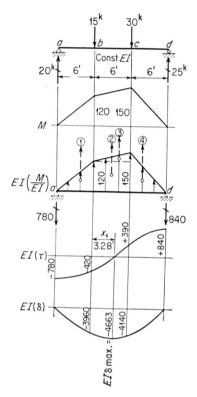

$\Sigma M_d = 0$

(1)	$120 \times 3 =$	$360 \times 14 =$	$5,040$
(2)	$120 \times 6 =$	$720 \times 9 =$	$6,480$
(3)	$30 \times 3 =$	$90 \times 8 =$	720
(4)	$150 \times 3 =$	$450 \times 4 =$	$1,800$
		$1,620$	$14,040$

$$\frac{14,040}{18} = 780 \;\updownarrow$$

$\Sigma M_a = 0$

$$
\begin{aligned}
360 \times 4 &= 1,440 \\
720 \times 9 &= 6,480 \\
90 \times 10 &= 900 \\
450 \times 14 &= 6,300 \\
\hline
\frac{15,120}{18} &= 840 \;\updownarrow
\end{aligned}
$$

$$
\begin{array}{lll}
\tau_a = -780 & -780 \times 6 = -4,680 & 0 = \delta_a \\
\quad\;\, +360 & +360 \times 2 = \; + 720 & \\
\cline{2-2}
& -3,960 = \delta_b & \\
\tau_b = -420 & -420 \times 6 = -2,520 & \\
\quad\;\, +720 & +720 \times 3 = +2,160 & \\
\quad\;\, + 90 & + 90 \times 2 = \; + 180 & \\
\cline{2-2}
& -4,140 = \delta_c & \\
\tau_c = +390 & +390 \times 6 = +2,340 & \\
\quad\;\, +450 & +450 \times 4 = +1,800 & \\
\tau_d = +840 & 0 = \delta_d &
\end{array}
$$

Maximum δ occurs where $\tau = 0$, that is, at the point where shear is zero on imaginary beam. This is between b and c, where

$$EI\tau = -420 + 120x_1 + \left(\frac{30}{6}\right)\frac{x_1^2}{2}$$

$$= -420 + 120x_1 + 2.5x_1^2 = 0$$

$$\therefore x_1^2 + 48x_1 = 168$$
$$(x_1 + 24)^2 = 168 + (24)^2 = 744$$
$$x_1 + 24 = +27.28 \quad \therefore x_1 = 3.28'$$

At this point,

$$EI\delta_{max} = -3,960 - (420)(3.28) + (120)(3.28)\left(\frac{3.28}{2}\right) + (5)(3.28)\left(\frac{3.28}{2}\right)\left(\frac{3.28}{3}\right)$$

$$= -3,960 - 1,378 + 646 + 29 = -4,663 \text{ kip-ft}^3$$

Discussion:

Note the units of these various numbers. M is in kip-feet. Therefore, the area under the M curve is in kip-feet², and the static moment of this area is in kip-feet³. Thus, if E and I are also substituted in kip and foot units, values of δ will be in feet and τ in radians.

Example 12.14 *Compute the slopes and deflections of this beam.*

$$E = 30 \times 10^3 \; k/''^2 \qquad I_1 = 600 \; in.^4 \qquad I_2 = 300 \; in.^4$$

The chord *bd* of this beam remains horizontal. Slopes and deflections with reference to this chord are therefore the actual slopes and deflections. Use the elastic-load method to obtain these, using an imaginary beam supported at *b* and *d*. The reaction at *b* on this beam gives the true slope of the tangent to the elastic curve at point *b*. With this slope known, it is easy to apply the moment-area theorems directly to obtain slopes and deflections in the cantilever portion *ab*.

$$\Sigma M_b = 0, \; \curvearrowright_+$$

(1) $96 \times 6 = -576 \times 4 = + 2,304$

(2) $72 \times 6 = \quad 432 \times 8 = - 3,456$

(3) $144 \times 6 = \quad 864 \times 16 = -13,824$

$$\begin{aligned}
&\qquad\qquad\qquad\qquad +720 \qquad \overline{-14,976} \\
&\qquad\qquad\qquad\qquad\qquad\qquad\qquad \overline{24} \\
&\qquad\qquad\qquad\qquad\qquad\qquad\; = 624 \; \updownarrow
\end{aligned}$$

$$\Sigma M_d = 0, \; \curvearrowright_+$$

$$\begin{aligned}
576 \times 20 &= -11,520 \\
432 \times 16 &= 6,912 \\
864 \times 8 &= 6,912 \\
& \;\; \frac{2,304}{24} = 96 \; \updownarrow
\end{aligned}$$

$$\tau_b = \begin{aligned}[t] &-96 \\ &-576 \\ &+432 \end{aligned}$$

$$\tau_c = \begin{aligned}[t] &-240 \\ &+864 \end{aligned}$$

$$\tau_d = +624$$

$$0 = \delta_b$$

$$\begin{aligned}
-96 \times 12 &= -1,152 \\
-576 \times 8 &= -4,608 \\
+432 \times 4 &= +1,728 \\
& \; \overline{-4,032} = \delta_c
\end{aligned}$$

$$\begin{aligned}
-240 \times 12 &= -2,880 \\
+864 \times 8 &= +6,912 \\
& \qquad 0 = \delta_d
\end{aligned}$$

Then at point *a*,

$$\begin{aligned}
EI_1\delta_a &= 96 \times 6 - 96 \times 3 \times 4 \\
&= -576 \; (down)
\end{aligned}$$

Maximum occurs just to right of point c, where $\tau = 0$.

$$EI_1\tau = +624 - (12x_1)\left(\frac{x_1}{2}\right) = 0 \qquad \therefore x_1^2 = 104 \qquad x_1 = \underline{10.22'}$$

$$EI_1\delta_{max} = -(624)(10.22) + \frac{(12)(10.22)^3}{(2)(3)} = -6,385 + 2,124 = \underline{-4,261} \ (down)$$

Substituting now for E and I_1,

$$\delta_{max} = \frac{-(4,261)^{k'^3}}{(30 \times 10^3 \times 144)^{k/'^2}(600/144^2)'^4} = \underline{-0.0341 \ ft} \ (down)$$

12.10   Application of Moment-area Theorems and Elastic-load Method to Deflection of Beams and Frames.   To utilize the moment-area approach at its maximum efficiency, it is often desirable to combine the direct application of the two theorems with the use of the elastic-load procedure.   This has already been illustrated in Example 12.14 and will be further illustrated in the examples that follow.   To plan the method of attack in a given problem, it is advisable first to sketch the elastic curve of the structure.   A certain amount of practice is necessary to develop proficiency in sketching such curves.   However, even the novice can get the curvature correct by simply following the bending-moment diagram of the member and noting whether the bending is plus or minus.

Once the elastic curve has been sketched approximately, it then is easy to plan the solution.   To obtain deflections with respect to a tangent, use the moment-area theorems directly.   To obtain deflections with respect to a chord, use the elastic-load method.   **In applying the elastic-load method as described here, the portion of the elastic curve of the actual beam corresponding to the span of the imaginary beam must never include an intermediate hinge.**   At such hinges, there may be a sharp change in the slope of the elastic curve.   This sudden change is not included in an elastic load that consists simply of the M/EI diagram.   Such cases may be handled by an extension of the elastic-load method called the conjugate-beam method, discussed in Art. 12.11, or by the combined use of the moment-area theorems and the elastic-load method as illustrated in the following examples.

For the reasons just noted, it is likewise true that **the moment-area theorems cannot be applied between two points on the elastic curve if there is a hinge within that portion of the beam.**

Example 12.15   *Compute the maximum deflection of this beam.*

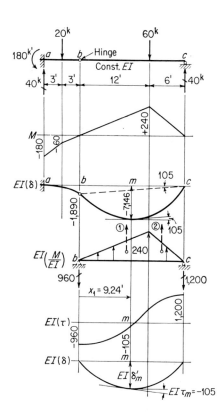

After studying the sketch of the elastic curve, it is apparent that δ_b may be computed by applying the second moment-area theorem to the portion ab. This deflection establishes the position of the chord bc. The deflections and slopes with reference to this chord may be obtained using the elastic-load method applied to an imaginary beam of span bc.

$$EI\,\delta_b = [(180)(\tfrac{3}{2})(5) + (60)(\tfrac{6}{2})(3)]$$
$$= 1{,}890 \; (\downarrow)$$

Rotation of chord $bc = \dfrac{1{,}890}{18} = 105$

(1) $240 \times 6 = 1{,}440 \times 10 = 14{,}400$
(2) $240 \times 3 = \phantom{1{,}}720 \times 4 = 2{,}880$
$$\overline{\phantom{1{,}440 \times 10 = }17{,}280}$$
$$\frac{}{18}$$
$$= 960 \;\updownarrow$$

$$1{,}440 \times 8 = 11{,}520$$
$$720 \times 14 = 10{,}080$$
$$\overline{21{,}600}$$
$$\frac{21{,}600}{18} = 1{,}200\updownarrow$$

The point of maximum δ occurs where the tangent to the elastic curve is horizontal, i.e., where the tangent slopes down to the right with respect to the chord bc, or $EI\tau_m = -105$.

$$EI\tau_m = -960 + (20x_1)\left(\frac{x_1}{2}\right) = -105$$
$$x_1^2 = 85.5$$
$$x_1 = 9.24'$$

$$EI\delta_m' = -(960)(9.24) + \frac{(20)(9.24)^3}{6}$$
$$= -6{,}225$$

$$EI\delta_m = -6{,}225 - (105)(18 - 9.24)$$
$$= -7{,}146$$

Discussion:

Note that it is not permissible to apply the elastic-load method to an imaginary beam of span ac because of the presence of the hinge at b.

Example 12.16　*Compute the slopes and deflections of this beam.　Constant E and I.*

Discussion:

The chord *dg* of the elastic curve does not move, and therefore slopes and deflections determined with reference to it by applying the elastic-load method to the imaginary beam *dg* are the true slopes and deflections of the beam in this portion.　These computations are straightforward and produce the results shown for the location and magnitude of the maximum deflections in the portion *dg*.

The reactions of this imaginary beam establish the slope of the tangent of the elastic curve at *d* and *g*.　Is is then easy to use the second moment-area theorem to compute the additional deflection of the hinges at *c* and *h* from these tangents.　The total deflections of these hinges from the original position of the beam are shown.

It is also easy to apply the second moment-area theorem to the cantilever portion *jk* and thus compute the deflection of the hinge at *j*.

In this manner, the position of the chords ac and hj is established, and it is now possible to compute the true slopes and deflections in these portions.   The position and magnitude of the maximum deflections in these portions are shown.   The slopes and deflections with respect to the chords ac and hj may be obtained by applying the elastic-load method to the imaginary beams of the same spans.

Note that there can be no point in the portion ac which deflects more than c, for the slope of the chord is greater than the slope of the tangent at c with respect to the chord.

The moment-area theorems and the elastic-load method may also be used advantageously in the computation of frame deflections.   The frame deflections computed in this manner, however, do not include the effect of axial changes in length of the members.   Fortunately, it is usually permissible to neglect the effect of axial deformation in most frame-deflection problems (see Example 12.9).

Example 12.17   *Compute the deflections of this frame.*

(1) $\quad 48 \times 12 = 576 \times 1\,{}^{2}\!\!/_{\!24} = 288 \downarrow$

(2) $\quad 48 \times 6 = 288 \times {}^{4}\!\!/_{\!24} = 48 \uparrow$

$$\overline{ 240 \downarrow}$$

(1) $\qquad\qquad 576 \times 1\,{}^{2}\!\!/_{\!24} = 288 \downarrow$

(2) $\qquad\qquad 288 \times 2\,{}^{0}\!\!/_{\!24} = 240 \uparrow$

$$\overline{ 48 \downarrow}$$

To find point of maximum deflection,

$$EI\tau_m = 0 = -240 + (4x)\left(\frac{x}{2}\right)$$

$$x^2 = 120 \qquad x = 10.98$$

$$EI\delta_m = -(240)(10.98) + (4)\frac{(10.98)^3}{6}$$

$$= -1{,}753 \; (\downarrow)$$

$$Ei\delta_d = (48)(6) - (48)(3)(4)$$

$$= -288 \; (\downarrow)$$

$$EI\delta_e = (48)(12) = 576 \; (\rightarrow)$$

Since the joint at c is rigid, the tangents to the elastic curves of all members meeting at that joint rotate through the same angle. Since there is no bending moment in the column, the elastic curve is a straight line inclined at the same angle as the tangent of the elastic curve of the beam.

Example 12.18   *Compute the deflection at point e on this frame.*

$$EI\tau_c = (360)(12)(1\tfrac{6}{24}) = 2{,}880$$
$$EI\delta_e = (2{,}880)(12) + (360)(6)(8)$$
$$\qquad = 51{,}840$$
$$\qquad (\leftarrow)$$

It should be apparent from these examples and the problems at the end of the chapter that the moment-area methods may be applied most advantageously when the moment diagram is composed of a series of straight lines, i.e., when the beam is acted upon by concentrated loads. In such cases, the area under the M/EI curve may be broken up into rectangles and triangles, and the necessary computations are quite simple. When the load is distributed, however, and the moment curve becomes a curved line, the computations become more difficult. When the load is uniformly distributed, the moment curve is parabolic, and the M/EI diagram may be broken up into triangles, rectangles, and parabolic segments.[1] In the case of more complicated distributions, however, it is usually necessary to divide the M/EI diagram into a series of short portions each of which may be broken up into essentially triangles and rectangles. Sometimes it is desirable to use Simpson's rule to improve the results of approximate summation.

Sometimes it is advisable to use graphical methods in applying the elastic-load method. Suppose, for example, that the M/EI diagram is very irregular in shape owing either to a complicated loading of the structure or to variation in the moment of inertia of the beam. In such cases, the shear and moment diagrams produced by the irregular elastic load acting on the imaginary beam may be obtained graphically in the manner discussed in Art. 5.10.

---

[1] Refer to the bending-moment diagram for portion hj of the beam in Example 12.16. Consider the shaded area between this parabolic curve and a chord of this curve. If the horizontal projection of this chord is a, prove that (1) the vertical intercept between the chord and the curve at the middle of this chord is $wa^2/8$, where w is the intensity of the uniformly distributed load on the beam; (2) the area of this shaded segment is $wa^3/12$; (3) the center of gravity of this shaded segment lies on a vertical line through the mid-point of this chord.

12.11 Conjugate-beam Method. From the examples of the previous article, it is apparent that deflection computations for any beam may be handled effectively by a proper combination of the use of the moment-area theorems and of the elastic-load method. The procedure involved in this combination, however, may be identified as nothing more

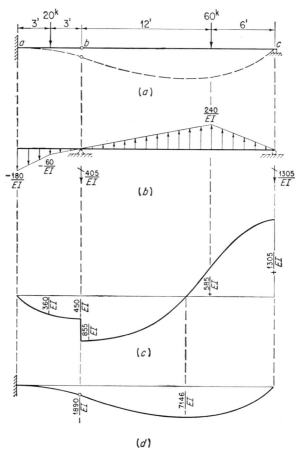

(a)

(b)

(c)

(d)

Figure 12.19 Development of conjugate-beam method

than a slight extension and variation of the elastic-load method. This extension is called the *conjugate-beam method.*

In order to develop these new ideas, consider the beam used in Example 12.15 and shown in a somewhat different manner in Fig. 12.19. In Fig. 12.19a are shown the real beam and its loading. Also shown by the dashed line is the deflection curve which has certain notable characteristics that are defined by the type of supports and by the hinge at *b*, even though at this stage it will be presumed that the magnitude of the deflections is unknown. (1) At support a both the deflection and slope of the elastic curve are zero; (2) at support c the deflection is zero but the elastic curve is free to assume any slope required; and (3) at hinge b, there can be a deflection, and in addition, a sudden change in slope can occur between the left and right sides of the hinge.

The objective is to select a *conjugate beam* (i.e., a corresponding fictitious beam) which has the same length as the real beam but is supported and detailed in such a manner that, **when the conjugate beam is loaded by the M/EI diagram of the real beam as an (elastic) load, the (elastic) shear in the conjugate beam at any location is equal to the slope of the real beam at the corresponding location and the (elastic) bending moment in the conjugate beam is equal to the corresponding deflection of the real beam.** Note that these slopes and deflections of the real beam are measured *with respect to its original position;* that is, they are the true slopes and deflections. It is always possible to select the proper supports for the conjugate beam to achieve the desired objective by simply noting the known characteristics of the elastic curve of the real beam at its supports or at any special construction features, such as the hinge at b.

To illustrate the selection of the supports of the conjugate beam, consider the beam in Fig. 12.19. At a, there is neither slope nor deflection of the real beam; therefore, there must be neither shear nor moment at this point of the conjugate beam. That is, point a of the conjugate beam must be free and unsupported. At c, there is slope but no deflection of the real beam; therefore, there must be shear but no moment in the conjugate beam. That is, point c of the conjugate beam must be provided with the vertical reaction of a roller support. At b, there is deflection and possibly a discontinuous slope in the real beam; therefore, a vertical reaction must be provided to create the sudden change in shear in the conjugate beam, and it must be capable of resisting bending moment. That is, point b of the conjugate beam must also be provided with a roller support. Thus, the conjugate beam is loaded and supported as shown in Fig. 12.19b.

If the reactions, shears, and bending moments are now computed as for any statically determinate beam, the (elastic) shear and the (elastic) bending-moment diagrams can be drawn as shown in Figs. 12.19c and d, respectively. The ordinates of these diagrams give, respectively, the slope and the deflection at corresponding locations in the real beam, measured with respect to the original undeflected position. **The convention used for sign of the (elastic) load, (elastic) shear, and (elastic) bending moment is the usual beam convention as described at the end of Art. 12.9 regarding the elastic-load method.**

These and similar considerations lead to the rules shown in Fig. 12.20

for selecting the supports and other details of conjugate beams. Illustrations of selection of supports and details of typical conjugate beams are shown in Fig. 12.21. **Note that statically determinate real beams always have corresponding conjugate beams which are also statically determinate. Statically indeterminate real beams appear to have unstable conjugate beams. However, such conjugate beams turn out to be in equilibrium since they are stabilized by the elastic loading corresponding to the M/EI diagram for the corresponding real beam.** For example, the last case shown

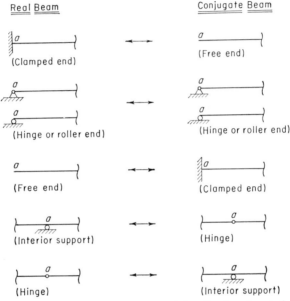

Figure 12.20   Selection of support and details of conjugate beams

is the real beam clamped at both ends, and the corresponding conjugate beam is completely free and unsupported. For any loading (such as the centrally applied concentrated load shown), it will be found that the M/EI diagram corresponds to an elastic loading which is completely self-equalizing and requires no supporting reactions whatsoever. In fact, in such cases, the stabilizing conditions required of the elastic loading furnish one method of obtaining the necessary equations for finding the redundant moments for such indeterminate beams.

If one uses the conjugate-beam method to solve problems such as Example 12.14, 12.15, or 12.16, one will find that one has made exactly the same computations as one would have if one solved the problems using a combination of the moment-area theorems and the elastic-load method. However, the conjugate-beam approach furnishes a straightforward pro-

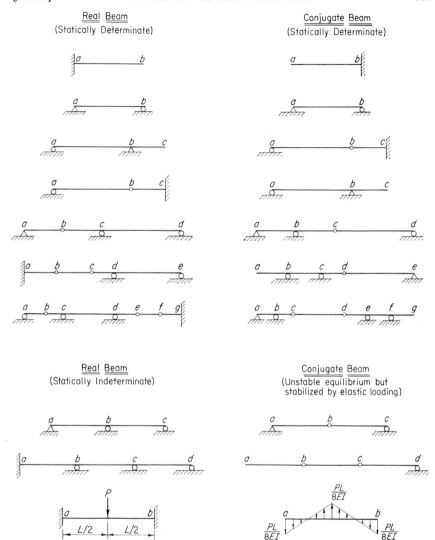

Figure 12.21   Typical real beams and corresponding conjugate beams

cedure for which a readily applied sign convention is available.   As a result, one is less likely to make mistakes when following the conjugate-beam routine.

12.12   Williot-Mohr Method.   When the method of virtual work is used to compute truss deflections, only one component of the deflection of a joint can be calculated at a time.   To obtain the magnitude and direction of the true absolute movement of a joint, both horizontal and vertical components of its movement must be determined.   Therefore, two separate applications of the method of virtual work are usually required in order to determine the resultant deflection of *each* truss joint. *One* graphical solution using the Williot-Mohr method, however, will determine the resultant deflection of *all* joints of the truss, and therefore this method obviously has a very important advantage in the solution of certain deflection problems.

The fundamentals of the Williot-Mohr method may be developed by considering the simple truss shown in Fig. 12.22. Assume that the changes of length of the members, ΔL, have been computed for the given condition of deformation, using Eq. (12.5a), (12.5b), or (12.5c). The deflected position of the truss may then be determined in the following manner as indicated by the dashed lines in Fig. 12.22a. First, remove the

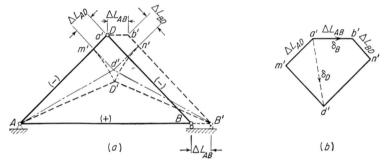

Figure 12.22   Kinematics of truss deflection

pin at joint D, and allow the change in length of member AB to take place. This will cause member DB to move parallel to itself as shown, and all points on this member will move horizontally to the right an amount equal to ΔL_{AB}. Now, upon allowing members AD and BD to change length, the D ends of each will move as shown if they remain connected to member AB at points A and B', respectively. Before pin D can be replaced and the truss connected together again, it is necessary to make the D ends of members AD and BD coincide again. This may be done by rotating AD about A and BD about B' until the arcs intersect. The deflection of any joint can then be determined from the original and deflected position of the joint.

This procedure is straightforward but difficult to apply in practice because the deflections and changes in length are actually very much smaller than have been indicated in this sketch, so that a very large scale drawing is necessary in order to obtain any accuracy. Since the deformations are small, however, the angular rotation of any member is also small, in fact so small that it is permissible to assume that, during the rotation of a member, a point moves along the tangent drawn normal to the original direction of the member rather than along the true arc, as shown by the dot-dash lines in Fig. 12.22a. If ΔL had not been tremendously exaggerated in this sketch, the dashed and dot-dash lines would coincide for all practical purposes. Introducing this simplification makes it possible to obtain the joint deflections without drawing the entire lengths of the members because it is no longer necessary to draw the arcs about the centers of rotation.

The simplified diagram shown in Fig. 12.22b is similar to the portion of Fig. 12.22a marked with the same letters. It involves only the changes in length of the members and the tangents to the arcs of rotation and enables one to find the relative movements of the various joints. Such a diagram is called a **Williot diagram** after the French engineer who suggested it. As before, imagine that the pin at D is temporarily removed, and allow the changes in length to take place one at a time. Upon selecting a suitable scale for ΔL and designating the points in this diagram by the lower-case letters of the corresponding truss joints, the diagram is started by locating point a'. In this simple truss, it is known that joint A remains fixed in position and member AB remains horizontal. Joint B therefore moves horizontally to the right relative to A an amount equal to ΔL_{AB} as indicated by the relative positions of points a' and b'. Owing to the shortening, ΔL_{AD}, the D end of member AD moves downward to the left parallel to AD with reference to joint A, as represented by the vector $\overline{a'm'}$; similarly, owing to the shortening, ΔL_{BD}, the D end of member BD moves downward to the right parallel to BD with reference to joint B, as represented by the vector $\overline{b'n'}$. In order to make the D ends coincide, member AD must be rotated about A and member BD about B. During these rotations, the D ends are assumed to move along the tangents as represented by the vectors $\overline{m'd'}$ and $\overline{n'd'}$, respectively. Note that these tangents are perpendicular to members AD and BD, respectively. The vectors $\overline{a'd'}$ and $\overline{a'b'}$ represent the deflections of joints D and B, respectively, with respect to joint A. In this case, since joint A is actually fixed in position, these vectors represent the true absolute movements of these joints. Of course, the lengths of these vectors are measured to the same scale as that used in plotting ΔL.

The construction of the Williot diagram for a more elaborate truss is carried out in essentially the same manner as described above. Temporarily, all members are assumed to be disconnected. Then, after the members are imagined to undergo their changes in length, they are reassembled one at a time, and the Williot diagram is constructed to show the resulting joint displacements. In such cases, the true relative movement of the two ends of a bar are not known as was true of joints A and B in the above simple case. The Williot diagram may be drawn, however, on the arbitrary assumption that some bar remains fixed in direction, i.e., that the relative movement of the joints at the end of this bar is parallel to the

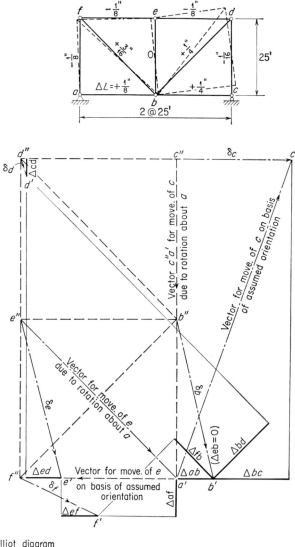

——— Williot diagram

— — Mohr correction diagram

—·— Vectors giving true deflections of truss joints

Figure 12.23   Williot-Mohr method

bar and equal to the change in its length. When these two points are located, a third point corresponding to the third joint of a truss triangle formed by these three joints may be located in the manner described above. The remainder of the construction may be carried out proceeding from joint to joint, always working with a triangle two joints of which have already been located, and locating the new joint from these two points. If the assumed orientation is correct, the vectors corresponding to certain known deflection conditions will be oriented correctly. If these vectors are not consistent with the known conditions, the Mohr correction diagram must be added to the Williot diagram.

The Williot diagram for the truss of Fig. 12.23 has been drawn on the assumption that joint a is fixed in position and member ab fixed in direction. If this orientation is correct, the vectors drawn from point a' to points b', c', d', etc., will be the true deflections of joints b, c, d, etc., respectively. Joint c on the truss, being a roller support, can have no vertical deflection and is constrained to move horizontally. On the basis of the assumed orientation, however, joint c moves upward to the right as shown by the vector $\overline{a'c'}$, and the other joints have moved as indicated to an exaggerated scale by the dashed lines on the line diagram of the truss. This means that the assumption that member ab remains fixed in direction is in error, and it is now necessary to rotate the truss, as a whole, clockwise about a to bring

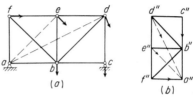

Figure 12.24 Mohr correction diagram

joint c back down on the support. The amount of rotation required may be determined by knowing that the true deflection of c must be a horizontal vector. This true deflection is the resultant of vector $\overline{a'c'}$ and the vector representing the movement of c during the rotation of the truss about a. During a small angular rotation of the truss about a, joint c may be assumed to move along the tangent to the true arc and hence normal to the line ac on the truss or, in this case, vertically. If this vector, giving the movement of c with reference to a during rotation, is added on the diagram as the vertical vector $\overline{c''a'}$ drawn through a', then the resultant of the vector $\overline{c''a'}$ ($\downarrow$) and the vector $\overline{a'c'}$ ($\nearrow$) must be the horizontal vector $\overline{c''c'}$ ($\rightarrow$), which is the true deflection of joint c, and thus point c'' is located.

During the rotation of the truss about a, not only joint c but all other joints may be assumed to move normal to the radius from the joint to the center of rotation a an amount equal to that radius times the angle of rotation. In Fig. 12.24a, the arrows on the joints indicate the direction of the joint movements as the truss is rotated clockwise about a through a small angle α. If all these vectors are drawn to scale and acting toward point a'', as shown in Fig. 12.24b, the movement of joint b during rotation is represented by vector $\overline{b''a''}$, of joint c by $\overline{c''a''}$, of joint d by $\overline{d''a''}$, etc. After these double-prime points have been connected as shown, consider any corresponding portions of these two figures such as triangles dac

and $d''a''c''$. Since $c''a''$ is perpendicular to ca and $d''a''$ is perpendicular to da, therefore angle dac = angle $d''a''c''$. Since $c''a''$ = αca and $d''a''$ = αda, then $c''a''/d''a''$ = ca/da. Therefore, triangles dac and $d''a''c''$ are similar. In this manner, it may be shown that Fig. 12.24a is similar to Fig. 12.24b. Such considerations lead to the following conclusion:

If a rigid body is rotated about some center of rotation O through a small angle, and if the movements of two points i and k are plotted as vectors $O''i''$ and $O''k''$ from or to a point O'', and if the shape of the body is then plotted to a scale with points i'' and k'' as a base, each line on this scale sketch will be perpendicular to the corresponding line on the actual body and the line drawn from any point on this scale sketch to the point O'' will represent, as a vector, the movement of the corresponding point on the real body during the rotation about O.

This principle is the basis for the **Mohr correction diagram.**

In the example in Fig. 12.23, the Mohr correction diagram $a'b''c''$-$d''e''f''$ is superimposed on the Williot diagram, using the vector $c''a'$ as a basis, every line on it being at 90° to the corresponding line of the line diagram of the truss. The vectors from the double-prime points to the pole a' give the movements of the corresponding joints during the rotation of the truss about joint a. The true deflection of any joint may now be determined as the resultant of the vector from the corresponding double-prime point to a' and the vector from a' to the corresponding single-prime point, i.e., **the true deflection of any joint may be found in magnitude and direction from the vector drawn from the double-prime point on the Mohr correction diagram to the single-prime point on the Williot diagram.**

12.13   Application of Williot-Mohr Method. The Williot diagram will be more compact and will require a smaller Mohr correction diagram if the orientation that is assumed to start the Williot diagram is reasonably correct. In many cases, it is quite apparent that certain bars do not change direction very much. For example, in the case of an end-support truss the center vertical remains essentially vertical and is therefore a good member to assume fixed in direction in starting the Williot diagram. This is illustrated in Example 12.19.

It is also interesting to note that the Mohr correction diagram may be eliminated entirely if the relative movements of the two ends of a bar are computed first by the method of virtual work. For example, consider the truss shown in Fig. 12.25. Joint a in this case does not move. Consider one of the bars that meet at joint a, such as bar ab. The relative movement of the two ends of this bar is the resultant of the relative movements parallel and perpendicular to the bar. The relative movement of the two ends parallel to the bar is simply equal to its change in length, while the relative movement normal to the bar may be computed by the method of virtual work. In this case, since point a does not move, all that is necessary is to compute the movement of point b normal to the bar, or vertically. Once this has been done, these two vectors may be laid out as shown, and the vector $\overline{a'b'}$ then gives the true relative movements of joints a and b. The Williot diagram may now be drawn on the basis of the positions of points a' and b', locating first point B' from the triangle

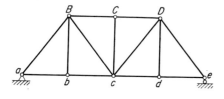

abB, etc. Since this diagram has been oriented correctly, the absolute movements of all the joints may be obtained from it directly without adding the Mohr correction diagram. This procedure is illustrated in Example 12.20.

Figure 12.25 Correct orientation of Williot diagram

Figure 12.26 Compound truss

The Williot diagram may be drawn without difficulty in the manner described in Art. 12.12 for any simple truss. It should be noted, however, that certain difficulties are encountered in applying these ideas to a compound truss such as that shown in Fig. 12.26. Suppose that the Williot diagram is started in this instance by assuming joint g fixed in position and bar gG in direction. Points F', f', e', and E' can be located without difficulty on the left side and similarly points H', h', i', and I' on the right. It is impossible to proceed beyond these points, however, by using the previously discussed procedures. One way of overcoming the difficulty is to recognize that the relative movement of joints C and e parallel to the line CDe is simply equal to the sum of the changes in length of bars CD and De and, similarly, that the relative movement of joints c and e along line cde is equal to the sum of the changes in length of cd and de. On this basis, temporarily consider that there are no joints at D and d and that bars cD and Dd have been omitted, and proceed as usual to locate points C' and c'. Having located these points, reinsert the omitted bars, and backtrack to locate points D' and d'. If the work has been done correctly, it is now possible to locate e' from D' and d' and see whether or not it coincides with the existing location of point e'. Points B', b', and a' can now be located without difficulty, and the remaining points to the right of

iI may be located in the manner just described for the points to the left
of *Ee*.

The application of the Williot-Mohr method to the case of a three-
hinged arch requires a somewhat different technique, which is illustrated
by Example 12.21.

Example 12.19   *Draw the Williot-Mohr diagram for this truss.*

Assume point c fixed in position.
Assume bar cC fixed in direction.

Point	Deflection	
	Horizontal	*Vertical*
A	0	0
B	0.063″ ←	0.130″ ↓
C	0.125″ ←	0.050″ ↓
D	0	0.125″ ↓
E	0.125″ →	0.700″ ↓
b	0.125″ →	0.130″ ↓
c	0.063″ ←	0.112″ ↓
d	0.250″ ←	0.083″ ↓
e	0.313″ ←	0.962″ ↓
f	0.438″ ←	1.513″ ↓

Discussion:

The vectors on the Williot diagram drawn from c' to A', B', b', C', etc., give the movements of joints A, B, b, C, etc., it being assumed that joint c remains fixed in position and bar cC remains fixed in direction. In such a case, the resulting joint deflections would be as shown to an exaggerated scale by the dashed lines on the line diagram. Obviously, the assumed orientation is incorrect; for joint A has moved off the hinge support, and the movement of joint d is not parallel to the supporting surface. Note, however, that the assumed orientation is not badly in error.

Joint A may be brought back to the hinge support by translating the truss as a rigid body parallel to the vector $\overline{A'c'}$ a distance equal to the scaled length of this vector. During such a translation, every joint would move the distance indicated by the vector $\overline{A'c'}$. After such translation, the resultant movement of any joint, such as E, would be the vector sum of the vector $\overline{A'c'}$ and the vector $\overline{c'E'}$, and therefore, the vector $\overline{A'E'}$. Therefore, it is apparent that the resultant movements of the various joints after joint A has been restored to its correct position are given by the vectors drawn from point A' to B', b', C', c', D', d', etc. Obviously, the truss is still not oriented correctly, for the vector $\overline{A'd'}$ does not indicate the proper direction for the movement of joint d. The truss must therefore be rotated counterclockwise about A so that d moves the amount given by the vector $\overline{d''A'}$. Then, the total movement of joint d is the vector sum of vectors $\overline{d''A'}$ and $\overline{A'd'}$, that is, the vector $\overline{d''d'}$, which is in the proper direction.

The Mohr correction diagram may then be completed as shown by the dotted lines, the line $d''A'$ being used as a base line. The final true resultant deflection of any joint is then given by the vector drawn from the corresponding double-prime point to the corresponding single-prime point.

Example 12.20   Draw the Williot diagram for the same truss as shown in Fig. 12.23. In this instance, however, first compute the true relative position of the two ends of a bar so that the Williot diagram may be drawn with the correct orientation and the Mohr correction diagram will thereby be eliminated.

In this case joint a is truly fixed in position. Computing simply the vertical deflection of joint b gives us the only additional information necessary to plot the true relative position of joints a and b.

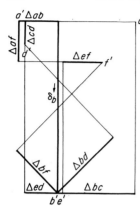

Bar	F_Q	ΔL	$F_Q\,\Delta L$
fe	−0.5	−0.125	+0.063
ed	−0.5	−0.125	+0.063
af	−0.5	−0.125	+0.063
cd	−0.5	−0.063	+0.031
fb	+0.707	+0.188	+0.133
bd	+0.707	+0.250	+0.177
Σ			+0.530

$$(1^k)(\delta_b^{\downarrow}) = \Sigma F_Q\,\Delta L = +0.530^{k''}$$
$$\therefore \ \delta_b = \underline{0.530\ in.}\ \downarrow$$

Note the much-reduced size of this diagram.

Example 12.21　*Find the deflections of this three-hinged arch, using the Williot-Mohr method.*

For left half:
　Assume a fixed in position.
　Assume aA fixed in direction.

For right half:
　Assume e fixed in position.
　Assume eE fixed in direction.

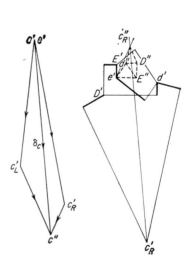

Discussion:

The presence of the hinge at point c introduces certain complications in applying the Williot-Mohr method to this problem. After making the assumptions indicated, draw the Williot diagrams in the usual manner for the two separate halves. On this basis, the vector $\overline{a'c_L'}$ on the left diagram indicates a certain deflection for joint c. Similarly, the vector $\overline{e'c_R'}$ on the right diagram indicates a different deflection for joint c. If the assumed orientations are correct, the deflection of joint c will be the same whether determined from the left or the right diagram. Since these vectors are not equivalent, the left half must be rotated about a, causing joint c to move normal to the radius ac. Similarly, the right half is rotated about e, causing joint c to move normal to the radius ec. These rotations must be such as to produce the same resultant displacement of joint c for either half. They are determined as indicated in the center vector diagram, being given by the vector $\overline{c_L'c''}$ for the left half and $\overline{c_R'c''}$ for the right half. These vectors, therefore, establish the bases $\overline{c_L''a'}$ and $\overline{c_R''e'}$ for the Mohr correction diagrams for the left and right halves, respectively. The true deflections of the various joints may now be obtained from the vectors drawn from the double- to the single-prime points.

12.14 Bar-chain Method. The bar-chain method is similar to the Williot-Mohr method in that by one application of the method we are able to compute the deflection

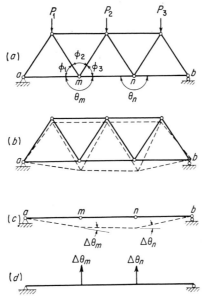

Figure 12.27 Fundamentals of bar-chain method

of several joints of a truss simultaneously. This method was first suggested by H. Müller-Breslau and is essentially an adaptation of the elastic-load method, applied to trusses instead of beams.

To develop the fundamentals of this procedure, consider the case of the simple truss shown in Fig. 12.27a, where it is desired to compute the vertical component of the deflection of the lower-chord panel points. For the given cause of deformation, the changes in length of the members may be computed from Eq. (12.5a), (12.5b), or

(12.5c).   As a result of these changes in length, the angles of the truss triangles will change by certain small amounts, and the truss may change shape as indicated to an exaggerated scale by the dashed lines in Fig. 12.27b.   The changes in the angles of the triangles may be computed rather easily by means of the expressions developed below. The bottom chord of this truss may be isolated and its deflected position drawn as shown in Fig. 12.27c.   This suggests to us immediately that the problem of computing the deflected shape of this bottom chord resembles that of computing the elastic curve of a straight beam by the moment-area or elastic-load method.   In the case of a beam, however, the elastic curve is a smooth, continuous curve the slope of which is continually changing, whereas the deflection curve of this bottom chord is composed of a series of straight lines which change slope only at the truss joints.   This series of straight lines is called a *bar chain*, and from this terminology the method gets its name.

In a beam, the change in slope between the tangents at the ends of a differential element of the elastic curve, dx, is equal to $M/EI\, dx$, which is the differential area under the M/EI diagram at that element.   At any joint m of the bar chain, however, the change in slope between the adjacent bars of the chain is equal to the change in the angle θ_m, that is, $\Delta\theta_m$, and between joints there is no change in slope.   When the moment-area method is applied to a bar chain, the M/EI diagram should be replaced, therefore, by a series of ordinates, one at each intermediate joint equal to $\Delta\theta$ at that joint.   Hence, the elastic load used for the bar chain consists of a series of concentrated loads such as those shown in Fig. 12.27d.   The technique of applying the moment-area or the elastic-load method to obtain the slope and deflection of the bar chain, however, is exactly the same as in the case of beams.   The angle θ should be considered as the angle included on the lower side between two adjacent bars of the chain. $\Delta\theta$ should be considered plus (and therefore an upward elastic load) when θ increases.

It is easy to compute the change in θ if the angle changes of the truss triangles are known.   For example, at joint m in this case, $\Delta\theta_m$ is numerically equal but opposite in sense to the algebraic sum of the angle changes in angles ϕ_1, ϕ_2, and ϕ_3.   An expression to be used for computing such changes in the angles of the truss triangles will now be developed.

Consider the triangle shown in Fig. 12.28.   Suppose that we want to compute the change in angle ϕ caused by these bars increasing in length by ΔL_1, ΔL_2, and ΔL_3.   The increase $\Delta\phi$ in angle ϕ may be computed by the method of virtual work, using the Q system shown.   Let α_1 represent the clockwise rotation of bar 1 and α_2 the counterclockwise rotation of bar 2.   Then, evaluating the external virtual work done by this Q system,

$$\Sigma Q\delta = (1)(\alpha \overset{\curvearrowright}{_1}) + (1)(\alpha \overset{\curvearrowleft}{_2}) = (1)(\alpha \overset{\curvearrowright}{_1} + \alpha \overset{\curvearrowleft}{_2}) = (1)\,\Delta\phi$$

since $\alpha \overset{\curvearrowright}{_1} + \alpha \overset{\curvearrowleft}{_2} = \text{increase in } \measuredangle\,\phi = \Delta\phi$

Applying now the law of virtual work,

$$\Sigma Q\delta = \Sigma F_Q\,\Delta L$$

$$(1)\ \Delta\phi = \left(\frac{1}{h_3}\right)\Delta L_3 + \left(-\frac{\cos\beta_2}{h_3}\right)\Delta L_2 + \left(-\frac{\cos\beta_1}{h_3}\right)\Delta L_1 \qquad (a)$$

From the geometry of the triangle, the following relations exist:

$$h_3 = L_2\sin\beta_2 \qquad \text{and} \qquad h_3 = L_1\sin\beta_1 \qquad (b)$$

Likewise, $L_3 = l_1 + l_2 = h_3\cot\beta_1 + h_3\cot\beta_2 = h_3(\cot\beta_1 + \cot\beta_2)$

$$\frac{1}{h_3} = \frac{\cot\beta_1 + \cot\beta_2}{L_3} \qquad (c)$$

Substituting from Eqs. (b) and (c) in Eq. (a),

$$\Delta\phi = \frac{\Delta L_3}{L_3}\,(\cot\beta_1 + \cot\beta_2) - \frac{\Delta L_2}{L_2}\cot\beta_2 - \frac{\Delta L_1}{L_1}\cot\beta_1$$

Or this may be written in the following convenient form, noting that $\Delta L = eL$:

$$\Delta\phi = (e_3 - e_1)\cot\beta_1 + (e_3 - e_2)\cot\beta_2 \qquad (12.11a)$$

Thus, the angle change $\Delta\phi$ is equal to the difference in the strain of the side opposite and one adjacent side multiplied by the cotangent of the angle between these sides, plus the difference in the strain of the side opposite and the other adjacent side of the

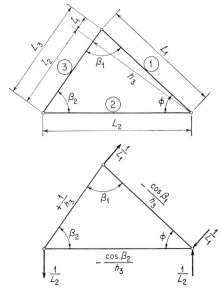

Figure 12.28   Angle changes of a truss triangle

triangle multiplied by the cotangent of the angle between these two sides. When the strain is due to an axial-stress intensity σ, this equation may be expressed more conveniently as

$$E\,\Delta\phi = (\sigma_3 - \sigma_1)\cot\beta_1 + (\sigma_3 - \sigma_2)\cot\beta_2 \qquad (12.11b)$$

A plus value of $\Delta\phi$ indicates an increase in angle ϕ and minus values a decrease.

After the angle changes of a simple truss have been computed by using either Eq. (12.11a) or (12.11b), $\Delta\theta$ may be computed at any joint of the bar chain. The moment-area method or the elastic-load procedure may then be applied to find the vertical components of the deflection of any bar chain that is *initially straight and horizontal*. This is illustrated in Examples 12.22 and 12.23. It should be recalled that, in applying the elastic-load method, the shears and moments of the imaginary beam give the slopes and deflections of the deflection curve, measured with reference to the chord corresponding to the support points of this imaginary beam. Thus, in Example 12.23, where the chord af rotates, the true deflections may be obtained by drawing the known line of zero deflections through points a and d and correcting the deflections measured from the chord af in the manner indicated.

Example 12.22   *Using the bar-chain method, compute the vertical component of the deflection of joint b of the truss in Fig. 12.23.*

The figures shown on the line diagram are $e \times 10^3$. The strains have all been multiplied by 1,000 to obtain more convenient numbers. The final results will then be divided by 1,000 to obtain the true answers.

⋏	$e_2 - e_1$	$\dfrac{cot}{\beta_1}$	$e_2 - e_2$	$\dfrac{cot}{\beta_2}$	$\Delta\phi$
abf	$-0.416 - 0.416$	0	$-0.416 - 0.442$	1	-0.858
fbe	$-0.416 - 0.442$	1	$-0.416 - 0$	0	-0.858
ebd	$-0.416 - 0$	0	$-0.416 - 0.590$	1	-1.006
dbc	$-0.208 - 0.590$	1	$-0.208 - 0.833$	0	-0.798
$\Sigma\Delta\phi$					-3.520

Since, in this case, $\Delta\theta$ is equal in magnitude but opposite in sense to $\Sigma \Delta\phi$ at joint b,

$$\therefore \ \Delta\theta_b = +3.520$$

and, therefore, an upward elastic load.

$$1.760 \times 25 = -44.0$$
$$\therefore \ \delta_b = \underline{0.044 \ ft} \ (down)$$
$$= \underline{\underline{0.528 \ in.}}$$

Example 12.23   *Using the bar-chain method, compute the vertical components of the deflection of the bottom-chord panel points.*

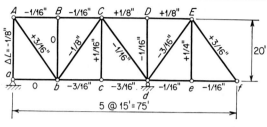

For convenience, multiply e by 10³, and divide the final results by 10³ to obtain true answers.

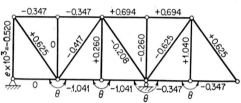

∡	$(e_3 - e_1) \times 10^3$ (1)	cot β_1 (2)	(1) × (2)	$(e_3 - e_2) \times 10^3$ (3)	cot β_2 (4)	(3) × (4)	$\Delta\phi \times 10^3$	$\Delta\theta \times 10^3$
abA	$-0.520 - 0 \quad = -0.520$	0	0	$-0.520 - 0.625 = -1.145$	1.3	-1.527	-1.527	
AbB	$-0.347 - 0.625 = -0.972$	0.75	-0.729	$-0.347 - 0 \quad = -0.347$	0	0	-0.729	$+1.301$
BbC	$-0.347 - 0 \quad = -0.347$	0	0	$-0.347 + 0.417 = +0.070$	0.75	$+0.052$	$+0.052$	
Cbc	$+0.260 + 0.417 = +0.677$	1.$\dot{3}$	$+0.903$	$+0.260 + 1.041 = +1.301$	0	0	$+0.903$	
bcC	$-0.417 + 1.041 = +0.624$	0.75	$+0.468$	$-0.417 - 0.260 = -0.677$	1.$\dot{3}$	-0.903	-0.435	$+0.435$
Ccd	$-0.208 - 0.260 = -0.468$	1.$\dot{3}$	-0.624	$-0.208 + 1.041 = +0.833$	0.75	$+0.625$	0	
cdC	$+0.260 + 1.041 = +1.301$	0	0	$+0.260 + 0.208 = +0.468$	1.$\dot{3}$	$+0.624$	$+0.624$	
CdD	$+0.694 + 0.208 = +0.902$	0.75	$+0.676$	$+0.694 + 0.260 = +0.954$	0	0	$+0.676$	-4.509
DdE	$+0.694 + 0.260 = +0.954$	0	0	$+0.694 + 0.625 = +1.319$	0.75	$+0.989$	$+0.989$	
Ede	$+1.040 + 0.625 = +1.665$	1.$\dot{3}$	$+2.220$	$+1.040 + 0.347 = +1.387$	0	0	$+2.220$	
deE	$-0.625 + 0.347 = -0.278$	0.75	-0.208	$-0.625 - 1.040 = -1.665$	1.$\dot{3}$	-2.220	-2.428	$+2.252$
Eef	$+0.625 - 1.040 = -0.415$	1.$\dot{3}$	-0.553	$+0.625 + 0.347 = +0.972$	0.75	$+0.729$	$+0.176$	

Using imaginary beam of span af,

$\Sigma M_f,$　↶+

$$1.301 \times 4 = \quad 5.204$$
$$0.435 \times 3 = +1.305$$
$$-4.509 \times 2 = -9.018$$
$$2.252 \times 1 = +2.252$$
$$5\,\overline{|-0.257}$$
$$\overline{0.521\downarrow} \qquad 0.051\,\text{⇕}$$

$\Sigma M_a,$　↷+

$$1.301 \times 1 = + \ 1.301$$
$$0.435 \times 2 = + \ 0.870$$
$$-4.509 \times 3 = -13.527$$
$$2.252 \times 4 = + \ 9.008$$
$$5\,\overline{|- \ 2.348}$$
$$\overline{0.470\,\text{⇕}}$$

$\tau \times 10^3$		$0 \ = \delta_a \times 10^3$
$+0.051$	$+0.051 \times 15 = + \ 0.77$	
$+1.301$		$+ \ 0.77 = \delta_b \times 10^3$
$+1.352$	$+1.352 \times 15 = +20.28$	
$+0.435$		$+21.05 = \delta_c \times 10^3$
$+1.787$	$+1.787 \times 15 = +26.81$	
-4.509		$47.86 = \delta_d \times 10^3$
-2.722	$-2.722 \times 15 = -40.83$	
$+2.252$		$+ \ 7.03 = \delta_e \times 10^3$
-0.470	$-0.470 \times 15 = - \ 7.05$	
$+0.470$		$-0.02 = \delta_f \times 10^3$
0		*0 essentially*

Certain modifications must be introduced into this approach before it can be applied to a bar chain that is not initially straight and horizontal. Suppose that we wish to compute the vertical components of the deflection of the lower-chord bar chain of the truss shown in Fig. 12.29a. The effect of the changes in the θ angles on the deflection of this bar chain can be computed in the same manner as if the bar chain were initially horizontal. This is evident when one considers the lower-chord bar chain shown in Fig. 12.29b. Imagine that we allow only the angle θ_b to change and that at the same time we hold the portion of the bar chain to the left of joint b fixed in position. The vertical component of the movement of point E would then be equal to $x' \, \Delta\theta_b$, the same value as it would have been if the bar chain were initially straight. Continuing in this manner, we may show that the vertical deflection of this lower-chord bar chain produced simply by the angle changes $\Delta\theta$ may be computed in the same manner as if the bar chain were initially horizontal, using the imaginary beam shown in Fig. 12.29c.

The total deflection of this lower-chord bar chain is produced, however, not only by the angle changes $\Delta\theta$ but also by the changes in length of the members of the bar chain themselves. For example, consider the effect of an elongation of bar cd. If all the joints of the bar chain were locked so that no angle changes could occur and if the bars to the left of c were held fixed in position, the elongation of bar cd would cause all joints to the right of c to move vertically an amount equal to $\Delta L_{cd} \sin \alpha$, as indicated by the ordinates to the solid line in Fig. 12.29d.　In order to return point E to its proper position, the entire bar chain must be rotated about point A as a rigid body, causing the vertical displacements shown by the dashed line in Fig. 12.29d.　The net effect of the two displacements shown in Fig. 12.29d is shown in Fig. 12.29e.　This displacement diagram would be the bending-moment diagram for the loads shown in Fig. 12.29f.　In the same manner, it could be shown that the contribution of the change in length of any

Figure 12.29　Bar chain (not initially straight)

bar of the chain to the vertical deflection would be equal to the bending moment produced by two similar equal and opposite loads acting at the joints at the ends of that bar.

These considerations lead us to the following conclusion: To compute the total deflections of a bar chain that is not initially straight, the bending moments may be computed on an imaginary beam that is acted upon by a modified elastic loading as indicated in Fig. 12.29g.　At any intermediate joint m of the bar chain, this loading is equal to the angle change $\Delta\theta_m$ modified by certain contributions proportional to the strains in the adjacent members of the bar chain.　Let this modified elastic load at joint m be called W_m.　Then,

$$W_m = \Delta\theta_m - e_L \tan \alpha_L + e_R \tan \alpha_R \qquad (12.12)$$

where e_L and α_L represent strain and initial slope with horizontal of adjacent member
    of bar chain on *left* of joint m

e_R and α_R represent similar quantities for adjacent member on *right* of joint m

$\Delta\theta_m$ represents change in angle θ_m, which, as defined above, is angle
    included on lower side between two adjacent members of chain

It is important for the proper sign convention to be adhered to in using this equation.

W_m is plus when indicating an upward elastic load

$\Delta\theta_m$ is plus when θ_m increases

e is plus when the member elongates

α is plus when the initial slope of the member is up to the right

---

Example 12.24   *Using the bar-chain method, compute the vertical components of the deflection of the lower-chord panel points.*

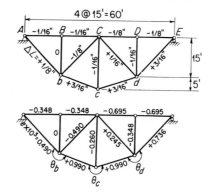

⅄	$(e_3 - e_1) \times 10^3$ (1)	$\cot \beta_1$ (2)	$(1) \times$ (2)	$(e_3 - e_2) \times 10^3$ (3)	$\cot \beta_2$ (4)	$(3) \times$ (4)	$\Delta\phi \times$ 10^3	$\Delta\theta \times$ 10^3
AbB	$-0.348 - 0.490 = -0.838$	1.0	-0.835	$-0.348 - 0 \quad = -0.348$	0	0	-0.838	
BbC	$-0.348 - 0 \quad = -0.348$	0	0	$-0.348 + 0.490 = +0.142$	1.0	$+0.142$	$+0.142$	$+0.883$
Cbc	$-0.260 + 0.490 = +0.230$	1.0	$+0.230$	$-0.260 - 0.990 = -1.250$	$0.\dot{3}$	-0.417	-0.187	
bcC	$-0.490 - 0.990 = -1.480$	0.500	-0.740	$-0.490 + 0.260 = -0.230$	1.0	-0.230	-0.970	$+0.838$
Ccd	$+0.245 + 0.260 = +0.505$	1.0	$+0.505$	$+0.245 - 0.990 = -0.745$	0.500	-0.373	$+0.132$	
cdC	$-0.260 - 0.990 = -1.250$	$0.\dot{3}$	-0.417	$-0.260 - 0.245 = -0.505$	1.0	-0.505	-0.922	
CdD	$-0.695 - 0.245 = -0.940$	1.0	-0.940	$-0.695 + 0.348 = -0.347$	0	0	-0.940	$+3.293$
DdE	$-0.695 + 0.348 = -0.347$	0	0	$-0.695 - 0.736 = -1.431$	1.0	-1.431	-1.431	

Then, $W_m = \Delta\theta_m - e_L \tan \alpha_L + e_R \tan \alpha_R.$

$$W_b \times 10^3 = +0.883 - (0.490)(-1.0) + (0.990)(-0.\dot{3}) = +1.043$$

$$W_c \times 10^3 = +0.838 - (0.990)(-0.\dot{3}) + (0.990)(0.\dot{3}) = +1.498$$

$$W_d \times 10^3 = +3.293 - (0.990)(0.\dot{3}) + (0.736)(1.0) = +3.699$$

Finding the reactions on the imaginary beam
AE,

$$\Sigma M_E, \qquad \overset{\curvearrowright}{+}$$

$$1.043 \times 3 = 3.129$$
$$1.498 \times 2 = 2.996$$
$$3.699 \times 1 = 3.699$$
$$\overline{4)9.824}$$
$$\overline{6.240\uparrow} \qquad \overline{2.456\downarrow}$$

$$\Sigma M_A, \qquad \overset{\curvearrowleft}{+}$$

$$1.043 \times 1 = 1.043$$
$$1.498 \times 2 = 2.996$$
$$3.699 \times 3 = 11.097$$
$$\overline{4)15.136}$$
$$\overline{3.784\downarrow}$$

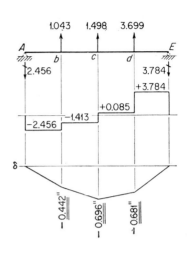

		0	$= \delta_A \times 10^3$
-2.456	$-2.456 \times 15 =$	-36.84	
$+1.043$		$\overline{-36.84}$	$= \delta_b \times 10^3$
-1.413	$-1.413 \times 15 =$	-21.20	
$+1.498$		$\overline{-58.04}$	$= \delta_c \times 10^3$
$+0.085$	$+0.085 \times 15 =$	$+1.28$	
$+3.699$		$\overline{-56.76}$	$= \delta_d \times 10^3$
$+3.784$	$+3.784 \times 15 =$	$+56.76$	
-3.784		$\overline{0}$	$= \delta_E \times 10^3$
$\overline{0}$			

Example 12.24 illustrates the application of this method to a bar chain that is not initially straight. It is important to note that the shear produced on the imaginary beam by the elastic load has no significance in such cases. Of course, in cases where the bar chain is initially straight and horizontal, such shears give the slope of the members of the deflected bar chain. The elastic load for the general case of a polygonal bar chain as expressed in Eq. (12.12), however, was determined so that the bending moment on the imaginary beam gave the deflection of the bar chain, but no significance was attached to the shear produced by this load. These statements may be verified by the computations in Example 12.24. In this case, since bar Bb does not change length, the vertical deflections of joints B and b are the same. The rotation of bar AB is therefore 0.002456 radian clockwise. Angle BAb is reduced by 0.000490 radian. Bar Ab, therefore, is found to rotate clockwise 0.001966 radian, but this value is not equal to the shear of 0.002456. Likewise, it will be found that none of the other rotations of the members of the bar chain are equal to the corresponding shears. Of course the rotation of bar Ab being known, the rotation of the remaining bars of the chain may be found by working from joint to joint along the chain and using the $\Delta\theta$ values already computed. In this manner, bar bc is found to rotate 0.001083 radian clockwise; cd, 0.000245 radian clockwise; and dE, 0.003048 radian counterclockwise.

The bar-chain method may be easily applied in a similar manner to any simple truss. A suitable bar chain is selected joining those joints the vertical deflection of which is desired. For any such bar chain, the elastic loads may be computed from Eq. (12.12). In the special cases where the bar chain is initially straight and horizontal (as illustrated in Examples 12.22 and 12.23), α will be zero for all bars and W_m equals simply $\Delta\theta_m$. Note that Eq. (12.12) cannot be used if the bar chain includes a vertical member since, then, $\alpha = 90°$ and $\tan \alpha = \infty$. It is never necessary to include such a member, however, since the difference in the vertical deflection of the ends of such a vertical is simply equal to the change in length of that member.

This method may also be applied to compound trusses such as that shown in Fig. 12.26. In such cases, however, it is necessary to insert imaginary bars between such joints as D and E, E and F, etc., so as to divide the truss into triangles for the computation of the angle changes. The changes in length of any one of these bars may be obtained by computing the relative deflection of the joints at the end of the bar by the method of virtual work. The method may likewise be applied to three-hinged arches such as that of Example 12.21. Here again, however, it is necessary to insert an imaginary bar between C and D before the angle changes may be computed. The change in length of this imaginary bar is equal to the relative deflection of joints C and D, which may likewise be computed by the method of virtual work.

12.15 Castigliano's Second Theorem. In 1879, Castigliano published the results of an elaborate research on statically indeterminate structures in which he used two theorems which bear his name. **Castigliano's second theorem** may be stated as follows:

In any structure the material of which is elastic and follows Hooke's law and in which the temperature is constant and the supports unyielding, the first partial derivative of the strain energy with respect to any particular force is equal to the displacement of the point of application of that force in the direction of its line of action.

In this statement, the words *force* and *displacement* should be interpreted also to mean *couple* and *angular rotation*, respectively. Further,

Figure 12.30 Derivation of Castigliano's second theorem

it also is implied that, during the deformation of the structure, there is no appreciable change in its geometry. The application of this theorem is therefore limited to cases where it is legitimate to superimpose deflections.

To derive this theorem, consider any structure that satisfies the stated conditions, such as the beam shown in Fig. 12.30. Suppose that this beam is loaded gradually by the forces P_1, P_2, . . . , P_n. Then, the external work done by these forces (let us call this W_E) is some function of these forces. According to the principle of the conservation of energy, we know that, in any elastic structure at rest and in equilibrium under a system of loads, the internal work or strain energy stored in the structure is equal to the external work done by these loads during their gradual application. Designating the internal work or strain energy by W_I, we may therefore write

$$W_I = W_E = f(P_1, P_2, \ldots, P_n) \qquad (a)$$

Suppose now that the force P_n is increased by a small amount dP_n; the internal work will be increased, and the new amount will be

$$W'_I = W_I + \frac{\partial W_I}{\partial P_n} dP_n \qquad (b)$$

The magnitude of the total internal work, however, does not depend upon the order in which the forces are applied—it depends only on the final value of these forces. Further, if the material follows Hooke's law, the deformation and deflection caused by the forces P_1, P_2, . . . , P_n and hence the work done by them are the same whether these forces are applied to a structure already acted upon by other forces or not, as long as the total stresses due to all causes remain within the elastic limit. If, therefore, the infinitesimal force dP_n is applied first and the forces P_1, P_2, . . . , P_n are applied later, the final amount of internal work will still be the same amount as that given by Eq. (b).

The force dP_n applied first produces an infinitesimal displacement $d\delta_n$, so that the corresponding external work done during the application of dP_n is a small quantity of the second order and can be neglected. If the forces P_1, P_2, . . . , P_n are now applied, the external work done just by them will not be modified owing to the presence of dP_n and hence will be equal to the value of W_E given by Eq. (a). However, during the application of these forces, the point of application of P_n is displaced an amount δ_n in the direction of the line of application of this force, and therefore dP_n does external work during this displacement equal to $(dP_n)(\delta_n)$. Let the total amount of external work done by the entire system during this loading sequence be W'_E. Then,

$$W'_E = W_E + dP_n\delta_n \qquad (c)$$

But, according to the principle of the conservation of energy, W'_E equals W'_I, and therefore

$$W_E + dP_n\delta_n = W_I + \frac{\partial W_I}{\partial P_n} dP_n \qquad (d)$$

However, since W_E is equal to W_I, Eq. (d) reduces to simply

$$\frac{\partial W_I}{\partial P_n} = \delta_n \qquad (12.13)$$

This latter equation is the mathematical statement of Castigliano's second theorem.

In order to use Castigliano's theorem, it is first necessary to develop suitable expressions for the strain energy stored, or the internal work done, by the stresses in a member. Consider first the case of the strain energy stored in a bar by an *axial force* F as this force gradually increases from zero to its final value. Consider a differential element of such a bar bounded by two adjacent cross sections, as shown in Fig. 12.31. Suppose that this element is acted upon by a force F_t, some intermediate value between zero and the final value of the force F. Suppose that this force is now increased by an amount dF_t, causing the element to change in length by an amount $\Delta(dL)_t$, where

$$\Delta(dL)_t = dF_t \frac{dL}{AE} \qquad (e)$$

Figure 12.31 Strain energy stored by axial force

Neglecting quantities of the second order, the internal work done during the application of dF_t is equal to $(F_t)[\Delta(dL)_t]$, and therefore the total internal work dW_I done in this element during the increase of the force F from zero to its final value is

$$dW_I = \int_0^F F_t \, \Delta(dL)_t = \int_0^F F_t \frac{dL}{AE} \, dF_t = \frac{F^2}{2AE} \, dL \qquad (f)$$

For the entire member, the internal work will be the sum of the terms dW_I for all the elements dL, or

$$W_I = \int_0^L \frac{F^2}{2AE} \, dL = \frac{F^2 L}{2AE} \qquad (g)$$

For all the members of the structure, the internal work will be the sum of such terms for every bar of the structure, or

$$\text{Strain energy stored by axial forces, } W_I = \sum \frac{F^2 L}{2AE} \qquad (12.14)$$

This equation may now be used to develop an expression for the strain energy stored in a beam by the stresses produced by a *bending moment* M. Consider a differential element of a beam having a length dL, as shown in Fig. 12.32. This element of the beam may be considered to be a bundle of little fibers each having a length dL, a depth dy, and a width normal to the plane of the paper of b. The axial force on such a fiber would be

$$F = \sigma b \, dy = \frac{My}{I} b \, dy \qquad (h)$$

Figure 12.32 Strain energy stored by bending moment

The strain energy stored in all such fibers of the beam may be evaluated by applying Eq. (12.14), summing up the contributions of all the fibers across the element dL, and then summing up these quantities for all the elements in the length of the beam, or

$$W_I = \int_0^L \int_{-c_2}^{c_1} \left(\frac{My}{I} b \, dy \right)^2 \frac{dL}{2(b \, dy)E} = \int_0^L \frac{M^2}{2EI} \int_{-c_2}^{c_1} \frac{y^2 b \, dy}{I} \, dL$$

$$= \int_0^L \frac{M^2}{2EI} \, dL \qquad (i)$$

since $\int_{-C_2}^{C_1} y^2 b \, dy = I$.   Hence, for all the beam elements of the structure,

$$\text{Strain energy stored by bending moment, } W_I = \sum \int \frac{M^2}{2EI} \, dL \quad (12.15)$$

As discussed previously in Art. 12.5, it is usually permissible to neglect the strain energy stored by the shear stresses in a beam.

12.16 Castigliano's First Theorem.[1] To complete the discussion of Castigliano's theorems, his first theorem is also presented here although it is a method for expressing equilibrium conditions and for analyzing statically indeterminate structures rather than a method for computing deflections. **Castigliano's first theorem** may be stated as follows:

In any structure the material of which is linearly or nonlinearly elastic and in which the temperature is constant and the supports are unyielding, the first partial derivative of the strain energy with respect to any particular deflection component is equal to the force applied at the point and in the direction corresponding to that deflection component.

This theorem may be derived in much the same fashion as the second theorem. Suppose a structure is in equilibrium under the action of the forces $P_1, P_2, \ldots, P_n$. These forces have done a certain amount of external work W_E and an equal amount of strain energy W_I in the structure. They likewise have produced certain deflections of the points of application of these forces, $\delta_1, \delta_2, \ldots, \delta_n$. If by varying the forces infinitesimal amounts the deflection δ_n is changed a small amount $d\delta_n$ while all other deflections $\delta_1, \delta_2, \ldots$ are held constant, the strain energy stored in the system will change to a value W_I, where

$$W_I' = W_I + \frac{\partial W_I}{\partial \delta_n} d\delta_n \qquad (a)$$

If the second-order contribution to the external work done by the differential force dP_n is neglected, the external work done on the structure will have increased to W_E' as a result of the introduction of the additional displacement $d\delta_n$, where

$$W_E' = W_E + P_n \, d\delta_n \qquad (b)$$

Since W_I' must equal W_E', equating the right-hand sides of Eqs. (a) and (b) results in

$$\frac{\partial W_I}{\partial \delta_n} = P_n \qquad (c)$$

which is a mathematical statement of Castigliano's first theorem.

Application of the first theorem is not considered here. The reader is referred to

[1] See A. Castigliano, "Théorem de l'equilibre des systémes elastiques et ses applications," translated by E. S. Andrews as "Elastic Stresses in Structures," Scott, Greenwood, 1919. Or see J. A. L. Matheson, "Hyperstatic Structures," vol. I, pp. 69 and 75, Butterworth's Scientific Publications, London, 1959.

Unfortunately there is considerable confusion in the literature regarding the nomenclature of Castigliano's theorems. Castigliano referred to his theorems as "theorem of the differential coefficients of the internal work, part I and part II." In this book, part I and part II are referred to, respectively, as Castigliano's first theorem and Castigliano's second theorem.

Matheson's fine book referred to above or to recent papers by Argyris.[1] In order to use this theorem, it is apparent that alternative expressions for the strain energy will have to be developed. The alternative expressions must express the strain energy in terms of the deflections δ_1, δ_2, . . . , δ_n.

12.17 Computation of Deflections, Using Castigliano's Second Theorem. Castigliano's second theorem is used principally in the analysis of statically indeterminate structures, although it is sometimes used to solve deflection problems. The technique of applying this method in the latter case is essentially the same as that of solving such problems by the method of virtual work. In fact, the following illustrative problems will demonstrate that the actual numerical computations involved in either of these methods are almost identical.

Example 12.25 illustrates how to apply this method when the deflection of the point of application of one of the loads is required. If this load has some numerical value, it should temporarily be denoted by a symbol, instead. Then, after the partial differentiation of the bending-moment expression has been performed, the symbol may be replaced by the given numerical value.

Example 12.25   *Compute the vertical deflection of point b, due to the load shown.*

$$W_I = \sum \int \frac{M^2 \, dx}{2EI}$$

but

$$\frac{\partial W_I}{\partial P} = \delta_b^{\downarrow} = \sum \int M \frac{\partial M}{\partial P} \frac{dx}{EI}$$

From b to a,

$$0 < x < L \qquad M = -Px \qquad \frac{\partial M}{\partial P} = -x$$

Therefore,

$$\delta_b^{\downarrow} = \int_0^L (-Px)(-x)\frac{dx}{EI} = \left[\frac{Px^3}{3EI}\right]_0^L$$

whence

$$\delta_b = \frac{PL^3}{3EI}$$

Sometimes we wish to compute the deflection at a point where no load is acting. In such cases, we may temporarily introduce an imaginary force (or couple) acting at the point and in the direction of the desired deflection component. Then, after the partial differentiation of the strain energy has been performed, we may let the introduced force equal zero and proceed with the numerical calculations. In this way, we obtain the desired deflection produced by only the given loads. Example 12.26 illustrates this procedure.

By introducing suitable imaginary loads in this manner, it is possible to compute any desired deflection component. The technique of selecting the appropriate imaginary loads in such cases is exactly the same as selecting the proper Q-force system in applying the method of virtual work. Example 12.27 illustrates this point and also demonstrates the close similarity between the solution by Castigliano's second theorem and that by the method of virtual work.

It should be noted that Castigliano's second theorem may be applied to any type of structure, whether beam, truss, or frame, the material of which behaves in a linearly elastic manner. Its use is restricted, however, to cases where the deflection is caused by loads. This theorem is not applicable to the computation of deflections produced by support settlements or temperature changes.

[1] J. H. Argyris, Energy Theorems and Structural Analysis, *Aircraft Eng.*, October, 1954, et seq.

Example 12.26 *Compute the change in slope of the cross section at a, due to the loads shown.*

Suppose that a couple M_1 was applied temporarily at a. Considering this as part of the load system, we may proceed as follows:

$$W_I = \sum \int \frac{M^2\, dx}{2EI}$$

but $\dfrac{\partial W_I}{\partial M_1} = \alpha_a{}^{\frown} = \sum \int M \dfrac{\partial M}{\partial M_1} \dfrac{dx}{EI}$

From a to b,

$$0 < x < 10 \qquad M = M_1 + \left(7 - \frac{M_1}{20}\right)x \qquad \frac{\partial M}{\partial M_1} = \left(1 - \frac{x}{20}\right)$$

From d to c,

$$0 < x < 4 \qquad M = \left(13 + \frac{M_1}{20}\right)x \qquad \frac{\partial M}{\partial M_1} = \frac{x}{20}$$

From c to b,

$$4 < x < 10 \qquad M = \left(13 + \frac{M_1}{20}\right)x - 10(x - 4) \qquad \frac{\partial M}{\partial M_1} = \frac{x}{20}$$

Then,

$$\frac{\partial W}{\partial M_1} = EI\alpha_a{}^{\frown} = \int_0^{10}\left[M_1 + \left(7 - \frac{M_1}{20}\right)x\right]\left(1 - \frac{x}{20}\right)dx$$
$$+ \int_0^4\left[\left(13 + \frac{M_1}{20}\right)x\right]\left(\frac{x}{20}\right)dx + \int_4^{10}\left[\left(13 + \frac{M_1}{20}\right)x - 10(x - 4)\right]\left(\frac{x}{20}\right)dx$$

In this equation, we may now let $M_1 = 0$ since it is an imaginary load. Then,

$$EI\alpha_a{}^{\frown} = \int_0^{10}(7x)\left(1 - \frac{x}{20}\right)dx + \int_0^4(13x)\left(\frac{x}{20}\right)dx + \int_4^{10}(3x + 40)\left(\frac{x}{20}\right)dx$$
$$= \left[\frac{7x^2}{2} - \frac{7x^3}{60}\right]_0^{10} + \left[\frac{13x^3}{60}\right]_0^4 + \left[\frac{3x^3}{60} + x^2\right]_4^{10} = \left(350 - \frac{700}{6}\right) + \left(\frac{208}{15}\right)$$
$$+ \left[\left(\frac{1{,}000 - 64}{20}\right) + (100 - 16)\right]$$

or $\qquad\qquad\qquad\qquad \alpha_a = \dfrac{378}{EI}$

If $E = 30 \times 10^3\ ^{k/''^2}$ and $I = 200$ in.^{4},

$$\alpha_a = \frac{(378)^{k'^2}}{(30 \times 10^3 \times 144)^{k/''^2}(200/144^2)^{'^4}} = 0.00907\ radian$$

Example 12.27   *Solve part a of Example 12.4, using Castigliano's second theorem.*

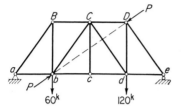

To solve for the relative deflection of joints b and D, add to the given load system the loads P acting as shown. Then

$$W_I = \sum \frac{F^2 L}{2AE}$$

and

$$\frac{\partial W_I}{\partial P} = \delta_{b-D} = \sum \frac{FL}{AE} \frac{\partial F}{\partial P}$$

Using the bar forces computed in Example 12.4 for the 60- and 120-kip loads and noting that the forces due to the loads P are P times the forces caused by the unit loads in that problem, we may now proceed as follows:

Bar	L	A	$\dfrac{A}{L}$	F	$\dfrac{\partial F}{\partial P}$	$F\dfrac{L}{A}\dfrac{\partial F}{\partial P}$
Units	$'$	$''^2$	$'/''^2$	k	k/k	$k'/''^2$
bc	15	5	3	$+\ 67.5\ -\ 0.416P$	-0.416	$-\ 84.5$
cd	15	5	3	$+\ 67.5\ -\ 0.416P$	-0.416	$-\ 84.5$
CD	15	5	3	$-\ 78.75\ -\ 0.831P$	-0.831	$+197.0$
bC	25	2.5	10	$-\ 18.7\ -\ 0.695P$	-0.695	$+130$
Cd	25	2.5	10	$+\ 18.7\ +\ 0.695P$	$+0.695$	$+130$
dD	20	5	4	$+105\ \ \ \ \ -\ 0.555P$	-0.555	-233
Σ						$+\ 55.0$

Before evaluating the product in the last column of this tabulation, set P equal to zero since only the contribution of the constant portion of F need be included in the product. Thus,

$$\delta_{b-D} = \frac{+55}{E} = \frac{(55)^{k'/''^2}}{(30 \times 10^3)^{k/''^2}} = +0.00183\ ft \qquad (together)$$

Note that those bars which have zero forces due to either the imaginary loads P or the given applied loads do not contribute to the products in the last column and therefore do not need to be included in the tabulation.

12.18   Deflection of Space Frameworks.   The deflections of the joints of a space framework may be computed without difficulty by either the method of virtual work or Castigliano's second theorem. The expressions developed previously in order to apply these methods to planar trusses may likewise be applied to space frameworks (which are simply three-dimensional "trusses"), as illustrated in Example 12.28.

Example 12.28   *Compute the z component of the deflection of joint d due to the load shown.   The cross-sectional area of all members is 2 sq in.   E = 30 × 10³ kips per sq in.*

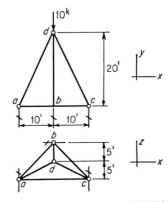

Bar	Projection			L
	x	y	z	
ab	10	0	10	14.14
bc	10	0	10	14.14
ac	20	0	0	20
ad	10	20	5	22.91
bd	0	20	5	20.62
cd	10	20	5	22.91

Using the method of virtual work,

$$\sum Q\delta = \sum F_Q \,\Delta L = \sum F_Q F_P \frac{L}{AE}$$

or

$$(1^k)(\delta_{dz}) = \frac{1}{AE}\sum F_Q F_P L$$

Bar	Components			F_Q
	X	Y	Z	
ab	+0.25	0	+0.25	+0.354
bc	+0.25	0	+0.25	+0.354
ac	−0.75	0	0	−0.75
ad	+0.5	+1	+0.25	+1.145
bd	0	−2	−0.5	−2.062
cd	+0.5	+1	+0.25	+1.145

Bar	Components			F_P
	X	Y	Z	
ab	+0.625	0	+0.625	+0.884
bc	+0.625	0	+0.625	+0.884
ac	+0.625	0	0	+0.625
ad	−1.25	−2.5	−0.625	−2.863
bd	0	−5	−1.25	−5.154
cd	−1.25	−2.5	−0.625	−2.863

Bar	L	F_Q	F_P	$F_Q F_P L$
Units	'	k	k	$k^{2\prime}$
ab	14.14	+0.354	+0.884	+ 4.4
bc	14.14	+0.354	+0.884	+ 4.4
ac	20	−0.75	+0.625	− 9.4
ad	22.91	+1.145	−2.863	+ 75.0
bd	20.62	−2.062	−5.154	+219.4
cd	22.91	+1.145	−2.863	− 75.0
Σ				+ 68.8

whence

$$(1^k)(\delta_{dz}) = \frac{+68.8^{k^{2\prime}}}{(2^{\prime\prime2})(30 \times 10^{3\,k/\prime\prime2})}$$

$$\delta_{dz} = \underline{+0.00115\ ft}$$

12.19 Other Deflection Problems. All the examples in this chapter have illustrated the computation of the deflection of statically determinate structures. All the methods presented may be applied, however, to both statically determinate and indeterminate structures. Of course, the stress analysis of an indeterminate structure must be completed before the deformation of the elements of the structure may be defined. Once this has been done, however, the computations of the resulting deflections of the structure are essentially the same as if it were statically determinate. Several examples illustrating such computations are included in Art. 13.17.

In this chapter, the discussion of beam deflections has been limited to cases where the centroidal axis of the beam is straight and where all the cross sections have axes of symmetry that lie in the same plane as the loads. Further, no discussion has been included concerning the deflections produced by shear. All such cases are beyond the scope of this book and are included in more advanced treatments of this subject. It should be noted, however, that either the method of virtual work or Castigliano's second theorem may be extended without difficulty to cover such cases. It is also possible to apply these methods to members that involve torsion.

12.20 Cambering of Structures. Cambering a structure consists in varying the unstressed shape of the members of the structure in a manner such that under some specified condition of loading the structure attains its theoretical shape. The purpose of such a procedure is twofold: (1) It improves the appearance of the loaded structure. (2) It ensures that the geometry of the loaded structure corresponds to the theoretical shape used in the stress analysis.

To illustrate this procedure, consider the problem of cambering a truss. In this case, the truss members are fabricated so that they are either longer or shorter than their theoretical lengths. Since the members receive their maximum stress under different positions of the live load, trusses cannot be cambered so as to assume their theoretical shape when each member receives its maximum stress. As a practical compromise, trusses are usually cambered so that they attain their theoretical shape under dead load or under dead load plus some fraction of full live load over the entire structure.

To camber a truss exactly, we compute the change of length of each member under the stresses produced by the cambering load and then fabricate the compression members the corresponding amounts too long and the tension members the corresponding amounts too short. Then, when the truss is erected and subjected to its cambering load, it will deflect into its theoretical shape. The advantage of this exact method is that any truss so cambered can be assembled free of initial stress. The disadvantage is that most members are affected and the required changes in length are sometimes small and difficult to obtain.

The practical method of cambering trusses, therefore, is to alter only the lengths of the chord members. For example, if each top-chord member of an end-supported truss is lengthened ³⁄₁₆ in. for every 10 ft of its horizontal projection, this is equivalent to changing both top and bottom chords by one-half of this amount. This change in length is the same as that produced by a stress intensity of

$$29,000,000 \times \tfrac{3}{32} \times \tfrac{1}{120} = 22{,}600 \text{ psi}$$

Since only the chords are being corrected, they must be overcorrected to allow for the contribution of the web members to the deflection. Assuming that the chords contribute 80 per cent of the deflection, the change in length specified above corresponds to that caused by a load which would produce a chord stress intensity of

$$0.8 \times 22{,}600 = 18{,}000 \text{ psi}$$

In other words, the rule of thumb suggested above corresponds to a cambering load essentially equal to dead load plus full live and impact over the entire structure.

This approximate method of cambering may be applied without difficulty to statically determinate trusses. It must be applied with caution, however, to statically indeterminate trusses; otherwise, the assembled truss may have to be forced together, initial stresses thus being introduced into the truss.

12.21   Maxwell's Law of Reciprocal Deflections.   Betti's Law.

Maxwell's law is a special case of the more general Betti's law. Both these laws are applicable to any type of structure, whether beam, truss, or frame. To simplify this discussion, however, these ideas will be developed by considering the simple truss shown in Fig. 12.33. Suppose that this truss is subjected to two separate and independent systems of forces, the system of forces P_m and the system of forces P_n. The P_m system develops the bar forces F_m in the various members of the truss, while the P_n system develops the bar forces F_n. Let us imagine two situations. First, suppose that the P_m system is at rest on the truss and that we then further deform the truss by applying the P_n system. As a second situation, suppose that just the reverse is true, i.e., that the P_n system is acting on the truss and that then we further deform the truss by applying the P_m system. In both situations, we may apply the law of virtual work and thereby come to a very useful conclusion known as Betti's law.

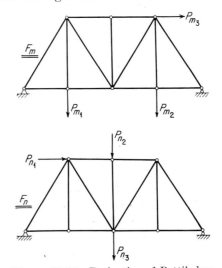

Figure 12.33   Derivation of Betti's law

For purposes of this derivation, we shall assume that the supports of the structure are unyielding and that the temperature is constant. Also, let

δ_{mn} = deflection of point of application of one of the forces P_m (in the direction and sense of this force) caused by application of P_n force system

δ_{nm} = deflection of point of application of one of the forces P_n caused by application of P_m force system

Consider now the application of the law of virtual work to the first situation. In this case, the P_m force system is in the role of the Q forces and will be given a ride as a result of the deformation caused by the P_n system. Thus, applying Eq. (12.5),

$$\Sigma P_m \delta_{mn} = \Sigma F_m \, \Delta L$$

where $\Delta L = F_n L / A E$, and thus

$$\sum P_m \delta_{mn} = \sum F_m F_n \frac{L}{AE} \qquad (a)$$

In the second situation, however, the P_n force system will now be in the role of the Q forces and will be given a ride as a result of the deformation caused by the P_m system. Then, applying Eq. 12.5,

$$\Sigma P_n \delta_{nm} = \Sigma F_n \, \Delta L$$

where $\Delta L = F_m L / A E$, and thus

$$\sum P_n \delta_{nm} = \sum F_n F_m \frac{L}{AE} \qquad (b)$$

From Eqs. (a) and (b), it may be concluded that

$$\Sigma P_m \delta_{mn} = \Sigma P_n \delta_{nm} \qquad (12.16)$$

which when stated in words is called **Betti's law.**

In any structure the material of which is elastic and follows Hooke's law and in which the supports are unyielding and the temperature constant, the external virtual work done by a system of forces P_m during the deformation caused by a system of forces P_n is equal to the external virtual work done by the P_n system during the deformation caused by the P_m system.

Betti's law is a very useful principle and is sometimes called the generalized Maxwell's law. This suggests that Maxwell's law of reciprocal deflections may be derived directly from Betti's law.

Consider any structure such as the truss shown in Fig. 12.34. Suppose that the truss is acted upon first by a load P at point 1; then suppose that the truss is acted upon by a load of the same magnitude P but applied now at point 2. Let

δ_{12} = deflection of point 1 in direction ab due to a load P acting at point 2 in direction cd

δ_{21} = deflection of point 2 in direction cd due to a load P acting at point 1 in direction ab

Applying Betti's law to this situation,

$$(P)(\delta_{12}) = (P)(\delta_{21})$$

and therefore $\delta_{12} = \delta_{21}$ (12.17)

which, when stated in words, is called **Maxwell's law of reciprocal deflections:**

In any structure the material of which is elastic and follows Hooke's law and in which the supports are unyielding and the temperature constant, the deflection of point 1 in the direction ab due to a load P at point 2 acting in a direction cd is numerically equal to the deflection of point 2 in the direction cd due to a load P at point 1 acting in a direction ab.

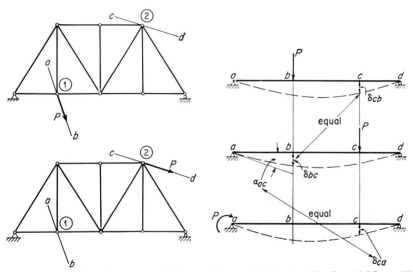

Figure 12.34 Development of Maxwell's law

Figure 12.35 Application of Maxwell's law

Maxwell's law is perfectly general and is applicable to any type of structure. This reciprocal relationship exists likewise between the rotations produced by two couples and also between the deflection produced by a couple of P and the rotation produced by a force P. This generality is illustrated by the beam in Fig. 12.35. That $\delta_{cb} = \delta_{bc}$ is a straightforward application of Maxwell's law. Note also that the rotation α_{ac} in radians produced by a force of P lb is numerically equal to the deflection δ_{ca} in feet produced by a couple of P ft-lb. In the latter case, be careful of the units.

It is important to become familiar with the subscript notations used in the above discussion to denote the deflections. **The first subscript denotes the point where the deflection is measured and the second subscript the point where the load causing the deflection is applied.**

12.22 Influence Lines for Deflections. Suppose that we wish to draw the influence line for the vertical deflection at point a on the beam

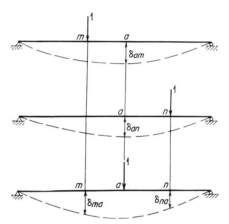

Figure 12.36 Influence lines for deflection

in Fig. 12.36. The ordinates of such an influence line may be computed and plotted by placing a unit vertical load successively at various points along the beam and in each case computing the resulting vertical deflection of point a. In this manner, when the unit load is placed at any point m, it produces a deflection δ_{am} at point a; or when placed at some other point n, it produces a deflection δ_{an} at point a. Note, however, the advantage of applying Maxwell's law to this problem. If we simply place a unit vertical load at point a, the deflections δ_{ma} and δ_{na} at points m and n will be equal, respectively, to δ_{am} and δ_{an} according to Maxwell's law. In other words, **the elastic curve of the beam when the unit load is placed at point a is the influence line for the vertical deflection at point a.** Thus by computing the ordinates of the elastic curve for one simple problem, we obtain the ordinates of the desired influence line.

This idea may be used to obtain the influence line for the deflection of any point on any structure. To obtain the influence line for the deflection of a certain point, simply place a unit load at that point, and compute the resulting elastic curve of the structure.

12.23   Problems for Solution

Problem 12.1   Using the method of virtual work, compute the vertical component of the deflection of joint d due to the load shown, for the structure of Fig. 12.37.   Bar areas in square inches are shown in parentheses. $E = 30 \times 10^3$ kips per sq in.

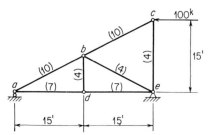

Figure 12.37   Problem 12.1

Problem 12.2   Using the method of virtual work, compute the horizontal component of the deflection of joint c due to the load shown, for the structure of Fig. 12.38. Bar areas in square inches are shown in parentheses. $E = 30 \times 10^3$ kips per sq in.

Figure 12.38   Problem 12.2

Problem 12.3   For the structure of Fig. 12.39, find the horizontal component of the deflection of joint d if bar cf is shortened 1 in.

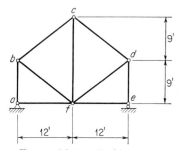

Figure 12.39   Problem 12.3

Problem 12.4   For the structure of Fig. 12.40, using the method of virtual work, determine the relative movement of joints M_3 and U_4 along the line M_3U_4 (a) due to the loading shown; (b) due to a uniform increase in temperature of 50°F in the bottom chord. Bar areas in square inches are shown in parentheses. $E = 30 \times 10^3$ kips per sq in. $\alpha_t = 1/150,000$ per °F.

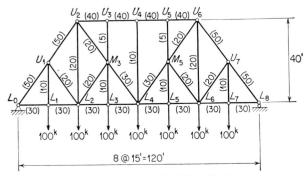

Figure 12.40   Problem 12.4

*Problem 12.5   For the structure of Fig. 12.41, using the method of virtual work, find the vertical deflection of point a due to the load shown. Cross-sectional areas of members in square inches are shown in parentheses. $E = 30 \times 10^3$ kips per sq in.

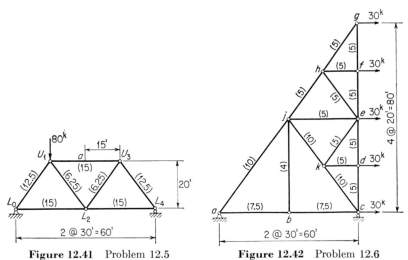

Figure 12.41   Problem 12.5   **Figure 12.42**   Problem 12.6

Problem 12.6   For the structure of Fig. 12.42, cross-sectional areas of members in square inches are shown in parentheses. $E = 30 \times 10^3$ kips per sq in. Compute the angular rotation of member bj, due to the loads shown.

*Problem 12.7   For the structure of Fig. 12.43, E_1 of member $gf = 20 \times 10^3$ kips per sq in., and E_2 of all the other members $= 30 \times 10^3$ kips per sq in. Cross-sectional areas in square inches are shown in parentheses. Using the method of virtual work,

    (a) Compute the vertical component of the deflection of point c due to the load shown.

    (b) If a turnbuckle in member gf were adjusted so as to shorten the member 0.5 in., what would be the vertical and horizontal components of the movement of point c due only to this adjustment?

Figure 12.43   Problem 12.7

Figure 12.44   Problem 12.8

*Problem 12.8**   Refer to Fig. 12.44.   During repairs to the right abutment of this truss, it was necessary to support the truss temporarily at joint L_2 on a hydraulic jack. If the gross dead reaction at L_4 is 50 kips, compute the distance the jack must raise the truss at joint L_2 in order to free the support at L_4 and lift it 2 in. above its normal position.   Cross-sectional areas of bars in square inches are shown in parentheses. $E = 30 \times 10^3$ kips per sq in.

*Problem 12.9**   Refer to Fig. 12.45.   Cross-sectional areas of members in square inches are shown in parentheses. E of member $ed = 20 \times 10^3$ kips per sq in. $= E_1$, and E of all other members $= 30 \times 10^3$ kips per sq in. $= E_2$.   Using the method of virtual work, determine the direction and magnitude of the resultant deflection of joint d due to load shown.

Figure 12.45   Problem 12.9

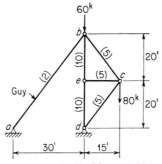

Figure 12.46   Problem 12.10

Problem 12.10   For the structure of Fig. 12.46, the cross-sectional areas of members in square inches are shown in parentheses. E of guy $= 20 \times 10^3$ kips per sq in. $= E_1$, and E of all other members $= 30 \times 10^3$ kips per sq in. $= E_2$.

(a) Compute the vertical component of the deflection of joint c due to the loads shown.

(b) How much would the length of the guy ab have to be changed, by adjusting a turnbuckle in the guy, to return joint c to its undeflected vertical elevation?

Problem 12.11   Using the method of virtual work, determine the vertical deflection and the change in slope of the cross section at point a of the beam of Fig. 12.47. E and I are both constant.

Figure 12.47   Problem 12.11

*Problem 12.12   For the girder of Fig. 12.48, using the method of virtual work,
(a) Compute the vertical deflection of point b due to the load shown.
(b) Compute the change in slope of the cross section at point d due to a uniformly
distributed load of 2 kips per ft applied over the entire span.

$$E = 30 \times 10^3 \text{ kips per sq in.} \qquad I_1 = 300 \text{ in.}^4 \qquad I_2 = 500 \text{ in.}^4$$

Figure 12.48   Problem 12.12

Problem 12.13   Compute the vertical deflection of point a of the frame of Fig.
12.49, considering the effect of deformation due to both axial stress and bending.
$E = 30 \times 10^3$ kips per sq in.

Figure 12.49   Problem 12.13   **Figure 12.50**   Problem 12.14

*Problem 12.14   For the structure of Fig. 12.50, I of member $ad = 3,456$ in.^{4}, and
$E = 30 \times 10^3$ kips per sq in.   Using the method of virtual work, compute the vertical
component of the deflection of point b.

Problem 12.15   For the truss of Fig. 12.51, the cross-sectional areas of members in
square inches are shown in parentheses. $E = 30 \times 10^3$ kips per sq in.   Compute the
relative deflection of point a and joint L_3 along the line joining them, due to the loads
shown.

Figure 12.51   Problem 12.15   **Figure 12.52**   Problem 12.16

Problem 12.16   Refer to Fig. 12.52.   Using the method of virtual work, compute the horizontal component of the deflection of point d, due to the following support movements:

Point a: Horizontal = 0.36 in. (to left)
        Vertical = 0.48 in. (down)
Point b: Vertical = 0.96 in. (down)

*Problem 12.17**   Refer to Fig. 12.53.   Using the moment-area method,

(a) Compute the vertical deflection of points a, c, and d and the slope of the elastic curve at points b and c in terms of E and I.

(b) If $E = 30 \times 10^3$ kips per sq in. and $I = 300$ in.⁴, compute from part a the vertical deflection of a in inches and the slope at b in radians.

Figure 12.53   Problem 12.17   **Figure 12.54**   Problem 12.18

Problem 12.18   Refer to Fig. 12.54.   Using the elastic-load procedure and the moment-area theorems,

(a) Find the vertical deflection at 3-ft intervals along the beam in terms of E and I.

(b) Find the position and magnitude of the maximum vertical deflection in span ce. E and I are constant.

Problem 12.19   Refer to Fig. 12.55.   Using the moment-area method, find, due to the load shown, the position and magnitude of the maximum vertical deflection in member bc. $E = 30 \times 10^3$ kips per sq in.

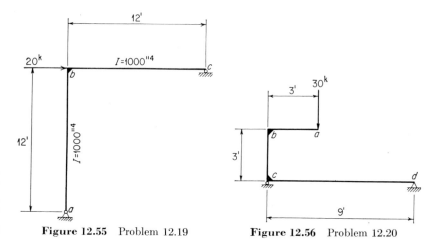

Figure 12.55   Problem 12.19   **Figure 12.56**   Problem 12.20

*Problem 12.20**   Refer to Fig. 12.56. E and I are constant throughout, $E = 30 \times 10^3$ kips per sq in., and $I = 432$ in.⁴   Due to the load shown, compute the vertical component of the deflection of point a on the bracket attached to this beam.

Problem 12.21   Refer to Fig. 12.57. E and I are constant, $E = 30 \times 10^3$ kips per sq in., and $I = 192$ in.[4]   Compute the location and magnitude of the maximum vertical deflection of the beam ab.

| Figure 12.57   Problem 12.21 | Figure 12.58   Problem 12.22 |

*Problem 12.22**   Refer to Fig. 12.58. $E = 30 \times 10^3$ kips per sq in., and $I = 1,440$ in.[4]   If the support at b settled downward ⅛ in., determine the location and magnitude of the maximum upward deflection in the portion of the beam ab resulting from both the load shown and the settlement.

Problem 12.23   Refer to Fig. 12.59.   Compute the position and magnitude of the maximum vertical deflection of this structure, using the moment-area theorems or their elastic-load adaptation. E and I are constant, $E = 30 \times 10^3$ kips per sq in., $I = 1,200$ in.[4]

Figure 12.59   Problem 12.23   Figure 12.60   Problem 12.24

Problem 12.24   Refer to Fig. 12.60. $E = 30 \times 10^3$ kips per sq in., and $I = 576$ in.[4]   Compute the maximum vertical deflection of this beam, using the conjugate-beam method.

*Problem 12.25**   Refer to Fig. 12.61.   Compute the position and magnitude of the maximum vertical deflection in this beam. E and I are constant, $E = 30 \times 10^3$ kips per sq in., $I = 432$ in.[4]

Figure 12.61   Problem 12.25

Problem 12.26   Refer to Fig. 12.62.   Using the conjugate-beam method, compute the position and magnitude of the maximum vertical deflection in the portion bc of this structure. E and I are constant, $E = 30 \times 10^3$ kips per sq in., $I = 1,440$ in.[4]

Figure 12.62   Problem 12.26

*Problem 12.27   Refer to Fig. 12.63.   Assuming that the couple of 120 kip-ft applied at b causes the moment reaction of 60 kip-ft acting as shown at support a, compute the position and magnitude of the maximum vertical deflection of this beam. $E = 30 \times 10^3$ kips per sq in., and $I = 576$ in.^{4}

Figure 12.63   Problem 12.27

*Problem 12.28   Refer to Fig. 12.64.   Find the horizontal and vertical components of the deflection of the joints of this truss, using the Williot-Mohr method.   Construct the Williot diagram, assuming point h fixed in position and bar hd in direction. Record the results in inch units.   Use a scale of 1 in. = 0.20 in. and place point h' in the lower right-hand corner of the page about 1 in. from the bottom and 3 in. from the right-hand edge. ΔL's of bars in inches are shown in parentheses.

Figure 12.64   Problem 12.28

Problem 12.29   Using the Williot-Mohr method, find the horizontal and vertical components of all the joints of the trusses in the following problems: (a) Prob. 12.6; (b) Prob. 12.7; (c) Prob. 12.4; (d) Prob. 12.9; (e) Prob. 12.10.

Problem 12.30   Using the bar-chain method, compute (a) the vertical deflection of the bottom-chord panel points of the truss of Prob. 12.15; (b) the vertical deflection of the top-chord panel points of the truss of Prob. 12.7; (c) the horizontal deflection of the panel points c, d, e, f, and g of the truss of Prob. 12.6; (d) the horizontal deflection of panel points a, j, h, and g of the truss of Prob. 12.6; (e) the vertical deflection of the joints of the bar chain $L_0 U_2 U_6 L_8$ of the truss of Prob. 12.4; (f) the vertical deflection of the lower-chord panel points of the three-hinged arch of Example 12.21.

13

Stress Analysis of
Statically Indeterminate Structures

13.1 Introduction. In the last 40 years, statically indeterminate structures have been used more and more extensively. This is no doubt due to their economy and increased rigidity under moving or movable loads. The details of reinforced-concrete and welded construction are such that structures of these types are usually wholly or partly continuous in their structural action and are therefore usually statically indeterminate. A knowledge of the analysis of indeterminate structures has thus become increasingly important as the use of these types of construction has become more extensive. Typical examples of indeterminate structures are continuous beams and trusses, two-hinged and hingeless arches, rigid-frame bridges, suspension bridges, and building frames.

Statically indeterminate structures differ from statically determinate ones in two important respects, viz.:

1. Their stress analysis involves not only their geometry but also their elastic properties such as modulus of elasticity, cross-sectional area, and moment of inertia. Thus, to arrive at the final design of an indeterminate structure involves assuming preliminary sizes for the members, making a stress analysis of this design, redesigning the members for these stresses, making a new stress analysis of the revised design, redesigning again, reanalyzing, etc., until one converges on the final design.

2. In general, stresses are developed in indeterminate structures, not only by loads, but also by temperature changes, support settlements, fabrication errors, etc.

In order to understand the stress analysis of indeterminate structures, it is imperative to understand first the fundamental difference between an unstable, a statically determinate, and a statically indeterminate structure. For this reason, a short review of certain fundamentals is justified. Suppose that bar AB is supported only by a hinge support at A, as shown in Fig. 13.1a. If the 10-kip load shown is then applied to the bar, it will obviously rotate freely about the hinge at A. A bar supported in this manner will therefore be an *unstable structure*. By means of an additional roller support at B, however, as shown in Fig. 13.1b, we obviously prevent rotation about A and therefore have arranged the structure so that it is *stable;* by inspection it is also a *statically determinate structure*.

If we add still another roller support at C, as shown in Fig. 13.1c, we then have more reactions than the minimum required for static equilibrium and no longer have a statically determinate structure but, instead, a

(a) Unstable	(a)
(b) Stable and Statically Determinate	(b)
(c) Stable and Statically Indeterminate	(c)

Figure 13.1 Classification of structures　　**Figure 13.2** Simple superposition of effects

statically indeterminate structure. With this new arrangement, not only do we prevent the bar from translating or rotating as a rigid body, but also by the addition of the roller support at C we prevent this point from deflecting vertically.

This observation, however, immediately suggests a method by which we can compute the vertical reaction at C. If the support at C is temporarily removed, suppose that the 10-kip load acting on the beam supported simply by the remaining supports causes a downward deflection of 3 in. at C, as shown in Fig. 13.2a. If the support at C is now reestablished, it will have to provide an upward reaction in order to return point C to a position of zero deflection. Just how much this upward reaction will have to be may be determined by first finding how much a 1-kip load will deflect point C. If a 1-kip load acting at point C on the beam supported at A and B deflected this point $\frac{1}{2}$ in., as shown in Fig. 13.2b, then an upward force of 6 kips at point C, together with the 10-kip load, will produce a net deflection of zero at this point, as shown in Fig. 13.2c. The vertical reaction at point C of the beam shown in Fig. 13.1c must therefore be 6 kips

acting upward.   Once this reaction has been determined, the remaining
reactions at A and B may easily be computed by statics.

**13.2   Use of Superposition Equations in Analysis of Statically
Indeterminate Structures.**   Many simple indeterminate structures
may be analyzed in the manner just discussed.   Such an informal
approach is confusing, however, in the case of more complicated structures.   It is therefore desirable to develop a more formal and orderly

Figure 13.3   Organization of analysis by superposition equations

procedure to facilitate the solution of the more complicated problems and
also to handle the simple problems with maximum efficiency.

The ideas and philosophy behind a more orderly approach may be
developed by considering a specific example such as the indeterminate
beam shown in Fig. 13.3a, the supports of which are unyielding.   This
beam is statically indeterminate to the first degree, i.e., there is one more
reaction component than the minimum necessary for static equilibrium.
One of the reaction components may be considered as being extra, or
redundant.   In this case, consider the vertical reaction at b as being the
redundant reaction.

Suppose that we remove from the actual structure the vertical support at b and the vertical reaction X_b which it supplies. The statically determinate and stable cantilever beam that remains after the removal of this redundant support at b is called the *primary structure* (see Fig. 13.3b). We may now subject this primary structure to the combined effect of the same loading as the actual structure plus the unknown redundant force X_b, as shown in Fig. 13.3c.

If the redundant force X_b acting on the primary structure has the same value as the vertical reaction at b on the actual structure, then the shear and bending moment at any point and the reactions at point a are the same for the two structures. If the conditions of stress in the actual structure and the primary structure are the same, then the conditions of deformation of the two structures must also be exactly the same. If the conditions of deformation of the two structures are the same and the deflections of the supports at point a on each are also identical, then the deflections at any other corresponding points must be the same. Therefore, since there is no vertical deflection of the support at b on the actual structure, the vertical deflection of point b on the primary structure, due to the combined action of the applied load and X_b, must also be equal to zero.

It is possible, however, to express this latter statement mathematically and thus obtain an equation from which the value of the unknown redundant X_b may be determined. Assuming the positive direction of the redundant X_b to be upward, let us introduce the following notation:

Let Δ_b = upward deflection of point b on primary structure, due to all causes (see Fig. 13.3c)

Δ_{bo} = upward deflection of point b on primary structure, due only to the applied load with the redundant removed, hereafter called "condition $X = 0$" (see Fig. 13.3d)

Δ_{bb} = upward deflection of point b on primary structure, due only to redundant X_b

It is impossible to compute Δ_{bb} until the magnitude of X_b is known. If, however, we also let

δ_{bb} = upward deflection of point b on primary structure, due only to a unit upward load at b, hereafter called "condition $X_b = +1$ kip" (see Fig. 13.3e)

then we can say, **as long as the principle of superposition is valid,** that

$$\frac{\Delta_{bb}}{X_b} = \frac{\delta_{bb}}{1^k} \qquad\qquad (a)$$

Hence, $\qquad\qquad \Delta_{bb} = \frac{X_b}{1^k}\,\delta_{bb} \quad \text{or} \quad \Delta_{bb} = X_b\delta_{bb} \qquad\qquad (b)$

where, since we have replaced $X_b/1^k$ by simply X_b, **we henceforth must think of X_b as being dimensionless and representing simply the numerical value of** X_b (that is, the number of 1-kip forces represented by this redundant).[1] It is a physical fact, however, that Δ_b, the total deflection due to all causes, is equal to the superposition of the contributions of the separate effects, viz., the applied load and the redundant X_b.   Thus,

$$\Delta_b = \Delta_{bo} + \Delta_{bb} \qquad (c)$$

or, substituting from Eq. (*b*),

$$\Delta_b = \Delta_{bo} + X_b \delta_{bb} \qquad (13.1)$$

This equation is called a *superposition equation* for the deflection of point *b* on the primary structure.

Since Δ_b must be zero, we may solve Eq. (13.1) for X_b and obtain

$$X_b = -\frac{\Delta_{bo}}{\delta_{bb}} \qquad (13.2)$$

It is a simple matter, of course, to compute the numerical value of Δ_{bo} and δ_{bb} by any of the methods available for computing beam deflections. In substituting these values in Eq. (13.2), they should be considered plus when the deflections are upward as specified above.   A plus value for X_b will then indicate that it acts upward; a minus value, that it acts downward.   The organization of the numerical computations in problems such as this is illustrated by the examples in Art. 13.4.

13.3   General Discussion of Use of Superposition Equations in Analysis of Statically Indeterminate Structures.   The method of attack suggested in Art. 13.2 is the most general available for the stress analysis of indeterminate structures.   There are other methods, of course, that are definitely superior for certain specific types of structures, but there is no other one method that is as flexible and general as the method based on using superposition equations.   It is applicable to any structure, whether beam, frame, or truss or any combination of these simple types. It is applicable whether the structure is being analyzed for the effect of loads, temperature changes, support settlements, fabrication errors, or any other cause.

There is only one restriction on the use of this approach, viz., that the

---

[1] Alternatively, we could have rearranged Eq. (*a*) as follows,

$$\Delta_{bb} = X_b \frac{\delta_{bb}}{1^k} \quad \text{or} \quad \Delta_{bb} = X_b d_{bb} \qquad (b')$$

where d_{bb} is called a **flexibility** (or **deflection**) **coefficient.** This coefficient d_{bb} denotes the upward vertical deflection of point *b* per unit upward force at point *b* and has units of distance per unit force.   If we had elected to use this system, henceforth X_b would have been a dimensional number with force units.

principle of superposition is valid. From the discussion in Art. 2.12, it will be recalled that the principle of superposition is valid unless the geometry of the structure changes an essential amount during the application of the loads or the material does not follow Hooke's law. All the other methods discussed here are likewise subject to this same limitation, however.

Before presenting numerical examples illustrating the application of this method to certain typical problems, it is desirable to emphasize and extend the ideas suggested in Art. 13.2. The student may find that he has difficulty understanding the somewhat generalized discussion that follows. If he will read this article, however, absorbing what he can, and then study the examples in Arts. 13.4 and 13.5, he should then be able to understand the remainder of this article when he rereads it.

Suppose that we wish to analyze some particular indeterminate structure for any or all of the various causes which may produce stress in the structure. The structure may be of any type or statically indeterminate to any degree. In any case, the very first step in the analysis is to determine the degree of indeterminacy. Suppose the structure is indeterminate to the nth degree. We then select n redundant restraints, remove them from the structure, and replace them by the n redundant stress components that they supply to the structure. All these n redundants X_a, X_b, . . . , X_n will then be acting together with the applied loads on the *primary structure* that remains after the removal of the n restraints.

A wide choice of redundants is available in most problems, but it is usually possible to minimize the numerical calculations by choosing them judiciously. Some of the principles to follow in selecting the redundants are discussed in Art. 13.6. Suffice it to say for the present that the redundants must be selected so that the resulting primary structure is stable and statically determinate.[1]

Having selected the redundants, we then may reason that, if the redundant forces acting on the primary structure have the same values as the forces supplied by the corresponding restraints on the actual structure, then the entire conditions of stress in the actual and primary structure are the same. As a result, the conditions of deformation of the two structures are the same. If, in addition, the deflections of the supports of the primary structure are the same as the deflections of the corresponding supports of the actual structure, then the deflections of any other corresponding points on the two structures must be identical. It may be concluded, therefore, that the deflections of the points of application of the n redundants on the primary structure must be equal to the specified deflections of the corresponding points on the actual structure.

[1] Occasionally it is advantageous to select a statically indeterminate and stable primary structure (see Art. 14.3).

If n superposition equations are written for these n deflections, they will involve among them all the n redundants as unknowns. Since all these n deflection equations must be satisfied simultaneously by the n unknowns, simultaneous solution of these equations leads to the values of the n unknown redundants.

In applying this method, it is convenient to have a definite notation for the various deflection terms involved in the solution. The total deflection of a point m on the primary structure, due to all causes, is denoted by Δ_m. The various supplementary deflections contributing to this total are identified, however, by two subscripts, the first of which denotes the point at which the deflection occurs and the second of which denotes the loading condition which causes that particular contribution. Thus, the deflection of a point m produced **on the primary structure** by certain typical causes would be denoted as follows:

Δ_m = total deflection of point m, due to all causes

Δ_{mo} = deflection of point m due to condition $X = 0$ (that is, applied load only with all redundants removed)

Δ_{mT} = deflection of point m, due to change in temperature

Δ_{mS} = deflection of point m, due to **settlement of supports of primary structure**

Δ_{mE} = deflection of point m, due to fabrication errors

δ_{ma} = deflection of point m, due to condition $X_a = +1$ kip

δ_{mb} = deflection of point m, due to condition $X_b = +1$ kip

δ_{mm} = deflection of point m, due to condition $X_m = +1$ kip

etc.

Note that the deflections produced by unit values of the various redundants are denoted by a small delta (δ).

Any redundant may be arbitrarily assumed to act in a certain sense, thus establishing the positive sense of that redundant. Any deflection of the point of application of that redundant should then be measured along its line of action and should be considered positive when in the same sense as that assumed for the redundant.

Thus, using the above notation and sign convention, we have the following form for the n superposition equations involving the n redundants—one equation for the known total deflection of the point of application of each of the n redundants, on the primary structure:

$$\Delta_a = \Delta_{ao} + \Delta_{aT} + \Delta_{aS} + \Delta_{aE} + X_a \delta_{aa} + X_b \delta_{ab} + \cdots + X_n \delta_{an}$$
$$\Delta_b = \Delta_{bo} + \Delta_{bT} + \Delta_{bS} + \Delta_{bE} + X_a \delta_{ba} + X_b \delta_{bb} + \cdots + X_n \delta_{bn}$$
$$\cdots \cdots \cdots \cdots \cdots \cdots \cdots \cdots \cdots \cdots \cdots \cdots \cdots \cdots \cdots \quad (13.3)$$
$$\Delta_n = \Delta_{no} + \Delta_{nT} + \Delta_{nS} + \Delta_{nE} + X_a \delta_{na} + X_b \delta_{nb} + \cdots + X_n \delta_{nn}$$

If the known values of Δ_a, Δ_b, . . . , Δ_n are substituted and the various deflection terms on the right-hand side of these equations are evaluated by *any* suitable method, then the n equations may be solved simultaneously[1] for the value of the redundants X_a, X_b, etc.[2] **Note that the values of X_a, X_b, etc., obtained from this solution are dimensionless.** This is obviously so, since X_a, X_b, etc., must be pure numbers in order that all the terms in each of Eqs. (13.3) may have the same deflection units. In order to assign units to these values for X_a, X_b, etc., it is necessary to note the units of the unit values of these redundants that were used in the computation of δ_{aa}, δ_{ab}, etc.

Note further that the redundants selected may be forces or couples. The deflections designated by Δ or δ may therefore represent a linear or angular deflection, depending on whether they represent the deflection of the point of application of a force or a couple. In the examples that follow, the positive direction of any particular deflection is indicated by the small arrow appended to the symbol, as $\Delta_a^{\uparrow}$, $\Delta_b^{\searrow}$, $\Delta_c^{\rightarrow\!\leftarrow}$, etc.

13.4 Examples Illustrating Stress Analysis Using Superposition Equations. The following examples illustrate the application of the superposition-equation approach to the stress analysis of typical indeterminate structures acted upon by specified external loads.

After determining the degree of indeterminacy, one has considerable latitude in selecting the redundants. However, **never make the mistake of selecting a statically determinate reaction component, bar force, shear, or moment, as a redundant. If such a quantity is statically determinate, it is necessary for the stability of the structure; to remove it would leave an unstable primary structure.** Such an error will never go undetected, however, since an attempted stress analysis of the primary structure would lead to impossible or inconsistent results.

The reader should consider alternative selections of the redundants in the following examples and try to decide whether in each case there is

---

[1] A convenient tabular method for solving simultaneous equations is discussed in connection with Example 13.22.

[2] If the alternative approach suggested in the footnote on p. 404 (of Art. 13.2) were used, the superposition equations (13.3) could be rewritten in terms of the flexibility coefficients d_{ij}, where d_{ij} represents the deflection of the point of application of redundant X_i in the assumed direction of redundant X_i due to a unit value of redundant X_j.

$$
\begin{aligned}
\Delta_a &= \Delta_{ao} + \Delta_{aT} + \Delta_{aS} + \Delta_{aE} + X_a d_{aa} + X_b d_{ab} + \cdots + X_n d_{an} \\
\Delta_b &= \Delta_{bo} + \Delta_{bT} + \Delta_{bS} + \Delta_{bE} + X_a d_{ba} + X_b d_{bb} + \cdots + X_n d_{bn} \\
&\;\;\cdots\cdots\cdots\cdots\cdots\cdots\cdots\cdots\cdots\cdots\cdots\cdots\cdots\cdots\cdots \\
\Delta_n &= \Delta_{no} + \Delta_{nT} + \Delta_{nS} + \Delta_{nE} + X_a d_{na} + X_b d_{nb} + \cdots + X_n d_{nn}
\end{aligned} \tag{13.3'}
$$

As noted previously, the redundants X in these equations would be dimensional numbers with appropriate force or couple units as the case may be.

some other selection involving less numerical calculation than those used. The question of selection of redundants is discussed further in Art. 13.6.

The positive sense of a redundant may be chosen arbitrarily. The deflection of the point of application of this redundant should likewise be considered positive when in the same sense. Consideration of any of these examples should make it apparent that the final interpretation of the direction of the redundants will not be affected by the initial choice of its positive sense.

In applying the superposition approach, any suitable method may be used to compute the various deflections involved. Of course, as in any deflection problem, care must be exercised in handling units and signs. **Note again that the values of X_a, X_b, etc., obtained from these solutions are simply numerical values, i.e., they are dimensionless.** Such numerical values indicate, for example, that X_a is, say, 10.5 times larger than the unit load in condition $X_a = +1$ kip. Thus, if this is a 1-kip unit load, X_a should be considered as 10.5 kips in stating the final results or in using it in subsequent computations.

The units will always be consistent if the same force and distance units are used throughout a given problem. If, however, we mix up feet, inches, pounds, and kips in problems involving more than one type of deformation, we may run into difficulty. Similar difficulty will be encountered if units are mixed in dealing with problems involving temperature changes, support settlements, etc., such as are discussed in Art. 13.5.

It should be noted that Δ_n, the total deflection of the point of application of a redundant X_n due to all causes, is almost always equal to zero. In fact, the only case in which Δ_n would have a value other than zero would be when X_n represented a redundant reactive force or couple at a support on the actual structure, which underwent a movement in the direction of X_n.

Example 13.1 *Compute the reactions of this beam. E and I are constant.*

Structure is indeterminate to first degree. Select X_b as redundant. Then

$$\Delta_b^\uparrow = \Delta_{bo} + X_b \delta_{bb} = 0$$

Evaluate Δ_{bo} and δ_{bb} by method of virtual work.

$$\sum Q\delta = \sum \int M_Q M_P \frac{ds}{EI}$$

Δ_{bo}: $M_Q = M_b$ $M_P = M_o$

$$(1^k)(\Delta_{bo}^\uparrow) = \int M_b M_o \frac{ds}{EI}$$

From b to a,

$$M_b = x \qquad M_o = -x^2$$

$$(1^k)(\Delta_{bo}^\uparrow) = \int_0^{20} (x)(-x^2) \frac{dx}{EI}$$

$$\Delta_{bo} = \frac{-40,000^{k'^3}}{EI}$$

δ_{bb}: $M_Q = M_b$ $M_P = M_b$

$$(1^k)(\delta_{bb}^\uparrow) = \int M_b^2 \frac{dx}{EI}$$

$$(1^k)(\delta_{bb}^\uparrow) = \int_0^{20} (x)^2 \frac{dx}{EI} \qquad \delta_{bb} = \frac{2,667^{k'^3}}{EI}$$

Then

$$\frac{-40,000}{EI} + \frac{2,667}{EI} X_b = 0$$

$$\therefore X_b = \underline{+15} \qquad \therefore upward$$

Then, by statics, the reactions at a are found to be as shown.

Example 13.2   *Compute the reactions and draw the bending-moment diagram for this beam.   E and I are constant.*

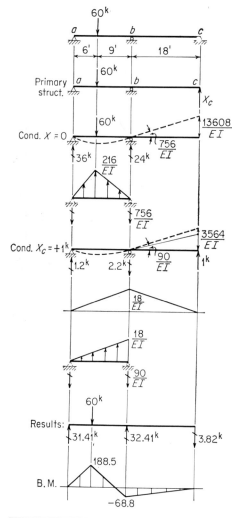

Structure is indeterminate to first degree. Select X_c as redundant.   Then,

$$\Delta \uparrow_c = \Delta_{co} + X_c \delta_{cc} = 0$$

Evaluate Δ_{co} and δ_{cc} by the elastic-load method.

Δ_{co}: Compute first the reaction at b on imaginary beam.

$$216 \times 3 \quad = 648 \times 4 = \quad 2{,}592$$
$$216 \times 4.5 = 972 \times 9 = \quad 8{,}748$$
$$\overline{ 11{,}340}$$
$$\frac{11{,}340}{15} = 756$$

Then,

$$EI\Delta_{co} = 756 \times 18 = 13{,}608\uparrow$$
$$\therefore \Delta_{co} = \frac{+13{,}608^{k'^3}}{EI}$$

δ_{cc}: Compute first the reaction at b on imaginary beam.

$$\tfrac{2}{3} \times 18 \times 7.5 = 90$$

Then,

$$EI\delta_{cc} = 90 \times 18 + 18 \times 9 \times 12$$
$$= 3{,}564\uparrow$$
$$\therefore \delta_{cc} = \frac{+3{,}564^{k'^3}}{EI}$$

Then,

$$\frac{13{,}608}{EI} + \frac{3{,}564}{EI} X_c = 0$$
$$\therefore X_c = \underline{-3.82} \qquad \therefore \; down$$

The reaction at a and b can now be computed easily by statics.   Likewise, the BM diagram may be constructed without difficulty.

Example 13.3 *Compute the reactions and bar forces for this truss. Cross-sectional areas in square inches are shown in parentheses. $E = 30 \times 10^3$ kips per sq in.*

Indeterminate to first degree. Select X_b as redundant. Then,

$$\Delta_b^\uparrow = \Delta_{bo} + X_b\delta_{bb} = 0$$

Evaluate Δ_{bo} and δ_{bb} by the method of virtual work.

$$\sum Q\delta = \sum F_Q\,\Delta L = \sum F_Q F_P \frac{L}{AE}$$

$\Delta_{bo}: F_Q = F_b \qquad F_P = F_o \qquad (1^k)(\Delta_{bo}^\uparrow) = \frac{1}{E}\sum F_b F_o \frac{L}{A}$

$\delta_{bb}: F_Q = F_b \qquad F_P = F_b \qquad (1^k)(\delta_{bb}^\uparrow) = \frac{1}{E}\sum F_b^2 \frac{L}{A}$

Primary struct. F

Bar	L	A	$\dfrac{L}{A}$	F_o	F_b	$F_bF_o\dfrac{L}{A}$	$F_b^2\dfrac{L}{A}$	X_bF_b	F
Units	$'$	$''^2$	$'/''^2$	k	k	$k^2'/''^2$	$k^2'/''^2$	k	k
ab	30	10	3	-60	-0.375	$+67.5$	$+0.422$	$+6.35$	-53.65
bc	30	10	3	-60	-0.375	$+67.5$	$+0.422$	$+6.35$	-53.65
ad	50	12.5	4	$+100$	$+0.625$	$+250$	$+1.563$	-10.6	$+89.4$
dc	50	12.5	4	-100	$+0.625$	-250	$+1.563$	-10.6	-110.6
bd	40	10	4	0	-1.0	0	$+4.0$	$+16.93$	$+16.93$
Σ						$+135$	$+7.970$		

Cond. $X = 0$ F_o

Cond. $X_b = +1^k$ F_b

$$(1^k)(\Delta_{bo}) = \frac{+135^{k^2'/''^2}}{E} \qquad \Delta_{bo} = \frac{135^{k'/''^2}}{E}$$

$$(1^k)(\delta_{bb}) = \frac{+7.97^{k^2'/''^2}}{E} \qquad \delta_{bb} = \frac{7.97^{k'/''^2}}{E}$$

$$\therefore \frac{135}{E} + \frac{7.97}{E}X_b = 0 \qquad X_b = \underline{-16.93} \qquad \therefore down$$

Results F

The remaining reactions and the bar forces can now be computed by statics. The bar forces could likewise be computed easily in a tabular manner by noting that by superposition

$$F = F_o + X_bF_b$$

Example 13.4 *Compute the reactions of this truss.   Cross-sectional areas in square inches are shown in parentheses. $E = 30 \times 10^3$ kips per sq in.*

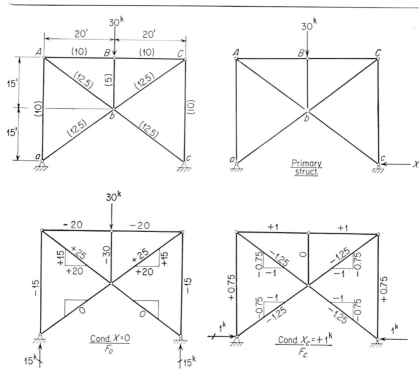

Indeterminate to first degree.   Select X_c as redundant.

$$\Delta_c^{\leftarrow} = \Delta_{co} + X_c \delta_{cc} = 0$$

Evaluate Δ_{co} and δ_{cc} by the method of virtual work.

Δ_{co}: $F_Q = F_c$ $F_P = F_o$ $(1^k)(\Delta_{co}^{\leftarrow}) = \dfrac{1}{E}\sum F_c F_o \dfrac{L}{A}$

δ_{cc}: $F_Q = F_c$ $F_P = F_c$ $(1^k)(\delta_{cc}^{\leftarrow}) = \dfrac{1}{E}\sum F_c^2 \dfrac{L}{A}$

Owing to symmetry of the load, structure, and redundant, only one-half of the bars have to be included in the tabulation.

$\dfrac{-272.5}{E} + \dfrac{19.875}{E} X_c = 0$

$\therefore X_c = +13.7$ $\therefore \leftarrow$

Results:

Bar	L	A	$\dfrac{L}{A}$	F_o	F_c	$F_o F_c \dfrac{L}{A}$	$F_c^2 \dfrac{L}{A}$
Units	$'$	$''^2$	$'/''^2$	k	k	$k^2'/''^2$	$k^2'/''^2$
AB	20	10	2	-20	$+1.0$	-40	$+2.0$
ab	25	12.5	2	0	-1.25	0	$+3.125$
Aa	30	10	3	-15	$+0.75$	-33.75	$+1.688$
Ab	25	12.5	2	$+25$	-1.25	-62.5	$+3.125$
$\frac{1}{2}Bb$	7.5	5	1.5	-30	0	0	0
$\frac{1}{2}\Sigma$						-136.25	$+9.938$

$$\therefore \Delta_{co} = \frac{-272.5^{k'/''^2}}{E} \qquad \delta_{cc} = \frac{19.875^{k'/''^2}}{E}$$

Example 13.5 *Compute the bar forces in the members of this truss. E and A are constant for all members.*

This truss is statically determinate externally, but indeterminate to the second degree with respect to its bar forces. Cut bars bC and Cd, and select their bar forces as the redundants. Then

$$\Delta_1 = \Delta_{10} + X_1\delta_{11} + X_2\delta_{12} = 0 \quad (1)$$

$$\Delta_2 = \Delta_{20} + X_1\delta_{21} + X_2\delta_{22} = 0 \quad (2)$$

By Maxwell's law, $\delta_{12} = \delta_{21}$, and by symmetry of the structure and in the selection of the redundants, $\delta_{11} = \delta_{22}$. Therefore, only four deflections need to be computed: Δ_{10}, Δ_{20}, δ_{12}, and δ_{11}. Using the method of virtual work, we find

$$(1^k)(EA\Delta_{10}) = \Sigma F_1 F_o L = -2{,}040^{k^{2\prime}}$$
$$(1^k)(EA\Delta_{20}) = \Sigma F_2 F_o L = +760^{k^{2\prime}}$$
$$(1^k)(EA\delta_{12}) = \Sigma F_1 F_2 L = +12.8^{k^{2\prime}}$$
$$(1^k)(EA\delta_{11}) = \Sigma F_1^2 L = +86.4^{k^{2\prime}}$$

Substituting these values in (1) and (2) and canceling out EA,

$$-2{,}040 + 86.4X_1 + 12.8X_2 = 0$$
$$+760 + 12.8X_1 + 86.4X_2 = 0$$

Solving these simultaneously,

$$X_1 = +25.5 \qquad X_2 = -12.6$$

In any bar,

$$F = F_o + X_1 F_1 + X_2 F_2$$

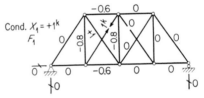

Bar	L	F_o	F_1	F_2	F_oF_1L	F_oF_2L	F_1^2L	F_1F_2L	F_1X_1	F_2X_2	F
Units	$'$	k	k	k	$k^2{'}$	$k^2{'}$	$k^2{'}$	$k^2{'}$	k	k	k
bc	15	+45	−0.6	0	−405	0	+ 5.4	0	−15.3	0	+29.7
cd	15	+15	0	−0.6	0	−135	0	0	0	+ 7.6	+22.6
BC	15	−30	−0.6	0	+270	0	+ 5.4	0	−15.3	0	−45.3
CD	15	−30	0	−0.6	0	+270	0	0	0	+ 7.6	−22.4
bB	20	+80	−0.8	0	−1,280	0	+12.8	0	−20.4	0	+59.6
cC	20	0	−0.8	−0.8	0	0	+12.8	+12.8	−20.4	+10.1	−10.3
dD	20	0	0	−0.8	0	0	0	0	0	+10.1	+10.1
Bc	25	−25	+1	0	−625	0	+25.0	0	+25.5	0	+ 0.5
bC	25	0	+1	0	0	0	+25.0	0	+25.5	0	+25.5
cD	25	+25	0	+1	0	+625	0	0	0	−12.6	+12.4
Cd	25	0	0	+1	0	0	0	0	0	−12.6	−12.6
Σ					−2,040	+760	+86.4	+12.8			

Discussion:

In tabulating the computations in such a truss, it is unnecessary to include bars having neither an F_1 nor an F_2 bar force. Be sure to include the redundant bars, however. Why?

There may be some question about cutting truss bars as was done in this problem. Students sometimes worry about the two ends of a cut bar being unstable, since as shown in the above line diagrams there is nothing to prevent these two ends from rotating about the pin joints. To be strictly correct, we should show the cut in such cases as shown in Fig. 13.4. Since the shear and moment in a straight bar hinged at both ends are statically

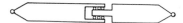

Figure 13.4   Visualization of removing capacity to transmit axial force

determinate, the restraints of this type cannot be removed. Thus, when we say that we cut such a bar, we mean that we remove its capacity to carry axial force but retain its ability to carry shear and moment. This could be accomplished by cutting through the member and then inserting a telescopic device in the manner shown.

It is impractical, however, to show such a detail every time we remove the capacity to carry axial force from a bar that is hinged at its ends. In such cases, therefore, we shall imply such a detail but show the cut as has been done in the line diagrams in this example. These remarks are likewise applicable to the tie rod in Example 13.8.

Example 13.6 *Compute the reactions and draw the bending-moment diagram for this beam.* $E = 30 \times 10^3$ *kips per sq in.*

This beam is statically indeterminate to the second degree. Select moments at supports as redundants. Then,

$$\Delta_b^{\rangle\,\langle} = \Delta_{bo} + X_b\delta_{bb} + X_c\delta_{bc} = 0 \quad (1)$$

$$\Delta_c^{\rangle\,\langle} = \Delta_{co} + X_b\delta_{cb} + X_c\delta_{cc} = 0 \quad (2)$$

Note $\delta_{bc} = \delta_{cb}$ by Maxwell's law. Use moment-area theorems to compute Δ_{bo}, Δ_{co}, δ_{bb}, δ_{cb}, and δ_{cc}.

$$EI_1\tau_{10} =$$
$$\frac{108}{15}\left[\frac{(9)(6)}{2}\right.$$
$$\left.+\frac{(6)(11)}{2}\right] = 432$$

$$EI_1\tau_{20} =$$
$$\frac{72}{15}\left[\frac{(9)(6)}{2}\right.$$
$$\left.+\frac{(6)(11)}{2}\right] = 288$$

$$\left. \right\} EI_1\Delta_{bo} = +720^{k'^2}$$

$$EI_1\tau_{30} =$$
$$\frac{72}{15}\left[\frac{(6)(4)}{2}\right.$$
$$\left.+\frac{(9)(9)}{2}\right] = 252$$

$$EI_1\tau_{40} =$$
$$\left(\frac{2}{3}\right)\frac{(81)(18)}{2} = 486$$

$$\left. \right\} EI_1\Delta_{co} = +738^{k'^2}$$

$$EI_1\tau_{1b} =$$
$$\left(\frac{1}{15}\right)\frac{(15)(10)}{2} = 5$$

$$EI_1\tau_{2b} =$$
$$\left(\frac{1}{3}\right)\frac{(15)(10)}{(15)(2)} = \frac{5}{3}$$

$$\left. \right\} EI_1\delta_{bb} = +6.67^{k'^2}$$

$$EI_1\tau_{3b} = \left(\frac{1}{3}\right)\frac{(15)(5)}{(15)(2)} = \frac{5}{6}$$

$$\therefore EI_1\delta_{cb} = +0.83^{k'^2}$$

$$EI_1\tau_{3c} =$$
$$\left(\frac{1}{3}\right)\frac{(15)(10)}{(15)(2)} = \frac{5}{3}$$

$$EI_1\tau_{4c} =$$
$$\left(\frac{1}{2}\right)\frac{(18)(12)}{(18)(2)} = 3$$

$$\left. \right\} EI_1\delta_{cc} = +4.67^{k'^2}$$

Substituting these values in (1) and (2) and canceling out EI_1,

$$720 + 6.67X_b + 0.83X_c = 0$$
$$738 + 0.83X_b + 4.67X_c = 0$$

Solving these simultaneously,

$$X_b = \underline{-90.3} \qquad X_c = \underline{-142.0}$$

With these moments known it is easy to isolate various portions of the beam and, by using statics, to compute shears, reactions, and bending moments, leading to the results shown.

Discussion:

When we select the support moments at b and c as the redundants, we remove the moment restraints from the actual structure at these points, i.e., we insert hinges at these points.

Note the manner in which the varying I is handled in this problem. One I is selected as a base, and all other I's are expressed in terms of the standard I. Once this is done, the actual values of the various I's need never be substituted in the solution of this problem.

Example 13.7 *Compute the reactions and draw the bending-moment diagram for this frame. E and I are constant. Consider only bending deformation.*

This frame is indeterminate to the first degree. Select X_c as the redundant. Then, $\Delta_c = \Delta_{co} + X_c\delta_{cc} = 0$. Compute Δ_{co} and δ_{cc} by the moment-area theorems.

$$EI\tau_{bo} = (720)(12)\left(\frac{12}{24}\right) = 4{,}320 \qquad \therefore \Delta_{co} = -\left(\frac{4{,}320}{EI}\right)(18) = \frac{-77{,}760^{k'^3}}{EI}$$

$$EI\tau_{bc} = (18)(12)\left(\frac{16}{24}\right) = 144 \qquad \therefore \delta_{cc} = \left(\frac{144}{EI}\right)(18) + \left(\frac{18}{EI}\right)(9)(12) = +\frac{4{,}536^{k'^3}}{EI}$$

Hence, $\qquad \dfrac{-77{,}760}{EI} + \dfrac{4{,}536}{EI}X_c = 0 \qquad X_c = +17.16 \qquad \therefore \;\longleftarrow$

The remaining computations may be easily done by using only statics.

Example 13.8 *Compute the force in the tie rod of this structure.*

Structure is indeterminate to the first degree. Cut the tie rod, and select its bar force as the redundant. Then,

$$\Delta_a = \Delta_{ao} + X_a \delta_{aa} = 0$$

Evaluate Δ_{ao} and δ_{aa} by the method of virtual work, including deformation due to both bending and axial force.

$$\sum Q\delta = \sum F_Q F_P \frac{L}{AE} + \sum \int M_Q M_P \frac{ds}{EI}$$

From A to B,

$$0 < x < 12 \qquad L = 12$$
$$M_o = 5x \qquad F_o = 0$$
$$M_a = -0.4x \qquad F_a = -0.6^k$$

Primary struct.

From C to E,

$$0 < x < 6$$
$$M_o = 15x \qquad F_o = 0$$
$$M_a = -0.4x \qquad F_a = 0$$

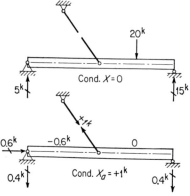

Cond. $X = 0$

From E to B,

$$6 < x < 12$$
$$M_o = 120 - 5x \qquad F_o = 0$$
$$M_a = -0.4x \qquad F_a = 0$$

Cond. $X_a = +1^k$

From D to B,

$$L = 10$$
$$M_o = 0 \qquad F_o = 0$$
$$M_a = 0 \qquad F_a = +1^k$$

$$(1^k)(\Delta_{ao}) = \sum F_a F_o \frac{L}{AE} + \sum \int M_a M_o \frac{ds}{EI} = 0 + \int_0^{12} (5x)(-0.4x) \frac{dx}{EI_2}$$
$$+ \int_0^6 (15x)(-0.4x) \frac{dx}{EI_2} + \int_6^{12} (120 - 5x)(-0.4x) \frac{dx}{EI_2}$$
$$\therefore EI_2 \Delta_{ao} = -3,168^{k'^3}$$

$$(1^k)(\delta_{aa}) = \sum F_a^2 \frac{L}{AE} + \sum \int M_a^2 \frac{ds}{EI} = \frac{(-0.6)^2(12)}{EA_2} + \frac{(1^2)(10)}{EA_1}$$
$$+ 2\int_0^{12} (-0.4x)^2 \frac{dx}{EI_2} \qquad \therefore EI_2 \delta_{aa} = +206.05^{k'^3}$$

Since

$$\frac{I_2}{A_2} = \left(\frac{600}{144^2}\right)\left(\frac{144}{20}\right) = \left(\frac{30}{144}\right)^{'2} \quad \text{and} \quad \frac{I_2}{A_1} = \left(\frac{600}{144^2}\right)\left(\frac{144}{2}\right) = \left(\frac{300}{144}\right)^{'2}$$

then,
$$\frac{-3,168}{EI_2} + \frac{206.05}{EI_2} X_a = 0 \qquad \therefore X_a = \underline{+15.38} \qquad \therefore \text{tension}$$

If the deformation due to axial force had been neglected, then

$$X_a = \frac{3,168}{184.32} = \underline{+17.2}$$

13.5   Additional Examples Involving Temperature, Settlement,

etc.   The following examples illustrate the application of the superposi-tion-equation approach to the stress analysis of typical indeterminate structures subjected to temperature changes, support movements, fabrica-tion errors, etc.

Fundamentally, these problems are no more difficult to handle than those involving simply the effect of loads.   **Always remember, how-ever, that the deflections Δ_{aT}, Δ_{aS}, etc., refer to deflections of points on the primary structure, due to a change in temperature of the primary structure, due to the settlement of the supports of the primary structure, etc.   These deflections when superimposed correctly with the contributions of each of the redundants must add up so that the total deflection of point a on the primary structure is equal to the known deflection of the corresponding point on the actual structure.**

Example 13.9   *Compute bar forces due to an increase of 60°F in the temperature at bars aB, BC, and Cd.   No change in the temperature of any other bars. $\alpha_t = 1/150,000$ per °F.   E = 30 × 10³ kips per sq in.   Cross-sectional areas in square inches are shown in parentheses.*

This truss is indeterminate to the first degree. Cut bar bC, and select its bar force as the redun-dant.   Then,

$$\Delta_a = \Delta_{aT} + X_a \delta_{aa} = 0$$

Using the method of virtual work,

Δ_{aT}: $F_Q = F_a$

$$(1^k)(\Delta_{aT}) = \sum F_a \alpha_t L = \alpha_t \sum F_a t L$$

δ_{aa}: $F_Q = F_P = F_a$ $(1^k)(\delta_{aa}) = \frac{1}{E} \sum F_a^2 \frac{L}{A}$

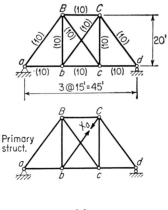

Bar	L	A	$\frac{L}{A}$	F_a	$F_a^2 \frac{L}{A}$	t	$F_a t L$	$X_a F_a$
Units	'	''²	'/''²	k	k²/''²	°F	k°F'	k
BC	15	10	1.5	−0.6	+0.54	+60	−540	− 7.5
bc	15	10	1.5	−0.6	+0.54	0	0	− 7.5
Bb	20	10	2	−0.8	+1.28	0	0	−10.0
Cc	20	10	2	−0.8	+1.28	0	0	−10.0
Bc	25	10	2.5	+1.0	+2.5	0	0	+12.5
bC	25	10	2.5	+1.0	+2.5	0	0	+12.5
Σ					+8.64		−540	

Primary struct.

Cond. $X_a = +1^k$
F_a

$$\Delta_{aT} = -(540)^{°F'} \left(\frac{1}{150,000}\right)^{/°F} = -0.0036 \, ft$$

$$\delta_{aa} = +\frac{8.64^{k'/''^2}}{30 \times 10^{3\,k/''^2}} = +0.000288 \, ft$$

$$-0.0036 + 0.000288 X_a = 0 \qquad X_a = +12.5$$

$$\therefore tension$$

Example 13.10   *Compute the bar forces of the two-hinged trussed arch in Example 13.4 caused by forcing member AB into place even though it had been fabricated $\frac{1}{8}''$ too short.*

In this case,

$$\Delta_c^{\leftarrow} = \Delta_{cE} + X_c \delta_{cc} = 0$$

Using the method of virtual work, Δ_{cE} may be evaluated as follows, using information from Example 13.4:

$$(1^k)(\Delta_{cE}^{\leftarrow}) = \Sigma F_c \,\Delta L_E = (+1^k)(-\tfrac{1}{96})' \qquad \Delta_{cE} = -0.0104'$$

From Example 13.4,

$$\delta_{cc} = +\frac{19.875^{k'/''^2}}{E} = +\frac{19.875^{k'/''^2}}{30 \times 10^{3\ k/''^2}} = +0.0006625'$$

$$\therefore\ -0.0104' + 0.0006625'X_c = 0 \qquad \therefore\ X_c = \underline{+15.7} \qquad \therefore\ +\!\!+$$

The bar force in any member can then be computed, since

$$F = X_c F_c = 15.7 F_c$$

Example 13.11   *Compute the bar forces in this truss due to the following support movements:*

$$\text{Support at } a, \ 0.24 \text{ in. down}$$
$$\text{Support at } c, \ 0.48 \text{ in. down}$$
$$\text{Support at } e, \ 0.36 \text{ in. down}$$

Cross-sectional area in square inches shown in parentheses.

$$E = 30 \times 10^3 \text{ kips per sq in.}$$

Selecting the vertical reaction at c as the redundant,

$$\Delta_c^\uparrow = \Delta_{cS} + X_c \delta_{cc} = -0.04'$$

Using the method of virtual work,

$$\Delta_{cS}: \qquad \Sigma Q \delta = 0$$

since $\Delta L = 0$ *(see Example 12.3).*

$$(1^k)(\Delta_{cS}^\uparrow) + (0.5^k)(0.02')$$
$$+ (0.5^k)(0.03') = 0$$
$$\therefore \ \Delta_{cS} = \underline{\underline{-0.025'}}$$

which checks the value obtained by geometry as shown on the sketch.

$$\delta_{cc}: \qquad (1^k)(\delta_{cc}^\uparrow) = \frac{1}{E} \sum F_c^2 \frac{L}{A}$$

Because of symmetry only one-half of the bars of the truss need be listed in the tabulation.

Primary struct.

Cond.
$X_c = +1^k$

Settlement cond.

Bar	L	A	$\dfrac{L}{A}$	F_c	$F_c^2 \dfrac{L}{A}$	$X_c F_c$
Units	$'$	$''^2$	$'/''^2$	k	$k^2/''^2$	k
ab	30	15	2	-0.375	$+0.281$	$+26.0$
bc	30	15	2	-0.375	$+0.281$	$+26.0$
BC	30	15	2	$+0.75$	$+1.125$	-52.1
aB	50	25	2	$+0.625$	$+0.781$	-44.1
Bc	50	25	2	-0.625	$+0.781$	$+44.1$
$\tfrac{1}{2}\Sigma$					$+3.25$	

$$\delta_{cc} = \frac{+6.50^{k'/''^2}}{30 \times 10^3 \, k/''^2} = \underline{\underline{+0.000216'}}$$

$$\therefore \ -0.025 + 0.000216 X_c = -0.04'$$

$$X_c = \frac{-0.015}{0.000216} = \underline{\underline{-69.5}} \qquad \therefore \ \text{down}$$

Example 13.12 *Compute the reactions and draw the bending-moment diagram for the beam in Example 13.6, due to the following support movements:*

Point a, 0.02 ft down
Point b, 0.04 ft down
Point c, 0.05 ft down
Point d, 0
$E = 30 \times 10^3$ *kips per sq in.*

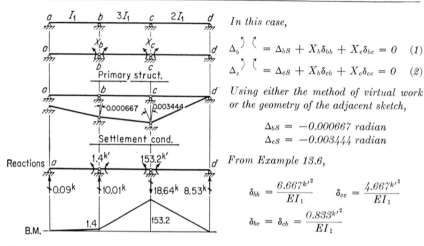

In this case,

$$\Delta_b{}^{)}{}^{(} = \Delta_b S + X_b \delta_{bb} + X_c \delta_{bc} = 0 \quad (1)$$

$$\Delta_c{}^{)}{}^{(} = \Delta_c S + X_b \delta_{cb} + X_c \delta_{cc} = 0 \quad (2)$$

Using either the method of virtual work or the geometry of the adjacent sketch,

$$\Delta_{bS} = -0.000667 \text{ radian}$$
$$\Delta_{cS} = -0.003444 \text{ radian}$$

From Example 13.6,

$$\delta_{bb} = \frac{6.667^{k'^2}}{EI_1} \qquad \delta_{cc} = \frac{4.667^{k'^2}}{EI_1}$$

$$\delta_{bc} = \delta_{cb} = \frac{0.833^{k'^2}}{EI_1}$$

Upon substituting these values, Eqs. (1) and (2) become

$$6.667X_b + 0.833X_c = 0.000667EI_1$$
$$0.833X_b + 4.667X_c = 0.003444EI_1$$

from which, since

$$EI_1 = (30 \times 10^3 \times 144)^{k''^2} \left(\frac{1,000}{144^2}\right)^{'4} = 0.208 \times 10^{6\ k'^2}$$

$$X_b = +0.00000685EI_1 = +1.4$$
$$X_c = +0.000736EI_1 = +153.2$$

The reactions and BM diagram may then easily be computed.

13.6 General Remarks Concerning Selection of Redundants.

From the previous discussion, we recognize that there is considerable latitude in selecting redundants, the only restriction being that they shall be selected so that a *stable* primary structure remains. By proper selection of the redundants, however, we may minimize the numerical computations. This objective may be achieved by adhering to the two following policies:

1. Take advantage of any symmetry of the structure.

2. Select the primary structure so that the effect of any of the various loading conditions is localized as much as possible.

Consideration of several alternative selections of the redundants for the continuous truss shown in Fig. 13.5 will illustrate the validity of these statements. This structure is indeterminate to the second degree. Any selection of the redundants will involve two equations of the following form:

$$\Delta_a = \Delta_{ao} + X_a \delta_{aa} + X_b \delta_{ab} = 0$$
$$\Delta_b = \Delta_{bo} + X_a \delta_{ba} + X_b \delta_{bb} = 0 \qquad (a)$$

Only the following five different deflection terms are involved, since δ_{ab} equals δ_{ba}:

$$(1)(\Delta_{ao}) = \sum F_a F_o \frac{L}{AE} \qquad (1)(\delta_{aa}) = \sum F_a^2 \frac{L}{AE}$$

$$(1)(\Delta_{bo}) = \sum F_b F_o \frac{L}{AE} \qquad (1)(\delta_{bb}) = \sum F_b^2 \frac{L}{AE} \qquad (b)$$

$$(1)(\delta_{ab}) = \sum F_a F_b \frac{L}{AE}$$

Before these terms can be evaluated, F_o, F_a, and F_b bar forces must be computed.

If the structure is symmetrical and if symmetrical redundants are selected, then the F_b forces can be obtained from the F_a forces by symmetry. Further, δ_{bb} will be equal to δ_{aa} in such a case, leaving only four deflection terms to be evaluated. The evaluation of these terms will involve less computation if the redundants are selected so as to restrict the effect of the various loading conditions to as few bars as possible. The latter will be true whether or not the structure is symmetrical.

All three alternative selections of the redundants shown in Fig. 13.5 take advantage of symmetry. The various loading conditions affect the portions of the structure indicated in each case. Comparison of these primary structures shows clearly that

ACTUAL STRUCTURE

PRIMARY STRUCTURE NO. 1

PRIMARY STRUCTURE NO. 2

PRIMARY STRUCTURE NO. 3

Figure 13.5 Selection of redundants

selection 3 is the best since it is most effective in localizing the effects of the various loading conditions.

There are several other items to be noted at this time. In the discussion of Example 13.5, it was pointed out that the shear and moment are statically determinate in a straight bar which is hinged at both ends. If such a bar is cut, only its axial force may be statically indeterminate and, therefore, considered as a redundant. On the other hand, the shear, moment, and axial force are often all statically indeterminate in a member that is rigidly connected at its ends to the rest of the structure. If such a member is cut, the shear, moment, and axial force may all be considered as redundants, provided that a stable structure remains when the restraints corresponding to all three of these elements are removed (as an illustration, see Example 13.14).

13.7 Analysis of Statically Indeterminate Structures, Using Castigliano's Second Theorem; Theorem of Least Work. The previous approach to the analysis of an indeterminate structure involves writing superposition equations for the deflections of the points of application of the redundants. Instead of doing this, however, expressions for these deflections may be set up, using Castigliano's second theorem. The latter approach is actually very similar to the former. It is a somewhat more automatic procedure, however, and is therefore preferred by some students and engineers. Since Castigliano's theorem should really be limited to the computation of the deflections produced simply by loads on the structure, this method lacks the generality of the superposition-equation approach.

Consider, for example, the indeterminate beam shown in Fig. 13.3. After the degree of indeterminacy has been established and the redundant and the resulting primary structure have been selected, the deflection of the point of application of redundant X_b may then be evaluated by using Castigliano's second theorem. In this particular case, only bending deformation is involved; therefore,

$$W_I = \sum \int M^2 \frac{ds}{2EI}$$

but
$$\frac{\partial W_I}{\partial X_b} = \Delta_b^{\dagger} \tag{a}$$

Since point b on the actual structure does not deflect, Δ_b on the primary structure must equal zero. As a result,

$$\frac{\partial W_I}{\partial X_b} = \sum \int M \frac{\partial M}{\partial X_b} \frac{ds}{EI} = 0 \tag{b}$$

However, M, being equal to the total bending moment on the primary structure due to all causes, may be expressed as being the superposition of the contribution of the applied load only and the contribution of the redundant X_b. Thus,

$$M = M_o + X_b M_b \qquad \frac{\partial M}{\partial X_b} = M_b \tag{c}$$

Equation (b), therefore, becomes

$$\sum \int M_o M_b \frac{ds}{EI} + X_b \sum \int M_b^2 \frac{ds}{EI} = 0 \qquad (d)$$

It is easy to evaluate these integrals for the primary structure and then solve for X_b.

If the superposition approach is used in this example, Δ_{bo} and δ_{bb} may be evaluated by the method of virtual work and found to be

$$(1)(\Delta_{bo}) = \sum \int M_o M_b \frac{ds}{EI} \qquad (1)(\delta_{bb}) = \sum \int M_b^2 \frac{ds}{EI} \qquad (e)$$

From Eqs. (e) it is immediately apparent that Eq. (d) is actually a statement that

$$\Delta_{bo} + X_b \delta_{bb} = 0 \qquad (f)$$

Thus, if the method of virtual work is used as a basis for evaluating Δ_{bo} and δ_{bb} in the superposition-equation approach, the two methods are essentially identical.

The above illustration involves a structure that is statically indeterminate to only the first degree. In more highly indeterminate structures, the procedure is essentially the same. After selecting the n redundants and the resulting primary structure, express the displacement of the point of application of each redundant by n separate applications of Castigliano's second theorem. This will result in n simultaneous equations involving the n redundants, the value of which may then be obtained by simultaneous solution of the equations. The procedure for analyzing a multiply redundant frame in this manner is illustrated by Example 13.14.

In the examples of Art. 13.8, equations comparable to Eq. (b) are evaluated in a slightly different manner. Thus it is possible to use Castigliano's theorem somewhat more automatically and effectively in certain problems. The procedure suggested in the above illustration may likewise be used to advantage in certain other problems. In cases of the latter type, however, there is no advantage to using the Castigliano approach instead of superposition equations.

If in the analysis of indeterminate structures the deflection of the point of application of a redundant is zero, then applying Castigliano's theorem as in Eq. (a) reduces to the statement that the first partial derivative of the strain energy with respect to that redundant is equal to zero. This is equivalent to stating that the value of the redundant must be such as to minimize the strain energy. This special case of Castigliano's second theorem is often called the **theorem of least work** and may be stated as follows:

In a statically indeterminate structure, if there are no support movements and no change of temperature, the redundants must be such as to make the strain energy a minimum.

13.8 Examples Illustrating Stress Analysis Using Castigliano's Second Theorem. The examples that follow have been chosen primarily to illustrate the use of Castigliano's second theorem in the stress analysis of indeterminate structures. If, in each case, we solved the problem by the superposition-equation approach, using the method of virtual work to evaluate the various deflection terms, we should find that the actual computations would be essentially the same as those involved in the Castigliano solution. The only difference in the two approaches lies in the somewhat more automatic manner of setting up the solution when the Castigliano approach is used.

There is a difference between the two approaches that is worthy of note. **In a Castigliano solution, the redundants carry their own units throughout a solution.** For example, in Eq. (a), X_b must be in kips if W_I is in kip-feet in order that the change in W_I divided by the change in X_b shall equal Δ_b in feet. As a result, if X_b is in kips, M_b must have units of kip-feet per kip if the units in Eqs. (c) are to be consistent. If it is recognized, therefore, that the redundants in a Castigliano solution carry their own units, dimensional checks should be consistent at all times.

Strictly speaking, Castigliano's theorem is applicable only when the deflection of the structure is caused by loads. It is possible, however, to handle the stress analysis of an indeterminate structure for the effect of temperature change, settlement of supports, etc., by proceeding as follows: Select the primary structure, and temporarily remove all the redundants. Now allow the temperature change or settlement to take place on the primary structure. Compute the resulting displacements of the points of application of the redundants on this primary structure. Such computations may be performed by means of the method of virtual work or some other suitable method. Now apply the redundants. As they are applied, they must restore their points of application to their correct positions. Castigliano's theorem may be used to evaluate the deflections produced by the redundants. Substituting the previously computed values for the restoring deflections, we thereby obtain equations containing only the redundants as the unknowns, which may then be obtained by simultaneous solution of these equations. While this procedure is often not so straightforward as that of the superposition-equation approach, there are nevertheless instances where it may be used advantageously.

Example 13.13 *Compute the bar forces in the members of this truss. Cross-sectional areas in square inches shown in parentheses. $E = 30 \times 10^3$ kips per sq in.*

Truss is indeterminate to first degree. Select force in bar bd as the redundant.

$$W_I = \sum \frac{F^2 L}{2AE} \qquad \frac{\partial W_I}{\partial X_1} = \Delta_1 \bigg\uparrow = 0$$

$$\therefore \frac{\partial W_I}{\partial X_1} = \frac{1}{E} \sum \frac{FL}{A} \frac{\partial F}{\partial X_1} = 0$$

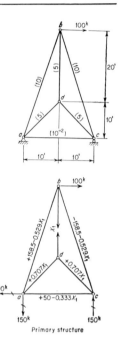

Bar	L	A	$\dfrac{L}{A}$	F	$\dfrac{\partial F}{\partial X_1}$	$F \dfrac{L}{A} \dfrac{\partial F}{\partial X_1}$
Units	$'$	$''^2$	$'/''^2$	k	k/k	$k'/''^2$
ab	31.7	10	3.17	$+158.5 - 0.529X_1$	-0.529	$-265 \quad + 0.886X_1$
bc	31.7	10	3.17	$-158.5 - 0.529X_1$	-0.529	$+265 \quad + 0.886X_1$
ca	20	10	2	$+ 50 \quad - 0.333X_1$	-0.333	$-33.3 + 0.222X_1$
ad	14.1	5	2.83	$+ 0.707X_1$	$+0.707$	$+ 1.414X_1$
bd	20	5	4	$+ 1.0 \quad X_1$	$+1.0$	$+ 4.000X_1$
cd	14.1	5	2.83	$+ 0.707X_1$	$+0.707$	$+ 1.414X_1$
Σ						$-33.3 + 8.822X_1$

$$\therefore \; -33.3 + 8.822X_1 = 0 \qquad X_1 = +3.78 \text{ kips}$$

The remaining bar forces may be found easily by statics or by extending the above tabulation.

Example 13.14   *Solve this frame using Castigliano's theorem.   Include the effect of deformation due to both axial force and bending.*

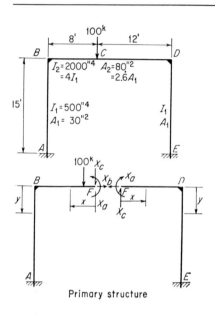

Primary structure

This frame is indeterminate to the third degree. Cut the girder at mid-span, and select the moment, axial force, and shear as the three redundants X_a, X_b, and X_c.

$$W_I = \sum \int M^2 \frac{ds}{2EI} + \sum \frac{F^2 L}{2AE}$$

But,

$$\frac{\partial W_I}{\partial X_a} = \Delta_a^{\,\curvearrowright\,\curvearrowleft} = 0$$

$$\frac{\partial W_I}{X_b} = \Delta_b^{\,\rightarrow\,\leftarrow} = 0$$

$$\frac{\partial W_I}{\partial X_c} = \Delta^{\,\downarrow\uparrow} = 0$$

Therefore, *differentiating and canceling out E,*

$$\sum \int M \frac{\partial M}{\partial X_a} \frac{ds}{I} + \sum F \frac{L}{A} \frac{\partial F}{\partial X_a} = 0 \quad (1)$$

$$\sum \int M \frac{\partial M}{\partial X_b} \frac{ds}{I} + \sum F \frac{L}{A} \frac{\partial F}{\partial X_b} = 0 \quad (2)$$

$$\sum \int M \frac{\partial M}{\partial X_c} \frac{ds}{I} + \sum F \frac{L}{A} \frac{\partial F}{\partial X_c} = 0 \quad (3)$$

From F to C,

$$0 < x < 2 \qquad M = X_a - xX_c \qquad \frac{\partial M}{\partial X_a} = 1 \qquad \frac{\partial M}{\partial X_b} = 0 \qquad \frac{\partial M}{\partial X_c} = -x$$

$$L = 2' \qquad F = X_b \qquad \frac{\partial F}{\partial X_a} = 0 \qquad \frac{\partial F}{\partial X_b} = 1 \qquad \frac{\partial F}{\partial X_c} = 0$$

From C to B,

$$2 < x < 10 \qquad M = X_a - xX_c - 100(x - 2) \qquad \frac{\partial M}{\partial X_a} = 1 \qquad \frac{\partial M}{\partial X_b} = 0 \qquad \frac{\partial M}{\partial X_c} = -x$$

$$L = 8' \qquad F = X_b \qquad \frac{\partial F}{\partial X_a} = \frac{\partial F}{\partial X_c} = 0 \qquad \frac{\partial F}{\partial X_b} = 1$$

From B to A,

$$0 < y < 15 \qquad M = X_a - yX_b - 10X_c - 800 \qquad \frac{\partial M}{\partial X_a} = 1 \qquad \frac{\partial M}{\partial X_b} = -y \qquad \frac{\partial M}{\partial X_c} = -10$$

$$L = 15' \qquad F = -100 - X_c \qquad \frac{\partial F}{\partial X_a} = \frac{\partial F}{\partial X_b} = 0 \qquad \frac{\partial F}{\partial X_c} = -1$$

From F to D,

$$0 < x < 10 \qquad M = X_a + xX_c \qquad \frac{\partial M}{\partial X_a} = 1 \qquad \frac{\partial M}{\partial X_b} = 0 \qquad \frac{\partial M}{\partial X_c} = x$$

$$L = 10' \qquad F = X_b \qquad \frac{\partial F}{\partial X_a} = \frac{\partial F}{\partial X_c} = 0 \qquad \frac{\partial F}{\partial X_b} = 1$$

From D to E,

$$0 < y < 15 \qquad M = X_a - yX_b + 10X_c \qquad \frac{\partial M}{\partial X_a} = 1 \qquad \frac{\partial M}{\partial X_b} = -y \qquad \frac{\partial M}{\partial X_c} = 10$$

$$L = 15' \qquad F = X_c \qquad \frac{\partial F}{\partial X_a} = \frac{\partial F}{\partial X_b} = 0 \qquad \frac{\partial F}{\partial X_c} = 1$$

Setting up Eq. (1),

$$\int_0^2 (X_a - xX_c)(1)\frac{dx}{4I_1} + \int_2^{10} (X_a - xX_c - 100x + 200)(1)\frac{dx}{4I_1}$$

$$+ \int_0^{15} (X_a - yX_b - 10X_c - 800)(1)\frac{dy}{I_1} + \int_0^{10} (X_a + xX_c)(1)\frac{dx}{4I_1}$$

$$+ \int_0^{15} (X_a + 10X_c - yX_b)(1)\frac{dy}{I_1} = 0$$

Combining, canceling, and integrating, we obtain

$$35X_a - 225X_b = 12,800 \qquad\qquad (1)$$

Now setting up Eq. (2)

$$\int_0^{15} (X_a - yX_b - 10X_c - 800)(-y)\frac{dy}{I_1} + \int_0^{15} (X_a - yX_b + 10X_c)(-y)\frac{dy}{I}$$

$$+ X_b \frac{(1)(10)}{2.6A_1} + X_b \frac{(1)(10)}{2.6A_1} = 0$$

Again combining and canceling before integrating, we obtain

$$(-225)X_a + \left(2,250 + 7.5\frac{I_1}{A_1}\right)X_b = -90,000$$

However, $\qquad\qquad \dfrac{I_1}{A_1} = \left(\dfrac{500}{144^2}\right)\left(\dfrac{144}{30}\right) = \dfrac{50}{432}$

and therefore $\qquad\qquad -225X_a + 2,250.87X_b = -90,000 \qquad\qquad (2)$

In a similar manner, Eq. (3) reduces to

$$\left(3,166.7 + 30\frac{I_1}{A_1}\right)X_c = -\left(125,866.7 + 1,500\frac{I_1}{A_1}\right)$$

$$3,170.14X_c = -126,040.2 \qquad\qquad (3)$$

Solving Eqs. (1), (2), and (3),

$$X_a = +304.2^{k'}$$
$$X_b = - \quad 9.56^k$$
$$X_c = - \quad 39.76^k$$

If the effect of axial deformation were neglected, all the terms containing A would be omitted.
Then, we should find

$$X_a = +304.0^{k'}$$
$$X_b = - \quad 9.60^k$$
$$X_c = - \quad 39.74^k$$

Discussion:

These results indicate that the effect of axial deformation may be neglected in comparison with the effect of bending in the rigid-frame type of structure.

Example 13.15   *Compute the force in the tie rod.   Include the effect of both axial force and bending.*

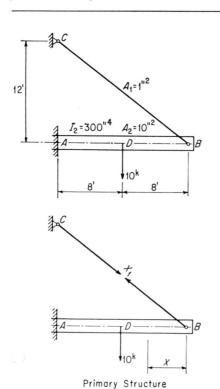

Primary Structure

This structure is indeterminate to the first degree.   Select the tie-rod force as the redundant.   Then

$$\frac{\partial W_I}{\partial X_1} = \Delta_1 \searrow\nwarrow = 0$$

$$\frac{\partial W_I}{\partial X_1} = \sum \int M \frac{\partial M}{\partial X_1} \frac{dx}{EI}$$

$$+ \sum F \frac{\partial F}{\partial X_1} \frac{L}{AE} = 0 \quad (1)$$

From B to C,

$$M = 0 \qquad F = X_1 \qquad \frac{\partial F}{\partial X_1} = 1$$

$$L = 20'$$

From B to D,

$$M = 0.6xX_1 \qquad F = -0.8X_1$$

$$\frac{\partial M}{\partial X_1} = 0.6x \qquad \frac{\partial F}{\partial X_1} = -0.8$$

$$0 < x < 8 \qquad L = 8'$$

From D to A,

$$M = 0.6xX_1$$
$$\quad - 10(x - 8) \qquad F = -0.8X_1$$

$$\frac{\partial M}{\partial X_1} = 0.6x \qquad \frac{\partial F}{\partial X_1} = -0.8$$

$$8 < x < 16 \qquad L = 8'$$

Evaluating Eq. (1),

$$\int_0^8 (0.6xX_1)(0.6x) \frac{dx}{I_2} + \int_8^{16} (0.6xX_1 - 10x + 80)(0.6x) \frac{dx}{I_2} + \frac{X_1(20)(1)}{A_1}$$

$$+ \frac{(-0.8X_1)(16)(-0.8)}{A_2} = 0$$

from which $\qquad X_1\left(491.52 + 20\frac{I_2}{A_1} + 10.24\frac{I_2}{A_2}\right) = 2,560$

$$\frac{I_2}{A_1} = \frac{25}{12} \qquad \frac{I_2}{A_2} = \frac{5}{24}$$

$$\therefore 535.32X_1 = 2,560$$
$$\therefore X_1 = \underline{+4.80^k}$$

whereas, if the axial force term were neglected,

$$X_1 = \underline{+5.20^k}$$

13.9   Development of the Three-moment Equation. The *three-moment equation* was first presented in 1857 by the French engineer Clapeyron. This equation is a relationship that exists between the moments at three points in a continuous member. It is particularly helpful in solving for the moments at the supports of indeterminate beams.

Designate three points on a continuous member as L, C, and R as shown in Fig. 13.6. Suppose that the moment of inertia is constant between point L and C and equal to I_L and likewise constant between C and R and equal to I_R.* The member is assumed to be straight initially,

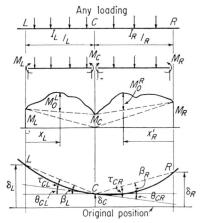

Figure 13.6   Derivation of three-moment equation

and the deflections from the original position are assumed to be δ_L, δ_C, and δ_R at points L, C, and R, respectively—all to be considered positive when upward as shown.

Let the moments at these three points be M_L, M_C, and M_R. Bending moments are to be considered plus when causing tension on the lower fibers of a member. The bending-moment diagram for the portion LC or CR may be considered to be that resulting from superposition of three separate effects: the contribution of each of the end moments acting separately, which is given by the ordinates of the triangles indicated by the dashed lines, and the contribution of the applied load acting by itself with the end moments removed, which is given by the ordinates M_o^L in the portion LC and by M_o^R in the portion CR.

From the sketch of the elastic curve,

$$\theta_{CL} = \beta_L - \tau_{CL} \qquad \text{and} \qquad \theta_{CR} = \tau_{CR} - \beta_R$$

---

* Theoretically it is possible, though cumbersome, to include the effect of variable I in this development.

However, since the elastic curve is continuous through point C,

$$\theta_{CL} = \theta_{CR}$$

Hence, $$\beta_L - \tau_{CL} = \tau_{CR} - \beta_R \qquad (a)$$

Since these are all small angles, it is permissible to consider that

$$\beta_L = \frac{\delta_L - \delta_C}{l_L} \qquad \beta_R = \frac{\delta_R - \delta_C}{l_R} \qquad (b)$$

If the bending-moment diagram were converted into an M/EI diagram, τ_{CL} and τ_{CR} could be evaluated easily by means of the second moment-area theorem,

$$\tau_{CL} = \frac{1}{EI_L l_L} \left(\frac{M_L l_L^2}{6} + \frac{M_C l_L^2}{3} + \int_0^{l_L} M_o^L x_L \, dx_L \right)$$
$$\tau_{CR} = \frac{1}{EI_R l_R} \left(\frac{M_R l_R^2}{6} + \frac{M_C l_R^2}{3} + \int_0^{l_R} M_o^R x_R' \, dx_R' \right) \qquad (c)$$

Let $$(\mathfrak{M}_o)_L = \int_0^{l_L} M_o^L x_L \, dx_L \qquad (\mathfrak{M}_o)_R = \int_0^{l_R} M_o^R x_R' \, dx_R' \qquad (13.4)$$

Substituting from Eq. (13.4) in Eqs. (c) and then from Eqs. (b) and (c) in Eq. (a), we obtain the so-called *three-moment equation*,

$$M_L \frac{l_L}{I_L} + 2M_C \left(\frac{l_L}{I_L} + \frac{l_R}{I_R} \right) + M_R \frac{l_R}{I_R} = - \frac{\mathcal{L}_o}{I_L} - \frac{\mathcal{R}_o}{I_R}$$
$$+ 6E \left[\frac{\delta_L}{l_L} - \delta_C \left(\frac{1}{l_L} + \frac{1}{l_R} \right) + \frac{\delta_R}{l_R} \right] \qquad (13.5)$$

where the load terms are

$$\mathcal{L}_o = + \frac{6(\mathfrak{M}_o)_L}{l_L} \qquad \mathcal{R}_o = + \frac{6(\mathfrak{M}_o)_R}{l_R} \qquad (13.6)$$

In using these equations, note particularly that:

1. M_L, M_C, and M_R are plus when causing tension on the lower fibers.
2. δ_L, δ_C, and δ_R are plus when upward from the original position.
3. $\mathcal{L}_o$ and $\mathcal{R}_o$ are load terms dependent on the applied load in the spans LC and CR, respectively.
4. The M_o diagram for a member is the bending-moment diagram drawn for the member if it is assumed to be a simple end-supported beam. $(\mathfrak{M}_o)_L$ represents the static moment of the area under this diagram, taken about an axis through the left end, while $(\mathfrak{M}_o)_R$ represents the static moment about an axis through the right end. The sign of both these static moments depends simply on the sign of the ordinates of the M_o diagram.

In the special case where $I_L = I_R = I$, Eq. (13.5) simplifies to

$$M_L l_L + 2M_C(l_L + l_R) + M_R l_R = -\mathcal{L}_o - \mathcal{R}_o$$
$$+ 6EI\left[\frac{\delta_L}{l_L} - \delta_C\left(\frac{1}{l_L} + \frac{1}{l_R}\right) + \frac{\delta_R}{l_R}\right] \quad (13.7)$$

The load terms in the cases of full uniform load and concentrated load are shown in Fig. 13.7.

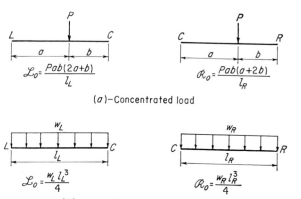

(a)–Concentrated load

(b)–Full uniformly distributed load

Figure 13.7   Load terms

13.10   Application of Three-moment Equation.   The three-moment equation is applicable to any three points on a beam as long as there are no discontinuities, such as hinges in the beam within this portion.   In applying the equation to a continuous beam, if we select three successive support points as being L, C, and R, the deflection terms on the right-hand side of the equation will be equal either to zero or to the known movements of the support points.   We thus obtain an equation involving the moments at the support points as the only unknowns.

In this manner, we may write an independent equation for any three successive support points along a continuous beam.   We shall obtain n independent equations involving n unknown support moments, which may then be obtained from the simultaneous solution of these equations.   There is a slight ambiguity in handling a fixed end on a continuous beam, but the technique of solving such problems is explained in the illustrative examples that follow.

The analysis of continuous beams by this method is straightforward.   Be careful, however, to follow the sign convention noted in Art. 13.9.   Likewise, be careful to use consistent units, particularly when there are movements of the supports.

Example 13.16   *Compute the reactions and draw the bending-moment diagram for this beam.*

Apply Eq. (13.5), taking a, b, and c as L, C, and R.

$$M_a = 0 \qquad M_b = ? \qquad M_c = 0$$

$$\delta_a = \delta_b = \delta_c = 0$$

$$\mathcal{L}_0 = \frac{(30)(6)(9)(21)}{15} = 2{,}268$$

$$\mathcal{R}_0 = \frac{(4)(18)^3}{4} = 5{,}832$$

$$0 + 2M_b\left(\frac{15}{I} + \frac{18}{1.5I}\right) + 0$$

$$= \frac{-2{,}268}{I} - \frac{5{,}832}{1.5I}$$

$$54M_b = -6{,}156 \qquad M_b = -114^{k'}$$

Example 13.17   *Compute the moments at the support points of this beam.   E and I are constant.*

In this case, there are four unknown moments, M_a, M_b, M_c, and M_d. Four equations are therefore required. A fixed end may be handled by replacing it by an additional span of essentially zero length, as shown. The required equations may then be obtained by applying Eq. (13.7) four separate times, considering L, C, and R in turn, as indicated.

$$\delta_{a'} = \delta_a = \delta_b = \delta_c = \delta_d = \delta_{d'} = 0$$

Consider a', a, and b as L, C, and R.

$$\mathcal{L}_0 = 0 \qquad \mathcal{R}_0 = \frac{(5)(8)(12)(32)}{20} + \frac{(6)(15)(5)(25)}{20} = 1{,}330.5 \qquad M'_a = 0$$

$$\therefore 40M_a + 20M_b = -1{,}330.5 \tag{1}$$

Consider a, b, and c as L, C, and R.

$$\mathcal{L}_0 = \frac{(5)(8)(12)(28)}{20} + \frac{(6)(15)(5)(35)}{20} = 1{,}459.5 \qquad \mathcal{R}_0 = \frac{(0.9)(18)^3}{4} = 1{,}312.2$$

$$\therefore 20M_a + 76M_b + 18M_c = -2{,}771.7 \tag{2}$$

Consider b, c, and d as L, C, and R.

$$\mathcal{L}_0 = 1{,}312.2 \qquad \mathcal{R}_0 = 0 \qquad \therefore 18M_b + 66M_c + 15M_d = -1{,}312.2 \tag{3}$$

Consider c, d, and d' as L, C, and R.

$$\mathcal{L}_0 = \mathcal{R}_0 = 0 \qquad M'_d = 0 \qquad \therefore 15M_c + 30M_d = 0 \qquad (4)$$

Solving Eqs. (1), (2), (3), and (4) simultaneously leads to the following values for the unknown moments:

$$M_a = -19.17^{k'} \qquad M_b = -28.20^{k'} \qquad M_c = -13.74^{k'} \qquad M_d = +6.87^{k'}$$

Example 13.18 *Compute the reactions and draw the bending-moment diagram for this beam, due to the following support settlement:*

Support a rotates 0.005 radian clockwise
Support b settles 0.0208 ft down
$E = 30 \times 10^3$ *kips per sq in.*

Consider a', a, and b as L, C, and R.

$$M'_a = 0 \qquad \delta_a = 0$$
$$\mathcal{L}_0 = \mathcal{R}_0 = 0 \qquad \delta_b = -0.0208'$$

As a result of rotation of support at a, δ'_a/l_L approaches $+0.005$. Applying Eq. (13.5),

$$2M_a\left(\frac{15}{I_1}\right) + M_b\left(\frac{15}{I_1}\right) = 6E(0.005)$$

$$+ 6E\left(-\frac{0.0208}{15}\right)$$

$$\therefore 30M_a + 15M_b = 0.02166EI_1 \qquad (1)$$

Consider a, b, and c as L, C, and R.

$$M_c = 0 \qquad \delta_b = -0.0208'$$
$$\delta_a = 0 \qquad \delta_c = 0$$

Applying Eq. (13.5),

$$M_a\left(\frac{15}{I_1}\right) + 2M_b\left(\frac{15}{I_1} + \frac{15}{4/3 I_1}\right)$$

$$= -6E(-0.0208)\left(\frac{1}{15} + \frac{1}{15}\right)$$

$$\therefore 15M_a + 52.5M_b = +0.01664EI_1 \qquad (2)$$

Solving Eqs. (1) and (2) simultaneously and substituting $EI_1 = 31.25 \times 10^4$ kip-ft²,

$$M_a = +0.000658EI_1 = +205.8^{k'}$$
$$M_b = +0.0001291EI_1 = +40.6^{k'}$$

13.11 Development of the Slope-deflection Equation.

The *slope-deflection method* was presented by Prof. G. A. Maney in 1915 as a general method to be used in the analysis of rigid-joint structures. This method extended the use of equations, originally proposed by Manderla and Mohr, for computing secondary stresses in trusses. It is useful in its own right; and even more important, it provides an excellent means of introducing the method of moment distribution.

The following fundamental equations are derived by means of the moment-area theorems. Thus, these equations consider deformation caused by bending moment but neglect that due to shear and axial force. Since the effect of axial force and shear deformation on the stress analysis of most indeterminate beams and frames is very small, the error that results from using these equations as a basis for the slope-deflection method of analysis is also very small (for corroboration, see the results of Example 13.14). **The fundamental slope-deflection equation is an expression for the moment on the end of a member in terms of four quantities, viz., the rotation of the tangent at each end of the elastic curve of the member, the rotation of the chord joining the ends of the elastic curve, and the external loads applied to the member.** It is convenient in the application of this equation to use the following sign convention:

1. Moments acting on the ends of a member are positive when **clockwise.**

2. Let θ be the rotation of the tangent to the elastic curve at the end of a member referred to the original direction of the member. The angle θ is positive when the tangent to the elastic curve has rotated **clockwise** from its original direction.

3. Let ψ be the rotation of the chord joining the ends of the elastic curve referred to the original direction of the member. The angle ψ is positive when the chord of the elastic curve has rotated **clockwise** from its original direction.

Figure 13.8 Derivation of slope-deflection equation

In designating the end moments, two subscripts will be used; these subscripts together designate the member under consideration, and the first one designates the end of the member to which the moment is applied. For example, M_{AB} designates the moment acting on the A end of member AB; M_{BA}, the moment on the B end of that member. The θ angles will be designated by one subscript indicating the end of the member. The ψ angles will be designated by two subscripts indicating the chord and, likewise, the member.

Using the above notation and convention, consider a member AB that has a constant E and I^* throughout its length and that is initially straight. Suppose that this member is acted upon by the positive end moments M_{AB} and M_{BA} and any condition of an applied load, as shown in Fig. 13.8. Let AB be the elastic curve of this beam and $A'B'$ represent its original unstrained position. θ_A, θ_B, and ψ_{AB} are positive as shown.

The bending-moment diagram for this member may be considered to be the superposition of three separate effects: the contribution of each of the end moments acting separately, which is given by the ordinates of the triangular portions, M' and M'', and the contribution of the applied load acting by itself with the end moments removed, which is given by the ordinates M_o. In other words, the M_o ordinates are the ordinates of the simple-beam bending-moment diagram. The total bending moment at any point will be the algebraic sum of M_o, M', and M'', but for this present derivation it is easier to consider these three contributions separately.

If the bending-moment diagram is converted into an M/EI diagram, Δ_A and Δ_B may be evaluated by the second moment-area theorem. Then,

$$\Delta_A = -\frac{L^2}{6EI}M_{AB} + \frac{L^2}{3EI}M_{BA} - \frac{(\mathfrak{M}_o)_A}{EI} \qquad (a)$$

$$\Delta_B = \frac{L^2}{3EI}M_{AB} - \frac{L^2}{6EI}M_{BA} + \frac{(\mathfrak{M}_o)_B}{EI} \qquad (b)$$

in which $(\mathfrak{M}_o)_A$ is the static moment about an axis through A of the area under the M_o portion of the bending-moment diagram and $(\mathfrak{M}_o)_B$ is a corresponding static moment about an axis through B.

Realizing that the angles and deformation shown in Fig. 13.8 are actually so small that an angle, its sine, and its tangent may all be considered equal, we see from the figure that

$$\frac{\Delta_A}{L} = \tau_B = \theta_B - \psi_{AB} \qquad \frac{\Delta_B}{L} = \tau_A = \theta_A - \psi_{AB} \qquad (c)$$

Solving Eqs. (a) and (b) simultaneously for M_{AB} and M_{BA} and substituting in the resulting expressions for Δ_A/L and Δ_B/L from Eqs. (c), we obtain

$$M_{AB} = \frac{2EI}{L}(2\theta_A + \theta_B - 3\psi_{AB}) + \frac{2}{L^2}[(\mathfrak{M}_o)_A - 2(\mathfrak{M}_o)_B]$$

$$M_{BA} = \frac{2EI}{L}(2\theta_B + \theta_A - 3\psi_{AB}) + \frac{2}{L^2}[2(\mathfrak{M}_o)_A - (\mathfrak{M}_o)_B] \qquad (d)$$

Up to this point, the condition of loading has not been defined, and Eqs. (d) are valid for any condition of transverse loading. The last term

_____

* It is theoretically possible, of course, to set up the slope-deflection equation considering the effect of variable I.

in brackets in each of these equations is a function of the type of loading,

Simple Beam B.M.

Figure 13.9 Concentrated load

and it is important that its physical significance be recognized. Suppose that θ_A, θ_B, and ψ_{AB} are all equal to zero. Then the last terms of Eqs. (d) are, respectively, equal to the moment at the A end and the moment at the B end of the member. If, however, θ_A, θ_B, and ψ_{AB} are all equal to zero, it means physically that both ends of the member are completely fixed against rotation or translation and, therefore, that this member is what we call a fixed-end beam. These last terms of Eqs. (d) are therefore equal to the so-called "fixed end moments." Calling fixed end moments FEM,

$$\text{FEM}_{AB} = \frac{2}{L^2}\left[(\mathfrak{M}_o)_A - 2(\mathfrak{M}_o)_B\right]$$

$$\text{FEM}_{BA} = \frac{2}{L^2}\left[2(\mathfrak{M}_o)_A - (\mathfrak{M}_o)_B\right]$$

(13.8)

Substituting in Eqs. (d) from Eqs. (13.8), we obtain

$$M_{AB} = \frac{2EI}{L}(2\theta_A + \theta_B - 3\psi_{AB}) + \text{FEM}_{AB}$$

$$M_{BA} = \frac{2EI}{L}(2\theta_B + \theta_A - 3\psi_{AB}) + \text{FEM}_{BA}$$

(13.9)

Closer inspection of Eqs. (13.9) reveals that these two equations can be summarized by one general equation by calling the near end of a member N and the far end F. Also, if we let

$$K_{NF} = \textbf{stiffness factor for member } NF = \frac{I_{NF}}{L_{NF}} \qquad (13.10)$$

then the fundamental slope-deflection equation may be written as follows:

$$M_{NF} = 2EK_{NF}(2\theta_N + \theta_F - 3\psi_{NF}) + \text{FEM}_{NF} \qquad (13.11)$$

Of course, the FEM may easily be determined for any given loading. If, in addition, the rotation of the tangent at each end and the rotation of the chord joining the ends of a member are known, the end moments in the member may easily be computed from Eq. (13.11). In Art. 13.12, the use of this equation in the solution of indeterminate beams and frames is discussed.

The FEM for any given loading may be evaluated by means of Eqs. (13.8) in the following manner:

Concentrated load (see Fig. 13.9):

$$(\mathfrak{M}_o)_A = \frac{Pab}{L}\left[\frac{a}{2}\left(\frac{2a}{3}\right) + \frac{b}{2}\left(a + \frac{b}{3}\right)\right] = \frac{Pab}{6}(2a + b)$$

$$(\mathfrak{M}_o)_B = \frac{Pab}{L}\left[\frac{b}{2}\left(\frac{2b}{3}\right) + \frac{a}{2}\left(b + \frac{a}{3}\right)\right] = \frac{Pab}{6}(2b + a)$$

$$\text{FEM}_{AB} = \frac{2}{L^2}\left[\frac{Pab}{6}(2a + b) - 2\frac{Pab}{6}(2b + a)\right] = -\frac{Pab^2}{L^2}$$

$$\text{FEM}_{BA} = \frac{2}{L^2}\left[2\frac{Pab}{6}(2a + b) - \frac{Pab}{6}(2b + a)\right] = +\frac{Pa^2b}{L^2}$$

(13.12)

Full uniform load (see Fig. 13.10):

$$(\mathfrak{M}_o)_A = (\mathfrak{M}_o)_B = \frac{wL^4}{24}$$

$$\text{FEM}_{AB} = -\frac{wL^2}{12} \qquad \text{FEM}_{BA} = +\frac{wL^2}{12}$$

(13.13)

It will be noted that the proper signs of the FEM work out automatically from these calculations. In most cases, we know the direction of the end moments by inspection, and in this way we are usually able to verify the signs of the FEM.

Note again the sign convention to be used in applying the slope-deflection method. Note also that the above equations have been derived for a member that is initially straight and of constant E and I.

Figure 13.10   Full uniform load   **Figure 13.11**   Isolation of joints

13.12   Application of Slope-deflection Method to Beams and Frames. Consider first the application of the slope-deflection method to continuous-beam problems, such as the beam shown in Fig. 13.11, the supports of which are assumed to be unyielding. Think of this beam as being composed of two members AB and BC rigidly connected together at joint B. We could write expressions for the end moments at each end of each member, using Eq. (13.11). These four end moments M_{AB}, M_{BA}, M_{BC}, and M_{CB} would then be expressed in terms of the θ and ψ angles and the FEM, which could be computed from Eqs. (13.12) and (13.13).

Since the supports are unyielding, we know in this case that θ_A, ψ_{AB}, and ψ_{BC} are all equal to zero. Further, since members BA and BC are rigidly connected together at joint B, the tangent to the elastic curve at the B end of member AB must rotate with respect to its original direction algebraically the same amount θ_B as the tangent at the B end of member BC.   Only the values of θ_B and θ_C are unknown, therefore, and involved in the expressions for the four end moments.   If we could in some way find the values of θ_B and θ_C, we could then compute all the end moments; and, having them, we could compute by statics any other moment, shear, or reaction we desired.   In other words, the stress analysis of this beam would be reduced to a problem in statics if we knew the values of θ_B and θ_C.

In this case, we are able to solve for these two unknowns by virtue of the fact that there are two convenient equations of statics which these end moments must satisfy.   These equations are obtained by isolating joints B and C as shown in Fig. 13.11 and writing the equations $\Sigma M = 0$ for each of these joints.   Thus,

$$\text{From } \Sigma M_B = 0 \qquad M_{BA} + M_{BC} = 0$$
$$\text{From } \Sigma M_C = 0 \qquad M_{CB} = 0$$

By substituting in these two equations the expressions for the end moments obtained by applying Eq. (13.11), we shall obtain two equations involving the two unknowns θ_B and θ_C.   After solving these equations simultaneously for these unknowns, we shall then be able to compute the end moments and complete the stress analysis of the beam.

The actual numerical solution of such a problem is illustrated by Example 13.19.   In Example 13.20, these ideas have been extended and applied to a case where the supports move.

Example 13.19 *Compute the reactions and draw the shear and bending-moment diagrams for this beam. Unyielding supports.*

Analyzing the θ and ψ angles,

$$\theta_a = 0 \qquad \psi_{ab} = \psi_{bc} = 0$$
$$\theta_b = ? \qquad \theta_c = ?$$

$$K_{ab} = \frac{I}{10} = K \qquad K_{bc} = \frac{3I}{15} = 2K$$

$$FEM_{ab} = -\frac{(20)(6)(4)^2}{(10)^2} = -19.2^{k'}$$

$$FEM_{ba} = +\frac{(20)(6)^2(4)}{(10)^2} = +28.8^{k'}$$

$$FEM_{bc} = -\frac{(2)(15)^2}{12} = -37.5^{k'}$$

$$FEM_{cb} = +37.5^{k'} \qquad M_{cd} = -25^{k'}$$

Using Eq. (13.11), write expressions for the end moments

$$M_{ab} = 2EK\theta_b - 19.2$$
$$M_{ba} = 4EK\theta_b + 28.8$$
$$M_{bc} = 8EK\theta_b + 4EK\theta_c - 37.5$$
$$M_{cb} = 8EK\theta_c + 4EK\theta_b + 37.5$$

Isolate joints b and c; write the joint equations; and substitute for M_{ba}, M_{bc}, etc.

$$\Sigma M_b = 0 \qquad M_{ba} + M_{bc} = 0 \qquad \therefore 12EK\theta_b + 4EK\theta_c - 8.7 = 0 \quad (1)$$
$$\Sigma M_c = 0 \qquad M_{cb} - 25 = 0 \qquad \therefore 4EK\theta_b + 8EK\theta_c + 12.5 = 0 \quad (2)$$

Solving Eqs. (1) and (2), we find

$$EK\theta_b = +1.495 \qquad EK\theta_c = -2.31$$

Hence, substituting back in end-moment expressions,

$$M_{ab} = +2.99 - 19.2 = -16.21^{k'} \qquad M_{bc} = +11.96 - 9.24 - 37.5 = -34.78^{k'}$$
$$M_{ba} = +5.98 + 28.8 = +34.78^{k'} \qquad M_{cb} = -18.48 + 5.98 + 37.5 = +25.0^{k'}$$

The remaining results may be computed by statics.

Discussion:

The cantilever portion *cd* adds no complications since the bending moment in this portion is statically determinate. The cantilever does, however, affect the joint equation at joint *c*. When isolating joints, assume unknown moments to be positive (i.e., to act clockwise on the end of the member and therefore counterclockwise on the end of the joint stub). Any known moment, however, should be shown acting with its known value in its known direction.

A convenient way of handling the *K* factor is to select one *K* factor as a standard and express all others in terms of this.

Units will always be consistent if all values are substituted in kip and foot units.

An alternative way of handling the cantilever effect is as follows. For moment equilibrium at any joint m with members connecting it to joints a, b, . . . , j,

$$M_{ma} + M_{mb} + \cdots + M_{mj} = 0$$

If any of these end moments are known, the proper sign and value may be substituted. For example, at joint c, $M_{cb} + M_{cd} = 0$, but $M_{cd} = -25$. Hence, $M_{cb} - 25 = 0$, which checks Eq. (2) above.

Note that the final results satisfy Eqs. (1) and (2). This check does not verify the work prior to setting up these equations, of course.

Example 13.20 Compute the end moments for the beam in Example 13.19 caused only by the following support movements (no load acting):

Support a, vertically 0.01 ft down, rotates 0.001 radian clockwise
Support b, vertically 0.04 ft down
Support c, vertically 0.0175 ft down
Assume $E = 30 \times 10^3$ kips per sq in., $I = 1,000$ in.[4]

In this case,

$$\theta_a = +0.001 \qquad \psi_{ab} = \frac{0.04 - 0.01}{10} = +0.003 \qquad \psi_{bc} = -\frac{(0.04 - 0.0175)}{15}$$

$$= -0.0015$$

but $\qquad\qquad\qquad\qquad \theta_b = ? \qquad and \qquad \theta_c = ?$

There are no loads; therefore all FEM's are zero. Using Eq. (13.11) to write expressions for end moments,

$$M_{ab} = 2EK(0.002 + \theta_b - 0.009) \quad = 2EK\theta_b - 0.014EK$$
$$M_{ba} = 2EK(2\theta_b + 0.001 - 0.009) \quad = 4EK\theta_b - 0.016EK$$
$$M_{bc} = 2E(2K)(2\theta_b + \theta_c + 0.0045) = 8EK\theta_b + 4EK\theta_c + 0.018EK$$
$$M_{cb} = 2E(2K)(2\theta_c + \theta_b + 0.0045) = 4EK\theta_b + 8EK\theta_c + 0.018EK$$

From the joint equations,

$$\Sigma M_b = 0 \qquad M_{ba} + M_{bc} = 0 \qquad 12EK\theta_b + 4EK\theta_c + 0.002EK = 0 \qquad (1)$$
$$\Sigma M_c = 0 \qquad M_{cb} = 0 \qquad 4EK\theta_b + 8EK\theta_c + 0.018EK = 0 \qquad (2)$$

Solving Eqs. (1) and (2) simultaneously,

$$\theta_b = +0.0007 \qquad \theta_c = -0.0026$$

Therefore, substituting back,

$$M_{ab} = -0.0126EK = -262.5^{k'} \qquad M_{bc} = +0.0132EK = +275.0^{k'}$$
$$M_{ba} = -0.0132EK = -275.0^{k'} \qquad M_{cb} = \quad 0 \qquad = \quad 0$$

since $\qquad\qquad EK = 30 \times 10^3 \times 144 \times \dfrac{1,000}{144^2 \times 10} = 20,833$ kip-ft

Discussion:

In this type of problem, be particularly careful to insert the correct signs for the known θ and ψ angles. Also be careful to keep units consistent.

Consider the rigid frames shown in Figs. 13.12*a* to *d*. Suppose that we neglect the change in length of the members due to axial force, as is usually permissible in rigid frames, and consider only the effect of bending deformation. With this assumption, it is easy to show in each of these four frames that the ψ angle is zero for every member (with the exception of the statically determinate cantilever portions, of course). In Fig. 13.12*b*, for example, neglecting the axial change in length of members AB and BE, it is obvious that joint B cannot move unless the supports move. If joint B does not move, we can reason in the same manner that joint C

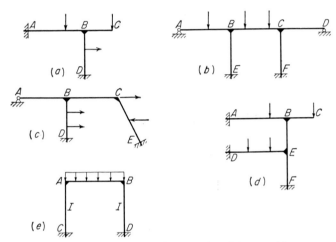

Figure 13.12   Typical rigid frames involving no sidesway

cannot move. The ψ angles must therefore be zero for all five members AB, BC, CD, BE, and CF.

At any particular joint, the θ angle will be the same for the ends of all members that are rigidly connected together at that joint. In the case of this frame, therefore, there will be only four unknown θ angles, θ_A, θ_B, θ_C, and θ_D. Hence, using Eq. (13.11), we shall obtain expressions for the end moments involving these four θ angles as the only unknowns. Since we may write a joint equation $\Sigma M = 0$ at each joint where there is an unknown θ, we are thereby able to obtain four equations containing the four θ angles as unknowns, in the same manner as in Example 13.19. After solving for the values of these θ angles, we may substitute back to obtain the values of the end moments, thus reducing the remainder of the stress analysis to a problem in statics.

In effect, we have shown that the slope-deflection solution of any frame in which there are no unknown ψ angles is essentially the same as that of a continuous beam. The solution of the frame in Fig. 13.12*e* is likewise in this category, provided that both the make-up and the loading are symmetrical. In this special case, the deflections will also be symmetrical and therefore there can be no horizontal deflection of the column tops. As a result, the ψ angles of all three members are zero.

In the most general type of rigid frame, both unknown θ and unknown ψ angles are involved even when we consider only the effect of bending deformation. In other words, there are both joint rotations and chord rotations, or "sidesway." Several examples of such frames are shown in Fig. 13.15. Certain new ideas must be introduced to handle such problems. For this purpose, consider the frame shown in Fig. 13.13.

Figure 13.13   Frame involving sidesway

If the supports are unyielding, there are only two unknown θ angles, θ_B and θ_C. In this case, however, there is nothing that would prevent joint B from moving. Since we are neglecting deformation due to axial force and since the chord rotations of the members are small, joint B moves essentially perpendicular to member AB, or in this case, horizontally. Suppose that this movement is Δ. In the same manner, we should reason that joint C at the top of column CD must likewise move horizontally. Since the axial change in length of BC is also neglected, the horizontal movement of C must also be Δ.

The deflected position of the chords is shown by the dashed lines in Fig. 13.13. Note that these dashed lines indicate, not the elastic curve of the frame, but simply the chords of the elastic curve. From the sketch it is apparent that

$$\psi_{BC} = 0 \qquad \psi_{AB} = \frac{\Delta}{20} = \psi_1$$

and therefore
$$\psi_{CD} = \frac{\Delta}{25} = \frac{4}{5}\psi_1$$

In this case, therefore, the ψ angles of the members of the frame may all be expressed in terms of one independent unknown, which we can call ψ_1.*

Applying Eq. (13.11) in this case leads to expressions for the end moments that involve θ_B, θ_C, and ψ_1 as unknowns. Two of the three equations required to solve for these unknowns may be obtained from the familiar joint equations at joints B and C. The third independent equa-

---

* In Example 13.22, this same technique is used on a more difficult problem to analyze the ψ angles assumed by the chords of the members and the relationships between these angles. This same basic approach may be used to study the ψ angles of a frame of any complexity, such as those shown in Fig. 13.15, and may be outlined as follows:

1. Temporarily, consider all rigid joints in the indeterminate portion of the frame to be pinned joints and all fixed supports to be hinge supports. Otherwise, consider the joint and support details of the structure to be as specified. Now investigate whether or not this modified structure is statically and geometrically stable. If one or more joints are free to translate without immediately encountering resistance, the structure is unstable and free to behave as a linkage or mechanism. If such behavior of the modified structure is possible, corresponding chords of members of the actual frame may rotate through certain ψ angles. In other words, in such a case sidesway of the actual structure is possible.

2. The degree of instability of the modified structure is equal to the number of roller (or link) supports which would have to be introduced in order to prevent movement of this structure as a linkage mechanism. The position of such additional supports may be located by proceeding as follows. Imagine that the members are disconnected from the supports and from one another at the joints. Now reassemble the structure one member at a time starting from the supports. As this reassembly proceeds, it will become apparent that in order to prevent instability as a mechanism, auxiliary holding supports must be introduced at any joint which is not prevented from translating by at least two noncollinear bars connecting it to the stable structure already reassembled.

3. The potential ψ angles in the actual frame and the relationships between them may now be studied by moving successively each of the stabilizing supports which were introduced into the modified structure described above. Each one of these supports may be moved an arbitrary amount and the resulting chord rotations thereby produced may then be evaluated. One of these chord rotations produced by a particular support movement may be designated as the one independent ψ angle associated with that support movement and all other chord rotations involved expressed in terms of it. The number of independent ψ angles involved in the actual frame is therefore equal to the degree of instability of the modified structure. Note that the chord rotations of some members of a frame may be related to more than one of the independent ψ angles.

A rigid frame is said to have one degree of freedom with respect to sidesway associated with each independent ψ angle. In Art. 13.14, it is shown that the organization of the moment-distribution solution of a frame is dependent on the proper recognition of the number of degrees of freedom with respect to sidesway.

When these procedures are applied to the frames shown in Fig. 13.15, the degree of instability of the corresponding modified structures (or the number of independent ψ angles of the actual structures) is found to be as follows: (a) 1, (b) 1, (c) 1, (d) 3, (e) 1, (f) 3, (g) 2, and (h) 2.

tion of statics that the end moments must satisfy must be obtained in some other manner. It may be derived as follows: Isolate each of the columns by cutting them out just below the girder and just above the foundation as shown in Fig. 13.14. Likewise, isolate the girder by cutting

Figure 13.14 Isolation of columns and girder

it out just below the top of the columns. Then, taking moments about the base of each isolated column,

$$M_{AB} + M_{BA} + 20H_1 = 0 \qquad (a)$$
$$M_{DC} + M_{CD} + 25H_2 = 0 \qquad (b)$$

Likewise from $\Sigma F_x = 0$ on the girder,

$$H_1 + H_2 = 5 \qquad (c)$$

Substituting for H_1 and H_2 in Eq. (c) from Eqs. (a) and (b), we obtain

$$M_{AB} + M_{BA} + 0.8M_{DC} + 0.8M_{CD} + 100 = 0 \qquad (d)$$

which is the required third independent equation of statics. From the two joint equations and this so-called "shear equation," we are able to arrive at three equations from which we can solve for θ_B, θ_C, and ψ_1 and then to complete the solution as in previous problems.

Examples 13.21 and 13.22 illustrate the slope-deflection solution of certain typical frames where sidesway is involved.

Example 13.21   *Compute the end moments and draw the bending-moment diagram for the frame.*

Analyzing the θ and ψ angles,

$\theta_A = \theta_D = \psi_{BC} = 0$
$\theta_B = ?$ $\theta_C = ?$ $\psi_{AB} = \psi_{CD} = \psi_1$

$$K_{AB} = K_{CD} = \frac{I_1}{15} = K \qquad K_{BC} = \frac{4I_1}{20} = 3K$$

$$FEM_{BC} = -\frac{(100)(8)(12)^2}{(20)^2} = -288^{k'}$$

$$FEM_{CB} = +\frac{(100)(8)^2(12)}{(20)^2} = +192^{k'}$$

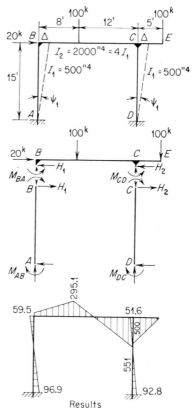

Using Eq. (13.11),

$$M_{AB} = 2EK\theta_B = 6EK\psi_1$$
$$M_{BA} = 4EK\theta_B - 6EK\psi_1$$
$$M_{BC} = 12EK\theta_B + 6EK\theta_C - 288$$
$$M_{CB} = 12EK\theta_C + 6EK\theta_B + 192$$
$$M_{CD} = 4EK\theta_C - 6EK\psi_1$$
$$M_{DC} = 2EK\theta_C - 6EK\psi_1$$

Joint B:

$$\Sigma M_B = 0 \qquad M_{BA} + M_{BC} = 0$$
$$\therefore\ 16EK\theta_B + 6EK\theta_C - 6EK\psi_1 - 288 = 0$$
$$\tag{1}$$

Joint C:

$$\Sigma M_C = 0 \qquad M_{CB} + M_{CD} - 500 = 0$$
$$\therefore\ 6EK\theta_B + 16EK\theta_C$$
$$- 6EK\psi_1 - 308 = 0 \quad (2)$$

Shear equations:

Col. AB: $M_{AB} + M_{BA} + 15H_1 = 0$
Col. DC: $M_{DC} + M_{CD} + 15H_2 = 0$
Girder: $H_1 + H_2 = 20$

$$\therefore\ M_{AB} + M_{BA} + M_{CD} + M_{DC} + 300 = 0 \quad (3)$$

Solving Eqs. (1), (2), and (3),

$$EK\theta_B = +18.63 \qquad EK\theta_C = +20.60 \qquad EK\psi_1 = +22.34$$

Then, $M_{AB} = -96.9^{k'}$ $M_{BC} = +59.2^{k'}$ $M_{CD} = -51.6^{k'}$

$M_{BA} = -59.5^{k'}$ $M_{CB} = +551.0^{k'}$ $M_{DC} = -92.8^{k'}$

Discussion:

Note that the dashed lines in the first sketch indicate the deflected position of the chords of the elastic curve of the columns, not the elastic curve itself.

When various portions of a frame are isolated as shown in the second sketch, all unknown end moments should be assumed to be positive, i.e., to act clockwise on the ends of the members. Shears and axial forces may be assumed to act in either direction, of course; but it having been assumed that a force such as H_1 acts in a certain direction on one isolated portion, it must be assumed that the force acts consistently on any subsequently isolated portions.

When plotting bending-moment diagrams for such frames, plot the ordinates on the side of the member that is in compression under the moment at that section of the frame.

Example 13.22   Compute the end moments and draw the bending-moment diagram for this frame.

To analyze ψ-angle relationships, imagine that the members are temporarily disconnected at the joints and from the supports and then reassembled one by one. First connect member AB at the base. If the chord of this member did rotate an amount ψ_{AB}, the B end would move essentially perpendicular to AB along the path BB'. Translate member BC parallel to itself so that the B ends of AB and BC can be connected together at point B'. If the chord of BC were now rotated, the C end would move along a path $C''C'$ perpendicular to the original direction of BC. Likewise, if member CD were connected to the support at D and the chord were rotated, the C end would have to move along a path CC' perpendicular to CD. The C ends of members BC and CD could be joined at point C' where these paths intersect. Then,

$$\psi_{AB} = \frac{BB'}{L_{AB}} = \frac{\Delta}{(\cos \alpha)L_{AB}} = \frac{\Delta}{20} = \frac{10}{13}\psi_1$$

$$\psi_{BC} = -\frac{C''C'}{10} = -\frac{\Delta}{10}(\tan \alpha + \tan \beta)$$

$$= -\frac{13}{200}\Delta = -\psi_1$$

$$\psi_{CD} = \frac{CC'}{L_{CD}} = \frac{\Delta}{(\cos \beta)L_{CD}} = \frac{\Delta}{25} = \frac{8}{13}\psi_1$$

Therefore all ψ angles can be expressed in terms of one unknown, ψ_1. Since $\theta_A = \theta_D = 0$, the independent unknown are θ_B, θ_C, and ψ_1.

$$K_{AB} = \frac{412}{20.6} = 20 = K \qquad K_{BC} = \frac{300}{10} = 30 = 1.5K \qquad K_{CD} = \frac{807}{26.9} = 1.5K$$

All FEM's are zero since no loads are applied between joints. Applying Eq. (13.11),

$$M_{AB} = 2EK\theta_B - {}^{60}\!\!/_{13}EK\psi_1 \qquad\qquad M_{CB} = 3EK\theta_B + 6EK\theta_C + 9EK\psi_1$$
$$M_{BA} = 4EK\theta_B - {}^{60}\!\!/_{13}EK\psi_1 \qquad\qquad M_{CD} = 6EK\theta_C - {}^{72}\!\!/_{13}EK\psi_1$$
$$M_{BC} = 6EK\theta_B + 3EK\theta_C + 9EK\psi_1 \qquad M_{DC} = 3EK\theta_C - {}^{72}\!\!/_{13}EK\psi_1$$

Joint B:

$$\Sigma M_B = 0 \qquad M_{BA} + M_{BC} = 0 \qquad \therefore \ 10EK\theta_B + 3EK\theta_C + 4.385EK\psi_1 = 0 \quad (1)$$

Joint C:

$$\Sigma M_C = 0 \qquad M_{CB} + M_{CD} = 0 \qquad \therefore \ 3EK\theta_B + 12EK\theta_C + 3.462EK\psi_1 = 0 \quad (2)$$

Shear equations:

$$\text{Col. } AB: \Sigma M_A = 0 \qquad M_{AB} + M_{BA} + 20H_1 - 5V_1 = 0 \qquad (a)$$
$$\text{Col. } CD: \Sigma M_D = 0 \qquad M_{DC} + M_{CD} + 25H_2 - 10V_2 = 0 \qquad (b)$$
$$\text{Girder: } \Sigma M_C = 0 \qquad M_{BA} + M_{CD} + 10V_1 = 0 \qquad (c)$$
$$\Sigma F_y = 0 \qquad V_1 = V_2 \qquad (d)$$
$$\Sigma F_x = 0 \qquad H_1 + H_2 = 100 \qquad (e)$$

Substitute in (a) and (b) for V_1, V_2, and H_2 from (c), (d), and (e); then eliminate H_1 from the modified Eqs. (a) and (b) and obtain

$$M_{AB} + 2.3M_{BA} + 2.1M_{CD} + 0.8M_{DC} + 2{,}000 = 0$$

or

$$11.2EK\theta_B + 15EK\theta_C - 31.292EK\psi_1 = -2{,}000 \qquad (3)$$

Now solve Eqs. (1), (2), and (3) in the following tabular form:

Eq.	Operation	$EK\theta_B$	+	$EK\theta_C$	+	$EK\psi_1$	$= const \times 10^{-2}$	Check
1		$+10$		$+ 3$		$+ 4.385$	0	$+17.385$
2		$+ 3$		$+12$		$+ 3.462$	0	$+18.462$
3		$+11.2$		$+15$		-31.292	-20	-25.092
3'	3×0.893	$+10$		$+13.393$		-27.939	-17.857	-22.404
3''	3×0.268	$+ 3$		$+ 4.018$		$- 8.382$	$- 5.357$	$- 6.721$
4	$1 - 3'$			-10.393		$+32.324$	$+17.857$	$+39.789$
5	$2 - 3''$			$+ 7.982$		$+11.844$	$+ 5.357$	$+25.183$
4'	4×0.768			$- 7.982$		$+24.825$	$+13.715$	$+30.559$
6	$5 + 4'$					$+36.669$	$+19.072$	$+55.742$
						$+ 1.0$	$+ 0.5201$	

$$7.982EK\theta_C = 5.357 - 6.159 = -0.802 \qquad EK\theta_C = -0.1005$$
$$3EK\theta_B = -5.357 + 4.359 + 0.404 = -0.594 \qquad EK\theta_B = -0.1980$$

The above results are for constants that are 0.01 of the actual constants. The actual results are 100 times the above.

$$EK\theta_B = -19.80 \qquad EK\theta_C = -10.05 \qquad EK\psi_1 = +52.01$$

The end moments are therefore

$$M_{AB} = -39.6 - 240.0 = -279.6^{k'}$$
$$M_{BA} = -79.2 - 240.0 = -319.2^{k'}$$
$$M_{BC} = -118.8 - 30.2 + 468.1 = +319.1^{k'}$$
$$M_{CB} = -59.4 - 60.4 + 468.1 = +348.7^{k'}$$
$$M_{CD} = -60.4 - 288.1 = -348.5^{k'}$$
$$M_{DC} = -30.2 - 288.1 = -318.3^{k'}$$

Discussion:

When analyzing the relations between the ψ angles, be sure to record the proper signs for them, thus indicating whether the chord rotates clockwise or counterclockwise.

In this problem, the solution of the simultaneous equations has been carried through in detail to illustrate a tabular procedure that is very convenient when there are three or more simultaneous equations to be solved. The important features of this procedure are as follows:

1. When eliminating an unknown, select the equation having the highest coefficient in that column. Operate on this equation so as to obtain several reduced versions of it, each version adjusted so as to match the coefficient of the unknown, which is being eliminated, in one of the original group of equations. Proceeding in this manner tends to minimize errors rather than to increase them.

2. Keep track of the operations performed on each equation, to facilitate checking.

3. In the check column, record the algebraic sum of all the coefficients and constant terms in each equation. Operate on this figure the same as on all other terms in an equation. After any operation, the new sum of the coefficients and constant terms should be equal to the new figure in the check column. Note that this is a necessary check but is not sufficient to catch occasional compensating errors.

4. The order of magnitude of the constant should be adjusted so as to be of the same order as the coefficients of the unknowns. This is done to make the check column most effective. After the solution of the equations is completed, the values of the unknowns may then be adjusted to give the answers corresponding to the actual constants.

By this time, the student should have started comparing the advantages and disadvantages of the different methods of stress analysis. He should have begun to form some idea as to when to use one method and when to use another. For example, he should study the structures in Figs. 13.12 and 13.15 and decide in each case whether the approach using superposition equations or Castigliano's theorem is or is not superior to the slope-deflection method.

The amount of computation is more or less proportional to the square of the number of simultaneous equations involved in the solution. Generally speaking, the superior method is that involving the fewest unknowns. Thus, comparing the superposition-equation approach with the slope-deflection method consists largely in comparing the number of redundant stress components with the number of unknown θ and ψ angles.

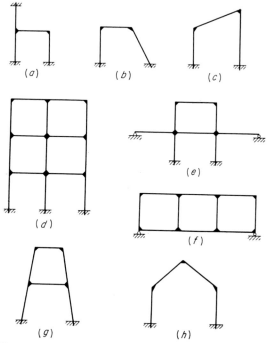

Figure 13.15   Typical rigid frames involving sidesway

13.13   Fundamentals of the Moment-distribution Method.

The moment-distribution method is an ingenious and convenient method of handling the stress analysis of rigid-joint structures.[1]   All the methods discussed previously involve the solution of simultaneous equations, which constitutes a major part of the computational work when there are more than three or four unknowns.   The method of moment distribution usually does not involve as many simultaneous equations and is often much shorter than any of the methods already discussed.   It has the fur ther advantage of consisting of a series of cycles, each converging on the precise final result; therefore the series may be terminated whenever one reaches the degree of precision required by the problem at hand.

[1] The moment-distribution method was presented by Prof. Hardy Cross in an article in *Trans. ASCE*, vol. 96, Paper 1793, 1932, and in several prior publications and is without a doubt one of the most important contributions to structural analysis in recent years.

If we refer to Eq. (13.11), the fundamental slope-deflection equation, we observe that the moment acting on the end of a member is the algebraic sum of four separate effects, viz.:

1. The moment due to the applied loads on the member if it were a fixed-end beam, i.e., the FEM

2. The moment caused by the rotation of the tangent to the elastic curve at the near end

3. The moment caused by the rotation of the tangent to the elastic curve at the far end

4. The moment caused by the rotation of the chord of the elastic curve joining the two ends of the member

Since the end moment is the superposition of these four effects, it is suggested that it might be possible to allow them to take place separately and thus arrive at their sum total.

To simplify the present discussion, we shall confine our attention to structures which are composed of prismatic members, i.e., members which have a constant I throughout their length, and also to structures in which there is no joint translation and in which, therefore, the ψ angles are all equal to zero.

Consider such a structure as that shown in Fig. 13.16. If the supports are unyielding, there is no joint rotation at a, d, c, or e, but there will be some joint rotation at b when the load is applied. However, suppose that we

Figure 13.16 Development of moment-distribution ideas (joint rotation only)

first consider the unloaded structure and imagine that we temporarily apply an external clamp which locks joint b against rotation. Then, if the load is applied, fixed end moments will be developed in member ab and these may be computed from Eqs. (13.13).

The moment FEM_{ba} causes a counterclockwise moment on the locked joint b. If the clamp is released, this moment will cause the joint to rotate counterclockwise. When this joint rotates, certain moments are developed throughout the length of all members meeting at this joint. The joint will continue to rotate until sufficient end moments are developed in the b ends of these members to balance the effect of FEM_{ba}. Of course, simultaneously certain end moments have been developed in the far ends of these members. When equilibrium is established at joint b, the structure in this case will have attained its final deformed position and the total end moment at the ends of the various members will be the algebraic sum of the fixed end moment and the moment caused by the rotation of joint b.

The procedure outlined above is essentially the moment-distribution method. It is convenient to adopt a certain terminology to simplify the description of the above procedure. We are already familiar with the term used to describe the end moments developed when the loads are applied to the structure with all joints locked against rotation—such moments are **fixed end moments.** When a joint is unlocked, it will rotate if the algebraic sum of the fixed end moments acting on the joint does not add up to zero; this resultant moment acting on the joint is therefore called the **unbalanced moment.** When the unlocked joint rotates under this unbalanced moment, end moments are developed in the ends of the members meeting at the joint. These finally restore equilibrium at the joint and are called **distributed moments.** As the joint rotated, however, and bent these members, end moments were likewise developed at the far ends of each; these are called **carry-over moments.**

Before evaluating these various moments numerically, it is desirable to adopt a convenient sign convention. Three different conventions are in use in the literature, but the authors prefer to use the same convention as that previously suggested for the slope-deflection method, viz., **end moments are plus when they act clockwise on the ends of the members.**

Figure 13.17 Joint rotation

Expressions for the *fixed end moments* have already been developed in Art. 13.11. The *unbalanced moment* acting on a joint n is simply the algebraic sum of the end moments at the n end of all members that are rigidly connected to this joint.

Some further analysis is necessary to explain how to compute the *distributed moments.* Consider the structure in Fig. 13.16 under the condition where joint b is unlocked and allowed to rotate under the unbalanced moment M. The structure deforms as shown in Fig. 13.17 and develops distributed moments M_{ba}, M_{bd}, etc., which restore the equilibrium of joint

b. These distributed moments, being unknown, are assumed to be positive and therefore to act clockwise

on the ends of the members and counterclockwise on the joint. The unbalanced moment M is assumed to be the resultant of posi-

Figure 13.18   Carry-over moment

tive fixed end moments and therefore also acts counterclockwise on the
joint. Since $\Sigma M_b = 0$,

$$M_{ba} + M_{bc} + M_{bd} + M_{be} + M = 0 \qquad (a)$$

However, the distributed moments may be evaluated by means of Eq.
(13.11), it being noted in this case that $\theta_a = \theta_d = \theta_c = \theta_e = 0$ and that
all ψ angles are zero.

$$\begin{aligned} M_{ba} &= 4EK_{ba}\theta_b & M_{bc} &= 4EK_{bc}\theta_b \\ M_{bd} &= 4EK_{bd}\theta_b & M_{be} &= 4EK_{be}\theta_b \end{aligned} \qquad (b)$$

By substituting in Eq. (a) from Eqs. (b), we can solve for θ_b, substitute this
value back in Eqs. (b), and obtain expressions for M_{ba}, etc.   For example,

$$M_{ba} = \frac{-K_{ba}}{K_{ba} + K_{bd} + K_{bc} + K_{be}}\, M \qquad \text{etc.} \qquad (c)$$

or, in general, the distributed moment in any bar bm is given by

$$M_{bm} = -\frac{K_{bm}}{\displaystyle\sum_b K}\, M \qquad (d)$$

where the summation is meant to include all members meeting at joint b.
Let

$$DF_{bm} = \textbf{distribution factor} \text{ for } b \text{ end of member } bm = \frac{K_{bm}}{\displaystyle\sum_b K} \qquad (13.14)$$

Then, $$M_{bm} = -DF_{bm}M \qquad (13.15)$$

Equation (13.15) may be interpreted as follows:
  **The distributed moment developed at the b end of member bm
as joint b is unlocked and allowed to rotate under an unbalanced
moment M is equal to the distribution factor DF_{bm} times the
unbalanced moment M with the sign reversed.**

An expression for *carry-over moment* must also be developed.   Consider any member, one end b of which has rotated θ_b, developing a distributed moment M_{bm} as shown in Fig. 13.18.   It should be noted that,
as joint b was unlocked and allowed to rotate, the joint at m remained

locked and therefore θ_m is equal to zero. Since ψ_{bm} is also zero, applying Eq. (13.11) leads to the following:

$$M_{bm} = 4EK_{bm}\theta_b \quad \text{and} \quad M_{mb} = 2EK_{bm}\theta_b$$

Hence, $\qquad\qquad M_{mb} = \frac{1}{2}M_{bm}$ $\qquad\qquad\qquad$ (13.16)

In words, **the carry-over moment is equal to one-half of its corresponding distributed moment and has the same sign.**

We have now developed all the fundamental ideas and relations required to solve the simpler moment-distribution problems. **Note, however, that the above discussion is restricted to structures composed of prismatic members.** These ideas are extended to members having variable I in Art. 13.15.

13.14 Application of Moment Distribution to Beams and Frames. For the first illustration of the application of moment distribution, consider the continuous beam shown in Fig. 13.19, the supports of which are unyielding. In this case, the ψ angles of both members are zero, and support a is permanently locked against rotation. Suppose that joints b and c are temporarily locked and the loads are applied, thereby developing the following fixed end moments:

$$\text{FEM}_{ab} = -9.6 \text{ kip-ft} \qquad \text{FEM}_{bc} = -18.75 \text{ kip-ft}$$
$$\text{FEM}_{ba} = +14.4 \text{ kip-ft} \qquad \text{FEM}_{cb} = +18.75 \text{ kip-ft}$$

In preparation for unlocking joints b and c and distributing the unbalanced moments, the stiffness factors K are computed, and from them the distribution factors at these joints are evaluated.

At b: $\qquad \Sigma K = 0.3I \qquad DF_{ba} = \frac{1}{3} \qquad DF_{bc} = \frac{2}{3}$

At c: $\qquad \Sigma K = 0.2I \qquad DF_{cb} = 1$

These distribution factors are then recorded in the appropriate box on the working diagram in Fig. 13.19. All the computations for the end moments are recorded on this diagram, the numbers referring to a particular end moment being recorded in a column normal to the member and running away from the member on the side first encountered in proceeding clockwise about the joint. Such an arrangement of the computations is, of course, not imperative but will be found highly desirable for frames.

After recording the fixed end moments, joints b and c are successively unlocked and allowed to rotate gradually into their equilibrium positions. Upon unlocking joint c, it rotates under an unbalanced moment of $+18.75$ until a distributed moment of -18.75 is developed to restore equilibrium. Joint c is relocked in this new position and a line is drawn under the -18.75 to indicate that the joint is now in equilibrium. As joint c

rotated, a carry-over moment of one-half of the distributed moment was developed at the b end of member bc, or in this case -9.38.

If joint b is now unlocked, it will rotate under an unbalanced moment equal to the algebraic sum of the two fixed end moments at this joint and the above carry-over moment, or -13.73. Using the appropriate distribution factors, the distributed moments that restore equilibrium are computed and are found to be $+4.58$ and $+9.15$; they are recorded and

Figure 13.19   Illustrative example

underlined, indicating that the joint is now in equilibrium. Relocking this joint in this new position and recording the carry-over moments developed at a and c by the rotation of joint b lead to $+2.29$ and $+4.58$, respectively.

Returning now to joint c and unlocking it a second time, it will rotate under a unbalanced moment of $+4.58$, developing a balancing distributed moment of -4.58. Again half of this distributed moment is carried over to the b end of this member. Joint c is locked in its new position. Now unlocking joint b a second time, it will rotate under an unbalance of -2.29, developing distributed moments of $+0.76$ and $+1.53$, which in turn induce carry-over moments at a and c of $+0.38$ and $+0.76$.

We may proceed in this manner, unlocking first joint c and then joint b, until the effects are so small that we are willing to neglect them. This problem has been carried through more cycles than required for practical purposes simply to illustrate the procedure. After the moment-distribution procedure is completed, the final end moments are obtained by adding algebraically all the figures in the various columns.

The convergence in the above solution has been rather slow owing to the fact that joint c is a hinged end and continually throws back sizable carry-over moments to joint b. Whenever there is such a hinged end at

Figure 13.20   Illustrative example using reduced stiffness factor

the extremity of a structure, the convergence may be improved by modifying the above procedure, as indicated in Fig. 13.20.

We start out as before, locking all joints against rotation, applying the loads, and developing the fixed end moments. Again as a first step, we unlock joint c and let it rotate and develop the distributed moment of -18.75, which then carries over -9.38 to joint b. At this point, we leave joint c unlocked so that it can rotate freely and hence can develop no end moment. Under these conditions, when we now proceed to joint b and unlock it, it will rotate under the unbalanced moment of -13.73 with the joint c unlocked instead of locked. Physically, this means that member bc is not so stiff as it was previously and hence does not take so much of the unbalanced moment. We shall now evaluate just how much its stiffness has been reduced.

Refer to Figs. 13.16 and 13.17 and the development of an expression for distributed moments. Suppose that the support at c were a roller or hinge support instead of a fixed support. Then, there would be a θ angle at c as well as b under the action of the unbalanced moment M, but M_{cb}

would be equal to zero.   Upon applying Eq. (13.11), the previous analysis
would be modified as follows:

$$M_{cb} = 4EK_{bc}\theta_c + 2EK_{bc}\theta_b = 0$$

from which

$$\theta_c = -\frac{\theta_b}{2}$$

and then

$$M_{bc} = 4EK_{bc}\theta_b + 2EK_{bc}\theta_c = 3EK_{bc}\theta_b = 4E(\tfrac{3}{4}K_{bc})\theta_b = 4EK_{bc}^R\theta_b$$

where $K_{bc}^R =$ **reduced stiffness factor** $= \tfrac{3}{4}K_{bc}$ (13.17)

Hence, our previous expressions for distribution factors may be used for
this new case provided that a reduced stiffness factor K^R instead of the
usual stiffness factor K is used for a member where the far end is hinged.[1]

We shall therefore revise the distribution factors at b, using the reduced
stiffness factor for member bc.

At b: Σ **eff K** $= 0.25I$ $DF_{ba} = 0.4$ $DF_{bc} = 0.6$

As a result, distributed moments of $+5.49$ and $+8.24$ are developed to
balance the unbalanced moment of -13.73.   There is no carry-over to
c, of course, since this joint was left unlocked.   There is the usual carry-
over, though, from b to a.   In this particular case, our solution is now
complete since joint c has not been unbalanced by the unlocking at b.
All joints are therefore in equilibrium and will not be disturbed if the
temporary locking device is permanently removed from joint b.   Adding
up the various columns will, in this case, now give us the exact end
moments for this beam.

The revised procedure will not always give exact results in one cycle as
it did in this problem, but in any case it will give more rapid convergence
than the original procedure.   Example 13.23 is designed to illustrate the
application of the above ideas to a somewhat more elaborate structure
that does not involve any unknown chord rotations.   In Example 13.24,
these ideas are extended to cover a case where the ψ angles are not zero
but their values are known.

---

[1] Inasmuch as the effective stiffness factor at b for member bm may be either K_{bm}
if the far end m is fixed or K_{bm}^R if the far end is hinged, it is desirable to rewrite Eq.
(13.14) as follows:

$$DF_{bm} = \textbf{distribution factor for } b \text{ end of member } bm = \frac{\text{eff } \mathbf{K_{bm}}}{\sum_b \text{eff } \mathbf{K}} \qquad (13.14a)$$

where the symbol **eff K** designates the **effective stiffness factor** of a member, which
may be equal to either K or K^R depending on whether the far end is fixed or hinged,
respectively.

Example 13.23 *Compute the end moments and draw the bending-moment diagram for this frame. Unyielding supports.*

Distribution factors:

At B: Σ eff $K = 2.8$ At C: Σ eff $K = 3.0$ At D: Σ eff $K = 3.788$

$DF_{BA} = 0.268$ $DF_{CB} = 0.417$ $DF_{DC} = 0.330$

$DF_{BC} = 0.446$ $DF_{CD} = 0.417$ $DF_{DJ} = 0.212$

$DF_{BG} = 0.286$ $DF_{CH} = 0.167$ $DF_{DE} = 0.248$

$\overline{1.000}$ $\overline{1.000}$ $DF_{DI} = 0.212$

$\overline{1.002}$

Fixed end moments:

$$FEM_{AB} = -\frac{(30)(6)(4)^2}{(10)^2} = -28.8^{k'} \qquad FEM_{BA} = +\frac{(30)(6)^2(4)}{(10)^2} = +43.2^{k'}$$

$$FEM_{BC} = -\frac{(3)(16)^2}{12} = -64^{k'} \qquad FEM_{CB} = +64^{k'}$$

$$FEM_{CD} = -\frac{(20)(12)}{8} = -30^{k'} \qquad FEM_{DC} = +30^{k'}$$

Cantilever moment:

$$M_{EF} = -(10)(6) = -60^{k'}$$

Moment distribution:

Final results:

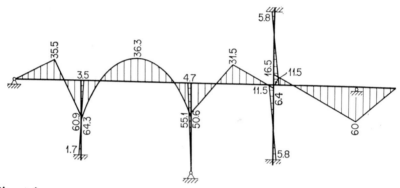

Discussion:

In this structure, when the loads are applied after all the joints have been locked against rotation, a moment will be developed at the E end of the cantilever, in addition to the usual fixed end moments at other points in the frame. The moment of 60 kip-ft contributes to the unbalanced moment at joint E, just as a fixed end moment would.

Note that the cantilever arm has no restraining effect on the rotation of joint E; that is, in effect, its stiffness factor is equal to zero. Any unbalanced moment is therefore carried entirely by the other members that meet at this joint.

Following the modified procedure, all hinged extremities must be unlocked first. This includes not only joints A and H but also E.

The remaining joints are unlocked in turn and gradually rotated into their equilibrium positions. If in doing this we start with the joint which has the largest unbalanced moment, the convergence of the solution will be somewhat more rapid, although the final results are independent of the order in which the joints are unlocked.

Example 13.24   *Solve Example 13.20, using moment distribution.*

Suppose that we temporarily lock all joints against rotation and that we then introduce the specified support movements, so that

$$\theta_a = +0.001 \text{ radian}$$
$$\psi_{ab} = +0.003 \text{ radian}$$
$$\psi_{bc} = -0.0015 \text{ radian}$$

In effect, we have bent the members and developed certain initial end moments that can be evaluated by using Eq. (13.11), or

$$M_{ab} = 2E(0.1I)(0.002 - 0.009)$$
$$= -0.0014EI = -292^{k'}$$
$$M_{ba} = 2E(0.1I)(0.001 - 0.009)$$
$$= -0.0016EI = -334^{k'}$$
$$M_{bc} = 2E(0.2I)(+0.0045)$$
$$= +0.0018EI = +376^{k'}$$
$$M_{cb} = +0.0018EI = +376^{k'}$$

since $EI = 30 \times 10^3 \times \dfrac{1,000}{144}$

$$= 208,333 \text{ kip-ft}^2$$

The remainder of the solution is handled in exactly the same manner as if these initial end moments were fixed end moments. Thus, the distribution, etc., is done exactly as it was in Fig. 13.20.

Once we understand the fundamental philosophy of moment distribution and the details of its application to the cases discussed above, it is quite easy to extend these ideas to more complicated cases involving sidesway, i.e., unknown ψ angles.[1]   Consider, for example, the frame shown in Fig. 13.21.   In this case, there is nothing to prevent a horizontal deflection of the column tops.   In addition to rotation of joints B and C, we therefore have certain unknown chord rotations developed in the columns.

In order to handle this problem by moment distribution, we may break it down into two separate parts.   First, suppose that we introduce a horizontal holding force R which prevents any horizontal movement of joint B.   With the structure restrained in this manner, we can apply

---

[1] See footnote on p. 445 for description of a method of determining the number of independent unknown ψ angles.   The number of degrees of freedom with respect to sidesway is equal to the number of independent unknown ψ angles.

all the given loads and determine the resulting end moments by moment distribution just as we would for any structure that involved no sidesway. Having the end moments, we can then back-figure the holding force R by statics.[1] This part of the solution is called case A in Fig. 13.21.

In the second, or case B, part of the solution, we imagine that we lock the joints against rotation, push on the frame at joint B, and introduce some arbitrary horizontal displacement Δ. (**Note that the pushing force P in case B must be applied at the same point and along the same line of action as the holding force R in case A.**) We can then analyze the ψ angles thus introduced into the columns. Using Eq. (13.11), we can compute the corresponding initial end moments developed

Final results   =   Case A + $B \times$ Case B

Figure 13.21 Moment distribution including effect of sidesway (joint translation)

in the members. These end moments will be expressed in terms of $E\Delta$; but since Δ is arbitrary, we can let $E\Delta$ equal unity or any convenient amount and obtain numerical values for the initial end moments. If we then unlock, distribute, and carry over through several cycles at joints B and C, we shall arrive at a set of end moments for the frame. Again by statics we can back-figure the force P that has pushed the frame into this position and developed these end moments.

We are now in a position to superimpose the case A and case B parts of the solution so as to obtain the answers for the specified loads. To simplify the discussion of this superposition, let us assume that R was computed to be a force of 12 kips acting to the left and P a force of 6 kips acting to the right. We must take the case A moments as they are, since the external loads for this case are the same as the specified ones; but we can combine these results with any multiple of the case B results that we desire. Using the assumed values for R and P, if we take twice the case B loads and superimpose them on the case A loads, we shall obviously obtain the specified load system. The final answers for the end moments

---

[1] Suppose in a particular problem that the holding force R was found from statics to be zero. What does this mean regarding sidesway? Is it necessary to proceed with a case B solution?

are therefore obtained by adding algebraically twice the case B moments to the case A moments.

Example 13.25   *Compute the end moments in this frame.*

At B: $K_{AB} = 15$ $DF_{BA} = 0.429$
        $K_{BD} = 20$ $DF_{BD} = 0.571$
        Σ eff $K = 35$

At D: $K_{DB} = 20$ $DF_{DB} = 0.426$
        $K_{DE}^{R} = 15$ $DF_{DE} = 0.319$
        $K_{DC}^{R} = 12$ $DF_{DC} = 0.255$
        Σ eff $K = 47$

Case A : *Prevent sidesway.   Hold frame at joint B.   Apply all given loads to the structure.*

$$FEM_{BD} = -250 \qquad M_{EF} = -400$$
$$FEM_{DB} = +250$$

By isolating columns, horizontal reactions at A and C may be computed.   Then, applying $\Sigma H = 0$ to the entire structure, we find the holding force at B to be 58.70^k acting toward the left.

Case B : *Introduce sidesway by pushing at point B, having first temporarily locked all joints (including C) against rotation.   Compute initial end moments from Eq. (13.11).*

$$M_{AB} = M_{BA} = -6E(15)\left(\frac{\Delta}{15}\right) = -6E\Delta$$

$$M_{CD} = M_{DC} = -6E(16)\left(\frac{\Delta}{20}\right) = -4.8E\Delta$$

Let $E\Delta = 100$; then

$$M_{AB} = M_{BA} = -600$$
$$M_{CD} = M_{DC} = -480$$

Combination of case A and case B: *Let B = factor by which we must multiply the case B solution. The superposition of B times the case B solution on the case A solution must be such that the modified pushing force from case B cancels the case A holding force at joint B, thereby leaving only the given loads acting on the structure. This cancellation may be expressed in equation form by considering forces acting to the right at joint B to be plus. Then,*

$$-58.70 + 66B = 0 \quad or \quad B = 0.89$$
$$\therefore \text{ Final results} = \text{case } A + (B) \text{ (case } B)$$

$M_{AB} = +78.9 - 421.5 = -342.6^{k'}$ $M_{DC} = -141.6 - 196.7 = -338.3^{k'}$

$M_{BA} = +157.8 - 310.5 = -152.7^{k'}$ $M_{DE} = +23.0 + 20.7 = +43.7^{k'}$

$M_{BD} = -157.8 + 310.5 = +152.7^{k'}$ $M_{ED} = +400 + 0 = +400^{k'}$

$M_{DB} = +118.6 + 176.0 = +294.6^{k'}$

Discussion:

When computing the initial end moments developed by a chord rotation, note that all joints, including hinged supports, are assumed to be locked against rotation. Note further that the stiffness factor K, not the reduced stiffness factor K^R, is used in these computations.

The reduced stiffness factor is used only to compute distribution factors and for no other purpose.

The end moments produced by any given horizontal load acting by itself at joint B can be computed by straight proportion from the case B part of the solution.

The ideas illustrated by Example 13.25 may be applied without modification to any frame involving only one independent ψ angle. It is also easy to extend the application of these ideas to frames involving more than one independent ψ angle. A frame having n independent ψ angles is said to have n *degrees of freedom with respect to sidesway.* For such a frame, the moment-distribution solution may be broken down into $(n + 1)$ separate cases: (1) a *case A* in which sidesway is completely prevented by introducing n holding forces; and (2) n separate sidesway cases, in each of which only *one* independent ψ angle is allowed to occur at a time by maintaining holding forces at $(n-1)$ of the n joints held in case A while pushing at the one remaining joint held in case A.

The results of these $(n+1)$ cases may be superimposed in the same manner as used in Example 13.25. The factor by which each of the sidesway cases must be multiplied in this superposition may be found from the solution of n simultaneous equations. The n simultaneous equations are obtained by writing one equation for each of the n joints held in case A. For a joint j, such an equation simply states that the

Figure 13.22   Multiple degrees of freedom with respect to sidesway

Note: Values noted above for pushing or holding forces have simply been assumed for illustrative purposes rather than being computed as would be done in solving an actual problem.   Dashed-line deflected shapes correspond to the initial position of the frame where joint displacements have been introduced with the joints locked against rotation.   The final elastic curve after the joints have been unlocked and have rotated into their final position corresponding to the completed moment distribution for each sidesway case has *not* been shown.

algebraic sum of the case A holding force at j, plus a factor B times the holding or pushing force at j for the sidesway case B, plus a factor C times the holding or pushing force at j for the sidesway case C, and so forth for each of the n sidesway cases, must be zero.

To illustrate this procedure for applying moment distribution to a frame having multiple degrees of freedom with respect to sidesway, consider the frame shown in Fig. 13.22.   This frame has three independent ψ angles corresponding to the independent horizontal displacements of joints B, C, and D.   The frame is therefore said to have three degrees of freedom with respect to sidesway.   The moment-distribution solution is therefore broken down into $(3+1)$, or four, separate cases: case A (sidesway prevented) and three sidesway cases (cases B, C, and D).

In case A after holding forces have been introduced at joints B, C, and D to prevent sidesway, all the given loads are applied and a regular no-sidesway moment-distribution solution is performed to obtain the end moments. Then by statics, the holding forces at B, C, and D are back-figured. For purposes of this discussion, these holding forces are assumed to have the values of 12, 8, and 4, respectively, and to be directed as shown in Fig. 13.22.

Then each of the three sidesway cases is considered separately. In case B, for example, joints C and D are held from displacing horizontally while joint B is displaced some arbitrary amount. If initially the joints are locked against rotation while this displacement is introduced, certain initial end moments are developed in members AB, BC, GH, and GF. These initial end moments can be computed for the arbitrary displacement as done above in case B of Example 13.25. A moment-distribution solution is performed for the end moments developed as a result of the introduction of these initial end moments. Then by statics the pushing force at B and the holding forces at C and D are back-figured. Also for purposes of the subsequent discussion, these forces are assumed to have the values and directions shown in Fig. 13.22 for case B. Similar solutions are conducted for the other two sidesway cases, case C and case D.

It now remains to find how much of each of the three sidesway cases should be superimposed on case A to obtain the final results for the actual given problem. In other words, we must obtain the factors B, C, and D by which cases B, C, and D, respectively, must be multiplied to obtain each of their contributions to the final results. These factors are obtained by solving three simultaneous equations, each of which is set up as follows. At joint B, for example, if forces to the right are considered as plus, we may write

$$12 + 22B - 13C + 9D = 0$$

At joint C: $\quad -8 - 6B + 14C - 21D = 0$

At joint D: $\quad -4 + 3B - 5C + 13D = 0$

The values of B, C, and D may be obtained from the simultaneous solution of these three equations. If we now multiply the external forces in case B by B, those in case C by C, and those in case D by D, and if we then superimpose these modified forces from these three cases on the forces in case A, we obtain simply the given loads (and their corresponding reactions). In other words, such a superposition has wiped out all the extra pushing and holding forces. Obviously, the final results (such as the end moments in the actual structure developed by the given loads) are then obtained by superimposing the results of the four cases, as indicated on Fig. 13-22.

It should be noted that one has considerable option as to how one introduces the arbitrary joint displacements in each of the sidesway solutions. The only requirement is that all of the sidesway cases be independent of one another. For example, in case B, we could have displaced joints B, C, and D equal amounts horizontally. In case C, we could have held joint B, and pushed C and D equal amounts. These new cases B and C could then have been combined with the previous cases A and D. A new set of simultaneous equations would be obtained from which new values of the factors B, C, and D would result. The superposition of the cases of this new solution would lead, however, to the same final results as were obtained from the first solution.

An alternative procedure that does not require simultaneous equations can be used for cases involving sidesway. In this method, we introduce joint displacements at the same time as we apply the loads that develop fixed end moments. After each cycle of distribution, we check the equilibrium equations and back-figure the joint loads. If the joint loads do not agree with the given ones, we introduce some additional joint displacements, carry through another cycle of distribution, check the forces again, etc.[1]

13.15   Moment-distribution Method Applied to Nonprismatic Members.
The fundamental philosophy of the moment-distribution procedure developed in Art. 13.13 is applicable to any beam or frame whether composed of members of constant or varying E and I. The expressions for fixed end moment, stiffness factor, and carry-over moment are derived specifically, however, for members of constant E and I and are not applicable to nonprismatic members. We shall now develop new expressions for these quantities for *the case of originally straight members of varying E and I.*

Carry-over Factor C. The carry-over moment is the moment induced at a fixed end of a member when the opposite end is rotated by an end moment. It is convenient to express the carry-over moment at B as being equal to the applied moment at A multiplied by the *carry-over factor C_{AB},* the order of the subscripts indicating the direction in which the effect is carried over, i.e., from A to B in this case, or

$$M_{BA} = C_{AB}M_{AB} \qquad (13.18)$$

From this equation, **the carry-over factor could be defined as the end moment induced at the fixed end of a member when the opposite end is rotated by an**

[1] Detailed discussion of this alternative procedure is beyond the scope of this book. For such information, the reader is referred to the more extensive treatment of the moment-distribution method found in the following textbooks: L. E. Grinter, "Theory of Modern Steel Structures," 2d ed., vol. 2, The Macmillan Company, New York, 1949; J. A. L. Matheson, "Hyperstatic Structures," vol. 1, Butterworth's Scientific Publications, London, 1959; J. I. Parcel and R. B. Moorman, "Analysis of Statically Indeterminate Structures," John Wiley & Sons, Inc., New York, 1955.

For more extensive treatments of the analysis of statically indeterminate structures in general, the reader is referred to the following texts as well as those mentioned above: S. F. Borg and J. J. Gennaro, "Advanced Structural Analysis," D. Van Nostrand Co., Inc., Princeton, N.J., 1959; L. C. Maugh, "Statically Indeterminate Structures," John Wiley & Sons, Inc., New York, 1946; S. P. Timoshenko and D. H. Young, "Theory of Structures," McGraw-Hill Book Company, Inc., New York, 1945; C.-K. Wang, "Statically Indeterminate Structures," McGraw-Hill Book Company, Inc., New York, 1953; J. S. Kinney, "Indeterminate Structural Analysis," Addison-Wesley Publishing Company, Reading, Mass., 1957.

end moment of unity. For a prismatic member, the carry-over factor is $\frac{1}{2}$. Note further that C_{AB} is equal to C_{BA} only when a member is symmetrical about its mid-point.

An outline of the procedure for computing the carry-over factor in any given case follows: Consider any member AB as shown in Fig. 13.23, and apply a moment of unity at A, thus inducing a moment C_{AB} at B. The resulting deflection of point A on the elastic curve from the tangent at B is equal to zero. Upon applying the second moment-area theorem, the static moment of the composite M/EI diagram taken about an axis through point A must therefore be equal to zero. C_{AB} may easily be evaluated from this equation.

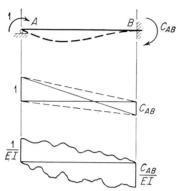

Figure 13.23   Carry-over factor

True Stiffness Factor K'. Let us refer to Art. 13.13, where the evaluation of distributed moments is discussed and consider that Figs. 13.16 and 13.17 now represent structures composed of nonprismatic members. In considering the effect of the rotation of joint B under the unbalanced moment M, we can no longer evaluate the distributed moments by Eq. (13.11). We can write, however,

$$M_{BA} = K'_{BA}\theta_B \qquad M_{BC} = K'_{BC}\theta_C \qquad \text{etc.} \quad (a)$$

where K'_{BA}, K'_{BC}, etc., are called the *true stiffness factors* for the B end of member BA, for the B end of member BC, etc. From these equations, **the true stiffness factor K'_{BA} may be defined as the end moment required to rotate the tangent at the B end of member BA through a unit angle when the far end A is fixed.**

For a prismatic member, the true stiffness factor is $4EK$. Note that K, previously called simply the "stiffness factor" of a member, gives the relative value of the true stiffness factors for prismatic members. Perhaps K should have been called the "relative stiffness factor," but this term is used so much that it is desirable to keep it as short as possible. Note further that, in general, a member has a different true stiffness factor at each end; only when the member is symmetrical will the true stiffness factor be the same at each end.

The true stiffness factor K'_{AB} for the A end of member AB shown in Fig. 13.24 may be computed as follows: By definition, an end moment of K'_{AB} applied at A will rotate the tangent at A through a unit angle when the far end B is fixed. Upon applying the first moment-area theorem, the net area under the composite M/EI diagram must therefore be equal to unity. If C_{AB} has previously been computed as described above, K'_{AB} may now be determined from this equation.

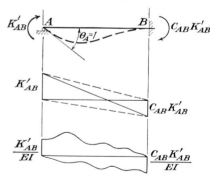

Figure 13.24   True stiffness factor

True Reduced Stiffness Factor K'^R. **The true reduced stiffness factor K'^R_{AB} may be defined as the end moment required to rotate the tangent at the A end through a unit angle when the far end is hinged.** K'^R_{AB} may easily be computed by proceeding as follows, provided that K'_{AB}, C_{AB}, and C_{BA} have already been computed: Consider a bar AB, and suppose temporarily that we lock the B end against rotation. A moment of K'_{AB} applied at the A end would produce a rotation of A of unity and induce a carry-over moment at the far end of $C_{AB}K'_{AB}$. If we now lock the A end in this position and unlock the B end, the latter end will rotate under the unbalanced moment $C_{AB}K'_{AB}$ and develop a distributed moment of $-C_{AB}K'_{AB}$. As a result, a carry-over moment of $-C_{BA}C_{AB}K'_{AB}$ is induced at A. The member will now be in the deformed condition shown in Fig. 13.25, and the total end moment at A will be equal to the true reduced stiffness factor K'^{R}_{AB}. Hence,

$$K'^{R}_{AB} = K'_{AB}(1 - C_{BA}C_{AB}) \qquad (13.19)$$

For a prismatic member where both C_{AB} and C_{BA} are equal to one-half, we see from Eq. (13.19) that K'^{R}_{AB} is equal to three-fourths of K'_{AB}, as it should be.

Figure 13.25 True reduced stiffness factor

Check Relationship Involving Stiffness and Carry-over Factors. A useful relationship between stiffness and carry-over factors may be derived and used for checking purposes. Consider the member AB shown in Fig. 13.26, where it is acted upon by two separate loading systems I and II. Applying Betti's law, we find that

$$C_{AB}K'_{AB} = C_{BA}K'_{BA} \qquad (13.20)$$

This expression proves very helpful when used as a check on the values of the carry-over and stiffness factors.

Distribution Factors and Distributed Moments. If we complete the evaluation of distributed moments using the expressions in Eqs. (*a*) of this article and proceeding as in Art. 13.13, we obtain expressions for the distribution factor which are the same

Figure 13.26 Check relationship

as Eqs. (13.14) or (13.14a) except that true stiffness factors K' are substituted for the stiffness factors K.

Sidesway Factor. It is likewise easy to develop expressions for the sidesway factor J that may be used to compute the initial end moments developed by a chord rotation. We can write the following expressions for such end moments:

$$M_{AB} = J_{AB}\psi_{AB}$$
$$M_{BA} = J_{BA}\psi_{AB} \qquad (13.21)$$

The sidesway factor J_{AB} may be defined as the end moment developed at the A end of member AB by a chord rotation of unity, both ends of the member being locked against joint rotation. For a prismatic member, the sidesway factor is $-6EK$. The sidesway factor will be the same at each end only when the member is symmetrical.

The sidesway factor for member AB in Fig. 13.27a may be expressed in terms of stiffness and carry-over factors by reasoning as follows: Suppose that the fixity is removed from the A and B ends temporarily and that the member is displaced as shown in Fig. 13.27b. Now lock the A end and rotate the B end until θ_B is restored to zero, thus developing end moments of $-K'_{BA}$ at B and $-C_{BA}K'_{BA}$ at A. Lock the B end in this position and rotate the A end until θ_A is likewise restored to zero, thus developing end moments of $-K'_{AB}$ at A and $-C_{AB}K'_{AB}$ at B. The member will now be in the same condition of deformation as shown in Fig. 13.27a, and the total end moments will be equal to the sidesway factor, or

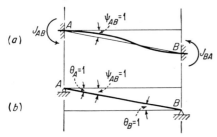

$$J_{AB} = -(K'_{AB} + C_{BA}K'_{BA})$$
$$J_{BA} = -(K'_{BA} + C_{AB}K'_{AB}) \qquad (13.22)$$

Figure 13.27 Sidesway factor

Fixed End Moments. The fixed end moments in a nonprismatic member may be computed as follows: Consider member AB acted upon by any loading. Assume temporarily that the load is applied to this member acting as an end-supported beam. For this condition, compute the resulting rotations of the tangents θ_{Ao} and θ_{Bo}, using the moment-area theorems. Then if we imagine that we lock the B end and rotate the A end back to a zero slope, and then lock the A end in this position and rotate the B end back, the resulting end moments will be found to be

$$\text{FEM}_{AB} = -K'_{AB}\theta_{Ao} + C_{BA}K'_{BA}\theta_{Bo}$$
$$\text{FEM}_{BA} = +K'_{BA}\theta_{Bo} - C_{AB}K'_{AB}\theta_{Ao} \qquad (13\text{-}23)$$

General Remarks. The above expressions are strictly applicable only to members the axes of which are originally straight. They may be used with satisfactory accuracy for members with slightly curved axes provided that the structure is arranged so that the axial thrust developed in such members is relatively small. Consideration of more accurate expressions for curved members is beyond the scope of this book.

Charts and tables have been prepared from which values of fixed end moments, stiffness, and carry-over factors may be readily obtained for typical haunched members encountered in practice.[1]

13.16 Stress Analysis of Statically Indeterminate Space Frameworks. Statically indeterminate space frameworks may be analyzed by means of superposition equations or Castigliano's theorem. Fundamentally, the stress analysis of such structures by these methods is accomplished in exactly the same manner as for an indeterminate truss. The detail of the analysis is more tedious, of course, for the

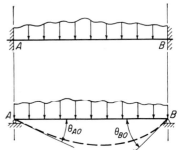

Figure 13.28 Supplementary computation relating to fixed end moment

---

[1] For example, refer to Concrete Beams and Columns with Variable Moment of Inertia, Portland Cement Association, Bulletin S.T. 41.

stress analysis of the statically determinate primary structure is more complicated when it is a three-dimensional framework instead of a planar truss. All the ideas discussed above for indeterminate trusses are applicable here, but a detailed extension of these ideas to indeterminate space frameworks is not within the scope of this book.

13.17　Deflection of Statically Indeterminate Structures. Once the stress analysis of an indeterminate structure has been completed, then the strains and the resulting deflections of the structure may be computed without difficulty by the same procedures as those discussed and applied to statically determinate structures in Chap. 12.

For example, suppose that we have computed the bar forces and the corresponding changes in length of the members of the truss shown in Fig. 13.29a, due to a given loading. Suppose that we then wish to com-

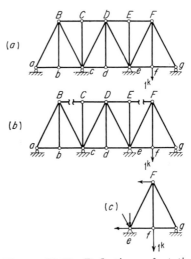

pute the resulting vertical deflection of joint f by the method of virtual work. We could proceed in the usual manner and apply a unit vertical load at joint f of the actual structure shown in Fig. 13.29a. This load would cause F_Q forces in most of the bars of the indeterminate truss. After these forces had been computed, we could apply Eq. (12.5) and compute the required deflection of joint f. But this procedure, though straightforward, is laborious since most of the bars of the truss are involved in the computations.

Deflection computations for indeterminate structures may be simplified considerably if we simply recognize that the redundants of such structures have been computed so that the stresses, strains, and deflections of the primary and actual structures are identical. Deflections may be computed, therefore, by using the statically determinate primary structure rather than the actual

Figure 13.29 Deflections of statically indeterminate truss

indeterminate structure. It is much easier to use the primary structure, of course. For example, in the above structure, suppose that we use the primary structure shown in Fig. 13.29b and proceed to compute the vertical deflection of joint f by the method of virtual work. In this case, the unit load at joint f would develop F_Q forces in only five bars, namely, ef, fg, eF, fF, and Fg. As a result, when Eq. (12.5) is applied, only these five bars contribute to the sum of $F_Q \Delta L$, the computations being thus tremendously reduced in this particular case.

To some, a descriptive explanation such as is given above is not adequate, and they prefer a mathematical demonstration. Although it will not be done here, it can be proved mathematically that the results are identical whether the unit Q load is considered to be applied to the actual indeterminate structure or to the statically determinate primary structure.

Physically, it seems obvious that the deflections computed for the right span of the actual structure must be identical with the deflections of this portion isolated as a simple span and considered to be acted upon by any given external loads and also by external forces corresponding to the bar forces in the members cut by the isolating section as shown in Fig. 13.29c. These ideas are even more obvious from a physical viewpoint in the case of the deflections of a continuous beam. In such a structure, it seems perfectly natural to isolate each span and compute its deflections by considering it as a simple end-supported beam acted upon by any loads which act in that span and also by end moments which are equivalent to the bending moments at the corresponding support points of the actual continuous beam.

13.18 Secondary Stresses in Trusses. In Chap. 4, it will be recalled that the elementary stress analysis of a truss is based upon the following assumptions:

1. The members are connected together at their ends by frictionless pin joints.

2. All external loads and reactions (including the weight of the members) are applied to the truss at the joints.

3. The centroidal axes of all members are straight, coincide with the lines connecting the joint centers, and lie in a plane that also contains the lines of action of all the loads and reactions.

A stress analysis based on these assumptions leads to the determination of so-called "primary stresses."

Stresses caused by conditions not considered in the primary stress analysis are called *secondary stresses*. Of these the most important are caused by the fact that the joints are rigid, and hence the members are not free to change their relative directions when the truss is deformed. Several classical methods[1] are available for making approximate analyses for secondary stresses. This problem can likewise be solved very efficiently by means of moment distribution. The latter method is the only one that will be discussed here.

A truss with rigid joints is actually a rigid frame. Theoretically, we could analyze such a frame by the use of superposition equations or Castigliano's theorem, considering deformation due to both bending and axial force. Such structures would be so highly statically indeterminate, however, that it would not be practical to carry through an exact stress analysis. We have already noted that the deflection of the joints is primarily a function of the axial forces in the members since the bending of the members has only a second-order effect on their axial change in length. Further, it can be shown that the axial forces in the members of a truss with rigid joints are essentially the same as those in an ideal pin-jointed truss, i.e., that the presence of shears and moments in the members has a small effect on the axial forces.[2] This suggests that the axial forces and the resulting joint deflections can be computed, assuming the truss to be pin-jointed. If the joint deflections are known, all the ψ angles of the members can be computed and the remainder of the problem solved either by slope deflection or moment distribution, in the same manner as for any frame in which only the joint rotations or θ angles are unknown.

The solution of a secondary stress problem using moment distribution may be outlined as follows:

1. Compute the bar forces assuming the truss to be pin-jointed.

2. Compute the joint deflections and the corresponding chord rotations of the members. This can be done conveniently by means of the Williot method or the angle-change procedure used in Example 13.26.

3. Compute the initial end moments developed if all the joints are locked against rotation and then the above joint deflections and chord rotations introduced. Likewise, compute any unbalanced moments that may act on the joints as a result of eccentricities of the bar.

4. Distribute and carry over through as many cycles as is necessary. The final

[1] A very comprehensive paper on these methods was presented by Cecil Vivian von Abo, *Trans. ASCE*, vol. 89, 1926.

[2] See J. I. Parcel and R. B. B. Moorman, "Analysis of Statically Indeterminate Structures," chap. 9, John Wiley & Sons, Inc.. New York, 1955.

end moments thus obtained will be the first approximation of the secondary end moments, from which the secondary stresses can be computed. From these end moments, the shears in the members can be computed as well and also, by statics, new values of the bar forces in the members.

5. If these new values of the bar forces are markedly different from those computed in step 1, repeat steps 2, 3, and 4, and thus arrive at a second approximation for the secondary stresses.

This procedure is illustrated by Example 13.26.

Example 13.26 *Compute the secondary stresses in the members of this truss.*

Bar	L	A	I	c	K	Make-up
	″	*″²*	*″⁴*	*″*	*″³*	
ab						
bc	300	18.0	174.9	6.375	0.583	4 ∡ s6 × 3½ × ½
Bb	336	15.88	153.4	6.375	0.456	4 ∡ s6 × 3½ × ⁷⁄₁₆
Bc	450.4	13.68	131.4	6.375	0.292	4 ∡ s6 × 3½ × ⅜
Cc	336	11.44	78.9	5.375	0.235	4 ∡ s5 × 3 × ⅜
aB	450.4	27.68	960.9	5.739 / 9.699	2.134	2[s 15″ − 33.9# 1Pl 18 × ⁷⁄₁₆
BC	300	26.55	922.7	5.921 / 9.453	3.076	2[s 15″ − 33.9# 1Pl 18 × ⅜

Bar forces ₵ Stress intensities

Notes: 1. Members ab, bc, Bb, Bc, and Cc assembled so:

2. Working lines of members aB and BC lie on ₵ of channels.

Step 1: *Primary bar forces and stress intensities shown on line diagram.*
Step 2: *Compute ψ angles using angle changes computed by Eq. (12.11b).*

Angle	$f_3 - f_1$	cot β_1	$f_3 - f_2$	cot β_2	1st term	2d term	$E\,\Delta\gamma$
B-a-b	+11.71+13.50=+25.21	1.12		0	+28.25	0	+28.25
b-B-a	+13.82+13.50=+27.32	0.893		0	+24.40	0	+24.40
a-b-B	-13.50-13.82=-27.32	0.893	-13.50-11.71=-25.21	1.12	-24.40	-28.25	-52.65
c-B-b	+13.82- 9.11=+4.71	0.893		0	+ 4.21	0	+ 4.21
B-b-c	+ 9.11-11.71=-2.60	1.12	+ 9.11-13.82=-4.71	0.893	- 2.91	- 4.21	- 7.12
b-c-B		0	+11.71- 9.11=+2.60	1.12	0	+ 2.91	+ 2.91
C-B-c		0	0 -9.11=- 9.11	1.12	0	-10.20	-10.20
c-C-B	+ 9.11-0=+9.11	1.12	+ 9.11+12.50=+21.61	0.893	+10.20	+19.30	+29.50
B-c-C		0	-12.50- 9.11=-21.61	0.893	0	-19.30	-19.30

Then, $E\psi_{Cc} = 0$ $E\psi_{aB} = +47.91$

$E\Delta_{BcC} = -19.30$ $E\Delta_{aBb} = +24.40$

$E\psi_{Bc} = +19.30$ $E\psi_{Bb} = +23.51$

$E\Delta_{Bcb} = + 2.91$ $E\Delta_{bBc} = + 4.21$

$E\psi_{bc} = +16.39$ $E\psi_{Bc} = +19.30$

$E\Delta_{Bbc} = - 7.12$ $E\Delta_{cBC} = -10.20$

$E\psi_{Bb} = +23.51$ $E\psi_{BC} = +29.50$

$E\Delta_{abB} = -52.65$ $E\Delta_{BCc} = +29.50$

$E\psi_{ab} = +76.16$ $E\psi_{Cc} = 0$

$E\Delta_{Bab} = +28.25$

$E\psi_{aB} = +47.91$

In this case, ψ_{Cc} is known to equal zero by symmetry. All these ψ angles are therefore oriented correctly. However, any ψ angle may be assumed to be zero and all other ψ angles computed to correspond. This is obviously permissible since it means in effect that the truss has been rotated as a rigid body which does not alter the condition of stress.

Step 3: *Compute initial end moments and eccentric moments.*

Joint a:

$M_e = +(374)(2.20) = \underline{+823^{k''}}$

Joint B:

Bar	K	$E\psi$	$-6EK\psi$
ab	0.583	+76.16	-266.0$^{k''}$
bc	0.583	+16.39	- 57.3$^{k''}$
aB	2.134	+47.91	-613.5$^{k''}$
BC	3.076	+29.50	-544.0$^{k''}$
Bb	0.456	+23.51	- 64.3$^{k''}$
Cc	0.235	0	0
Bc	0.292	+19.30	- 33.8$^{k''}$

$M_e = -(374)(2.20) + (332)(1.953)$

$= \underline{-174^{k''}}$

Step 4: *Distribute, carry over, and obtain secondary end moments. These end moments are underlined. With the section moduli known, it is simple to compute the secondary stress intensities from these.*

Note in this case that because of symmetry only half the truss needs to be considered; further, it is known, therefore, that joints C and c do not rotate. These joints never have to be unlocked.

13.19 Supplementary Remarks—Symmetrical and Antisymmetrical Loads, Elastic Center, and Column Analogy.

In presenting an elementary discussion of any subject, the writer must draw a rather arbitrary line between the fundamental and advanced aspects of the field, since there are always marginal topics that may or may not be included. It is desirable, however, to mention some of these topics briefly so as to suggest transitional reading material for those who intend to study further.

Here and there in previous discussions we have mentioned and used symmetry to a limited extent. Whenever we are dealing with a symmetrical structure, we should always be on the alert to utilize symmetry as effectively as possible. For example, consider the closed-ring type of structure shown in Fig. 13.30. Strictly speaking, this structure is indeterminate to the third degree. If both the frame and the loading are symmetrical about both the x and the y axis, however, then we can reason from symmetry that the shear is zero and the axial force is 6 kips compression at the mid-point cross section of the girder. Only the moment remains unknown. Because of symmetry, therefore, only one statically indeterminate quantity remains, instead of three.

The gain from symmetry in the above situation suggests that we can gain considerable simplification even when we have an *unsymmetrical load* acting on a *symmetrical structure*. Consider such a situation as that shown in Fig. 13.31. Suppose that this frame (called a "Vierendeel truss") is symmetrical about the vertical axis only. Consider the solution of the frame under the given unsymmetrical load as shown in Fig. 13.31a. If the slope-deflection method is used, there is a total of

11 unknowns—8θ and 3ψ angles. Suppose that the load is broken down into two separate systems, one a symmetrical system shown in Fig. 13.31b and one an antisymmetrical system shown in Fig. 13.31c. Obviously, the sum of these two systems is equal to the given load, and therefore the sum of the results for the two separate systems is equal to the results for the given load.

Let us now compare the computational work of analyzing the structure for the given unsymmetrical load with the sum of the computational works for the symmet-

Figure 13.30 Symmetrical structure, symmetrically loaded

Figure 13.31 Use of symmetrical and antisymmetrical loads

rical and antisymmetrical loads. For the case of the symmetrical loads, there are only five independent unknowns—four θ angles and one ψ angle—since, by symmetry,

$$\theta_a = -\theta_d \qquad \theta_b = -\theta_c \qquad \theta_e = -\theta_h \qquad \theta_f = -\theta_g$$
$$\psi \text{ cols} = \psi_{fg} = 0 \qquad \psi_{ef} = -\psi_{gh}$$

For the case of the antisymmetrical loads, there are six independent unknowns—four θ and two ψ angles—since in this case, by antisymmetry,

$$\theta_a = \theta_d \qquad \theta_b = \theta_c \qquad \theta_e = \theta_h \qquad \theta_f = \theta_g \qquad \psi_{ef} = \psi_{gh}$$

Since the computational work is roughly proportional to the square of the number of unknowns, using symmetrical and antisymmetrical loads almost cuts the computational work in half. This idea is very useful when we are dealing with symmetrical structures and deserves further study.[1]

The so-called "elastic center" is another useful idea that we have not discussed.[2] The elastic-center technique is applicable to the closed-ring type of structures; a frame such as that shown in Fig. 13.32 would be classified as this type if we consider the ground as being the closing side of the ring. We may analyze this structure by means of superposition equations, selecting the redundants as shown in Fig. 13.32b, which is the same selection as that used in Example 13.14. Proceeding with this

[1] J. S. Newell, Symmetric and Anti-symmetric Loadings, *Civil Eng.*, April, 1939, pp. 249–251. W. L. Andrée, Das B = U Verfahren, R. Oldenbourg-Verlag, Munich, 1919.

[2] W. M. Fife and J. B. Wilbur, "Theory of Statically Indeterminate Structures," pp. 114–120, McGraw-Hill Book Company, Inc., New York, 1937.

Figure 13.32 Use of elastic center

solution involves three simultaneous equations of the following form:

$$\Delta_{ao} + X_a\delta_{aa} + X_b\delta_{ab} + X_c\delta_{ac} = 0$$
$$\Delta_{bo} + X_a\delta_{ab} + X_b\delta_{bb} + X_c\delta_{bc} = 0$$
$$\Delta_{co} + X_a\delta_{ac} + X_b\delta_{bc} + X_c\delta_{cc} = 0$$

If we can select the three redundants in such a manner that δ_{ab}, δ_{ac}, and δ_{bc} are all equal to zero, then each of these equations will contain only one redundant and we will not have to solve them simultaneously. We can do this if we apply the redundants at some point o as shown in Fig. 13.32c, where the two coordinates of point o and the inclination α of the x axis are selected so as to make δ_{ab}, δ_{ac}, and δ_{bc} all equal to zero simultaneously. The redundants acting at point o are assumed to be connected by two rigid (nondeformable) arms to the two sides of the cut in the girder. Note that the two sets of redundants in Figs. 13.32b and c are statically equivalent but do not have the same values, of course.

The detailed calculations involved in using this elastic-center procedure are found to be similar to computing static moments and products and moments of inertia of areas. Professor Hardy Cross recognized this and suggested organizing the computations as in computing the stresses in a column subjected to combined bending and direct stress. He called this suggested procedure "column analogy."[1]

13.20 Problems for Solution

*Problem 13.1 Find all the reactions of the structure shown in Fig. 13.33, using superposition equations as the basis for the solution. $L/A = 1$ for all members.

Figure 13.33 Problem 13.1

[1] H. Cross and N. D. Morgan, "Continuous Frames of Reinforced Concrete," John Wiley & Sons, Inc., New York, 1932.

Problem 13.2   Compute the bar forces in the members of the truss shown in Fig. 13.34, using the superposition-equation method.   Cross-sectional areas of members, in square inches, are shown in parentheses.

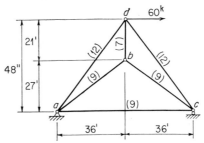

Figure 13.34   Problem 13.2

*Problem 13.3   Using superposition equations, compute the bar force in the tie rod ad of the structure of Fig. 13.35.   Cross-sectional areas of the members, in square inches, are shown in parentheses.

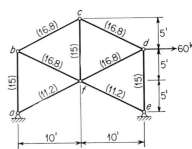

Figure 13.35   Problem 13.3   **Figure 13.36**   Problem 13.4

*Problem 13.4   Using superposition equations, compute the bar force in all members of the arch of Fig. 13.36.   Cross-sectional areas in square inches are shown in parentheses. $E = 30 \times 10^3$ kips per sq in., $\alpha_t = 1/150,000$ per °F.

*Problem 13.5   Find the horizontal component of the right reaction of the arch in Prob. 13.4, due to each of the following conditions: (a) Increase of temperature of 50°F in bars ab, bc, cd, de.   No change in remaining bars.   (b) If bars bc and cd are ¼ in. too short and bar cf is ⅛ in. too long owing to errors in fabrication and it was necessary to force them into place.   (c) If the supports settle as follows:

Left support: Vertical   = 0.48 in. down
                    Horizontal = 0.24 in. to left
Right support: Vertical   = 0.24 in. down
                    Horizontal = 0.36 in. to right

Problem 13.6   Compute the reactions and the bar forces in all members of the structure shown in Fig. 13.37.   Cross-sectional areas in square inches are shown in parentheses.   Calibration of spring de indicates that a force of 20 kips elongates it 1 in. $E = 30,000$ kips per sq in.

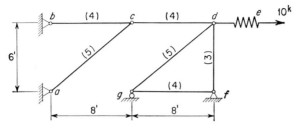

Figure 13.37   Problem 13.6

Problem 13.7   Compute the horizontal component of the deflection of joint d due to the load acting on the structure shown in Fig. 13.38.   The stiffness of spring bc is such that it elongates 0.036 in. under a tensile force of 1 kip.   For all other members, $A = 2$ sq in. and $E = 30,000$ kips per sq in.

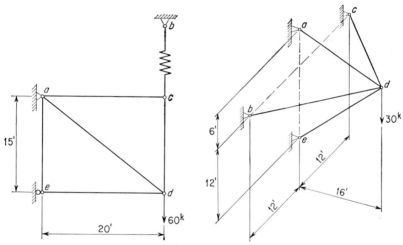

Figure 13.38   Problem 13.7   **Figure 13.39**   Problem 13.8

Problem 13.8   All joints of the structure shown in Fig. 13.39 are frictionless ball-and-socket joints.   Joints b, c, and d lie in the same horizontal plane.   For all members, $A = 3$ sq in. and $E = 30,000$ kips per sq in.   Compute the bar forces in all members due to the 30-kip vertical load shown.

Problem 13.9   Consider the beam shown in Fig. 13.40.

(a) Estimate in some reasonable manner (which you should describe) the reactions developed in this beam by the loads shown.   Be sure that your estimated reactions at least satisfy static equilibrium.   Draw the shear and bending-moment diagrams for your solution, and sketch the elastic curve for the beam.

(b) Using the superposition equations as a basis for the solution, analyze the beam for the load shown and draw the shear and bending-moment diagrams corresponding to your results.

(c) Analyze the beam only for the effect of a vertical settlement of support b of 0.24 in. and a clockwise rotation of support a of 0.005 radian. $E = 30,000$ kips per sq in.

(d) The values which you estimated in part a for the reactions will not, in general, give consistent deflections for the structure.   For example, instead of the supports being immovable as intended in this part of the solution, your values may imply certain support movements in addition to the given loads.   What movements are implied by your estimate?

Figure 13.40   Problem 13.9

Figure 13.41   Problem 13.10

*Problem 13.10   Draw the bending-moment diagram for the frame shown in Fig. 13.41.   Use Castigliano's theorem as a basis for the solution.   Consider only the effect of bending deformation.

*Problem 13.11   Compute the reactions of the structure shown in Fig. 13.42. Neglect deformation due to axial force. E and I are constant.

Figure 13.42   Problem 13.11

*Problem 13.12   Compute the reactions on the structure shown in Fig. 13.43. Neglect deformation due to axial force. E and I are constant.

Figure 13.43   Problem 13.12

*Problem 13.13   Draw the shear and bending-moment diagrams for member AB of the frame shown in Fig. 13.44.   Neglect deformation due to axial force.

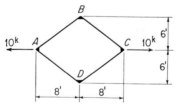
Figure 13.44   Problem 13.13

Problem 13.14   Analyze the structure shown in Fig. 13.45 and draw the bending-moment diagram for member *CD*.

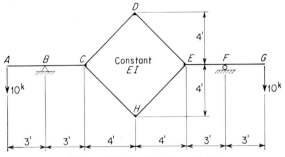

Figure 13.45   Problem 13.14

*Problem 13.15   Referring to Fig. 13.46, draw the bending-moment curve for the beam *AB*, using Castigliano's theorem.

Figure 13.46   Problem 13.15

Problem 13.16   Referring to Fig. 13.47, compute the axial forces in the members of the king-post truss, due to the load shown.   Also, draw the bending-moment curve for member *AC*.

Member *AC*: $A = 12$ sq in.   and $I = 432$ in.[4]
Member *AD*: $A = 3$ sq in.
Member *DC*: $A = 3$ sq in.
Member *BD*: $A = 2$ sq in.

Figure 13.47   Problem 13.16

*Problem 13.17   In the structure shown in Fig. 13.48, the cross-sectional areas of members, in square inches, are shown in parentheses. $E = 30 \times 10^3$ kips per sq in.,

I of beam = 4,000 in.[4]   Compute the force in the tie rod, which is connected to the beam and the truss by hinged ends.

Figure 13.48   Problem 13.17

Figure 13.49   Problem 13.18

Problem 13.18   Compute the reactions of the structure shown in Fig. 13.49.

Problem 13.19   Refer to the structure shown in Fig. 13.50.

(a) Compute the reactions due to the load shown.

(b) Suppose that the tie rod ec were removed and the beam were supported at c by a roller support.   Compute the reactions which would be developed in this modified structure if it were unloaded but subjected to the following support movements:

   a settles 0.72 in. downward

   c settles 0.12 in. downward

   d rotates 0.005 radian counterclockwise

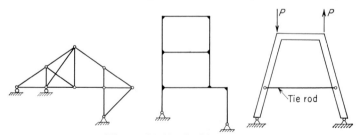

Figure 13.50   Problem 13.19

Problem 13.20   Discuss each of the structures shown in Fig 13.51 with respect to stability and statical indeterminany.   If indeterminate, indicate what you would

Figure 13.51   Problem 13.20

select for redundants.   For the right structure, what can you reason about the stress analysis by applying principles of symmetry and antisymmetry?

Problem 13.21   Consider the two-span continuous beam used in Prob. 13.9.   Suppose that the moments of inertia in each span were doubled by the addition of flange plates.   What effect would this modification of the structure have on the following results previously computed in the solution of that problem?

(a) The bending moments computed for the given loading.
(b) The bending moments computed for the given support movements.
(c) The bending deflections computed for the given support movements.
(d) The bending stress intensities computed for the given support movements.

*Problem 13.22   Refer to Fig 13.52.   Compute the end moments in all the members of this frame, using the slope-deflection method.   Draw the moment curves for members *AB* and *BD*.

Figure 13.52   Problem 13.22   **Figure 13.53**   Problem 13.23

*Problem 13.23   Refer to Fig. 13.53.   Compute the end moments in all members of this frame, using the slope-deflection method.   Draw the shear and moment curves for member *ab*.

Problem 13.24   Solve parts *b* and *c* of Prob. 13.9, using the slope-deflection method.

*Problem 13.25   Using the slope-deflection method, find all the end moments and support reactions of the frame shown in Fig. 13.54.

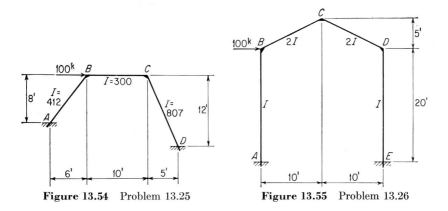

Figure 13.54   Problem 13.25   **Figure 13.55**   Problem 13.26

Problem 13.26   Using the slope-deflection method, find all the end moments and support reactions of the frame shown in Fig. 13.55.

Problem 13.27   A complete solution of the structure shown in Fig. 13.56 is not required.   However,

(a) Indicate the independent θ and ψ angles.   If some ψ angles are related, indicate the relationships.

(b) Write the equations of statics which are the basis of the slope-deflection solution of this structure.

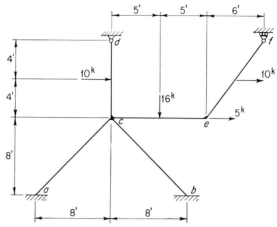

Figure 13.56   Problem 13.27

Problem 13.28   Assume that the structure shown in Fig. 13.57 is symmetrical about its vertical center line.

(a) Indicate the independent θ and ψ angles, and write the appropriate equations of statics, assuming that the loading is symmetrical about the vertical center line.

(b) Do likewise for an antisymmetrical loading.

Figure 13.57   Problem 13.28   **Figure 13.58**   Problem 13.29

*Problem 13.29**   Refer to Fig. 13.58.   Using moment distribution, compute the end moments in the members of this frame, and draw the shear and moment curves for member *AB*.

Problem 13.30   Solve parts *b* and *c* of Prob. 13.9, using moment distribution.

*Problem 13.31   Refer to Fig. 13.59.   Find the end moments of this frame, using the moment-distribution method.

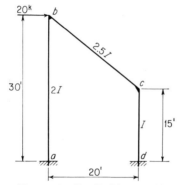

Figure 13.59   Problem 13.31   Figure 13.60   Problem 13.32

*Problem 13.32   Compute the end moments in the members of the frame shown in Fig. 13.60, using the moment-distribution method.

Problem 13.33   Refer to Fig. 13.61.   Find the end moments in the members of this frame, using the moment-distribution method.

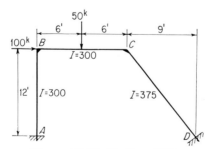

Figure 13.61   Problem 13.33

*Problem 13.34   Refer to Fig. 13.62.   Find the end moments in this frame, using the moment-distribution method.

Figure 13.62   Problem 13.34

*Problem 13.35   For the frame shown in Fig. 13.63, draw the bending-moment curves, using the moment-distribution method.

Figure 13.63   Problem 13.35

Problem 13.36   Consider the structure shown in Fig. 13.64.

(a) Using the moment-distribution method, compute the end moments produced in all members by the load shown.

(b) Using the results of part a, describe how you would compute the horizontal deflection of C.

(c) How large a horizontal force would now have to be applied at joint C in order to push it back to its original position?

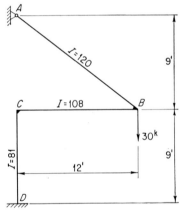

Figure 13.64   Problem 13.36

Problem 13.37   Consider the structure shown in Fig. 13.65.

(a) Using the moment-distribution method, compute the end moments produced in all members by the load shown.

(b) Suppose that this structure were altered by pin-connecting joint B to a support 12 ft above it by means of a tie rod.   Compute the axial force developed in this tie rod by the 10-kip vertical load at joint C.   Neglect the effect of the axial change in length of the tie rod.

(c) Describe how you could incorporate the effect of the axial change of length of the tie rod on the moment-distribution solution.

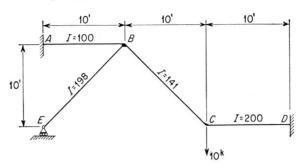

Figure 13.65   Problem 13.37

Problem 13.38   Assuming that the structures shown in Fig. 13.66 are unsymmetrical and using suitable sketches to describe your ideas, indicate the various cases into which you would divide the moment-distribution solution of each of the structures.

Figure 13.66   Problem 13.38

*Problem 13.39   Compute the end moments in all members of the frame shown in Fig. 13.67.

Figure 13.67   Problem 13.39

Problem 13.40   Utilizing principles of symmetry and antisymmetry, compute the end moments in all members of the frame shown in **Fig. 13.68** by the moment-distribution method.

Figure 13.68   Problem 13.40

Problem 13.41   Consider the beam shown in Fig. 13.69, in which $I = 500$ in.[4], $A = 30$ sq in., and $E = 30 \times 10^3$ kips per sq in.   Compare the solution of this problem by the theorem of three moments, slope deflection, and superposition equations.   *Hints:* To what degree is the beam indeterminate?   Can you find the horizontal reactions by three moments or slope deflection?   Which method do you consider to be superior?   How many simultaneous equations are involved in each solution?

Figure 13.69   Problem 13.41

Problem 13.42   Determine the number of independent θ and ψ angles in each of the structures shown in Figs. 13.12 and 13.15.

14

Influence Lines for Statically Indeterminate Structures

14.1 Introduction. In Chap. 13, various methods of analyzing indeterminate structures are discussed; in all cases, however, the structures are subjected to some particular condition of loading. Often it is necessary to analyze an indeterminate structure for the effect of a movable or a moving load. In such cases, it is convenient to prepare influence lines or influence tables for the various stress components, since from these we can determine both how to load the structure to produce a maximum effect and likewise the magnitude of this maximum effect.

In Chap. 6, the preparation and use of influence lines for statically determinate structures are discussed. In such cases, we found that after a little practice we could draw an entire influence line by figuring a few key ordinates and connecting them with straight lines. Influence lines for indeterminate structures cannot be drawn so easily, however, since in general they are curved lines or, at best, a series of chords of a curved line.

Fortunately, influence lines of the latter type occur quite frequently. When an indeterminate structure is loaded at the panel points by floor beams, which in turn support stringers, which act as simple beams between the floor beams, it is easy to show that the various influence lines for the indeterminate structure are straight lines between panel points. If, however, the stringers are continuous over several floor beams, the influence lines are curved lines between panel points, though in most practical cases the departure of these curves from a straight line between panel points is rather slight. If the moving load does not act through a stringer-floor-beam system and can be applied to the structure at any point along its length, the influence lines are likewise curved lines.

The first step in preparing influence lines for the various stresses in an indeterminate structure is to determine the influence lines for the redundants. Once this has been done, the influence lines for any other reaction, bar force, shear, or moment can be computed by statics.

14.2 Influence Line by Successive Positions of Unit Load. In Chap. 6, it is pointed out that the ordinates of an influence line for some particular quantity can always be obtained by placing a unit load successively at each possible load point on the structure and computing the value of that quantity for each of these positions. This same procedure may be followed to obtain the influence lines for the redundants of an indeterminate structure. Doing so means solving a number of problems in just the same way as in Chap. 13.

Offhand this might seem a long and tedious process. It will be found, however, that the computations may be organized very efficiently, as is illustrated in Example 14.1. Moreover, once the influence lines for the redundants have been obtained, the influence lines for all other stress components can be obtained very easily, simply by superimposing quantities already computed. In Example 14.1, once the influence-line ordinates have been computed for the redundants X_1 and X_2, the ordinates for all other bar forces may be computed in tabular form, by means of the relation

$$F = F_o + X_1 F_1 + X_2 F_2$$

Note that this is very easy, for F_o bar forces have already been computed for all bars for every position of the unit load. While it takes longer to compute simply the influence lines for the redundants of an indeterminate truss by this method, influence lines for all the bar forces and reactions may be obtained essentially as fast by this method as by any other.

Example 14.1   *Assuming A to be constant for all bars, prepare influence lines for the forces in the redundant bars of this truss.*

Select forces in bars *CD* and *FG* as redundants. Compute these redundants for a unit load at any joint *n*, using superposition equations.

$$\Delta_1^{\rightarrow +\leftarrow} = \Delta_{1n} + X_1\delta_{11} + X_2\delta_{12} = 0 \quad (1)$$
$$\Delta_2^{\rightarrow +\leftarrow} = \Delta_{2n} + X_1\delta_{21} + X_2\delta_{22} = 0 \quad (2)$$

By symmetry, $\delta_{11} = \delta_{22}$
By Maxwell's law, $\delta_{12} = \delta_{21}$
Equations (1) and (2) therefore become

$$\Delta_{1n} + X_1\delta_{11} + X_2\delta_{12} = 0 \quad (1a)$$
$$\Delta_{2n} + X_1\delta_{12} + X_2\delta_{11} = 0 \quad (2a)$$

Using the method of virtual work to evaluate these deflection terms, the constants of the structure are

$$(1^k)(\delta_{11}) = \frac{1}{EA}\sum F_1^2 L$$

$$(1^k)(\delta_{12}) = \frac{1}{EA}\sum F_1 F_2 L$$

while the load terms are

$$(1^k)(\Delta_{1n}) = \frac{1}{EA}\sum F_1 F_n L$$

$$(1^k)(\Delta_{2n}) = \frac{1}{EA}\sum F_2 F_n L$$

Since *EA* is constant for all bars and the right-hand sides of Eqs. (1a) and (2a) are zero, for convenience we can let *EA = 1* for the rest of the solution. By symmetry, X_1 due to a unit load at *b* is equal to X_2 due to a unit load at *h*, etc. As a result, if we compute both X_1 and X_2 for a unit load placed successively at points *b, d,* and *e,* we shall have enough information to plot the complete influence lines for both X_1 and X_2.

Constants of structure:

Bar	L	F_1	F_2	F_1F_2L	F_1^2L
ac	30	-0.5	0	0	$+\ 7.5$
ce	30	-0.75	-0.25	$+5.625$	$+\ 16.875$
eg	30	-0.25	-0.75	$+5.625$	$+\ 1.875$
BD	30	$+1.0$	0	0	$+\ 30.0$
DF	30	$+0.5$	$+0.5$	$+7.5$	$+\ 7.5$
aB	25	$+0.8\dot{3}$	0	0	$+\ 17.35$
Bc	25	$-0.8\dot{3}$	0	0	$+\ 17.35$
cD	25	$-0.41\dot{6}$	$+0.41\dot{6}$	-4.345	$+\ 4.345$
De	25	$+0.41\dot{6}$	$-0.41\dot{6}$	-4.345	$+\ 4.345$
eF	25	$-0.41\dot{6}$	$+0.41\dot{6}$	-4.345	$+\ 4.345$
Fg	25	$+0.41\dot{6}$	$-0.41\dot{6}$	-4.345	$+\ 4.345$
Σ				$+1.37$	$+115.83$

$$\therefore \delta_{11} = +115.83 \qquad \delta_{12} = +1.37$$

Load terms:

		Unit load in left span					Unit load in center span						
			At b						At d			At e	
Bar	L	F_1	F_n	F_1F_nL	Bar	L	F_1	F_2	F_n	F_1F_nL	F_2F_nL	F_n	F_1F_nL
ac	30	-0.5	$+0.375$	$-\ 5.625$	ce	30	-0.75	-0.25	$+0.563$	-12.66	$-\ 4.22$	$+0.375$	$-\ 8.44$
aB	25	$+0.83$	-0.625	-13.0	eg	30	-0.25	-0.75	$+0.188$	$-\ 1.41$	$-\ 4.22$	$+0.375$	$-\ 2.81$
Bc	25	-0.83	-0.625	$+13.0$	DF	30	$+0.5$	$+0.5$	-0.375	$-\ 5.63$	$-\ 5.63$	-0.75	-11.25
Σ				$-\ 5.625$	cD	25	-0.416	$+0.416$	-0.938	$+\ 9.78$	$-\ 9.78$	-0.625	$+\ 6.50$
					De	25	$+0.416$	-0.416	-0.313	$-\ 3.26$	$+\ 3.26$	$+0.625$	$+\ 6.50$
					eF	25	-0.416	$+0.416$	$+0.313$	$-\ 3.26$	$+\ 3.26$	$+0.625$	$-\ 6.50$
					Fg	25	$+0.416$	-0.416	-0.313	$-\ 3.26$	$+\ 3.26$	-0.625	$-\ 6.50$
					Σ					-19.70	-14.07		-22.50

Note:
When load is at b, $\Delta_{2b} = 0$.
When load is at e, $\Delta_{1e} = \Delta_{2e}$.

Solution of equations:

Eq.	Operation	X_1	X_2	b	d	e	Check
(1) (2)		+115.83 + 1.37	+ 1.37 +115.83	+5.625 +0	+19.70 +14.07	+22.50 +22.50	+165.025 +153.77
(1')	(1) × 0.01182	+ 1.37	+ 0.016	+0.066	+ 0.233	+ 0.266	+ 1.951
(3)	(2) − (1')		+115.814	−0.066	+13.837	+22.234	+151.819
			+ 1.0	−0.00057	+ 0.1196	+ 0.1920	+ 1.3100
		− 1.37		+0.00078	− 0.1638	− 0.2610	
		+115.83		+5.6258	+19.5362	+22.2390	
		+ 1.0		+0.0486	+ 0.1688	+ 0.1920	

14.3   Müller-Breslau's Principle for Obtaining Influence Lines.

Müller-Breslau's principle provides a very convenient method of computing[1] influence lines and likewise is the basis for certain indirect methods of model analysis.   This principle may be stated as follows:

The ordinates of the influence line for any stress element (such as axial force, shear, moment, or reaction) of any structure are proportional to those of the deflection curve which is obtained by removing the restraint corresponding to that element from the structure and introducing in its place a corresponding deformation into the primary structure which remains.

This principle is applicable to any type of structure, whether beam, truss, or frame or whether statically determinate or indeterminate.   **In the case of indeterminate structures, this principle is limited to structures the material of which is elastic and follows Hooke's law.**   This limitation is not particularly important, however, since the vast majority of practical cases fall into this category.

The validity of this principle may be demonstrated in the following manner: For this purpose, consider the two-span continuous beam shown in Fig. 14.1a.   Suppose that the influence line for the vertical reaction at a is required.   The influence line may be plotted after the reaction has been evaluated for a unit vertical load applied successively at various points n along the structure, each evaluation being carried out

[1] Likewise, by applying Müller-Breslau's principle, it is often possible to sketch the shape of an influence line roughly and thus determine, accurately enough for design purposes, how to load the structure so as to produce a maximum effect.

as follows: Temporarily remove the roller support at a from the actual structure, leaving the primary structure shown in Fig. 14.1b. Suppose that this primary structure is acted upon by the unit load at a point n and a vertical upward force R_a at point a. If this force has the same value as the vertical reaction at point a on the actual structure, then the stresses—and hence the deformation—of the primary structure will be exactly the same as those of the actual structure. The elastic curve of the primary structure under such conditions will therefore be as indicated in Fig. 14.1b, the vertical deflection at point a being zero.

Suppose that we now consider the primary structure to be acted upon by simply a vertical force F at point a. In this case, the primary structure will deflect as shown in Fig. 14.1c. Thus we have considered the primary structure under the action of two separate and distinct force systems: (1) the forces in sketch b and (2) those in sketch c.

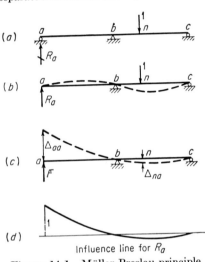

Influence line for R_a

Figure 14.1   Müller-Breslau principle

Applying Betti's law to this situation, we may write

$$(R_a)(\Delta_{aa}) + (1)(\Delta_{na}) = (F)(0)$$

and therefore

$$R_a = -\frac{\Delta_{na}}{\Delta_{aa}}(1) \qquad (14.1)$$

where the same notation is used to designate these deflections as that in the superposition-equation method.

From this equation, it is apparent that the reaction R_a when the unit vertical load is at point n is proportional to the deflection Δ_{na} at that point. The shape of the influence line for R_a is therefore the same as the shape of the elastic curve of the structure when it is acted upon by a force F at point a. The magnitude of the influence line ordinate at any point n may be obtained by dividing the deflection at that point on this elastic curve by the deflection at point a. In this manner, we have demonstrated that influence lines may be obtained in the manner outlined by Müller-Breslau's principle.

In a similar manner, the validity of this principle may be demonstrated for any stress element of any structure. In the general case, Eq. (14.1) may be written as follows for any stress element X_a:

$$X_a = -\frac{\Delta_{na}}{\Delta_{aa}}(1) \qquad (14.2)$$

It is important to note the sign convention of this equation, viz., X_a is plus when in the same sense as the introduced deflection Δ_{aa}, and Δ_{na} is plus when in the same sense as the applied unit load, the influence of which is given by the ordinates of the influence line. Note further that X_a may represent either a force or a couple. If X_a is a force, the corresponding Δ_{aa} is a linear deflection; but if X_a is a couple, the corresponding Δ_{aa} is an angular rotation.

It is also important to note that the magnitude of any influence-line ordinate is independent of the magnitude of the force F which must be applied to introduce the deflection Δ_{aa} into the primary structure. **For computation of the influence-line ordinates, F is usually taken as unity and Δ_{aa} and Δ_{na} are computed to correspond.**

Examples 14.2 and 14.3 illustrate the application of this procedure to continuous beams. **When applying this method, note that, if the actual structure is indeterminate to more than the first degree, the primary structure which remains after the removal of a redundant is still a statically indeterminate structure.** This does not cause any real difficulty, however. It simply means that, before the deflections Δ_{aa} and Δ_{na} can be computed, the statically indeterminate primary structure must be analyzed by one of the methods of Chap. 13.

Example 14.2 *Prepare an influence line for the vertical reaction at b of this beam.*

Applying Müller-Breslau's principle, we may select the primary structure shown and write that

$$X_b^\uparrow = -\frac{\Delta_{nb}^\downarrow}{\Delta_{bb}^\uparrow}\,(1^k)$$

where the plus direction of the various terms is shown.

If, for convenience, we decide to call Δ_{nb} plus when up, we must reverse the sign of the right-hand side of this equation and write

$$X_b^\uparrow = \frac{\Delta_{nb}^\uparrow}{\Delta_{bb}^\uparrow}\,(1^k)$$

By the second moment-area theorem,

$$EI\Delta_{nb} = (20)\left(\frac{x}{2}\right)\left(\frac{2x}{3}\right)$$
$$+ (20 - x)\left(\frac{x}{2}\right)\left(\frac{x}{3}\right) = \frac{x^2}{6}(60 - x)$$

$$EI\Delta_{bb} = \frac{(20)^2}{6}(60 - 20) = \frac{8,000}{3}$$

$$\therefore\ X_b^\uparrow = \frac{x^2(60 - x)}{16,000}$$

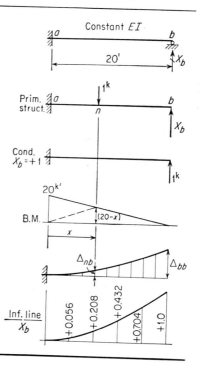

Example 14.3 *Prepare an influence line for the moment at support b of this beam.*

Using Müller-Breslau's principle,

$$X_b^{\,\rangle\,\langle} = -\frac{\Delta_{nb}^{\downarrow}}{\Delta_{bb}^{\,\rangle\,\langle}}\,(1^k) \qquad or \qquad X_b^{\,\rangle\,\langle} = +\frac{\Delta_{nb}^{\uparrow}}{\Delta_{bb}^{\,\rangle\,\langle}}\,(1^k)$$

if we reverse the sign convention for Δ_{nb}.

Computing Δ_{nb} and Δ_{bb} by the moment-area or elastic-load procedure,

$EI_1\tau_1 = (0.5)(7.5) = 3.75$

$EI_1\tau_2 = (1.1)(6)(\frac{2}{3}) - (0.305)(6)(\frac{1}{3}) = 3.834$

$\therefore EI_1\Delta_{bb} = 3.75 + 3.83 = \underline{\underline{7.58}}$

Span *ab*:

$$EI_1\Delta_{nb}^{\uparrow} = \left(\frac{x}{15}\right)\left(\frac{x^2}{6}\right) - \left(\frac{1}{2}\right)\left(\frac{x}{2}\right)\left(\frac{2x}{3}\right) - \left(\frac{1}{2} - \frac{x}{30}\right)\left(\frac{x^2}{6}\right) = \frac{x^3}{60} - \frac{x^2}{4}$$

$$\therefore X_b = \frac{1}{7.58}\left(\frac{x^3}{60} - \frac{x^2}{4}\right)$$

Span *bc*:

$$EI_1\Delta_{nb}^{\uparrow} = -3.834x + (1.1)\left(\frac{x^2}{3}\right) + (1.1 - 0.0928x)\left(\frac{x^2}{6}\right) - (0.02542)\left(\frac{x^3}{6}\right)$$

$$= -3.834x + 0.556x^2 - 0.0197x^3$$

$$\therefore X_b = \frac{1}{7.58}(-3.834x + 0.556x^2 - 0.0197x^3)$$

etc., for spans cd and de. From these equations, the ordinates every 3 ft are found to be as noted.

14.4   Influence Lines Obtained by Superposition of the Effects of Fixed End Moments.   This method is very useful for determining influence lines for the end moments of indeterminate beams or frames. It involves using moment distribution to determine the separate effects of each of the fixed end moments of the various loaded members. These separate effects may then be superimposed to give the total end moments. When properly organized as illustrated in Example 14.4, it is a very effective method of obtaining influence lines for the end moments.

Essentially this method consists of the following steps:

1. Apply a fixed end moment of unity at one end of a member.   Using the moment-distribution procedure, compute the resulting end moments in all members.   Repeat this process for each end of every member that can have a fixed end moment developed by the applied loads.

2. Compute the fixed end moments developed by a unit load placed in turn at each of the various load points.

3. Combine the data from steps 1 and 2 to find the end moments throughout caused by a unit load at each of the various load points of the structure.

Of course, when the influence lines have been computed for the end moments, other influence lines may be computed by statics.

When computing step 1 of the above procedure, note that actually only one moment-distribution solution is required for each joint of the frame.   This may be done for a fixed end moment of unity in any member at a joint.   Once this is done, the effect of a fixed end moment of unity in any of the other members meeting at that joint may be determined by inspection.   This is evident in the solution of Example 14.4.

Example 14.4 *By superimposing the effects of fixed moments, prepare an influence table for the end moments of the frame used in Example 13.25.   Give ordinates every 5 ft along girder BDEF.*

In this case, there can be a sidesway of the columns. To consider this we need to combine a case A and a case B type of solution.

Use the case B end moments from Example 13.25, dividing the data there by 60.

Step 1: *Find the end moments caused by an FEM = +1 in ends of girder members.*

$F.E. M_{BD} = +1.0$

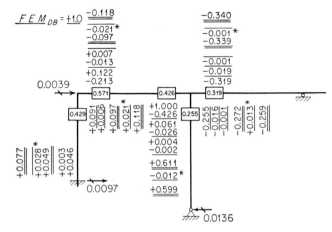

These are the only actual moment-distribution solutions that need to be carried through. The end moments caused by $FEM_{DE} = +1.000$ can be written by inspection simply by shifting the $+1.000$ figure from the DB to the DE column of figures. Likewise, the end moments due to either $FEM_{ED} = +1.0$ or $FEM_{EF} = +1.0$ will be equal to one-half those due to $FEM_{DE} = +1$, with the exception of the ends ED and EF.

Summary of end moments caused by FEM = +1 at the various points.

$FEM = +1$ at point	M_{AB}	M_{BD}	M_{DB}	M_{DE}	M_{DC}	M_{ED}
BD	+0.071	+0.236	−0.300	+0.083	+0.217	0
DB	+0.077	−0.118	+0.599	−0.340	−0.259	0
DE	+0.077	−0.118	−0.401	+0.660	−0.259	0
ED	−0.038	+0.059	+0.201	−0.330	+0.129	0
EF	−0.038	+0.059	+0.201	−0.330	+0.129	−1.0

Step 2: FEM due to unit load at various load points:

Load at	FEM developed at end				
	BD	DB	DE	ED	EF
1	−2.8125	+0.9375			
2	−2.50	+2.50			
3	−0.9375	+2.8125			
4			−2.8125	+0.9375	
5			−2.50	+2.50	
6			−0.9375	+2.8125	
F					−4.00

Step 3: *Influence table for end moments:*

Load at	Factor × [end moment corresponding to FEM = +1 at point (−)]	M_{AB}	M_{BD}	M_{DB}	M_{DE}	M_{DC}	M_{ED}
1	−2.8125 × BD	−0.199	−0.664	+0.844	−0.233	−0.610	
	+0.9375 × DB	+0.072	−0.111	+0.561	−0.318	−0.243	
		−0.127	−0.775	+1.405	−0.551	−0.853	0
2	−2.50 × BD	−0.172	−0.590	+0.750	−0.207	−0.543	
	+2.50 × DB	+0.192	−0.295	+1.498	−0.850	−0.648	
		+0.020	−0.885	+2.248	−1.057	−1.191	0
3	−0.9375 × BD	−0.067	−0.221	+0.281	−0.078	−0.203	
	+2.8125 × DB	+0.216	−0.332	+1.682	−0.956	−0.729	
		+0.149	−0.553	+1.963	−1.034	−0.932	0
4	−2.8125 × DE	−0.216	+0.332	+1.128	−1.852	+0.729	
	+0.9375 × ED	−0.036	+0.054	+0.188	−0.308	+0.120	
		−0.252	+0.386	+1.316	−2.160	+0.849	0
5	−2.50 × DE	−0.192	+0.295	+1.002	−1.648	+0.648	
	+2.50 × ED	−0.095	+0.145	+0.500	−0.820	+0.320	
		−0.287	+0.440	+1.502	−2.468	+0.968	0
6	−0.9375 × DE	−0.072	+0.111	+0.376	−0.619	+0.243	
	+2.8125 × ED	−0.107	+0.163	+0.565	−0.922	+0.360	
		−0.179	+0.274	+0.941	−1.541	+0.603	0
F	−4.0 × EF	+0.152	−0.232	−0.804	+1.321	−0.521	+4.0

14.5   Problems for Solution

Problem 14.1   (*a*) Assuming L/A to be constant for all bars, prepare an influence line for the force in bar CD of the truss shown in Fig. 14.2.

(*b*) Using the data from part *a*, likewise prepare influence lines for the force in bars Bc and bc.

Figure 14.2   Problem 14.1

Problem 14.2   Prepare influence lines for the forces in bars bC and Cd of the truss shown in Example 13.5.

Problem 14.3   Using Müller-Breslau's principle, prepare influence lines for (*a*) the moment at point *c* of the beam shown in Example 14.3; (*b*) the vertical reaction at point *b* of this same beam.

Problem 14.4   Using the method described in Art. 14.4 prepare influence lines for the end moments of the beam shown in Example 14.3.

15

Introduction to Matrix Methods of Structural Analysis

15.1 Introduction. For many years, structural engineers have been investigating the application of methods and notations used by mathematicians in linear algebra to the solution of structural analysis problems. Much of this work has been done in the last twenty-odd years and has more or less paralleled the development of improved procedures for solving linear simultaneous equations. Of course, even more recently, the general availability of the modern electronic digital computer has stimulated an intense interest in the use of matrix methods to formulate structural theory.

Matrix formulation provides a means of systematizing generalized procedures for the machine computation of structural problems. Such methods are particularly useful for dealing with complex highly redundant systems. Most of the published information on this subject is located in the periodical literature.[1] Only a few textbooks include treatments of matrix methods, though several more are in the process of being published.

15.2 Classification of Methods of Structural Analysis. It is of interest to discuss the methods of structural analysis presented in the

[1] Aeronautical structural engineers have played a leading role in utilizing matrix methods. The following references primarily from the civil engineering literature have been selected to introduce the reader to this subject:

S. H. Crandall, "Engineering Analysis," McGraw-Hill Book Company, Inc., New York, 1956. (Brief discussion of matrix notation and manipulation.)

J. L. Matheson, "Hyperstatic Structures," Butterworth's Scientific Publications, London, 1959. (See chap. 9, Matrix Methods, written by Dr. R. K. Livesley, for an excellent introductory treatment.)

P. B. Morice, "Linear Structural Analysis," The Ronald Press Company, New previous chapters from a more generalized point of view. This discussion will furnish a basis for classifying these methods, which will provide a better background for the matrix formulation of structural analysis.

Structural analysis involves computing not only the external reactions, and the internal forces (and stresses) of a structure, but also strains and deflections throughout. In so-called statically determinate structures, almost invariably the external reactions and internal forces (and stresses) are computed first; then, from the stresses, the strains can be determined, and subsequently deflections can be computed. This same order of computations is followed in many methods of analyzing statically indeterminate structures; that is, first the redundants and corresponding statically determinate primary structure are selected; then these redundant forces (and/or couples) are computed by solving an equal number of simultaneous equations, each of which expresses a known deflection condition for the primary structure in terms of the redundants; and then once the redundants are known, the stresses, strains, and deflections for the entire structure may be computed as in the case of a statically determinate structure. Such a method of structural analysis is referred to as a **force method of structural analysis,** since the first step in the computations involves computing the unknown external and internal forces (and/or couples) in the structure.

In other cases of statically indeterminate structures (and, very occasionally, of determinate structures), the above order of computation is completely inverted. Such a method of analysis is called a **displacement method of structural analysis.** In this approach, first the internal forces (and couples) are expressed in terms of the key displacement components of the structure; such expressions are substituted into the key equilibrium equations of the structure, thereby obtaining a system of linear simultaneous equations involving the key displacements as the unknowns; then the values of the displacements obtained from the

York, 1959. (Introductory text concerning the flexibility matrix method of structural analysis.)

S. U. Benscotter, Matrix Analysis of Continuous Beams, *Trans. ASCE*, vol. 112, p. 1109, 1947.

P. P. Chen, The Matrix Analysis of Pin-connected Structures, *Trans. ASCE*, vol. 114, p. 181, 1949.

G. Kron, Tensorial Analysis of Elastic Structures, *J. Franklin Inst.*, vol. 238, no. 6, December, 1944.

R. W. Clough, Matrix Analysis of Beams, *J. Eng. Mech. Div.*, *ASCE*, vol. 84, no. EMI, January, 1958.

R. W. Clough, Use of Modern Computers in Structural Analysis, *J. Struct. Div.*, *ASCE*, vol. 84, no. ST3, May, 1958.

J. H. Argyris, Energy Theorems and Structural Analysis, *Aircraft Eng.*, vol. 27, p. 347, 1955; and subsequent issues.

J. H. Argyris, Die Matrixentheorie der Statik, *Ingr.-Arch.*, vol. 25, no. 3, p. 174, 1957.

solution of these equations are substituted into the original expressions for the internal forces (and couples) to obtain the values of the latter; and finally, once all the internal forces (and couples) are known, it is easy to compute the reactions of the structure.

According to this classification, the methods discussed in Chap. 13 may be grouped as follows. The superposition-equation method, the application of Castigliano's second theorem, and the use of the three-moment equation are all force methods of analysis. The slope-deflection method is a displacement method. The moment-distribution method is a successive approximation procedure based on the same philosophy as the displacement methods.

15.3 Comparison of Force and Displacement Methods for Planar Trusses. The comparison of these two general methods of structural analysis can be focused more sharply by considering their application to a specific type of structure. For this purpose consider pin-jointed planar trusses. The complete structural analysis of such a structure having n joints, b bars, and r reaction components involves a total of $(2n + b)$ unknowns, namely, $(2n - r)$ joint displacement components (i.e., a horizontal and vertical component at each joint except from the support joints, where the displacement components corresponding to the r reaction components are known and usually equal to 0) and b bar forces and r reaction components.

If the structure is stable and statically determinate with respect to external and internal forces, $(b + r)$ is equal to $2n$. If a force method of solution is selected, there are $2n$ independent equations of statics ($\Sigma H = 0$ and $\Sigma V = 0$ at each joint) available to solve for the equal number of $(b + r)$ unknown forces. These $2n$ equations could be solved simultaneously, but usually it is more convenient to proceed as discussed in detail in Chap. 4. If the structure is stable and statically indeterminate, $(b + r)$ is greater than $2n$. In such a case, to solve for the $(b + r)$ unknown forces it is necessary to supplement the $2n$ equations of statics with $[(b + r) - 2n]$ deflection equations—one concerning the displacement of each of the $[(b + r) - 2n]$ redundants selected. Here again, the $(b + r)$ equilibrium and deflection equations could be solved simultaneously for the $(b + r)$ unknown forces. Usually, however, it is more convenient to proceed as discussed in Chap. 13 regarding the superposition-equation method or the use of Castigliano's second theorem. In effect, in this procedure, the equations of statics are used in the solution as described in Chap. 4, and only the $[(b + r) - 2n]$ deflection equations need to be solved simultaneously for the $[(b + r) - 2n]$ redundant forces contained in them as the unknowns. To summarize, in applying a force method of solution, usually the solution is arranged so as to avoid solving the entire number of equations of statics simultaneously. Only in the statically indeterminate structures is it necessary to solve equations simultaneously; and then it is the deflection equations which are solved for an equal number of unknown redundant forces.

So far here a displacement method of solution has not been formulated for the analysis of a truss, but it is easy to do so. Consider a typical

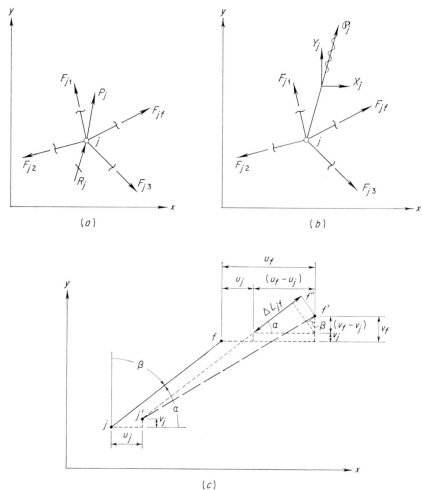

Figure 15.1 Displacement method for planar truss

joint j of a planar truss to which a certain number of bars b_j are connected. This joint might also be supported by a reactive force R_j and also acted upon by a known load P_j. If this joint were isolated, the equilibrium equations for the joint, $\sum_{}^{j} F_x = 0$ and $\sum_{}^{j} F_y = 0$, would involve the concurrent force system shown in Fig. 15.1a. For convenience, however, the load P_j and the reaction R_j are replaced by their resultant $\mathcal{P}_j$ and the system shown in Fig. 15.1b is used in the development below. Thus, for equilibrium of the joint,

$$\sum^{j} F_x = 0, \; \overset{\rightarrow}{+} \qquad X_j + \sum^{j} (F_{jf} \cos \alpha_{jf}) = 0$$

$$\sum^{j} F_y = 0, \; \uparrow + \qquad Y_j + \sum^{j} (F_{jf} \cos \beta_{jf}) = 0$$

(15.1)

in which X_j and Y_j are, respectively, the x and y components of the resultant joint force $\mathcal{P}_j$ and $\sum^{j}$ indicates that such contributions from the bar force F_{jf} for each bar jf at joint j are to be evaluated and summed algebraically.

By considering the kinematics of displacement of a bar jf, it is possible to relate the change in length of the bar ΔL_{jf} to the x and y components of the displacements of joints j and f. The displacements are exaggerated tremendously in Fig. 15.1c, but in the derivation of the following relation it is recognized that the rotation of the bar is in fact a small angle so that $f''f'$ is substantially normal to the original direction of the bar. Therefore,

$$\Delta L_{jf} = (u_f - u_j) \cos \alpha_{jf} + (v_f - v_j) \cos \beta_{jf}$$

(15.2)

However, for a bar of constant cross section and material,

$$\Delta L_{jf} = \frac{F_{jf} L_{jf}}{A_{jf} E_{jf}} \qquad \text{or} \qquad F_{jf} = \left(\frac{EA}{L} \right)_{jf} \Delta L_{jf}$$

(15.3)

Hence,

$$F_{jf} = \left(\frac{EA}{L} \right)_{jf} [(u_f - u_j) \cos \alpha_{jf} + (v_f - v_j) \cos \beta_{jf}]$$

(15.4)

which is the desired equation relating the bar force F_{jf} to the components of the displacements of the joints at each end of it: u_j and v_j, and u_f and v_f.

Substitution from Eq. (15.4) for F_{jf} in Eqs. (15.1) results in the following equations:

$$X_j = u_j \sum^{j} \left[\left(\frac{EA}{L} \right)_{jf} \cos^2 \alpha_{jf} \right] + v_j \sum^{j} \left[\left(\frac{EA}{L} \right)_{jf} \cos \alpha_{jf} \cos \beta_{jf} \right]$$

$$+ \sum^{jf} \left[u_f \left(\frac{EA}{L} \right)_{jf} (-\cos^2 \alpha_{jf}) \right] + \sum^{jf} \left[v_f \left(\frac{EA}{L} \right)_{jf} (-\cos \alpha_{jf} \cos \beta_{jf}) \right]$$

$$Y_j = u_j \sum^{j} \left[\left(\frac{EA}{L} \right)_{jf} \cos \alpha_{jf} \cos \beta_{jf} \right] + v_j \sum^{j} \left[\left(\frac{EA}{L} \right)_{jf} \cos^2 \beta_{jf} \right]$$

$$+ \sum^{jf} \left[u_f \left(\frac{EA}{L} \right)_{jf} (-\cos \alpha_{jf} \cos \beta_{jf}) \right] + \sum^{jf} \left[v_f \left(\frac{EA}{L} \right)_{jf} (-\cos^2 \beta_{jf}) \right]$$

(15.5)

In these equations, $\overset{j}{\sum}$ indicates that such contributions for each bar at joint j are to be evaluated and summed algebraically. Also, $\overset{jj}{\sum}$ indicates that such terms are to be evaluated for each bar at joint j, although, when these are summed, as many terms as there are bars will be obtained, each containing a different u or v as the case may be. At any rate, Eqs. (15.5) represent the two equilibrium equations for a joint j, expressed in terms of the u and v displacements at joint j and the u and v displacements of the joints at the far ends of all members connected to joint j.

For any planar truss (whether it is statically determinate or statically indeterminate with respect to either or both external reaction components and internal bar forces), a displacement method of solution utilizing equilibrium equations such as Eqs. (15.5) can be formulated. A total of $2n$ equilibrium equations may be obtained by applying Eqs. (15.5) to each of the n joints of the truss. *For an unsupported joint*, the values of X_j and Y_j in the equations are known, being defined simply by the value and direction of the known load P_j at the joint, and the unknowns are the joint displacement components involved. *For a joint supported by a hinge support*, the u and v components for this joint are known (and usually zero); but since the reactive force is unknown, both X_j and Y_j are unknown. *For a joint supported by a roller support*, the two equilibrium equations may be written for directions *parallel and perpendicular to the roller surface*. In the equation for the parallel direction, the joint load component is known but the parallel joint displacement is unknown, while in the equation for the perpendicular direction, the perpendicular joint displacement component is known (and usually zero) but the joint reaction component is unknown.

Therefore, the $2n$ equilibrium equations may be divided in two groups. From the x and y directions at the unsupported joints and the direction parallel to the roller surface at the roller-supported joints, a total of $(2n - r)$ equilibrium equations such as Eqs. (15.5) are obtained in the first group, involving *known* joint load components (such as X_j and Y_j) and the $(2n - r)$ *unknown* joint displacement components (such as u_j and v_j). The second group of r equilibrium equations are also obtained by applying Eqs. (15.5), but involve r unknown reaction components and certain of the $(2n - r)$ unknown displacement components. However, simultaneous solution of the $(2n - r)$ equations of the first group leads to the values of the $(2n - r)$ joint displacement components involved. Once these values are obtained, they may be substituted into the equations of the second group, and the reaction components then may be computed. Once the values of the displacement components are available, they may also be substituted into equations such as Eq. (15.4) to obtain the bar forces (such as F_{jf}), thereby completing the structural analysis of the truss.

It is of interest to compare the force-method solutions of several typical planar trusses, such as shown in Fig. 15.2, with the displacement-method solutions. This comparison is made simply on the basis of the number of equations which must be solved simultaneously, since the

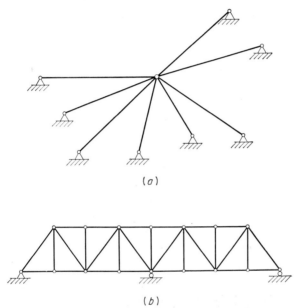

(a)

(b)

Figure 15.2 Examples of planar trusses

solution of these equations often represents the major part of the computational effort when slide rules or desk calculators are used. Ignored in the comparison are the time to set up the equations and the time to complete the solution after the simultaneous equations have been solved. For truss (a), $n = 9$, $b = 8$, and $r = 16$. Therefore, there are $[(b + r) - 2n]$ or six unknown redundant forces involved, but only $[2n - r]$ or two unknown joint displacements. Solution by the displacement method is preferable, therefore, since it involves only two simultaneous equations. For truss (b), $n = 16$, $b = 29$, and $r = 4$. Therefore, there is only one redundant force involved, but 28 unknown joint displacements. Solution by a force method is vastly superior in this case.

15.4 Generalization of Displacement Method. The displacement method developed above may be interpreted and generalized in a form which can be applied to any member-type structure, whether it is a framework or a frame, or whether it is two- or three-dimensional.

Refer to the first of Eqs. (15.5). Suppose that $u_j = 1$, but that $v_j = 0$ and that both u and v are zero at the joints at the far ends of all members meeting at joint j. In this case, the equation reduces to

$$X_j = (1) \sum_{}^{j} \left[\left(\frac{EA}{L} \right)_{jf} \cos^2 \alpha_{jf} \right]$$

Or, in other words, this summation can be interpreted to be equal to the x force which must be applied at j in order to produce only a unit x displacement at j and no other displacement at j or at the joints at the far ends of the members meeting at j. In this same fashion, the coefficients of the other displacement components in this equation could be interpreted to have similar physical significances.

The coefficients of the displacement terms on the right-hand side of Eqs. (15.5) are referred to as **stiffness coefficients** and denoted by k. Actually, two subscripts are used with k; for example, $k_{j_x f_y}$ designates the force which must be applied at joint j in the x direction when a unit displacement is introduced at joint f in the y direction, with all other joint displacement components controlled to be equal to zero. To illustrate the use of this notation, if the first of Eqs. (15.5) is applied to joint j in Fig. 15.1b and if the joints at the far ends of the four members shown are numbered 1, 2, 3, and 4, the following equation results:

$$X_j = k_{j_x j_x} u_j + k_{j_x j_y} v_j + k_{j_x 1_x} u_1 + k_{j_x 2_x} u_2 + k_{j_x 3_x} u_3$$
$$+ k_{j_x 4_x} u_4 + k_{j_x 1_y} v_1 + k_{j_x 2_y} v_2 + k_{j_x 3_y} v_3 + k_{j_x 4_y} v_4$$

This form of expressing the first of Eqs. (15.5) is a considerable improvement over the original. Further simplification of notation results if only one symbol is used to denote joint displacement components (whether it is an x, y, or z component of translation, or whether it is one of the joint rotations in the case of a frame) and if only one symbol is used to designate joint force (or couple) components. This simplified notation can also be interpreted more generally.

The following system will therefore be used to formulate the analysis of any member-type structure by the displacement method. First, on a suitable sketch of the structure, identify by a sequence of numbers the displacement components which are to be used to define the displacement of each joint. Thus, for example, in the case of a planar truss, 1 and 2 denote, respectively, the x and y components of joint a; 3 and 4, the x and y components of joint b; etc.   Next, resolve the joint forces (and couples, if involved) into components in the same direction as used for displacements, and use the same numbering system to denote these forces.   Now, let

P_m = joint force component at joint and in direction denoted by number m

D_m = joint displacement component at joint and in direction denoted by number m

k_{ml} = stiffness coefficient denoting joint force component acting at joint and in direction denoted by m when unit displacement is introduced at joint and in direction denoted by l when all other joint displacement components are equal to zero (i.e., prevented)

Then for a structure involving *s unknown joint displacement components*, the following *s equilibrium equations* are available to solve for these unknowns in the structural analysis by the *generalized displacement-method approach:*

$$P_1 = k_{11}D_1 + k_{12}D_2 + k_{13}D_3 + \cdots + k_{1s}D_s$$
$$P_2 = k_{21}D_1 + k_{22}D_2 + k_{23}D_3 + \cdots + k_{2s}D_s$$
$$\cdot \qquad \cdot \qquad \cdot \qquad \cdot \qquad \cdots \qquad \cdot \qquad (15.6)$$
$$P_s = k_{s1}D_1 + k_{s2}D_2 + k_{s3}D_3 + \cdots + k_{ss}D_s$$

If the structure has r *reaction components*, there are r corresponding *known joint displacement components* which are *assumed to be zero*.[1]   A total of $(r + s)$ equilibrium equations may be written, s of which are represented by Eqs. (15.6).   The remaining r equilibrium equations are of the following form, where the r reaction components are expressed in terms of the s unknown joint displacement components:

$$R_a = k_{a1}D_1 + k_{a2}D_2 + k_{a3}D_3 + \cdots + k_{as}D_s \qquad (15.7)$$

Once the s joint displacement components have been computed by the simultaneous solution of Eqs. (15.6), their values may be substituted into equations such as Eq. (15.7) to determine the values of the r reaction components.   The joint displacements may also be substituted into the stress-displacement relations for the structure in order to define the internal stresses.   For example, the bar forces F_{jf} may be determined by substituting the values of the displacements into Eq. (15.4).

Above it was noted that there are $(2n - r)$ unknown joint displacement components involved in a planar truss (or two-dimensional frame-

---

[1] It is possible to include the effect of support movements, temperature changes, and fabrication errors, but these effects will not be included in this discussion.

work). In a three-dimensional space framework, x, y, and z components are required to specify the displacement of each joint; therefore, there are a total of $(3n - r)$ unknown joint displacement components involved in such a structure. In the planar frame all joints of which are rigid, it is necessary to specify not only the x and y components of the lineal displacement of each joint, but also the rotation of each joint; there are therefore $(3n - r)$ unknown joint displacement components. In the three-dimensional space frame with rigid joints, it is necessary to specify the x, y, and z components of the lineal translation of the joint and the rotation of the joint about each of the three reference axes; there are therefore $(6n - r)$ unknown joint displacement components involved in such a structure.

So far it has been presumed that the loads (and/or couples) were applied only at the joints of the structure. If some of the members are subjected to distributed or concentrated loads between joints, the analysis of the structure may be handled as follows:

1. Assume temporarily that all the joints are temporarily locked against translation or rotation. Apply all the loads which are applied to the members between joints. It is easy to compute the moments, shears, and axial forces developed in each member if both ends are completely locked against translation or rotation. Compute the forces and couples which must be acting on each joint to lock all the members meeting there against translation and rotation.

2. Apply to the structure all the given joint loads (and couples), and in addition apply to each joint forces and couples which are equal in magnitude but opposite in sense to the joint locking forces and couples computed in (1). The structure may now be analyzed for all of these joint forces and couples, using Eqs. (15.6) as described above.

The total bending moment, shear, and axial force at any location in the structure will be the algebraic sum of the contributions computed from (1) and (2).

15.5   Structural Analysis for Large Number of Loading Conditions. If a complete structural analysis (including the computation of joint deflections as well as the internal stress condition) of a complex structure were to be performed for a large number of loading conditions, the analysis may be organized in a different manner from that described above for a single loading condition.

This procedure involves using a set of load-deflection relationships which are just the reverse of those represented by Eqs. (15.6). Those equations are expressions for the joint load components in terms of the joint displacement components and involve the stiffness coefficients k.

The following load-deflection equations are simply superposition equations expressing the joint displacement components in terms of the joint load components and involve the flexibility (or deflection) coefficients d. Thus,

$$
\begin{aligned}
D_1 &= d_{11}P_1 + d_{12}P_2 + d_{13}P_3 + \cdots + d_{1s}P_s \\
D_2 &= d_{21}P_1 + d_{22}P_2 + d_{23}P_3 + \cdots + d_{2s}P_s \\
&\ \cdot \qquad\quad \cdot \qquad\quad \cdot \qquad\ \cdots \qquad\quad \cdot \\
D_s &= d_{s1}P_1 + d_{s2}P_2 + d_{s3}P_3 + \cdots + d_{ss}P_s
\end{aligned}
\tag{15.8}
$$

where d_{ml} = flexibility (or deflection) coefficient denoting the joint displacement component at the point and in the direction denoted by m produced by a unit joint force acting at the point and in the direction denoted by l.

These flexibility coefficients could be obtained by using one of the force methods, but they are laborious to compute compared with the stiffness coefficients k. They may be computed, however, from Eqs. (15.6) as follows. To obtain d_{12}, d_{22}, $\ldots$, d_{s2}, apply to the structure a single unit load, namely, $P_2 = 1$; then solve Eqs. (15.6) simultaneously for $D_1, D_2, \ldots , D_s$, these values being equal, respectively, to $d_{12}, d_{22}, \ldots ,$ d_{s2} (by definition of these flexibility coefficients). Thus, if Eqs. (15.6) were solved s times for unit values of $P_1, P_2, \ldots , P_s$ in turn, these s solutions for the $D_1, D_2, \ldots , D_s$ would give in turn all the d coefficients for each of the s columns on the right-hand sides of Eqs. (15.8). (This procedure in matrix terminology is referred to as inverting the stiffness matrix to obtain the flexibility matrix.)

Once the flexibility coefficients have been computed, the joint deflection components $D_1, D_2, \ldots , D_s$ may be computed for any desired loading condition defined by $P_1, P_2, \ldots , P_s$. If the values of the joint deflection components are available, reactions can be computed from Eq. (15.7) and bar forces, etc., from equations such as Eq. (15.4).

15.6 Matrix Methods of Structural Analysis. Even the abbreviated discussion of this chapter makes it apparent that setting up the elements and manipulating large numbers of simultaneous equations become very cumbersome using conventional notation, terminology, and methods. The difficulties pyramid with the complexity and redundancy of the structure. Mathematicians have developed matrix notation and methods to expedite the discussion and solution of linear algebra.

No attempt will be made here to summarize the fundamentals of matrix notation and matrix algebra, or to introduce the application of these methods to the structural analysis problem. The above discussion of this chapter is designed to set the stage for the reader to pursue this subject elsewhere, such as in the references listed at the beginning of this chapter.

However, the following illustrative example is included to serve as a basis for correlating the above discussion with other presentations. The planar truss involved is shown in Fig. 15.3, and it is seen to involve six joints, eleven bars, and five reaction components. The structure is therefore statically indeterminate to the fourth degree with respect to bar forces and reaction components. On the other hand, there are seven unknown joint displacement components.

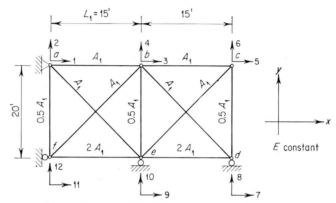

Figure 15.3   Illustrative example

The solution of this truss by the displacement method is formulated below. For this purpose, the x and y components of the joint forces and the joint displacements are identified by the heavy-line arrows and the numbers shown adjacent to the joints in Fig. 15.3, the odd numbers being assigned to the x direction and the even to the y direction; for example, 1 and 2 at joint a, 3 and 4 at joint b, etc. It is assumed that there are a large number of loading conditions involved, for each of which the values of the joint force components ($P_3, P_4, P_5, P_6, P_7, P_9,$ and P_{12}) are specified.

By applying Eqs. (15.6), seven equilibrium equations may be set up for this problem, in which the seven known joint force components P_m for any particular loading condition are expressed in terms of the seven unknown joint displacement components D_m and the stiffness coefficients k_{ml}. These seven equations may be represented as follows using matrix notation:

$$\mathbf{P} = \mathbf{kD} \qquad\qquad (a)$$

where $\mathbf{P}$ and $\mathbf{D}$ represent the column matrices (or column vectors),

$$\mathbf{P} = \begin{bmatrix} P_3 \\ P_4 \\ P_5 \\ P_6 \\ P_7 \\ P_9 \\ P_{12} \end{bmatrix} \quad \text{and} \quad \mathbf{D} = \begin{bmatrix} D_3 \\ D_4 \\ D_5 \\ D_6 \\ D_7 \\ D_9 \\ D_{12} \end{bmatrix}$$

and **k** represents the following square **stiffness matrix:**

$$\mathbf{k} = \begin{bmatrix} k_{33} & k_{34} & k_{35} & k_{36} & k_{37} & k_{39} & k_{3,12} \\ k_{43} & k_{44} & k_{45} & k_{46} & k_{47} & k_{49} & k_{4,12} \\ k_{53} & k_{54} & k_{55} & k_{56} & k_{57} & k_{59} & k_{5,12} \\ k_{63} & k_{64} & k_{65} & k_{66} & k_{67} & k_{69} & k_{6,12} \\ k_{73} & k_{74} & k_{75} & k_{76} & k_{77} & k_{79} & k_{7,12} \\ k_{93} & k_{94} & k_{95} & k_{96} & k_{97} & k_{99} & k_{9,12} \\ k_{12,3} & k_{12,4} & k_{12,5} & k_{12,6} & k_{12,7} & k_{12,9} & k_{12,12} \end{bmatrix}$$

Equations (*a*) may be solved simultaneously to obtain the unknown displacements D_m for the column vector **P** associated with each of the loading conditions. Where there are a large number of loading conditions, however, it is usually easier to proceed as follows. By applying Eqs. (15.8), set up seven load-deflection equations which may be represented, using matrix notation, as

$$\mathbf{D} = \mathbf{dP} \qquad (b)$$

where **d** represents the following square **flexibility matrix:**

$$\mathbf{d} = \begin{bmatrix} d_{33} & d_{34} & d_{35} & d_{36} & d_{37} & d_{39} & d_{3,12} \\ d_{43} & d_{44} & d_{45} & d_{46} & d_{47} & d_{49} & d_{4,12} \\ d_{53} & d_{54} & d_{55} & d_{56} & d_{57} & d_{59} & d_{5,12} \\ d_{63} & d_{64} & d_{65} & d_{66} & d_{67} & d_{69} & d_{6,12} \\ d_{73} & d_{74} & d_{75} & d_{76} & d_{77} & d_{79} & d_{7,12} \\ d_{93} & d_{94} & d_{95} & d_{96} & d_{97} & d_{99} & d_{9,12} \\ d_{12,3} & d_{12,4} & d_{12,5} & d_{12,6} & d_{12,7} & d_{12,9} & d_{12,12} \end{bmatrix}$$

However, since it is laborious to compute the deflection coefficients d_{ml}, it is easier to replace the flexibility matrix **d** by its equivalent, the inverse of the stiffness matrix, $\mathbf{k}^{-1}$. Thus, Eq. (*b*) may be rewritten as

$$\mathbf{D} = \mathbf{k}^{-1}\mathbf{P} \qquad (c)$$

The solution of this problem may now be formulated as follows. First, evaluate the stiffness coefficients k_{ml} and set up the stiffness matrix **k**. Then invert this stiffness matrix to obtain $\mathbf{k}^{-1}$. Using Eq. (*c*), obtain the unknown joint displacement components D_m for each of the loading conditions. Obtain the reactions by substituting the values of D_m into equations such as Eq. (15.7) which have been written for this structure. Obtain the bar forces in the members by substituting the values of D_m into equations such as Eq. (15.4) for each bar.

The key to the solution of this problem is to evaluate the stiffness coefficients and set up the stiffness matrix **k**. By using the coefficients

of appropriate terms in Eqs. (15.5), the following formulas are obtained
for the various stiffness coefficients for joint j and for the joints f at the
far ends of the bars jf meeting at joint j:

If $u_j = +1$,

$$k_{j_x j_x} = \sum^{j} \left[\left(\frac{EA}{L} \right)_{jf} \cos^2 \alpha_{jf} \right] \tag{d}$$

$$k_{j_y j_x} = \sum^{j} \left[\left(\frac{EA}{L} \right)_{jf} \cos \alpha_{jf} \cos \beta_{jf} \right] \tag{e}$$

$$k_{f_x j_x} = \left(\frac{EA}{L} \right)_{jf} (-\cos^2 \alpha_{jf}) \tag{f}$$

$$k_{f_y j_x} = \left(\frac{EA}{L} \right)_{jf} (-\cos \alpha_{jf} \cos \beta_{jf}) \tag{g}$$

If $v_j = +1$,

$$k_{j_x j_y} = \sum^{j} \left[\left(\frac{EA}{L} \right)_{jf} (\cos \alpha_{jf} \cos \beta_{jf}) \right] \tag{h}$$

$$k_{j_y i_y} = \sum^{j} \left[\left(\frac{EA}{L} \right)_{jf} (\cos^2 \beta_{jf}) \right] \tag{i}$$

$$k_{f_x j_y} = \left(\frac{EA}{L} \right)_{jf} (-\cos \alpha_{jf} \cos \beta_{jf}) \tag{j}$$

$$k_{f_y j_y} = \left(\frac{EA}{L} \right)_{jf} (-\cos^2 \beta_{jf}) \tag{k}$$

In Table 15.1, the EA/L of each bar is listed in terms of EA_1/L_1; and, in
addition, the values of $\cos^2 \alpha$, $\cos^2 \beta$, and $\cos \alpha \cos \beta$ for each bar are

Table 15.1

Bar	$\dfrac{EA}{L} \Big/ \dfrac{EA_1}{L_1}$	$\cos \alpha$	$\cos \beta$	$\cos^2 \alpha$	$\cos^2 \beta$	$\cos \alpha \cos \beta$
ab	1	1	0	1	0	0
bc	1	1	0	1	0	0
fe	2	1	0	1	0	0
ed	2	1	0	1	0	0
af	0.375	0	1	0	1	0
be	0.375	0	1	0	1	0
cd	0.375	0	1	0	1	0
ae	0.6	0.6	-0.8	0.36	0.64	-0.48
fb	0.6	0.6	$+0.8$	0.36	0.64	$+0.48$
bd	0.6	0.6	-0.8	0.36	0.64	-0.48
ec	0.6	0.6	$+0.8$	0.36	0.64	$+0.48$

Table 15.2

$k \Big/ \dfrac{EA_1}{L_1}$	3	4	5	6	7	9	12
3	+2.432	0	−1.0	0	−0.216	0	−0.288
4	0	+1.143	0	0	+0.288	0	−0.384
5	−1.0	0	+1.216	+0.288	0	−0.216	0
6	0	0	+0.288	+0.759	0	−0.288	0
7	−0.216	+0.288	0	0	+2.216	−2.0	0
9	0	0	−0.216	−0.288	−2.0	+4.432	0
12	−0.288	−0.384	0	0	0	0	+0.759

listed. The various stiffness coefficients may be computed using the formulas (d) through (k). These results are tabulated in Table 15.2. In effect, the stiffness matrix **k** may be obtained by multiplying each of the elements listed in Table 15.2 by EA_1/L_1.

16

Plastic Behavior of Structures

16.1 Introduction. In the previous discussions of the computation of deflections and the analysis of statically indeterminate structures, attention is focused almost exclusively on linearly elastic behavior. However, structural engineers are becoming increasingly interested in basing some of their designs on the ultimate strength of the structure. It is therefore important to consider the plastic behavior of some typical structural members as background for the plastic-design procedures which are being developed.

Many structural materials are ductile. Of these, structural steel exhibits the most suitable postelastic properties from the standpoint of applying the principles of plastic design. Of course, as soon as yield stress intensities are developed at the most highly stressed section, *statically determinate* steel structures can carry very little more load without undergoing excessive deflections. In the case of a *statically indeterminate* structure, however, plastic deformation can occur at such a section with no substantial loss of resistance while additional load is applied to the structure. During this additional loading, the structure is somewhat more flexible but not excessively so. The load may be increased still further until yield stresses are developed at enough locations so that the structure is on the point of deflecting as a mechanism and undergoing excessive deflections. In certain cases, this reserve load-carrying capacity of a statically indeterminate steel structure, over and beyond the load which first produced yield stresses, can be utilized in design.

This reserve capacity beyond the yield load P_{yp} (that is, the load which produced yield stresses at the first location) is most impressive in structures where material is used inefficiently. Note that this does not necessarily mean structures which are uneconomically designed. For example, it is often economical to use a rolled beam the capacity of which is utilized only at the one most highly stressed section. On the other hand, if it is economical to vary the size of the members and thereby design the "one-horse-shay" type of structure with substantially constant stresses throughout, excessive deflections impend at loads only slightly greater than the yield load.

Plastic design is most appropriate when the dominant portion of the design loading is an immovable and essentially nonreversing loading. Under severe reversing loadings, *plastic fatigue* could occur, as exemplified by breaking a nail or wire by bending it back and forth into the plastic range. If heavy moving loads were involved, it is possible to produce additional plastic deformation with each passage of the load and eventually accumulate excessive permanent deflections. In many building design situations, the most important design loadings may be considered as "static" loadings, and it is to such situations that plastic design is intended to apply.

Here the plastic behavior of certain important cases will be discussed. This is not intended, however, to be a comprehensive treatment of either the plastic analysis or the plastic design of structures.[1]

16.2 Mechanical Properties of Steel. The important properties of structural steel from a design standpoint are depicted in Figs. 16.1 and 16.2. In Fig. 16.1 is shown the complete (engineering) stress-strain curve of a typical A7 structural steel, illustrating the exceptional ductility of such a steel before actual tensile rupture occurs. From a practical design viewpoint, major interest is focused on the initial portion of this curve, say up to an elongation of 2 per cent. This initial portion is idealized and shown with an expanded scale for strain in Fig. 16.2.

In the idealized stress-strain curve, structural steel is assumed to be linearly elastic up to the **yield-point stress** σ_{yp} of 34 kips per sq in. Note that the **yield-point strain** ϵ_{yp} is a little more than 0.001, or 0.1 per cent. Actually, steel is linearly elastic up to a **proportional limit** of about two-thirds of the yield-point stress. Strains are still recoverable upon unloading up to the **elastic limit,** which is about three-quarters of the yield-point stress. When steel is unloaded after being loaded beyond the elastic limit, there will be some permanent set or residual strain apparent. In other words, plastic behavior actually starts at the elastic limit. Such behavior is not marked, however, until

[1] For such information the reader is referred to books such as: J. F. Baker, M. R. Horne, and J. Heyman, "The Steel Skeleton," vol. II, "Plastic Behavior and Design," Cambridge University Press, London, 1956; L. S. Beedle, "Plastic Design of Steel Frames," John Wiley & Sons, Inc., New York, 1958; "Plastic Design in Steel," American Institute of Steel Construction, New York, 1958; P. G. Hodge, Jr., "Plastic Analysis of Structures," McGraw-Hill Book Company, Inc., New York, 1959.

Figure 16.1 Typical stress-strain curve for A7 structural steel

Figure 16.2 Idealized stress-strain curve for A7 structural steel (idealization of initial portion of complete stress-strain curve shown in Fig. 16.1)

the yield-point stress level is reached. Actually at this level, the steel goes through an "upper yield" and subsequently a "lower yield" before settling down to the yield stress level commonly referred to. The magnitude of the "wiggle" associated with this upper and lower yield-point phenomenon is accentuated with the speed of loading and is depicted at the start of the yield plateau in Fig. 16.1. For static or quasi-static loading, this phenomenon has no importance and is therefore ignored in the idealized curve shown in Fig. 16.2. For all practical purposes, when the yield-point stress level is reached, structural steel will deform plastically at no increase in stress up to a strain of 1 or 1.5 per cent. At this

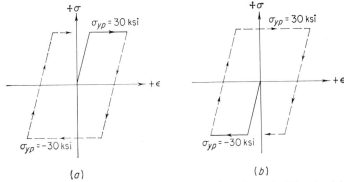

Figure 16.3   Behavior of steel assumed for discussion of plastic behavior (a) starting with tensile strains, (b) starting with compressive strains

point, so-called "strain hardening" begins, and again an increase in stress is required to produce an increase of strain. In the early stages of strain hardening the slope of the stress-strain curve corresponds to the modulus E_{sh} of about 700 kips per sq in. compared with Young's modulus of elasticity E of 29,000 kips per sq in. in the elastic range.

In the subsequent discussion, structural steel will be assumed to be linearly elastic up to the (tensile) yield point, and then to yield *indefinitely* at the constant yield-point stress (in other words, strain hardening will be ignored).[1] If, after yielding a certain amount, an element is unloaded, it will be assumed to unload (as shown by the dot-dash line) along a path which is parallel to the initial elastic line. If the element is then loaded in the opposite sense, it will be assumed to continue straining, as shown by the dot-dash line, until a yield stress level of −34 kips per sq in. is reached. At this point, if required, it would be assumed to be capable of yielding indefinitely in compression at this constant stress level.

[1] In plastic design, the maximum strains in the structure corresponding to the ultimate load at which excessive deflections impend will seldom exceed 0.015. Neglect of the strain-hardening range therefore seldom has any important effect on the computation of the ultimate load. Further, neglect of this effect leads to a conservative estimate of the ultimate load.

For simplicity in the following discussion, the assumed behavior of structural steel is depicted by the sketches shown in Fig. 16.3. Note that the yield-point stress in both tension and compression is rounded off to a value of 30 kips per sq in.

16.3 Plastic Behavior of Simple Truss Structure. For purposes of this discussion, the very simple three-bar truss shown in Fig. 16.4 is used. It will be assumed that buckling is prevented. Therefore, these bars with a cross-sectional area of 1 sq in. will yield indefinitely at a bar

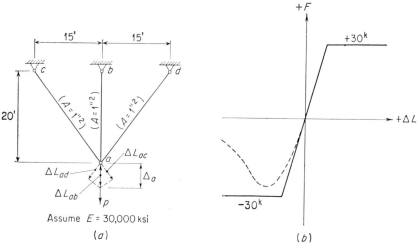

Figure 16.4 Simple truss structure

force of + or −30 kips for a yield stress of 30 kips per sq in., as shown in Fig. 16.3. In actuality, slender compression members have an F vs. ΔL relationship as shown by the dotted line in Fig. 16.4b, where in this case ΔL is interpreted as the relative movement of the two ends of a buckled bar rather than the axial change in length of the bar.[1] Whereas this hypothetical example is not representative of actual trussed structures, it does provide an excellent vehicle for developing the important concepts involved in the plastic behavior of structures.

Before starting the discussion of the truss shown in Fig. 16.4, it is interesting to note the behavior of several statically determinate modifications of this structure. Suppose that the structure consisted simply of two bars, say ab and ac (or ab and ad). For such a structure, when the vertical load P reached a value of 30 kips, the force in bar ab would reach

---

[1] This characteristic inability of compression members to hold their maximum compressive load indefinitely over the same yield range as a tension member is the main reason why the plastic behavior of truss structures cannot be relied on in design.

its yield value of 30 kips and excessive vertical deflections of joint a would impend. Therefore, the value of both P_{yp} and P_{ult} is 30 kips.* On the other hand, if the structure consisted of simply the two bars ac and ad, a vertical load P of 48 kips would produce yield stresses of 30 kips per sq in. in both bars simultaneously. Therefore, the value of both P_{yp} and P_{ult} is again identical but equal to 48 kips.

Considering now the actual indeterminate structure in Fig. 16.4, it is easy to analyze by any of the standard methods its behavior during the initial linearly elastic range. In this simple case, it is even easier to recognize that, for consistent deformation of the three bars,

$$\Delta L_{ac} = \Delta L_{ad} = 0.8 \Delta L_{ab}$$

as shown by the dotted lines in Fig. 16.4a. Therefore,

$$F_{ac}(25)/(1)E = (0.8)(F_{ab})(20)/(1)E$$

or $F_{ac} = F_{ad} = 0.64 F_{ab}$. However, for vertical equilibrium of joint a, $0.8 F_{ac} + 0.8 F_{ad} + F_{ab} = P$. Hence, $2.024 F_{ab} = P$. Since bar ab starts to yield when $F_{ab} = 30$ kips, $P_{yp} = 60.72$ kips. For this load, note that bars ac and ad are still well within their elastic range since

$$F_{ac} = F_{ad} = (0.64)(30) = 19.2 \text{ kips}$$

Since bars ac and ad are available to resist further loading of the structure even though bar ab is yielding at a constant resisting force of 30 kips, load P may be increased an additional 17.28 kips to a total value of 78 kips before the force in members ac and ad is built up an additional 10.8 kips to a total of 30 kips. Since all three bars are now on the point of yielding, excessive deflections impend and P_{ult} therefore is equal to 78 kips. Note that this value could also be computed directly by noting that excessive deflections impend when all three bars are at their yield value of 30 kips. Hence, simply from $\Sigma V = 0$,

$$P_{ult} = 30 + (2)(0.8)(30) = 78 \text{ kips}$$

During the initial elastic stage, Δ_a, the vertical deflection of joint a, is equal to the change in length of bar ab, or

$$\Delta_a = F_{ab}(20)/(1)E = P(20)/(2.024)E$$

If E is 30,000 kips per sq in, $\Delta_a = P/3,036$. Thus at P_{yp}, $\Delta_a = 0.02$ ft.

---

* In this discussion, the subscripts yp and ult attached to the load symbol have the following significance:

P_{yp} is the load at which yield stress intensities are reached in the most highly stressed element.

P_{ult} is the load at which excessive deflection of the structure impends.

Of course, during the increment of loading between P_{yp} and P_{ult}, only the bars ac and ad are resisting the additional load ΔP, and the structure is about twice as flexible as a result. Thus, $\Delta(\Delta_a) = (1.25)(\Delta F_{ac})(25)/(1)E$, or $\Delta(\Delta_a) = \Delta P/1,536$. Hence, for the last 17.28 kips of load, the additional deflection is 17.28/1,536, or 0.01125 ft. Thus, at P_{ult} the total deflection of a is $(0.02 + 0.0112)$, or 0.0312 ft.

The behavior of this structure through this stage is depicted graphically by the initial-loading portions of the graphs shown in Fig. 16.5. Plotted are both the bar forces versus P and the vertical deflection of joint a versus P.

Now suppose that the structure is gradually unloaded. During the removal of the load, the stress and strain decrease, as indicated by the initial portion of the dashed lines in Fig. 16.3a. In other words, the structure unloads in a linearly elastic fashion parallel to the initial elastic loading stage. As a result, as shown graphically in Fig. 16.5, after the load has been entirely removed, there is a residual deflection of joint a equal to 0.0054 ft downward, and there are the following residual bar forces: $F_{ab} = -8.6$ kips and $F_{ac} = F_{ad} = +5.4$ kips.

If the structure were now reloaded, it would behave in a linearly elastic manner. In fact, over the entire reapplication of the 78 kips, the structure would behave elastically and come back to the identical stresses, strains, and deflections which existed when P_{ult} of 78 kips was first acting on the structure. Further, the structure can be unloaded and reloaded an indefinite number of times without any further plastic deformation beyond that which occurred during the initial loading up to 78 kips.

The behavior of this simple structure illustrates very effectively the elastic-plastic behavior of indeterminate structures when subjected to a load system, the points of application, distribution, and directions of which are unchanging. During the initial application of such a load, plastic deformation occurs only during the stage in which the structure mobilizes its reserve strength between P_{yp} and P_{ult}. As a result of this permanent set (which, in the illustrative example, is an elongation of 0.0112 ft in bar ab), **the structure has in effect "prestressed itself" so that this particular loading can be removed and reapplied an indefinite number of times in an elastic manner and with no further plastic deformation.**

Note further in this structure the situation if the members were disconnected from one another at joint a after the first cycle of loading and unloading. It would be found that members ac and ad were still 25 ft long, but member ab would be 0.0112 ft longer than its original length of 20 ft. To reassemble the members at a would require that bars ac and *ad* be stretched with tensions of 5.4 kips and that bar *ab* be compressed 0.0057 ft with a compressive force of 8.6 kips. This of course corresponds with the residual stresses which are noted above to exist in the unloaded structure after the load of 78 kips had been applied and removed the first time.

Figure 16.5   Behavior of three-bar truss structure shown in Fig. 16.4

Now consider what would happen if the direction of the load were reversed and an upward load were applied to the structure. (Remember that it is assumed that the members can carry compressive forces without buckling.) During the initial stages of this upward loading, the structure would behave elastically. However, when an upward load has been applied sufficient to increase the force in ab from its residual value of -8.6 kips to its compressive yield value of -30 kips, the structure is on the point of undergoing plastic deformation in the upward sense. This upward load P_{yp} will be $P_{yp} = (2.024)(-21.4) = -43.3$ kips. During the application of this load, the force in bars ac and ad will have changed from $+5.4$ kips to a value of $[+5.4 + (0.64)(-21.4)]$ or -8.3 kips. Whereas bar ab is now on the point of being compressed plastically, bars ac and ad still have considerable reserve capacity before they too are on the point of being compressed plastically. An additional load of $(2)(0.8)(30 - 8.3)$, or 34.7, kips can be applied before bars ac and ad reach their compressive yield force of 30 kips. Thus, the upward $P_{ult} = -43.3 - 34.7 = -78$ kips. **This is of course the same as the downward P_{ult} and likewise can be computed simply from statics and the yield capacity of the three bars.**

Note that, during the application of the last 34.7 kips of upward load, bar ab is compressed plastically $(2)(0.0112)$, or 0.0224, ft. If it were disconnected from the other bars at joint a, it would be 0.0112 ft shorter than its original length of 20 ft.

If the upward load of 78 kips is removed, the unloaded structure will have residual bar forces and deflections numerically the same but opposite in sense to those remaining after the removal of the downward load of 78 kips.

If the structure were now reloaded with a downward load, bar forces and deflections would change in a linearly elastic manner for the first 43.3 kips of loading. Bar ab would then have a force of $+30$ kips and would stretch plastically during the application of the additional 34.7 kips of loading which is required to bring bars ac and ad to their tension yield value of 30 kips. **Thus, a reversing load of 78 kips applied first down and then up can be applied without producing excessive deflection. With each cycle of downward and upward loading, bar ab is subjected to the plastic fatigue condition of first being stretched plastically 0.0224 ft and then compressed plastically the same amount.** A steel member could not stand too many cycles of such abuse.

To avoid alternating plastic deformation with each cycle of downward and upward loading, note that the absolute sum of the downward and upward load cannot exceed $2P_{yp}$, or $(2)(60.72) = 121.4$ kips. If 60.7 kips is applied downward, 60.7 kips could be applied upward; if 78 kips is applied downward, only 43.4 kips can be applied upward; if 65 kips is applied downward, 56.4 kips can be applied upward; etc. This behavior is typical of the effect of reversing loads in situations involving plastic deformation.

Now consider the behavior of this structure in its original unstressed condition but acted upon by an entirely different loading, say a horizontal load H acting to the right at joint a. Under linear elastic conditions, such a loading would produce the following bar forces: $F_{ab} = 0$, $F_{ac} = -F_{ad} = 5H/6$. In this case, $H_{yp} = 1.2F_{ac} = 36$ kips. Since both ac and ad are on the point of yielding, one in tension and one in compression, no reserve load-carrying capacity is available. Therefore, $H_{ult} = H_{yp} = 36$ kips. **This illustrates the property that the reserve strength above the yield load depends both on the properties of the structure and on the nature of the loading.**

This simple problem has served to illustrate all the most important characteristics of plastic behavior except the effect of alternating loadings. Such loadings can cause an accumulation of plastic deformation first at one location, then at another location in the structure. With each such cycle of loading, the structure deflects more and more out of its original shape. Such behavior is illustrated in Art. 16.6.

16.4 Moment-Curvature Relations for Flexural Members. It is convenient to start the discussion of the plastic behavior of flexural members by considering the case of pure bending of a simple beam of rectangular cross section acted upon by equal end couples. Such a case involves no shear or axial force and no transverse loads. Hence, plane cross sections before bending remain plane after bending, and it is easy to develop, for both the elastic and the elastic-plastic ranges, relations between σ_1 (the stress in the extreme fiber) and M (the bending moment) and between ϕ (the curvature) and M. Note that the curvature ϕ is equal to $d\theta/ds$, the rate of change of slope of the cross sections of the beam. In other words, the curvature of ϕ is equal to the relative rotation of two adjacent cross sections a unit distance apart.

In Fig. 16.6 are shown several stages in the bending of a differential element of this beam, starting with the end of the elastic range where σ_1 has just reached the value σ_{yp}, and concluding with the fully plasticized cross section where fibers close to the center of the cross section have reached the yield strain ϵ_{yp}. It is assumed that the material is following the idealized stress-strain curve shown in Fig. 16.2. The width of the rectangular cross section is b and the depth d.

Throughout the elastic range, the bending moment M is equal to $\sigma_1 S$, where S is the section modulus of the cross section and the curvature ϕ is equal to M/EI. At the end of the elastic range, the stress in the extreme fiber σ_1 reaches the yield-point stress σ_{yp}. Therefore,

$$M_{yp} = \sigma_{yp}S \tag{16.1}$$

$$\phi_{yp} = \frac{M_{yp}}{EI} \tag{16.2}$$

A beam is an assemblage of an infinite number of elements or fibers, and

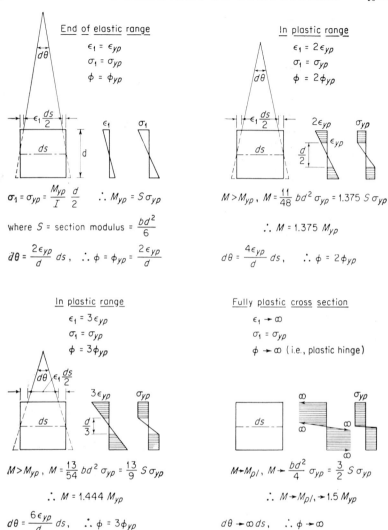

End of elastic range

$\epsilon_1 = \epsilon_{yp}$
$\sigma_1 = \sigma_{yp}$
$\phi = \phi_{yp}$

$\sigma_1 = \sigma_{yp} = \dfrac{M_{yp}}{I}\dfrac{d}{2}$ $\therefore M_{yp} = S\sigma_{yp}$

where S = section modulus = $\dfrac{bd^2}{6}$

$d\theta = \dfrac{2\epsilon_{yp}}{d}ds$, $\therefore \phi = \phi_{yp} = \dfrac{2\epsilon_{yp}}{d}$

In plastic range

$\epsilon_1 = 2\epsilon_{yp}$
$\sigma_1 = \sigma_{yp}$
$\phi = 2\phi_{yp}$

$M > M_{yp}$, $M = \dfrac{11}{48}bd^2\sigma_{yp} = 1.375\,S\,\sigma_{yp}$

$\therefore M = 1.375\,M_{yp}$

$d\theta = \dfrac{4\epsilon_{yp}}{d}ds$, $\therefore \phi = 2\phi_{yp}$

In plastic range

$\epsilon_1 = 3\epsilon_{yp}$
$\sigma_1 = \sigma_{yp}$
$\phi = 3\phi_{yp}$

$M > M_{yp}$, $M = \dfrac{13}{54}bd^2\sigma_{yp} = \dfrac{13}{9}S\,\sigma_{yp}$

$\therefore M = 1.444\,M_{yp}$

$d\theta = \dfrac{6\epsilon_{yp}}{d}ds$, $\therefore \phi = 3\phi_{yp}$

Fully plastic cross section

$\epsilon_1 \to \infty$
$\sigma_1 = \sigma_{yp}$
$\phi \to \infty$ (i.e., plastic hinge)

$M \to M_{pl}$, $M \to \dfrac{bd^2}{4}\sigma_{yp} = \dfrac{3}{2}S\,\sigma_{yp}$

$\therefore M \to M_{pl}, \to 1.5\,M_{yp}$

$d\theta \to \infty\,ds$, $\therefore \phi \to \infty$

Figure 16.6   Moment-curvature relations for pure bending of beam with rectangular cross section

the internal stress distribution among these elements must result in consistent deformation of them as well as satisfying equilibrium requirements.   In other words, a beam is a structure which is statically indeterminate to an infinite degree.   Just as in the case of the simple indeterminate truss discussed in Art. 16.3, the fact that the outer fibers of the beam are on the point of yielding does not mean that excessive deflections impend immediately, because the entire inner core of the beam is still elastic and capable of resisting additional bending moment.

The postelastic behavior of a beam may be studied by considering successive stages of deformation, as shown in Fig. 16.6 for a beam of rectangular cross section. In these considerations it is assumed that cross sections continue to remain plane and, therefore, that the bending strains vary linearly across the beam. Since the material is being assumed to follow the idealized stress-strain curve, the stress in any fiber which is strained more than ϵ_{yp} is constant and equal to σ_{yp}. Thus, in any postelastic stage, there is an inner elastic core in which the bending

Figure 16.7 Nondimensional moment-curvature relationships for typical beam cross sections

strains are equal to or less than ϵ_{yp} and over which the normal stresses σ vary in a linear manner. This core is flanked above and below by plasticized layers in which the bending strains are equal to or more than ϵ_{yp} and in which the normal stresses are constant and equal to σ_{yp}. At any stage it is easy to compute the resisting moment furnished by the bending stresses and thereby define the equivalent bending moment involved. Note that the curvature at any stage is defined by the depth of the elastic core of the beam.

By considering various stages of plastification and computing the bending moment and curvature associated with each, it is possible to obtain the data for plotting the nondimensional moment-curvature relationship shown in Fig. 16.7. In the limit, the elastic core shrinks to a differential depth, the upper half of the beam is plasticized compressively, and the lower half is plasticized in tension. This is called the *fully plasticized stage* and represents the ultimate bending resistance (M_{pl}) the cross section can provide.

$$M_{pl} = \sigma_{yp}\mathbf{Z} \qquad (16.3)$$

where $\mathbf{Z}$ is called the **plastic modulus** of the cross section. For the rectangular cross section, $\mathbf{Z} = bd^2/4$. Note that

$$\frac{M_{pl}}{M_{yp}} = \frac{\mathbf{Z}}{\mathbf{S}} = \mathfrak{F} \qquad (16.4)$$

where $\mathfrak{F}$ is called the **form factor** of the cross section. For the rectangular cross section, $\mathfrak{F} = 1.5$.

Figure 16.8 Idealized wide-flange (W) beam cross section

Beams of other types of cross sections could be studied in exactly the same manner as described above for the rectangular cross section. If this were done, results such as shown in Fig. 16.7 would be obtained for typical cross sections. Of these, the most important is the idealized W-beam cross section shown in Fig. 16.8. For the W cross section, the following values would be obtained for the section modulus $\mathbf{S}$ and the plastic modulus $\mathbf{Z}$:

$$\mathbf{S} = \left[\frac{b_1 h_1^3}{6h} + \frac{b(h^2 - h_1^2)(h + h_1)}{8h} \right] \qquad (16.5)$$

$$\mathbf{Z} = \left[\frac{b_1 h_1^2}{4} + \frac{b(h^2 - h_1^2)}{4} \right] \qquad (16.6)$$

If these formulas are applied to typical W beams, the form factor $\mathfrak{F}$ will be found to range from 1.10 to 1.18 and to be about 1.12 for the most commonly used sizes. Note that in the limit, if half the area of the beam were concentrated on a line at the top edge and the other half on a line at the bottom edge with an infinitesimally thin web in between, the form factor $\mathfrak{F}$ of such an I beam would be 1.0.

The moment-curvature relation of the W beam is such a flat curve for the portion between M_{yp} and M_{pl} that often the idealized version shown by the short-dash line in Fig. 16.7 is used. In fact, sometimes the more conservative version shown by the long-dash line is used, as is done in the discussion of the statically indeterminate beams in Art. 16.5. When either of these idealizations is used, the concept is that, when the moment reaches the level defined by the horizontal lines, an indefinite amount of flexing or curvature can occur without increase in resisting moment. In other words, the beam acts from then on as if a friction hinge had been installed, which allowed flexing to occur while it resisted at a constant moment. In the subsequent discussions, this concept will be referred to by stating that "a **plastic hinge** with a resisting moment of ——— kip-ft forms ———."

The above considerations are based on the assumption of pure bending. This study of the moment-curvature relations could be extended to consider the effect of using the actual stress-strain curve, including the effect of strain hardening, the effect of residual stresses, the effect of shear and axial force in combination with bending moment, etc. The reader is referred to books such as noted in Art. 16.1 for a more detailed discussion. The introduction of such refinements would not alter in any major way the subsequent discussion of the plastic behavior of beams, and these details are therefore not included in this presentation.

16.5 Plastic Behavior of Typical Beams. The following discussion of the plastic behavior of beams parallels that given in Art. 16.3 regarding trusses and is prefaced by the consideration of a beam supported in a statically determinate manner.

Simple End-supported Beam. Consider the simple end-supported beam acted upon by a single concentrated load P at mid-span, as shown in Fig. 16.9. A beam of rectangular cross section and a W beam are considered. Either of these beams behaves in a linearly elastic manner up to the load P_{yp}, which develops a moment M_{yp} at mid-span.

Consider first that the true $M - \phi$ relations shown by the solid lines in Fig. 16.7 pertain. Whereas either of these beams starts to undergo plastic deformation at the yield load, either will accept more load before excessive deflections occur. The beam of rectangular cross section can be loaded to a P_{ult} of $1.5P_{yp}$ before the mid-span cross section is fully plasticized. At this ultimate load, the plasticized zone (shown in black) will have spread out one-sixth of the span on either side of the load on the top and bottom edges of the beam. In the case of the W beam if $\mathfrak{F} = 1.12$, the plasticized zone is much more localized and will have spread out only $0.0536L$ on either side of the ultimate load of $1.12P_{yp}$.

Note also how flat the load-deflection curve of the W beam is for loads greater than P_{yp}. In fact, if the conservative version of the idealized $M - \phi$ relation in Fig. 16.7 were used, it could be said that a plastic hinge forms when the load reaches P_{yp} and excessive deflections impend immediately.

Fixed-end Beam. In the following discussion of the behavior of a W beam fixed at both ends, it is assumed that the conservative idealization of the $M - \phi$ curve shown in Fig. 16.7 pertains. For illustrative purposes, it will be assumed that for this W cross section

$$M_{yp} = M_{pl} = 100 \text{ kip-ft}$$

The beam is shown in Fig. 16.10 acted upon by a uniformly distributed load of w kips per ft. Note that the clamped end is detailed so that it is impossible to develop even secondary horizontal reactions.

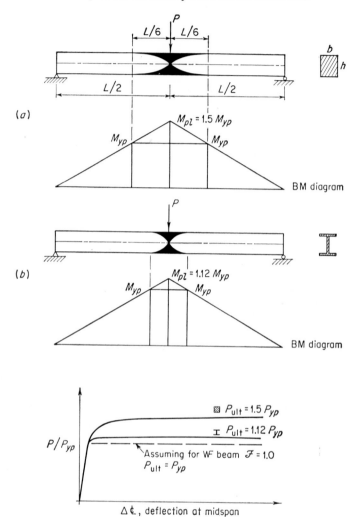

Figure 16.9   Plastic behavior of simple end-supported beam

During the initial application of the downward loading, the beam behaves in a linear elastic manner, developing end moments of $wL^2/12$ and a moment at mid-span of $wL^2/24$. A load of 12 kips per ft will develop end moments of -100 kip-ft, the plastic moment capacity of the beam. Therefore $w_{yp} = 12$ kips per ft. Plastic hinges are now on the point of forming at A and C if additional downward load is applied,

Figure 16.10   Behavior of fixed-ended beam

but the member is capable of carrying an additional increment Δw as an end-supported beam.   The load Δw may be increased to a value such that the simple beam moments caused by it increase the moment at B by 50 kip-ft, thereby bringing the total moment at B up to $+100$ kip-ft. A plastic hinge is now on the point of forming at B, and the beam will collapse as a two-bar mechanism if any further loading is attempted. Therefore, $\Delta w = (50)(8)/100 = 4$ kips per ft, and $w_{ult} = 12 + 4 = 16$ kips per ft.

The fixed-ended beam deflections under the first 12 kips per ft and the simple beam deflections under the last 4 kips per ft are shown in Fig. 16.10c. Also noted is the plastic rotation which occurs at the plastic hinges A and C under this last 4 kips per ft of loading, with the beam acting as a simple end-supported one.

If the load were now removed, the beam would act in the linear elastic manner of a fixed-ended beam. The change in bending moments during the removal of the load would be identical to the fixed-ended beam bending moments caused by an upward load of 16 kips per ft, or

$$\frac{+(16)(100)}{12} = +133 \text{ kip-ft}$$

at A and C and $-(16)(100)/(24) = -67$ kip-ft at B. When these values are superimposed on the dashed-line curve in Fig. 16.10b, the residual moments of $+33$ kip-ft shown in Fig. 16.10d are obtained. These residual moments and the residual deflections are locked in the beam as a result of the permanent plastic rotation which occurred at the plastic hinges at A and C.

Note that in effect the beam is now "prestressed" so that w_{ult} of 16 kips per ft may be applied and removed an indefinite number of times without further plastic deformation taking place.

However, if an upward loading were now applied to the unloaded structure, only 8 kips per ft could be applied elastically, since this load would bring the moment at A and C up to a value of $+100$ kip-ft. An additional upward load of 8 kips per ft could be applied with plastic hinges acting at A and C, before the collapse as a two-bar mechanism is imminent due to the formation of a third plastic hinge at point B. During the application of this last 8 kips per ft of loading, plastic rotation of $333/EI$ (in an upward sense) would take place at the plastic hinges A and C. When this total upward loading of 16 kips per ft is removed, residual moments and deflections numerically the same but opposite in sense to those shown in Fig. 16.10d would now be locked in the beam. This reversing plastic deformation which would have then taken place at A and C would be exactly the same as the phenomena used to break a wire or nail.

As in the case of the truss example of Art. 16.3, the only way to avoid reversing plastic deformation is to keep the absolute sum of the upward and downward load less than twice w_{yp}. Figure 16.10e shows the behavior of this beam in the same manner as is used in Fig. 16.5.

Comparison of Yield and Ultimate Loadings for Several Typical Beams.
For a uniform downward loading, the fixed-ended beam just considered
exhibits a reserve load capacity of $\frac{4}{12}$, or $33\frac{1}{3}$ per cent, between w_{yp}, the
load at which plastic deformation starts, and w_{ult}, the load at which
excessive deflections or collapse impends. **For a nonreversing and
immovable loading on any indeterminate structure, the magnitude of this reserve load capacity depends both on the distribution of the strength characteristics of the structure and on the
distribution of the loading on the structure.** As a result, a particular structure may exhibit considerable reserve capacity under one
loading, but very little or no reserve under another loading.

To illustrate this principle, consider the same fixed-ended beam as
used above, but loaded by a single concentrated load P at mid-span, as
shown in Fig. 16.11. For this loading, in the elastic range the bending
moments at both ends and at mid-span are all numerically equal to $PL/8$.
Therefore, M_{yp} (and in this case M_{pl}) is developed simultaneously at
both ends and at mid-span under a load of $(100)(8)/10$, or 80, kips. Therefore, both P_{yp} and P_{ult} equal 80 kips and there is *no* reserve capacity
exhibited under this type of loading.

In Fig. 16.11*b*, *c*, and *d*, both the yield and ultimate loads for several
typical continuous beams and loadings are illustrated in order to define
the reserve capacity which is developed during the plastification of the
structure. Note that it is possible to compute the ultimate loading without first computing the yield loading, as is illustrated in Fig. 16.12. **To
compute the yield load, it is necessary to perform an elastic
indeterminate analysis of the structure. To compute the ultimate load, it is necessary to perform only a plastic analysis of the
structure.**

The reader is referred to "Plastic Design of Steel Frames" by L. S.
Beedle for a full discussion of various methods of plastic analysis. Here,
it will simply be noted that there are primarily two basic methods: the
mechanism method and the statical method. The mechanism method
is illustrated in Fig. 16.12 and consists of the following steps:

1. Identify the location of potential plastic hinges (supports, joints,
concentrated load points, and points of zero shear in portions subjected
to distributed loadings).

2. Consider various combinations of these hinges to form possible
collapse mechanisms.[1]

3. Compute the loads associated with each of these possible mecha-

---

[1] Note that the ultimate loading may be associated with a collapse mechanism
which *may* or *may not* involve the entire structure. For example, in Fig. 16.11*d*, only
the left span is on the point of collapsing; the other two spans are well within the
elastic range.

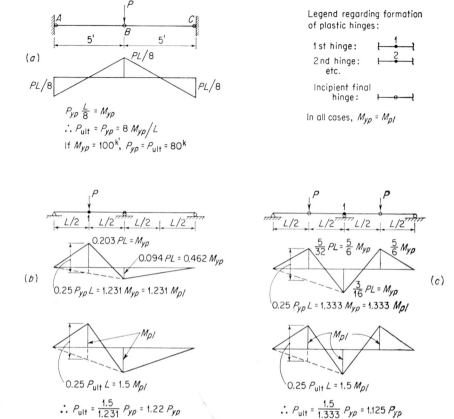

$$P_{yp} \frac{L}{8} = M_{yp}$$
$$\therefore P_{ult} = P_{yp} = 8 \, M_{yp}/L$$
If $M_{yp} = 100^{k'}$, $P_{yp} = P_{ult} = 80^k$

Legend regarding formation
of plastic hinges:

1st hinge: |—•—| $\frac{1}{}$

2nd hinge: |—•—| $\frac{2}{}$
etc.

Incipient final
hinge: |—∘—|

In all cases, $M_{yp} = M_{pl}$

(a)

(b)

0.203 $PL = M_{yp}$

0.094 $PL = 0.462 \, M_{yp}$

0.25 $P_{yp} L = 1.231 \, M_{yp} = 1.231 \, M_{pl}$

M_{pl}

0.25 $P_{ult} L = 1.5 \, M_{pl}$

$$\therefore P_{ult} = \frac{1.5}{1.231} P_{yp} = 1.22 \, P_{yp}$$

(c)

$\frac{5}{32} PL = \frac{5}{6} M_{yp}$

$\frac{5}{6} M_{yp}$

$\frac{3}{16} PL = M_{yp}$

0.25 $P_{yp} L = 1.333 \, M_{yp} = 1.333 \, M_{pl}$

M_{pl}

0.25 $P_{ult} L = 1.5 \, M_{pl}$

$$\therefore P_{ult} = \frac{1.5}{1.333} P_{yp} = 1.125 \, P_{yp}$$

(d)

0.2 $PL = M_{yp}$ 0.1 $PL = 0.5 \, M_{yp}$

0.25 $P_{yp} L = 1.25 \, M_{yp} = 1.25 \, M_{pl}$

M_{pl}

0.25 $P_{ult} L = 1.5 \, M_{pl}$ $\therefore P_{ult} = \frac{1.5}{1.25} P_{yp} = 1.20 \, P_{yp}$

Figure 16.11   Yield and ultimate loadings for typical continuous beams

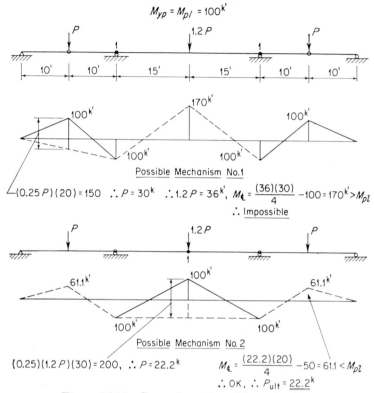

$M_{yp} = M_{pl} = 100^k$

Possible Mechanism No.1

$(0.25P)(20) = 150$ ∴ $P = 30^k$ ∴ $1.2P = 36^k$, $M_t = \dfrac{(36)(30)}{4} - 100 = 170^k > M_{pl}$

∴ Impossible

Possible Mechanism No. 2

$(0.25)(1.2P)(30) = 200$, ∴ $P = 22.2^k$ $M_t = \dfrac{(22.2)(20)}{4} - 50 = 61.1 < M_{pl}$

∴ OK, ∴ $P_{ult} = \underline{22.2^k}$

Figure 16.12   Comparison of possible mechanisms

nisms.   The correct mechanism of failure will be the one associated
with the lowest load.   This will be the ultimate loading, provided that
the moment at any section does not exceed M_{pl} at that section.

**16.6   Plastic Behavior of Continuous Beam under Alternating
Loading.**   One more aspect of plastic behavior will be discussed using
as an illustration the two-span continuous beam shown in Fig. 16.13.
Assume that for this W beam $M_{yp} = M_{pl} = 100$ kip-ft.   Shown in Fig.
16.13 are the yield and the ultimate values of two loading conditions: (1)
a single concentrated load applied at the center of one span and (2) equal
concentrated loads applied simultaneously at the center of both spans.
These ultimate loads are computed on the assumption that each of the
loadings is nonreversible and immovable.

During the application of the ultimate value of the single concentrated
load, plastic rotation occurs at a plastic hinge which forms in the beam
at the load point d.   During the application of the ultimate value of the
two concentrated loads, plastic rotation occurs at a plastic hinge located
over the center support.   In the case of the single load, during the appli-

cation of the loading between the yield and ultimate condition, rotation occurs at the plastic hinge at d and the last 10.8 kips of load is carried by portion $abcd$, which is supported at a and c and cantilevered from c to d. The bending moments change by the shaded amount between the dashed and solid lines. Similarly, in the case of the two equal loads, the last 6.7 kips of each load is carried by ac and ce acting as end-supported beams while rotation occurs at the plastic hinge located at point c. Of

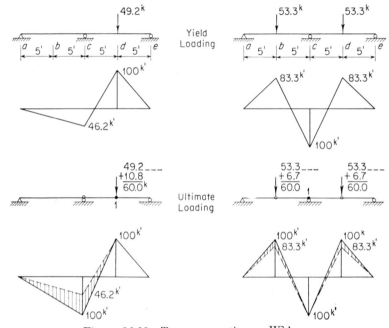

Figure 16.13   Two-span continuous W beam

course, in the case of either of these loading conditions, if it were the only loading condition involved, it could be removed and reapplied an indefinite number of times without any further plastic deformation beyond that which occurred during the first application of the ultimate value of the loading.

Consider now the behavior of the beam if it is subjected alternately to the ultimate loading of each of these two loading systems. First the single 60-kip load is applied at d, and then removed; then the two 60-kip loads are applied one at b and one at d, and later removed; then the single 60-kip load is again applied at d, and then removed; then the two 60-kip loads are applied and removed; etc.

The following sequence of events is recorded in Fig. 16.14. As described above, the last 10.8 kips of the 60-kip load at d causes the plastic rotation α_1 of the plastic hinge at point d. When this 60-kip load is

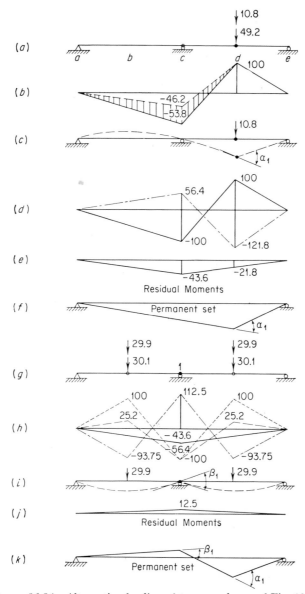

Figure 16.14   Alternating loading of two-span beam of Fig. 16.13

removed, the beam behaves elastically and causes changes in the bending moments, as noted on the dot-dash diagram in (d). These changes in moment are $-60/49.2$ times those shown in Fig. 16.13 for the elastic application of the 49.2-kip load at d. The superposition of the dot-dash diagram on the solid-line diagram in (d) gives the residual moments shown in (e). Note that, if the support at c were removed, the member would be kinked as shown in (f) because of the plastic rotation α_1 at d. The upward force required to push c up to its proper position would be found to be equal to 8.72 kips and therefore would produce the residual moments noted in (e).

Suppose that two equal loads are now applied at b and d to the beam with these residual moments, noted again by the solid line in (h). During the first 30.1 kips of such loads, the member would behave elastically and the change in moments thereby produced would be 30.1/53.3 times those shown in Fig. 16.13 for the 53.3-kip loads. These changes in moment would bring the moment c to a value of -100, and when superimposed on the residual moments give the dashed-line curve in (h). An additional 29.9 kips can be applied at b and d, with the structure behaving as the two end-supported beams shown in (i), and with a plastic rotation β_1 occurring at the plastic hinge at c. As the two 60-kip loads are now removed, the member behaves elastically and the change in moments developed during the removal is $-60/53.3$ times those shown in Fig. 16.13 and is indicated by the dot-dash line in (h). The residual moments left in the beam after the removal of the two 60-kip loads are shown in (j). Note that, if the support at c were again removed, the member would be kinked as shown in (k) because of the plastic deformations α_1 at d and β_1 at c.

If the single 60-kip loads were applied again at d, the member would behave elastically for the first 46.2 kips, thereby bringing the moment at d up to 100 kip-ft. During the last 13.8 kips of loading, the load would be carried similarly to the manner shown in (c), but the plastic rotation at d would be α_2 and equal to 13.8/10.8 times α_1. Removal of this 60-kip load would leave the same residual moments as shown in (e), but the permanent set would involve two kinks: β_1 at c and $(\alpha_1 + \alpha_2)$ at d.

If the two 60-kip loads were applied at b and d and then removed, an additional plastic rotation of β_1 would be produced at c. If the single 60-kip load were applied again at d and removed, an additional plastic rotation of α_2 would be produced at d. Subsequently, alternating the two 60-kip loads at b and d with the single 60-kip load at d would cause with every cycle an additional plastic rotation β_1 at c and α_2 at d. As a result, with each cycle the member is kinked more and more at c and d, and before long the member will be so badly deformed that it is no longer serviceable.

Computations show that plastic deformations will not accumulate if no more than a 50.5-kip load at d is alternated with two 50.5-kip loads, one at b and one at d. During the first 49.2 kips of the single load at d, the member behaves elastically. During the next 1.3 kips, plastic deformation occurs at the plastic hinge at d. As a result, when the

50.5-kip load is removed, triangularly varying residual moments are left in the beam with peak value of 5.3 kip-ft at c.   When the two 50.5-kip loads are now applied at b and d, the member behaves elastically, bringing the total moment at c just up to 100 kip-ft but producing no plastic deformation at this point.   Such loadings can subsequently be alternated an indefinite number of times with no further plastic deformation.   In other words, the first application of the 50.5-kip load at d "prestressed" the beam so that subsequent alternations of this load with the two 50.5-kip loads could take place elastically with no further plastic deformation.   Thus, 50.5 kips is called the value of the **shakedown loading.** Note that it is very little greater than the yield value of a single load at d.

16.7   Stress Control of Indeterminate Structures.   It may not seem appropriate to discuss stress control and the normal and hybrid action of statically indeterminate structures in this chapter on plastic behavior.   Actually, however, it will be shown that all these subjects are very closely related to one another.

First note that a statically determinate structure can be designed to operate with any stress desired, since the structure is free to change its shape to correspond.   For example, the members of a statically determinate truss may be designed to operate at any suitable stress level, since the truss is free to adjust its configuration as may be required.   **In general, however, the stress level (and hence the strain level, also) cannot be set arbitrarily in the various portions of a statically indeterminate structure since the various portions must fit together in a consistent manner, so that simultaneously both the equilibrium and the deformation requirements for the structure are satisfied.**

It is possible, however, to control the erection of an indeterminate structure in such a manner that a **desired stress (and strain) pattern is realized for one particular static load condition.**   For example, the two-span continuous beam shown in Fig. 16.14 (and assumed as weightless for this discussion) could be erected as follows: (1) the beam could be connected to the supports at a and e, both of which are capable of providing either an upward or a downward reaction; (2) then a jack could be placed under the beam at c and an upward force of 8.72 kips applied to the beam; (3) the support at c could then be shimmed to fit the jacked position of the beam; and (4) if the jack were then removed, the reactions of the beam would be 8.72 kips upward at c and 4.36 kips downward at a and e, and the initial moments would be as shown in Fig. 16.14e.   Now the beam has been prestressed so that a 60-kip downward load can be applied at d with the structure behaving completely elastically and no plastic deformation would be involved.   This process is called **stress control** of a statically indeterminate structure.

The truss structure shown in Fig. 16.4 furnishes another convenient example of stress control. Refer to the previous discussion in Art. 16.3. Suppose that members ac and ad of this structure were fabricated exactly 25 ft long, but member ab was deliberately made 0.0112 ft too long. Then during the erection the member could be forced into place, thereby creating a compressive force of 8.6 kips in ab and tensile forces of 5.4 kips in ac and ad. This structure has now been prestressed so that a vertical

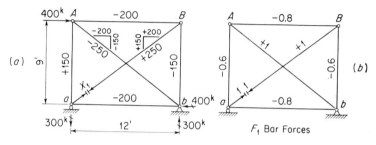

$$(1)(\Delta_1) = \sum F_1 \frac{F}{A} \frac{L}{E} = \frac{1}{E} \sum F_1 \frac{F}{A} L = \frac{3684}{30 \times 10^3}, \quad \therefore \Delta_1 = 0.1228 \text{ in. (together)}$$
$$\therefore \text{Make bar } aB \ 0.1228 \text{ in. short}$$

Bar	L (in.)	$\frac{F}{A}$ (ksi)	F_1	$F_1 \frac{F}{A} L$
AB	144	−14	−0.8	+1,612
ab	144	−14	−0.8	+1,612
Aa	108	+18	−0.6	−1,167
Bb	108	−14	−0.6	+907
Ab	180	−14	+1.0	−2,520
aB	180	+18	+1.0	+3,240

$$\Sigma = +3,684$$

Figure 16.15   Example of stress control

load of 78 kips at a will bring the force in all three bars up to their tensile yield capacity of 30 kips simultaneously.

A third example of stress control is given for the simple truss structure shown in Fig. 16.15. Suppose that it is desired to operate the compression members at 14 kips per sq in. and the tension members at 18 kips per sq in. Further, suppose that it is desired to divide the horizontal load equally between the two diagonals. In order to satisfy static equilibrium, this choice results in the bar forces shown in Fig. 16.15a. Suppose that the areas of the bars were now selected so as to obtain exactly the desired stress intensities. Select aB as the redundant bar, cut it, and apply the tensile redundant forces of 250 kips acting toward each other on each side of the cut. If the desired conditions are to be obtained, there must be no relative deflection of the two sides of the cut. The computations in Fig.

16.15 show, however, that the two sides of the cut have come together (i.e., tried to telescope one another) 0.1228 in. If, however, member aB had been made 0.1228 in. too short, the two sides of the cut would fit together perfectly. Therefore, if in the fabrication of this truss member aB were made 0.1228 in. too short and all other members were made perfectly, then during the erection aB could be forced into place. This would create a prestressed condition in the truss such that, when the 400-kp load was applied, the desired stress conditions would be obtained exactly.

16.8 Normal and Hybrid Action of Statically Indeterminate Trusses. In the previous article, it is shown that statically indeterminate structures are susceptible to stress control. By this technique, *any* statically indeterminate structure may be made to operate at any prescribed stress condition (consistent with equilibrium requirements) for *any* particular static loading condition. To accomplish this, it is necessary to control the displacements of the point of application of the redundants in a suitable way, as illustrated above.

If stress control is to be used, a designer usually wants to use it to achieve maximum economy (which for illustrative purposes will be assumed to be coincident with minimum volume of material). He therefore starts investigating what values he should use for the redundants to obtain minimum volume of material. Such a study leads him to recognize two distinct types of action of indeterminate structures: **normal action** and **hybrid action.**[1] These ideas apparently are applicable to any type of statically indeterminate structure and to any degree of indeterminacy. However, here only a simple indeterminate truss, indeterminate to the first degree, is considered.

Consider the structure shown in Fig. 16.16. It is recognized that, by using stress control, X, the bar force in the redundant bar aB, may have any desired value, and the tension bars may be made to operate at 18 kips per sq in. and the compression bars at 14 kips per sq in. Assuming that the required bar areas are exactly obtained, the volume in cubic inches for each bar could be computed easily, as shown for various values of X. The volumes so obtained are plotted in Fig. 16.16 for each bar, and the volumes of all bars are added to obtain the total volume of material in the entire truss, as shown by the dot-dash line. Note that the vertical scale that is used for the individual bars is twice that of the total volume of the truss.

[1] This general subject has interested a number of structural engineers over the years. Apparently one of the first was F. H. Cilley about 1900, and very recently L. M. Laushey. See F. H. Cilley, The Exact Design of Statically Indeterminate Frameworks. An Exposition of Its Possibility, but Futility, *Trans. ASCE*, June, 1900; L. M. Laushey, Direct Design of Optimum Indeterminate Trusses, *J. Structural Div., ASCE*, vol. 84, December, 1958.

The interesting fact here is that the minimum volume for the truss is obtained when $X = 0$.   In other words, the minimum volume is obtained when the truss is reduced to the two-bar statically determinate truss formed by aA and Ab.   This illustrates so-called **hybrid action** of a statically indeterminate structure.

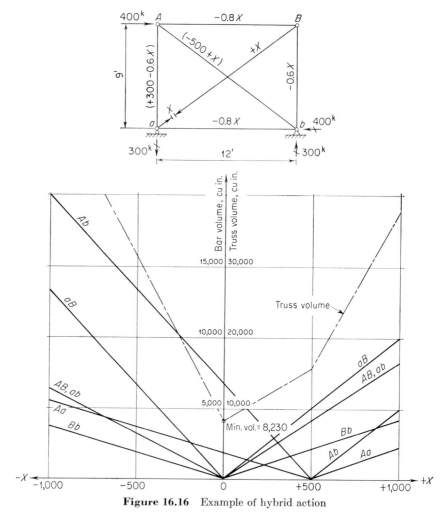

Figure 16.16   Example of hybrid action

Now consider the same truss, but this time it is loaded at B as shown in Fig. 16.17.   By proceeding in the same fashion as above, it is easy to obtain the volume curves noted.   The interesting feature of this case is the minimum range of the volume curve for the truss, between $X = 0$ and $X = 500$ kips.   The volume of material is the same for any value

selected for the redundant between these limits.   This range is called
the **normal range,** and the action illustrated is called the **normal
action** of a statically indeterminate structure.

For values of redundants selected within the normal range, direct
design is possible without using stress control.   In other words, if X

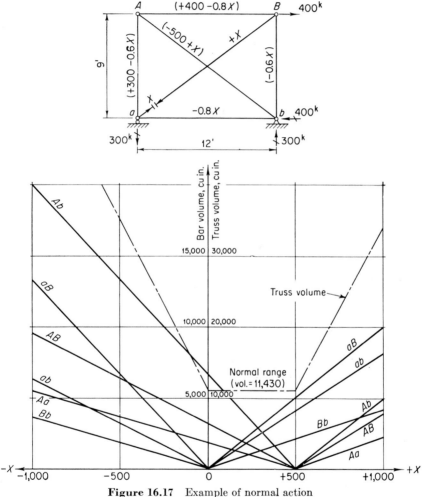

Figure 16.17   Example of normal action

is selected within this range and the areas are determined to satisfy the
desired stresses, it will be found that the two sides of the cut in the redundant match perfectly without making any adjustment in the length of this
bar.   Also within this range, the deflected configurations of the structure
are identical.

Note the structures defined by the values of the redundants at the ends of the normal range. When $X = 0$, the structure reduces to the statically determinate truss composed of AB, Aa, and Ab. When $X = +500$, the structure reduces to the statically determinate truss composed of Ba, Bb, and ab.

16.9   Application of Principles of Normal and Hybrid Action to Structural Design.   Whereas the considerations of the previous article are restricted to a very simple indeterminate truss, more extensive studies indicate that the following conclusions regarding normal and hybrid action are valid for any type of indeterminate structure which is to be designed for **a system of immovable static loads:**

1. For every statically indeterminate structure, there is a statically determinate version which, if designed by itself, will have the minimum volume of material, and for the volume used, minimum deflections.

2. For some structures under some loadings, a normal range exists through which identical minimum volumes of material and identical deflections are obtained.

3. Through the normal range, direct design is possible without resorting to stress control.

4. For any statically indeterminate structure for which a direct design is not obtainable, successive approximation leads to the most economical design which will be statically determinate if the original layout and loading involve hybrid action.

5. Apparently from the standpoint of strength and stiffness, there is no theoretical economy achieved by using statically indeterminate structures for static load systems.

These conclusions do not pertain to situations where significant moving or movable loads must be provided for in the design. Under such loadings, maximum stresses at various locations in the structure occur for different positions of the moving loads.

It is interesting to note that standard practice is consistent with the above conclusions. For the very-long-span structures where the design is controlled largely by the dead weight of the structure (i.e., a static load), the most commonly used structures are statically determinate, such as cantilever trusses or girders, three-hinged arches, etc.

16.10   Plastic Design of Steel Structures.   The above considerations are not presented as a complete and comprehensive treatment of the subject of plastic analysis and design. Rather this chapter is intended as an introduction to some of the fine textbooks and reference books and to the extensive periodical literature which are now available.

The concept of basing design on the ultimate load capacity of a structure is about forty years old, though most of the present knowledge in this area has been developed in the last twenty years. At the present time, there is a great deal of interest in incorporating these ideas into standard practices wherever they are appropriate. Of course, there are many examples of the tacit acceptance of plastic behavior: joint designs based on uniform distribution of load to rivets, bolts, and welds; neglect of stress concentrations under static load conditions where brittle fracture is unlikely; neglect of residual stresses due to straightening or other fabrication and manufacturing procedures; etc.

Plastic-design ideas are most appropriate for substantially static load conditions. When severe reversing or alternating loads are involved, the possibility of plastic fatigue or the accumulation of plastic deformation must be recognized. Modern construction and design usually involve statically indeterminate structures even though the above considerations of hybrid and normal action suggest that, on the basis of strength and stiffness requirements, there is no economy in statically indeterminate construction for substantially immovable and static loadings. It has also been shown that, for static loads, stress-control techniques lead to the same design as plastic-design procedures. The plastic-design philosophy, however, offers the structure the opportunity to exercise its own stress control by introducing plastic deformations at its plastic hinges.

From many points of view, it is important for the modern structural engineer to understand both the elastic and the plastic behavior of his structures and to blend this knowledge into his analytical and design practices.

16.11 Problems for Solution

Problem 16.1 Compute the key points of and draw the load-deflection curve (P vs. Δ_a) for the structure shown in Fig. 16.18 for each of the following assumptions for the stress-strain curve for member ab: (1) that the member yields indefinitely at a constant yield stress of 30 kips per sq in. in compression; in other words, this member yields indefinitely with an effective E of zero; (2) that the member yields, as shown by line 2, where the effective E is $-45,000$ ksi.

Figure 16.18 Problem 16.1

Problem 16.2 In the following discussion of plastic behavior and plastic design vs. elastic design of beams, assume that I-beam cross sections are involved and, in such cases, that the form factor $\mathfrak{F}$ of the cross sections is equal essentially to 1.0; or in other words the section modulus and the plastic modulus of the cross section are essentially equal. Consider the design of a two-span beam of constant EI to carry the two 40-kip loads shown in Fig. 16.19. Assume that σ_{yp} of the structural steel is 33 kips per sq in.

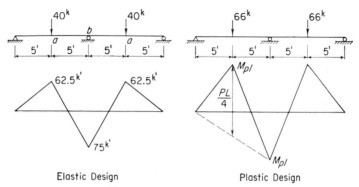

Elastic Design   Plastic Design

Figure 16.19   Problem 16.2

1. On an *elastic-design* basis, using a factor of safety of 1.65, the allowable bending stress is 33/1.65, or 20, kips per sq in. Therefore, the section modulus required to carry the maximum moment of 75 kip-ft is $\mathbf{S} = (75)(12)/20 = 45$ in.[3]

2. On a *plastic-design* basis, using the factor of safety of 1.65, the beam should be designed for ultimate loads of $(40)(1.65)$, or 66, kips. Therefore, $1.5M_{pl} = P_{ult}L/4$, or $M_{pl} = (66)(10)/(1.5)(4) = 110$ kip-ft. The plastic modulus (and also the section modulus if $\mathfrak{F} = 1.0$) required to provide this M_{pl} at σ_{yp} of 33 kips per sq in. is $\mathbf{Z} = (110)(12)/33 = 40$ in.[3], thereby showing a saving of 40 vs. 45 over the elastic design above.

3. Stress control can be used to equalize the moments at points a and b for the elastic design. For example, during construction the end supports can be jacked up enough to create the following initial moments:

Figure 16.20   Initial moments

When these are superimposed on the elastic moments produced by the 40-kip loads, the following totals are obtained:

Figure 16.21   Superposition of initial and elastic moments

The section modulus required to carry the maximum moments of 66.67 kip-ft is $S = (66.67)(12)/20 = 40$ in.[3]   This demonstrates that the elastic-design approach in combination with stress control leads to the same cross section as plastic design.

Suppose that this beam is designed on an elastic basis, with the intention that stress control will be used to produce the initial moments noted above.   Suppose in fact, however, that because of an error the beam was jacked twelve times the intended amount.

(a) Describe the behavior of the beam under these circumstances when the 40-kip loads are applied.

(b) What would be the ultimate value of the loads and what would be the factor of safety against excessive deflections?

Problem 16.3   Consider the two-span continuous beam shown in Fig. 16.22. Assume that it is an I beam and that the form factor $\mathfrak{F}$ is essentially equal to 1.0, and therefore that $M_{pl} = M_{yp} = 100,000$ ft-lb.

Figure 16.22   Problem 16.3

(a) Compute the ultimate value of equal concentrated loads P applied at the center of each span.

(b) Compute in terms of EI of the beam the ductile deformation (i.e., the relative rotation of the cross sections on each side of a plastic hinge) which would occur at the plastic hinges developed in the beam during the first application of these ultimate loads.

(c) In the example shown in Fig. 16.13 which had a roller support at the right end instead of being fixed, the ultimate value of the concentrated loads was 60 kips.   What would be the ultimate value if the middle support in this example settled $\frac{1}{4}$ in.?

17

Introduction to Advanced Structural Mechanics

17.1 Introduction. In general, structures may be built up out of one or more members or panels. A *member* is an element which is relatively long compared with its cross-sectional dimensions, such as a beam or strut. *Panels* may be defined as elements the length and the breadth of which are of the same order of magnitude, but the thickness of which is considerably smaller, such as plates, slabs, and shells.

Elementary theories for the stress distribution in structural members are developed in introductory courses in mechanics and strength of materials. Such theories are adequate to handle many of the conventional structural problems concerning member-type structures. Little consideration is given in most introductory courses to the analysis of plates and shells or to the analysis of buckling or vibrational characteristics of either member or panel elements.

These more advanced aspects are discussed in advanced structural mechanics courses. Here, a very brief introduction to the following areas of advanced structural mechanics is presented.

Theory of Elasticity. This subject denotes the area of structural mechanics in which are developed methods of determining the stresses, strains, and displacements in *linearly elastic bodies*. Actually, the fundamentals regarding force equilibrium and the geometry of deformation are applicable to nonlinear elastic or to plastic bodies. The restriction of linear elasticity enters only when the stress-strain relations are introduced. The fundamental relations of the theory of elasticity are applicable to both member and panel-type elements. They also pertain both to the determination of stress distributions and to the analysis of buckling and dynamic behavior.

548

Theory of Plates and Shells. The elastic theory of plates and shells is developed by introducing certain simplifications into the fundamental relations of the theory of elasticity and by adapting these relations to the solution of typical plate and shell problems. The nonlinear elastic theory and the plastic theory of plates and shells are beyond the scope of the present discussion.

Buckling of Structural Elements. Usually the static equilibrium position of an actual structure or structural element is a *stable* one to which the system returns after being slightly disturbed. Sometimes, however, the equilibrium position is an *unstable* one from which the system continues to move or *buckle* after being slightly disturbed. The stability of the equilibrium position is dependent on the stiffness or rigidity of the system rather than on the strength. Often the buckling of a system can be studied by using the stiffness obtained from approximate load-deflection characteristics defined by elementary theory.

Dynamic Response of Structures. The static deflection of a structure is a function only of the applied static loads and the stiffness of the system. For a dynamic loading, however, the response is also a function of the mass of the system since accelerations are involved.

For detailed discussion of these subjects, the reader is referred to the books listed on page 7 of the Foreword.

17.2 Basic Definitions and Relationships Involved in the Theory of Elasticity. The methods of the theory of elasticity are developed for application to a body the material of which is uniformly distributed over a volume of a specific undeformed shape and which is supported and then subsequently loaded and/or deformed in some specific manner. It is assumed that the material is *homogeneous, isotropic,* and *linearly elastic*—all of which are properties that can be approached but never realized exactly in actuality. For such a specified problem, it is desired to compute the state of stress, strain, and displacement throughout the body.

For purposes of the mathematical solution of such problems, it is necessary to locate points and portions of the body with respect to some suitable system of coordinate axes. Although special coordinate systems are more convenient for certain problems, the conventional rectangular coordinate system of x, y, and z axes is the most general and will be used here.

Notation and convention. The *external forces* acting on a body are of two types: *surface forces* and *body forces*. Isolation of a portion of a body and consideration of its equilibrium demonstrate the existence of *internal forces* on the exposed internal faces of such a portion. The notation and convention used for describing external and internal forces are shown in Fig. 17.1. In all cases, forces are shown in their positive senses.

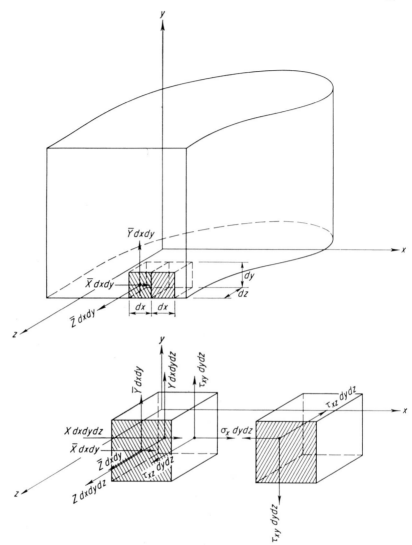

Figure 17.1 Notation and convention for force and stress intensities

For isolated differential portions such as shown, the variation of intensity over a differential area (or volume) is so small that the total force on an area (or volume) may be represented as the intensity at the center of the face (or volume) multiplied by the area of the face (or by the volume of the portion).

The surface forces are distributed over the surface of the body and can be resolved into three coordinate components, the intensities (force per unit area) of which are denoted by $\bar{X}$, $\bar{Y}$, and $\bar{Z}$. The body forces are distributed over the volume of the body and may be caused by gravity, magnetism, or acceleration (inertia forces) and can be represented by three coordinate components, the intensities (force per unit volume) of which are denoted by X, Y, and Z. Note that the positive sense of the surface or body force components is the same as the positive sense of the corresponding coordinate axis.

The resultant internal force distributed over an internal face may be resolved into two components: a *normal* component perpendicular to the face and a *shear* component parallel to the face. Usually this shear component is further resolved into two components acting in the plane of the face. The intensities (force per unit area) of the normal and shear components are called, respectively, the *normal stress* σ and the *shear stress* τ. Usually the stress condition at a point is defined by specifying the normal and shear stresses on the three coordinate planes at a point, the x, y, or z plane being perpendicular to the x, y, or z coordinate axis, respectively.

One subscript is used with σ to denote the plane on which the normal stress acts; thus σ_y denotes the normal stress on a plane normal to the y axis. Normal stresses will be considered plus when tensile.

Two subscripts are used with τ, the first to denote the plane on which it acts and the second to denote the direction in which it acts in this plane; thus τ_{xy} denotes the shear stress on the x plane acting parallel to the y axis. Shear stresses will be considered plus when acting in plus coordinate directions on the most positive face of a portion.

As a result of deformation, points on a body are displaced. The resultant displacement of a point may be represented by its three coordinate components u, v, and w, which represent components in the x, y, and z directions, respectively. Displacement components are considered plus when in the positive sense of the corresponding coordinate axes.

Once the displacements of all points are defined, it is easy to compute the strains. The *lineal strain* of a line element is denoted by ϵ and considered plus when an elongation. One subscript is used with ϵ to denote the original direction of the element involved. The change in the right angle between two originally perpendicular line elements is called the *shear strain* between these elements and is denoted by γ and is considered plus when the original right angle between the positive extension of these line elements is reduced. Two subscripts are used with γ to denote the original direction of these two line elements.

Independent components of stress. It is easy to show that the normal and shear stresses on any plane through a point may be computed if the normal stress and two shear stress components are known on each of three mutually perpendicular planes (i.e., three orthogonal planes) at a point. It would appear therefore that nine stress components (three on each of three planes) must be known at each point in order to define completely the state of stress at each point. It is easy to show, however, that there are only six independent components of stress at each point.

Usually for convenience the independent components of stress at a point are considered to be those acting on the three coordinate planes at a point. Consider the stresses on three such planes at the center of the differential particle shown in Fig. 17.2 to be σ_x, τ_{xy}, and τ_{xz}; σ_y, τ_{yx},

Note: Shown are stresses and body–force intensities. To obtain forces on faces multiply stresses shown by face area; to obtain body forces multiply body–force intensities by particle volume

Figure 17.2   Equilibrium considerations of differential particle

and τ_{yz}; and σ_z, τ_{zx}, and τ_{zy}. Then, considering the change of stress which occurs between the center of the particle and the center of one of the faces, the stresses at the center of each face are as shown. Suppose now that the equation for moment equilibrium about the x axis, $\Sigma M_x = 0$, is written. If only the lowest-order differential terms (third order) are retained, this equation becomes

$$\tau_{yz}\, dx\, dy\, dz - \tau_{zy}\, dx\, dy\, dz = 0 \qquad \text{or} \qquad \tau_{yz} = \tau_{zy}$$

Similarly, moment equilibrium equations about the y axis and about the z axis lead to the conclusions that

$$\tau_{xz} = \tau_{zx} \qquad \text{and} \qquad \tau_{xy} = \tau_{yx}$$

Thus, it is apparent that **there are only six independent components of stress at each point:** three normal stresses, σ_x, σ_y, and σ_z; and three shear stresses, τ_{xy} $(=\tau_{yx})$, τ_{xz} $(=\tau_{zx})$, and τ_{yz} $(=\tau_{zy})$. If these six stress components are known for the coordinate planes at any particular point, it is easy to compute the stresses on any other plane through this point by considering the force equilibrium of a differential tetrahedron at this location formed by the intersection of this plane with three coordinate planes. In this manner, so-called *stress-transformation equations* are obtained. Such equations may be found in any standard textbook on elasticity.

Such considerations may be extended to prove that through any point there are three mutually perpendicular planes on which the resultant stress is normal to the plane (i.e., on which there are no shear stresses). Such planes are called the *principal planes*, and the normal stresses on these planes are called *principal stresses*. One of these principal stresses is the algebraically largest normal stress on any plane through this point and is called the *major principal stress;* one is the algebraically smallest and is called the *minor principal stress;* and the third is an intermediate value.

It is important to note that all these conclusions regarding stress components are based only on equilibrium considerations and, therefore, are valid for any material whether it exhibits linear or nonlinear stress-strain properties.

Definition of components of strain. Once the displacements u, v, and w are known at each and every point in a body, it is easy to compute by simple geometrical considerations any aspect of the deformation of the body. Such computations are particularly easy if the displacements are small so that the small-angle assumptions ($\alpha \simeq \sin \alpha \simeq \tan \alpha$ and $\cos \alpha \simeq 1$) are valid and so that squares of the first derivatives of the displacement can be neglected in comparison with the first derivative itself.

For example, as shown in Fig. 17.3, consider three line elements at point O: OA, OB, and OC. After deformation, these elements have moved to the positions $O'A'$, $O'B'$, and $O'C'$, the displacements having been exaggerated tremendously to clarify the geometry involved. Note that, if u, v, and w are the displacements of point O, the displacements of A, B, and C are

Point A:

$$u + \frac{\partial u}{\partial x}\,dx \qquad v + \frac{\partial v}{\partial x}\,dx \qquad \text{and} \qquad w + \frac{\partial w}{\partial x}\,dx$$

Point B:

$$u + \frac{\partial u}{\partial y}\,dy \qquad v + \frac{\partial v}{\partial y}\,dy \qquad \text{and} \qquad w + \frac{\partial w}{\partial y}\,dy$$

Point C:

$$u + \frac{\partial u}{\partial z}\, dz \qquad v + \frac{\partial v}{\partial z}\, dz \qquad \text{and } w + \frac{\partial w}{\partial z}\, dz$$

In view of the small displacements, substantially the true lengths of and the true angle between elements such as $O'A'$ and $O'C'$ will be seen in the projection of these lines on the xz plane. In such a projection, for

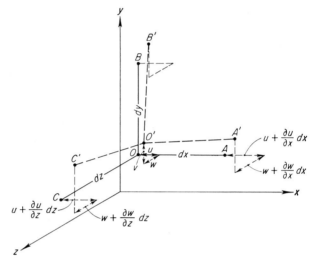

Figure 17.3   Geometrical relations between displacements and strains

example, it will be apparent that $\Delta(OA)$, the change in the length of OA, is substantially

$$\Delta(OA) = O'A' - OA = \frac{\partial u}{\partial x}\, dx$$

Hence, the *unit elongation* or *lineal strain* of this element which was originally parallel to the x axis is called ϵ_x and is equal to $\partial u/\partial x$. In a similar manner, $\Delta(\angle AOC)$, the change in the angle between the originally perpendicular elements OA and OC, is substantially

$$\Delta(\angle AOC) = \angle AOC - \angle A'O'C' = \frac{\partial u}{\partial z} + \frac{\partial w}{\partial x}$$

This reduction in the original right angle between these two elements which were originally parallel to the x and z axis is called *shear strain* γ_{xz}. Thus, the six strain components at point O (three lineal strains and three shear strains) are found in this manner to be related to the three displacements u, v, and w by the following expressions:

$$\epsilon_x = \frac{\partial u}{\partial x} \qquad \gamma_{xy} = \frac{\partial u}{\partial y} + \frac{\partial v}{\partial x}$$

$$\epsilon_y = \frac{\partial v}{\partial y} \qquad \gamma_{xz} = \frac{\partial u}{\partial z} + \frac{\partial w}{\partial x} \qquad (17.1)$$

$$\epsilon_z = \frac{\partial w}{\partial z} \qquad \gamma_{yz} = \frac{\partial v}{\partial z} + \frac{\partial w}{\partial y}$$

Note that these six components of strain are not independent since they are expressed in terms of only three quantities: u, v, and w.

This interdependency of the six strain components is very important. In the terminology of elasticity literature, it is said that **the strains must be compatible.** The test for compatibility is that the six strain components must satisfy six compatibility equations—three of the following type:

$$\frac{\partial^2 \epsilon_x}{\partial y^2} + \frac{\partial^2 \epsilon_y}{\partial x^2} = \frac{\partial^2 \gamma_{xy}}{\partial x \, \partial y} \qquad (17.2a)$$

and three of the following type:

$$2 \frac{\partial^2 \epsilon_x}{\partial x \, \partial y} = \frac{\partial}{\partial x} \left(- \frac{\partial \gamma_{yz}}{\partial x} + \frac{\partial \gamma_{xz}}{\partial y} + \frac{\partial \gamma_{xy}}{\partial z} \right) \qquad (17.2b)$$

The validity of these identities may be verified by substitution from Eq. (17.1). Actually, the satisfaction of these six compatibility equations is the unique characteristic of an exact elasticity solution for a given problem. **There are an infinite number of stress distributions which satisfy the statical requirements and the boundary force requirements, but there is only one which also satisfies the strain compatibility equations and the boundary displacement requirements.**

Once the six strain components have been computed at a point for three elements originally parallel to x, y, and z axes, it is easy to compute the six strain components with respect to any other three orthogonal directions at the point. This may be done using the *strain-transformation equations* found in standard elasticity textbooks.

As in the case of stresses, it can be shown that there are at a point three directions which were mutually perpendicular before deformation and which remain so after deformation (i.e., there are three mutually perpendicular axes between which there is no shear strain). These three directions are called the axes of *principal strain*. The algebraically largest of these three lineal strains is called the *major principal strain;* and the algebraically smallest, the *minor principal strain.*

Note that these considerations regarding strain are limited only by the geometrical approximations dependent on small dis-

placements; and they are therefore valid for a material of any stress-strain characteristics. Also, note that, if the material is homogeneous and isotropic, the directions of the axes of principal strain and the directions of the principal stresses are coincident.

Differential equations of equilibrium. In the previous discussion of stress, only the relations of stress at a point are considered. The variation of stress between adjacent points must now be considered to establish the equilibrium requirements between the rates of change of the six stress components. Consider the particle shown in Fig. 17.2, and first write the equation for force equilibrium in the x direction, $\Sigma F_x = 0$. This equation simplifies to

$$\frac{\partial \sigma_x}{\partial x} + \frac{\partial \tau_{yx}}{\partial y} + \frac{\partial \tau_{zx}}{\partial z} + X = 0$$

and $\Sigma F_y = 0$ to

$$\frac{\partial \tau_{xy}}{\partial x} + \frac{\partial \sigma_y}{\partial y} + \frac{\partial \tau_{zy}}{\partial z} + Y = 0 \qquad (17.3)$$

and $\Sigma F_z = 0$ to

$$\frac{\partial \tau_{xz}}{\partial x} + \frac{\partial \tau_{yz}}{\partial y} + \frac{\partial \sigma_z}{\partial z} + Z = 0$$

These three equations are called the *differential equations of equilibrium* and must be satisfied at all points throughout the volume of a body. The solution for the stresses which satisfies Eq. (17.3) is also required to be in equilibrium with the specified forces at all points on the boundary of the body.

Linearly elastic stress-displacement equations. So far no specific stress-strain relations have been introduced. Such relations can be discussed in a more rigorous mathematical manner. The following, however, will be presented simply on the basis of experimental evidence regarding *linearly elastic, homogeneous,* and *isotropic* materials. Such evidence shows that a normal stress such as σ_x produces a lineal strain of σ_x/E in the x direction, lineal strains of $-\nu\sigma_x/E$ in both the y and z directions, and no shear strains between x and y, x and z, or y and z axes. Likewise, a shear stress such as τ_{xy} produces only a shear strain γ_{xy} but no other strains regarding the x, y, and z elements. Thus, the following six stress-strain relations may be written by superimposing the contributions of all six strain components:

$$\epsilon_x = \frac{1}{E}[\sigma_x - \nu(\sigma_y + \sigma_z)] \qquad \gamma_{xy} = \frac{\tau_{xy}}{G}$$

$$\epsilon_y = \frac{1}{E}[\sigma_y - \nu(\sigma_x + \sigma_z)] \qquad \gamma_{xz} = \frac{\tau_{xz}}{G} \qquad (17.4)$$

$$\epsilon_z = \frac{1}{E}[\sigma_z - \nu(\sigma_x + \sigma_y)] \qquad \gamma_{yz} = \frac{\tau_{yz}}{G}$$

where E = Young's modulus of elasticity in tension and compression

ν = Poisson's ratio

$G = E/2(1 + \nu)$ = modulus of elasticity in shear

The above stress-strain relations may be converted into the desired stress-displacement equations by substitution from Eqs. (17.1):

$$\frac{\partial u}{\partial x} = \frac{1}{E}\left[\sigma_x - \nu(\sigma_y + \sigma_z)\right] \qquad \frac{\partial u}{\partial y} + \frac{\partial v}{\partial x} = \frac{\tau_{xy}}{G}$$

$$\frac{\partial v}{\partial y} = \frac{1}{E}\left[\sigma_y - \nu(\sigma_x + \sigma_z)\right] \qquad \frac{\partial u}{\partial z} + \frac{\partial w}{\partial x} = \frac{\tau_{xz}}{G} \qquad (17.5)$$

$$\frac{\partial w}{\partial z} = \frac{1}{E}\left[\sigma_z - \nu(\sigma_x + \sigma_y)\right] \qquad \frac{\partial v}{\partial z} + \frac{\partial w}{\partial y} = \frac{\tau_{yz}}{G}$$

17.3   Formulation of the Solution of the Elasticity Problem. Now that the basic definitions and relations of the theory of elasticity are available, it is possible to formulate the method of solution of typical problems. Given in such problems are the geometry and material characteristics of the body involved, together with the definition of the forces on and/or displacements of the boundary surface of this body. Required are the stresses and displacements throughout the volume of the body. **As unknowns, therefore, there are nine unknown functions of x, y, and z. Six of these functions—σ_x, σ_y, σ_z, τ_{xy}, τ_{xz}, and τ_{yz}— define the six independent stress components throughout the body; and three of these—u, v, and w—define the three displacement components.**

Available to determine these nine unknown functions are **nine partial differential equations, three of which are the differential equations of equilibrium (17.3) and six of which are the stress-displacement equations (17.5). The nine unknown functions must satisfy not only these nine equations, but also the force and/ or displacement conditions on the boundary in order to be the true elasticity solution to a given problem.**

Note that, in general, the elasticity problem is a *statically indeterminate* one. There are only three equations of static equilibrium, which alone are insufficient to determine the six stress components involved in these equations. Only when the six stress-displacement equations are also considered can a unique solution be obtained.

Elasticity problems may be categorized as being one of three types, depending on the nature of the boundary conditions:

Type I. To determine the stress distribution and displacements when the body forces and boundary forces are prescribed and when there are no prescribed boundary displacements. *Example:* Simple end-supported beam.

Type II. To determine the stress distribution and displacements when the body forces are prescribed and when the boundary forces are prescribed except at discrete points where, instead, displacements are prescribed. *Example:* Two-span continuous beam.

Type III. To determine the stress distribution and displacements when the body forces are prescribed and when the displacements are prescribed over the entire boundary.

Civil engineering problems usually belong to the type I or II category. Further, by using the familiar primary structure technique as described in Chap. 13, type II problems may be converted into several type I problems.

To solve type I problems, the nine partial differential equations are condensed to six by eliminating u, v, and w from the stress-displacement equations. This procedure results in six equations which are exactly the same as those which would be obtained by substituting for the strains in the compatibility equations (17.2) from the stress-strain relations (17.4). These six equations will involve only the six independent stress components as the unknowns. When the stress components have been determined so as to satisfy these six equations and the boundary-force conditions, these values may be substituted into Eqs. (17.5) and the displacements u, v, and w determined from the resulting equations.

The reader is referred to standard elasticity textbooks for solutions to typical problems. Actually, relatively few problems have been solved, and those which have are relatively simple compared with many actual practical problems. Nevertheless, these solutions have been particularly useful as a means of improving our understanding and knowledge of the behavior of structures and structural members.

17.4 Small Deflection Theory of Flat Plates. In the Foreword, the behavior of a plate is visualized as being analogous to that of two layers of beam strips. One approximate method of computing plate behavior is based on this analogy and involves approximating a plate by a rectangular grid of beams. The analysis involves dividing the applied load between the two systems of intersecting beams so that the deflection and slope of each system are identical at all intersection points of the grid. In the following discussion, however, the classical theory for analyzing the behavior of the continuum of a flat plate is summarized.

Plates are subjected primarily to loadings which act transversely to the original middle plane of the plate. Most commonly the resulting transverse bending deflections of the plate are small and may be evaluated by a so-called **small deflection theory.** According to this theory, even when the *transverse loading* is accompanied by *middle-plane loads* (which act parallel to the original position of the middle plane of the plate), only the transverse loading contributes to the transverse bending of the plate. This is comparable, in cases of beam struts which are subjected simultaneously to transverse and axial loading, to assuming that the transverse bending of the beam struts is caused only by the transverse loading and is independent of the axial loading.

For more flexible plates, bending deflections increase and the modification of the transverse bending by the middle-plane loading becomes relatively more important. A more refined theory which includes this modification in the computation of the transverse bending of a plate is called **approximate large deflection theory.** This is comparable to computations for slender beam struts which include the bending moment contributed by the axial forces acting with lever arms which depend on the transverse bending deflections of the member.

The most accurate form of plate theory is called **large deflection theory.** In this theory, not only is the effect of the middle-plane loading on the transverse bending considered, but in addition the following refinements are evaluated. As a plate bends, the edges of the plate tend to move parallel to its original plane. If the edges are restrained against such movement, middle-plane reactions (usually called *membrane reactions*) are developed. Moreover, plates usually are bent into non-developable surfaces, and as a result further modification of the middle-plane (or *membrane*) stresses are induced. In large deflection theory, therefore, the complete interaction of membrane and transverse bending behavior is considered. It is a nonlinear theory and difficult to apply, but it must be considered for the thin plates undergoing large transverse bending deflection in the presence of large membrane forces. Such plates deflect so much that they are behaving much more like shallow shells than flat plates; and, in the latter stages of such behavior, the loading is primarily carried by membrane forces.

Simplifying assumptions and approximate elasticity relations. The following limitations are imposed on the ensuing discussion: (1) the thickness of the plate h is very small compared with the length and breadth; (2) if the thickness is not constant, the rate of change of thickness is very small; and (3) the transverse bending deflections are small compared with the thickness of the plate.

Actually, the problem of finding the stresses and deflections of a flat plate is a three-dimensional elasticity problem. By introducing certain valid approximations, it is possible in the case of *small deflection theory* to separate the three-dimensional problem into two two-dimensional elasticity problems, each of which gives a reasonably good solution for the unknowns involved. These approximations may be justified by considering the order of magnitude of the six independent stress components involved.

Consider a flat plate such as shown in Fig. 17.4a. The six stresses may be grouped into three classifications: the transverse normal stress σ_z; the transverse shear stresses τ_{xz} and τ_{yz}; and the stresses parallel to the middle plane of the plate σ_x, σ_y, and τ_{xy}.

Note that σ_z is of the order of magnitude of q, where q is usually in the range of 1 to 10 psi, occasionally 10 to 100 psi, and rarely in the range of hundreds of pounds per square inch. The total transverse load on the plate is of the order of qL^2. For transverse equilibrium, this load is

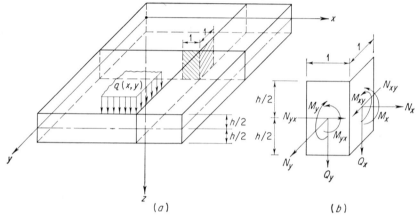

Figure 17.4   Thin-plate notation and convention

balanced by transverse shearing forces of the order of $\tau_{xz}Lh$ or $\tau_{yz}Lh$. Therefore, τ_{xz} and τ_{yz} are of the order of $(q)(L/h)$. If a bending of a strip of the plate of unit width is considered, the bending moment is of the order of qL^2, whereas the resisting moment is of the order of $\sigma_x h^2$ or $\sigma_y h^2$. Therefore, σ_x or σ_y (and, it is assumed, τ_{xy} also) is of the order of $(q)(L/h)^2$. Thus, since L/h is relatively large for thin plates, σ_x, σ_y, and τ_{xy} are greater than τ_{xz} and τ_{yz} and much greater than σ_z.

Since τ_{xz}, τ_{yz}, and σ_z are relatively small, their effect on the deflections of the plate will be neglected. As a result, the exact stress-displacement equations, Eqs. (17.5), will be approximated by the following approximate stress-displacement equations for thin plates:

$$\frac{\partial u}{\partial x} = \frac{1}{E}[\sigma_x - \nu\sigma_y] \qquad \frac{\partial u}{\partial y} + \frac{\partial v}{\partial x} = \frac{\tau_{xy}}{G}$$

$$\frac{\partial v}{\partial y} = \frac{1}{E}[\sigma_y - \nu\sigma_x] \qquad \frac{\partial u}{\partial z} + \frac{\partial w}{\partial x} = 0 \qquad (17.6)$$

$$\frac{\partial w}{\partial z} = 0 \qquad \frac{\partial v}{\partial z} + \frac{\partial w}{\partial y} = 0$$

Whereas τ_{xz}, τ_{yz}, and σ_z are being neglected as far as deformations are concerned, **all six stress components will be retained for any equilibrium considerations.** Note that this is comparable to elementary beam theory wherein transverse shearing stresses are considered in equilibrium considerations, but are usually neglected in the computation of bending deflections.

Notation and convention. When considering the equilibrium of a plate, it is convenient to isolate portions by passing transverse cutting planes or surfaces. The stresses on such surfaces, σ_x, σ_y, τ_{xy}, τ_{xz}, and τ_{yz}, vary over the thickness of the plate, of course. To avoid having to deal with these distributed stresses, it is convenient to represent them by their resultant forces and couples. For this purpose, it is convenient to introduce the definitions of the **stress resultants** N_x, N_y, N_{xy} $(= N_{yx})$, Q_x, and Q_y and the **stress couples** M_x, M_y, and M_{xy} $(= -M_{yx})$, as shown in their positive sense in Fig. 17.4b and as defined mathematically in Eqs. (17.7):

$$N_x = \int_{-h/2}^{+h/2} \sigma_x \, dz \qquad\qquad N_y = \int_{-h/2}^{+h/2} \sigma_y \, dz$$

$$N_{xy} = \int_{-h/2}^{+h/2} \tau_{xy} \, dz \quad = \quad N_{yx} = \int_{-h/2}^{+h/2} \tau_{yx} \, dz$$

$$Q_x = \int_{-h/2}^{+h/2} \tau_{xz} \, dz \qquad\qquad Q_y = \int_{-h/2}^{+h/2} \tau_{yz} \, dz \qquad (17.7)$$

$$M_x = \int_{-h/2}^{+h/2} \sigma_x z \, dz \qquad\qquad M_y = \int_{-h/2}^{+h/2} \sigma_y z \, dz$$

$$M_{xy} = -\int_{-h/2}^{+h/2} \tau_{xy} z \, dz \quad = \quad -M_{yx} = -\int_{-h/2}^{+h/2} \tau_{yx} z \, dz$$

In other words, these stress resultants and stress couples are, respectively, the force per unit length (pounds per inch) and the couple per unit length (inch-pounds per inch) supplied by the stresses involved. Note $N_{xy} = N_{yx}$ and $M_{xy} = -M_{yx}$ in view of the fact that $\tau_{yx} = \tau_{xy}$ and because of the sign convention adopted for all of these quantities. Note that each of the stress couples and stress resultants is defined by a function only of x and y.

The displacements of points lying in the middle surface of the plate in the x, y, or z direction are denoted by u_o, v_o, and w_o, respectively, all of which are functions only of x and y.

Formulation of small deflection theory. If the stress condition in a plate is represented by the stress resultants and stress couples, there will be a total of 11 independent unknowns required in order to define completely the stress and displacement condition of a plate:

5 stress resultants: N_x, N_y, N_{xy} $(=N_{yx})$, Q_x, and Q_y
3 stress couples: M_x, M_y, and M_{xy} $(= -M_{yx})$
3 displacements: u_o, v_o, and w_o

In order to solve for these unknowns, 11 equations are required. As shown below, there are 6 independent stress-displacement equations and 5 independent equilibrium equations available.

According to the third of Eqs. (17.6), w is independent of z. Therefore, at any location (x,y) the value of w is the same regardless of the value

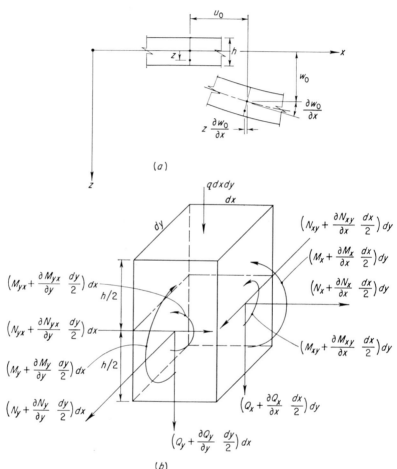

(a)

(b)

Figure 17.5 Small deflection theory for thin plates

of z and equal to w_o, the value of w at the middle surface. Then, by integrating the last two of Eqs. (17.6),

$$u(x,y,z) = u_o(x,y) - z\frac{\partial w_o}{\partial x}(x,y)$$

and

$$v(x,y,z) = v_o(x,y) - z\frac{\partial w_o}{\partial y}(x,y)$$

(17.8)

As shown by Fig. 17.5a, these equations are equivalent to stating that lines perpendicular to the middle surface before bending of the plate will remain perpendicular to it after bending (this is called the Bernoulli-Navier hypothesis). Equations (17.8) may be substituted into the first, second, and fourth of Eqs. (17.6) to obtain the following relations:

$$
\begin{aligned}
\sigma_x &= \frac{E}{1 - \nu^2} \left[\left(\frac{\partial u_o}{\partial x} + \nu \frac{\partial v_o}{\partial y} \right) - z \left(\frac{\partial^2 w_o}{\partial x^2} + \nu \frac{\partial^2 w_o}{\partial y^2} \right) \right] \\
\sigma_y &= \frac{E}{1 - \nu^2} \left[\left(\frac{\partial v_o}{\partial y} + \nu \frac{\partial u_o}{\partial x} \right) - z \left(\frac{\partial^2 w_o}{\partial y^2} + \nu \frac{\partial^2 w_o}{\partial x^2} \right) \right] \\
\tau_{xy} &= G \left[\frac{\partial u_o}{\partial y} + \frac{\partial v_o}{\partial x} - 2z \frac{\partial^2 w_o}{\partial x \, \partial y} \right]
\end{aligned}
\tag{17.9}
$$

The six stress-displacement equations may then be obtained by substituting from Eqs. (17.9) into the expressions of Eqs. (17.7) for the N's and the M's, thus:

$$
\begin{aligned}
N_x &= \frac{Eh}{1 - \nu^2} \left[\frac{\partial u_o}{\partial x} + \nu \frac{\partial v_o}{\partial y} \right] \\
N_y &= \frac{Eh}{1 - \nu^2} \left[\frac{\partial v_o}{\partial y} + \nu \frac{\partial u_o}{\partial x} \right] \\
N_{xy} &= N_{yx} = Gh \left[\frac{\partial u_o}{\partial y} + \frac{\partial v_o}{\partial x} \right]
\end{aligned}
\tag{17.10}
$$

and

$$
\begin{aligned}
M_x &= - \frac{Eh^3}{12(1 - \nu^2)} \left[\frac{\partial^2 w_o}{\partial x^2} + \nu \frac{\partial^2 w_o}{\partial y^2} \right] \\
M_y &= - \frac{Eh^3}{12(1 - \nu^2)} \left[\frac{\partial^2 w_o}{\partial y^2} + \nu \frac{\partial^2 w_o}{\partial x^2} \right] \\
M_{xy} &= - M_{yx} = \frac{2Gh^3}{12} \frac{\partial^2 w_o}{\partial x \, \partial y}
\end{aligned}
\tag{17.11}
$$

The required differential equations of equilibrium may be obtained by considering the equilibrium of the differential portion of the plate shown in Fig. 17.5b. Considering that N_x, N_y, M_x, etc., represent the stress couples and stress resultants on x and y planes at the center of the element, the forces and couples acting on the positive faces of the element will be as shown. In addition, but not shown, are similar forces and couples on the negative faces, such as $\left(N_x - \frac{\partial N_x}{\partial x} \frac{dx}{2} \right) dy$, etc. For equilibrium of this portion, the following equations must be satisfied:

$$
\begin{aligned}
\sum F_x = 0 && \frac{\partial N_x}{\partial x} + \frac{\partial N_{yx}}{\partial y} = 0 \\
\sum F_y = 0 && \frac{\partial N_{xy}}{\partial x} + \frac{\partial N_y}{\partial y} = 0
\end{aligned}
\tag{17.12}
$$

$$\sum F_z = 0 \qquad \frac{\partial Q_x}{\partial x} + \frac{\partial Q_y}{\partial y} + q = 0$$

$$\sum M_y = 0 \qquad \frac{\partial M_x}{\partial x} + \frac{\partial M_{yx}}{\partial y} - Q_x = 0 \qquad (17.13)$$

$$\sum M_x = 0 \qquad -\frac{\partial M_{xy}}{\partial x} + \frac{\partial M_y}{\partial y} - Q_y = 0$$

Note that $\Sigma M_z = 0$ results simply in $0 = 0$ since $N_{xy} = N_{yx}$ and does not yield a usable equation.

Consideration of the 11 equations from Eqs. (17.10) to (17.13) shows that they separate into two groups: (1) Eqs. (17.10) and (17.12) containing N_x, N_y, N_{xy} ($= N_{yx}$), u_o, and v_o; (2) Eqs. (17.11) and (17.13) containing M_x, M_y, M_{xy} ($= -M_{yx}$), Q_x, Q_y, and w_o. Thus, the small deflection theory for thin plates separates the solution into two parts, the first of which is called the **membrane problem** involving the **membrane stress resultants** N_x, N_y, and N_{xy} and the **membrane displacements** u_o and v_o, which will not be considered further, and the second of which is called the **transverse bending problem,** which is discussed below.

Transverse bending problem. In the following discussion of the transverse bending portion of small deflection plate theory, it is assumed that the thickness h of the plate is constant. The symbol D is used to designate the flexural rigidity of the plate:

$$D = \frac{Eh^3}{12(1 - \nu^2)} \qquad (17.14)$$

The six unknowns involved in the transverse bending problem will be designated as

w_o	the **transverse bending deflection**
M_x, M_y	the **bending stress couples**
M_{xy} ($= -M_{yx}$)	the **twisting stress couples**
Q_x, Q_y	the **transverse shear stress resultants**

Available for the solution of these unknowns are the three differential equations of equilibrium, Eqs. (17.13), and the three stress-displacement equations, Eqs. (17.11).

These six equations may be consolidated into one partial differential equation involving only w_o as the unknown. Substitute for Q_x and Q_y in the first of Eqs. (17.13) from the last two of these equations. Then substitute in the resulting equation from Eqs. (17.11) and obtain

$$D\left[\frac{\partial^4 w_o}{\partial x^4} + 2\frac{\partial^4 w_o}{\partial x^2\,\partial y^2} + \frac{\partial^4 w_o}{\partial y^4}\right] = q(x,y) \qquad (17.15)$$

This is the equation which governs the transverse bending deflection of the plate. If w_o can be determined so as to satisfy Eq. (17.15) and the boundary conditions concerning w_o, then w_o can be substituted into Eqs. (17.11) to obtain M_x, M_y, and M_{xy} $(= -M_{yx})$. Subsequently, these stress couples can be substituted into the last two of Eqs. (17.13) to obtain Q_x and Q_y.*

Once the stress couples and stress resultants are known, it is easy to compute the stress intensities associated with the transverse bending of the plate, using the following expressions:

$$\sigma_x = \frac{12z}{h^3} M_x \qquad \sigma_y = \frac{12z}{h^3} M_y \qquad \tau_{xy} = -\frac{12z}{h^3} M_{xy}$$

$$\tau_{xz} = \frac{3}{2} \frac{Q_x}{h} \left[1 - 4\frac{z^2}{h^2} \right] \qquad \text{and} \qquad \tau_{yz} = \frac{3}{2} \frac{Q_y}{h} \left[1 - 4\frac{z^2}{h^2} \right]$$

The following boundary conditions regarding w_o on various types of boundaries can be developed:

FIXED (OR CLAMPED) EDGE. Along such an edge, both the transverse bending deflection and the slope of the middle surface normal to the edge must be zero. For example, if the fixed edge is parallel to the x axis at $y = b$,

$$[w_o]_{y=b} = 0 \qquad \text{and} \qquad \left[\frac{\partial w_o}{\partial y} \right]_{y=b} = 0$$

SIMPLY SUPPORTED EDGE. Along such an edge, both the transverse bending deflection and the bending stress couple normal to the edge are zero, which results in the following conditions for an edge parallel to the x axis at $y = b$:

$$[w_o]_{y=b} = 0 \qquad \text{and} \qquad \left[\frac{\partial^2 w_o}{\partial y^2} \right]_{y=b} = 0$$

FREE EDGE. Such an edge must be entirely free of bending or twisting stress couples and of transverse shear stress resultants. It can be shown that such conditions are substantially obtained if, along an edge $x = a$, for example,

$$\left[\frac{\partial^3 w_o}{\partial x^3} + (2 - \nu) \frac{\partial^3 w_o}{\partial x \partial y^2} \right]_{x=a} = 0$$

and

$$\left[\frac{\partial^2 w_o}{\partial x^2} + \nu \frac{\partial^2 w_o}{\partial y^2} \right]_{x=a} = 0$$

Solution of transverse bending problems. Application of the above theory to various plate problems will be found in standard textbooks on plates and shells and will not be discussed here. For example, the solution for a rectangular plate simply supported on all four edges as shown in Fig. 17.6 would be found to be given by the following Fourier

---

* Note that this proposed method of analysis is one of the type described in Chap. 15 as displacement methods of analysis.

series:

$$w_o = \sum_{m=1}^{\infty} \sum_{n=1}^{\infty} A_{mn} \sin \frac{m\pi x}{a} \sin \frac{n\pi y}{b} \qquad (17.16)$$

where $\qquad A_{mn} = \dfrac{P_{mn}}{\pi^4 D[(m/a)^2 + (n/b)^2]^2}$ $\qquad (17.17)$

and $\qquad P_{mn} = \dfrac{4}{ab} \displaystyle\int_0^a \int_0^b q(x,y) \sin \frac{m\pi x}{a} \sin \frac{n\pi y}{b}\, dx\, dy$ $\qquad (17.18)$

from which P_{mn} can be evaluated for any specified transverse loading $q(x,y)$. Although this solution is not derived here, it is easy to verify that the expression for w_o given by Eq. (17.16) satisfies Eq. (17.15) and the boundary conditions for the simply supported edges along all four sides of this rectangular plate.

17.5 Large Deflection Theory of Plates. As the transverse bending deflections become larger and larger, the contribution of the middle-plane forces to the transverse bending becomes more and more significant. This effect may be accounted for by considering the equilibrium

Figure 17.6 Rectangular plate—simply supported on all four edges

of the element in Fig. 17.5b in its deflected, rather than its undeflected, position. As a result of the displacement of this particle, the side faces and the stress resultants and stress couples acting on them are rotated through small angles. If these slight changes in direction are considered in rewriting the equilibrium equations, it is found that only the first of Eqs. (17.13) is revised significantly and becomes

$$\frac{\partial Q_x}{\partial x} + \frac{\partial Q_y}{\partial y} + q + N_x \frac{\partial^2 w_o}{\partial x^2} + N_y \frac{\partial^2 w_o}{\partial y^2} + 2N_{xy} \frac{\partial^2 w_o}{\partial x\, \partial y} = 0 \qquad (17.19)$$

The last two of Eqs. (17.13) and Eqs. (17.12) remain unchanged.

In addition to this modification, large transverse bending deflections have an effect on the strains of the middle surface of the plate. To evaluate this effect refer to Fig. 17.3, and suppose that in this figure the displacements v in the y direction were much larger than the displacements in the xz plane. Such large displacements would now modify the strain of fibers OA and OC, whereas previously, when these displacements were small, it was found that they had only a second-order effect which was legitimately neglected. If such effects were included in the plate theory derived above, the stress-displacement equations, Eqs. (17.10), would become

$$N_x = \frac{Eh}{1 - \nu^2}\left[\frac{\partial u_o}{\partial x} + \frac{1}{2}\left(\frac{\partial w_o}{\partial x}\right)^2 + \nu\frac{\partial v_o}{\partial y} + \frac{\nu}{2}\left(\frac{\partial w_o}{\partial y}\right)^2\right]$$

$$N_y = \frac{Eh}{1 - \nu^2}\left[\frac{\partial v_o}{\partial y} + \frac{1}{2}\left(\frac{\partial w_o}{\partial y}\right)^2 + \nu\frac{\partial u_o}{\partial x} + \frac{\nu}{2}\left(\frac{\partial w_o}{\partial x}\right)^2\right] \qquad (17.20)$$

$$N_{xy} = N_{yx} = Gh\left[\frac{\partial u_o}{\partial y} + \frac{\partial v_o}{\partial x} + \frac{\partial w_o}{\partial x}\frac{\partial w_o}{\partial y}\right]$$

The remaining three stress-displacement equations, Eqs. (17.11), would remain unchanged, however.

When these refinements are introduced to obtain large deflection theory, it becomes apparent that the solution no longer separates into the two independent parts, the membrane problem and the transverse bending problem, as it does in small deflection plate theory. There are still 11 equations involving 11 unknowns, but the solution of these equations is very difficult. A few simple problems have been solved by large deflection theory. The reader is referred to the literature for further discussion of this subject. See, for example, "Theory of Plates and Shells" by Timoshenko and Woinowsky-Krieger.

17.6 Analysis of Thin Shells. In the Foreword, the structural behavior of shells is described in a qualitative manner. In the following discussion, fundamentals of plate theory are extended to include shells. This brief presentation covers little more than an introduction to the classical theory of shells and is intended to assist the reader in starting his studies of the standard textbooks and the extensive periodical literature devoted to the analysis and design of shell structures.

Limitations, assumptions, notation, and convention. In the following discussion, it will be assumed that h, the thickness of the shell, is small compared with the radii of curvature and the span of the shell. Essentially the same assumptions are used for thin shells as are used for thin plates, namely:

1. Normal stresses perpendicular to the middle surface of the shell are disregarded.

2. Contributions of the radial shear stresses to the deformation and deflection of the shell are neglected.

3. Points on lines normal to the middle surface of the shell before deformation remain on lines normal to the middle surface after deformation.

Basically the same definitions and notation as used for plates are used for thin shells.

Strains, stresses, and displacements at a given location in the shell are referenced to orthogonal coordinate axes with an origin O at a point

Figure 17.7   Thin shell notation

lying on the middle surface.   The x and y axes are taken coincident with the tangents to the lines of curvature of the middle surface at point O, and the z axis is taken coincident with the normal to the middle surface. The principal radii of curvature of the surface in the xoz and yoz planes are called r_x and r_y, respectively.   Refer to Fig. 17.7a.

The internal stresses acting on a differential shell element such as shown in Fig. 17.7a may be represented by a system of equivalent stress resultants and stress couples, which is similar to that used for plates. In the case of a small element of a shell, the exposed side faces, because of the initial curvature of the shell, are of a trapezoidal form rather than rectangular as in the case of plates. In the case of thin shells, however, *where h is very small compared with* r_x *or* r_y, the effect of this trapezoidal form may be neglected and the stress couples and stress resultants may be defined by Eqs. (17.7), the same definition as used for plates. These definitions are in terms of per unit length of the side faces *at the middle surface of the shell*. The stress couples and stress resultants are shown in their positive senses in Fig. 17.7b.

The definition of strains in a *thin shell* may be developed by considering the deformation of a small element of the shell such as shown in Fig. 17.7c, where lines normal to the middle surface are considered to be so both before and after deformation. Without considering the details of the derivation, the strains ϵ_x, ϵ_y, and γ_{xy} for x and y elements lying at a distance z from the middle surface may be defined as

$$\epsilon_x = \epsilon_{xo} - z\chi_x$$
$$\epsilon_y = \epsilon_{yo} - z\chi_y \tag{17.21}$$
$$\gamma_{xy} = \gamma_{xyo} - 2z\chi_{xy}$$

where ϵ_{xo}, ϵ_{yo}, and γ_{xyo} refer to the strain of x and y elements lying in the middle surface of the shell, and where

χ_x = change of curvature of middle surface in xoz plane
χ_y = change of curvature of middle surface in yoz plane
χ_{xy} = change of twist of middle surface

The strain expressions, Eqs. (17.21), may be substituted into approximate stress-strain equations, comparable to Eqs. (17.6). From the resulting equations, expressions for the stresses in terms of the strains may be substituted into Eqs. (17.7), the definitions of the stress couples and stress resultants, to obtain the following relationships:

Stress-Strain Relations for Membrane Stress Resultants

$$N_x = \frac{Eh}{1 - \nu^2} [\epsilon_{xo} + \nu\epsilon_{yo}]$$

$$N_y = \frac{Eh}{1 - \nu^2} [\epsilon_{yo} + \nu\epsilon_{xo}] \tag{17.22}$$

$$N_{xy} = N_{yx} = \frac{Eh}{2(1 + \nu)} \gamma_{xyo}$$

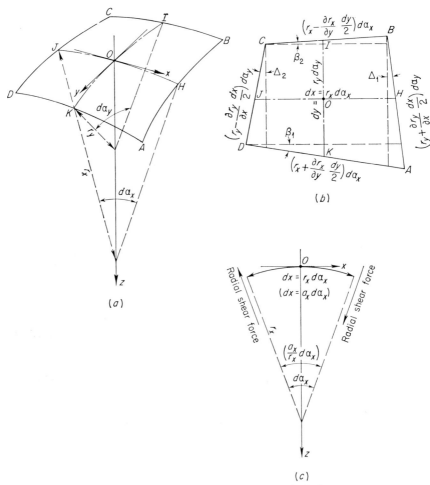

Figure 17.8   Geometry of differential shell element

Stress-Strain Relations for Bending and Twisting Stress Couples

$$M_x = -D[\chi_x + \nu\chi_y]$$
$$M_y = -D[\chi_y + \nu\chi_x] \qquad (17.23)$$
$$M_{xy} = -M_{yx} = D(1 - \nu)\chi_{xy}$$

In any given problem, these equations may be converted into stress-displacement equations by replacing the strains and changes in curvature by suitable expressions in terms of the displacements of the shell, u_o, v_o, and w_o.

Formulation of analysis of shells.   As in plate analysis, the analysis of a shell involves a total of 11 unknown functions of x and y, which describe the three membrane stress resultants N_x, N_y, and N_{xy} ($= N_{yx}$); the five bending stress couples and stress resultants, two of which are the bending stress couples M_x and M_y, one of which is the twisting stress couple M_{xy} $(= -M_{yx})$, and two of which are the radial shear stress resultants Q_x and Q_y; and the three displacements u_o, v_o, and w_o. Available to find these unknowns are 11 partial differential equations: the six stress-displacement equations which may be obtained in any given problem by converting the six stress-strain equations, Eqs. (17.22) and (17.23); and the five differential equations of equilibrium which may be derived as described below.

For purposes of the following derivation, a differential element such as shown in Fig. 17.7a is used. **This element is isolated by pairs of adjacent planes which are normal to the middle surface and are assumed to contain lines of curvature of the middle surface.** Only the middle surface of this element is shown in Figs. 17.8 and 17.9. The origin is selected at the center of the element, and the x and y axes lie in the tangent plane and coincide with the tangents to the lines of curvature. Note that none of the four sides of this element is exactly normal or parallel to *any* of the three coordinate axes. Further, none of the middle surface lengths of the four faces will be the same. For purposes of writing the three force-equilibrium equations, all five stress resultants are shown in Fig. 17.9a, while for purposes of deriving the moment-equilibrium equations, the moment vectors representing the stress couples are shown in Fig. 17.9b. The intensity of the resultant load is designated by q, the x, y, and z components of which are designated by q_x, q_y, and q_z.

Five equations of equilibrium may be written for the shell element: $\Sigma F_x = 0$, $\Sigma F_y = 0$, $\Sigma F_z = 0$, $\Sigma M_x = 0$, and $\Sigma M_y = 0$. Of course, the equation $\Sigma M_z = 0$ is identically satisfied and as in the case of thin plates does not yield a usable equation. In order to save space, the detailed derivation of these equations is omitted. These derivations are straight-forward but somewhat tedious to perform because of the inclinations of the four faces. These five equations become as follows when the central angles α_x and α_y are used as the independent variables in the differentiation:

$$\frac{\partial}{\partial \alpha_x}(N_x r_y) + \frac{\partial}{\partial \alpha_y}(N_{yx} r_x) + N_{xy}\frac{\partial r_x}{\partial \alpha_y} - N_y\frac{\partial r_y}{\partial \alpha_x} - Q_x r_y + q_x r_x r_y = 0$$

$$\frac{\partial}{\partial \alpha_y}(N_y r_x) + \frac{\partial}{\partial \alpha_x}(N_{xy} r_y) + N_{yx}\frac{\partial r_y}{\partial \alpha_x} - N_x\frac{\partial r_x}{\partial \alpha_y} - Q_y r_x + q_y r_x r_y = 0$$

$$\frac{\partial}{\partial \alpha_x}(Q_x r_y) + \frac{\partial}{\partial \alpha_y}(Q_y r_x) + N_x r_y + N_y r_x + q_z r_x r_y = 0$$

$$\frac{\partial}{\partial \alpha_x}(M_{xy} r_y) - \frac{\partial}{\partial \alpha_y}(M_y r_x) - M_{yx}\frac{\partial r_y}{\partial \alpha_x} + M_x\frac{\partial r_x}{\partial \alpha_y} + Q_y r_x r_y = 0$$

$$-\frac{\partial}{\partial \alpha_y}(M_{yx} r_x) - \frac{\partial}{\partial \alpha_x}(M_x r_y) + M_{xy}\frac{\partial r_x}{\partial \alpha_y} + M_y\frac{\partial r_y}{\partial \alpha_x} + Q_x r_x r_y = 0$$

$$(17.24)$$

In the above derivation, it is presumed that the shell surface is defined by the lines of curvature which are two orthogonal families of curves, along any one of which the normals to the shell surface at consecutive points intersect. It is also presumed that the osculating planes (that is, the planes containing three consecutive points, or two

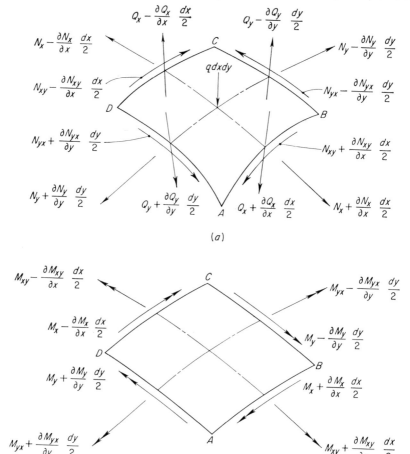

Figure 17.9   Stress resultants and stress couples

consecutive tangents, on a space curve) of these lines of curvature are normal to the surface. However, in general, the osculating planes of the lines of curvature are not normal to the surface; for example, in the case of a surface of revolution, the lines of curvature of which are the meridians and the parallels of latitude. The meridional plane is normal to the surface, and the radius of curvature of the meridian at any point is identical to one of the principal radii of curvature of the surface at that point. However, the plane of the parallel is not normal to the surface, and the radius of curvature of the parallel is not identical to the other principal radius of curvature of the surface at that point.

In such cases, the differential element shown in Figs. 17.8 and 17.9 would be isolated by pairs of curves from the two families of lines of curvature. The lengths of the sides would be described by the radii of curvature of these lines of curvature, which would be called a_x and a_y, but these might not be principal radii of curvature of the surface. However, the z axis would still be taken radially and normal to the tangent plane of the surface at O. The radial shears Q_x and Q_y would also act normal to the surface and in the direction of the principal radii of curvature. Therefore, in computing the component of Q_x in the x direction, for example, the angle involved would not be $d\alpha_x/2$ but (as shown in parentheses in Fig. 17.8c) would be $a_x\,d\alpha_x/2r_x$. Likewise, in setting up the equation $\Sigma F_z = 0$, components of the normal stress resultants N_x and N_y would be computed in the z direction, using this same modified angle.

Thus, when the surface is defined by lines of curvature, the osculating planes of one or both of which are not perpendicular to the surface, the following version of Eqs. (17.24) must be used:

$$\frac{\partial}{\partial\alpha_x}(N_x a_y) + \frac{\partial}{\partial\alpha_y}(N_{yx}a_x) + N_{xy}\frac{\partial a_x}{\partial\alpha_y} - N_y\frac{\partial a_y}{\partial\alpha_x} - Q_x\frac{a_x a_y}{r_x} + q_x a_x a_y = 0$$

$$\frac{\partial}{\partial\alpha_y}(N_y a_x) + \frac{\partial}{\partial\alpha_x}(N_{xy}a_y) + N_{yx}\frac{\partial a_y}{\partial\alpha_x} - N_x\frac{\partial a_x}{\partial\alpha_y} - Q_y\frac{a_x a_y}{r_y} + q_y a_x a_y = 0$$

$$\frac{\partial}{\partial\alpha_x}(Q_x a_y) + \frac{\partial}{\partial\alpha_y}(Q_y a_x) + N_x\frac{a_x a_y}{r_x} + N_y\frac{a_x a_y}{r_y} + q_z a_x a_y = 0$$

$$\frac{\partial}{\partial\alpha_x}(M_{xy}a_y) - \frac{\partial}{\partial\alpha_y}(M_y a_x) - M_{yx}\frac{\partial a_y}{\partial\alpha_x} + M_x\frac{\partial a_x}{\partial\alpha_y} + Q_y a_x a_y = 0$$

$$-\frac{\partial}{\partial\alpha_y}(M_{yx}a_x) - \frac{\partial}{\partial\alpha_x}(M_x a_y) + M_{xy}\frac{\partial a_x}{\partial\alpha_y} + M_y\frac{\partial a_y}{\partial\alpha_x} + Q_x a_x a_y = 0$$

$$(17.25)$$

Membrane theory of shells. Over the major portion of most civil engineering shells, there are substantially no bending and twisting stress couples and no radial-shear stress resultants. Therefore, the load is carried substantially by the membrane stress resultants: N_x, N_y, and N_{xy} $(= N_{yx})$. Bending and twisting couples and radial shears are significant only in the vicinity of the boundaries or near discontinuities in the loading or in the geometry of the shell surface.

If there are no bending and twisting couples or radial shears (that is, if $M_x = M_y = M_{xy} = Q_x = Q_y = 0$), the *five* equilibrium equations are reduced to *three* equations involving only the membrane stress resultants:

N_x, N_y, and N_{xy} $(= N_{yx})$.   Or, from Eqs. (17.25),

$$\frac{\partial}{\partial \alpha_x}(N'_x a_y) + \frac{\partial}{\partial \alpha_y}(N'_{yx} a_x) + N'_{xy}\frac{\partial a_x}{\partial \alpha_y} - N'_y \frac{\partial a_y}{\partial \alpha_x} + q_x a_x a_y = 0$$

$$\frac{\partial}{\partial \alpha_y}(N'_y a_x) + \frac{\partial}{\partial \alpha_x}(N'_{xy} a_y) + N'_{yx}\frac{\partial a_y}{\partial \alpha_x} - N'_x \frac{\partial a_x}{\partial \alpha_y} + q_y a_x a_y = 0 \quad (17.26)$$

$$N'_x \frac{a_x a_y}{r_x} + N'_y \frac{a_x a_y}{r_y} + q_z a_x a_y = 0$$

The values of the membrane stresses defined by these equations constitute the analysis of a shell by so-called **membrane theory.** These values are designated by the prime marks N'_x, N'_y, and N'_{xy} $(= N'_{yx})$ to indicate that they are first approximations of the membrane stress resultants which would be determined as part of the general solution of the problem, which included the effect of the bending and twisting couples and the radial shears.

It is important to note that **the membrane-theory solution is a statically determinate one defined simply by the above three equilibrium equations and the boundary conditions of the structure.**[1] Such a structure, because of its initial curvature, could maintain a *continuous distributed loading* in equilibrium even if it had no bending stiffness and therefore simply utilized its membrane strength.   In making this statement, the possibility of buckling of the shell is ignored.   Note that a flat plate is incapable of doing this, as is evident from the first of the equilibrium equations, Eqs. (17.13).   If the bending and twisting couples and radial shears are zero, there is no way of satisfying the equilibrium equation $\Sigma F_z = 0$.   Only after the plate has undergone considerable transverse deflection and curvature can the membrane forces be brought to bear and help to stabilize the plate.   (This is one of the factors considered in the large deflection theory for plates.)

It is interesting to note that the structural action of a shell is very similar to that of a truss.   A truss does not *need* rigid joints or bending stiffness in its members (if the possibility of buckling is ignored) in order to carry a system of *joint* loads and reactions.   It can carry these loads simply by using axial forces (that is, "membrane forces") in its members. If the truss *does have* rigid joints and the bending capacity of its members *is recognized*, it *does mobilize* some of this strength in carrying joint loads, but most of such loads are carried by the axial forces in the members. In other words, just as for a shell carrying *distributed loadings*, a "membrane solution" for a truss computed on the basis that it carries its joint

---

[1] In the membrane-theory solution, it is assumed that the boundary supports supply only the membrane-type boundary forces as required by the theory and that the boundaries are free to displace as required by the membrane-theory strains.

loads as a pin-connected truss is a very good first approximation for the axial forces in the members of the actual truss with rigid joints.

Application of membrane theory to shells of revolution.   Shells of revolution such as cones, spheres, etc., may be generated by rotation

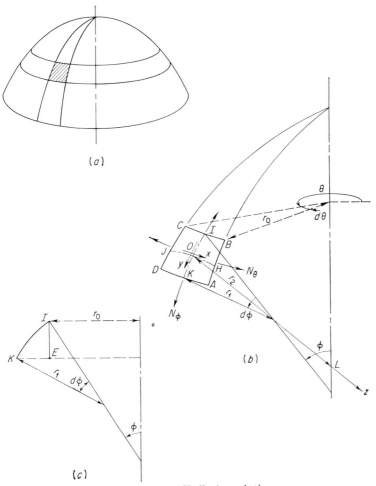

(a)

(b)

(c)

Figure 17.10   Shell of revolution

of a plane curve about an axis lying in the plane of the curve, as shown in Fig. 17.10.   Various positions of the generating curve are called meridians of the surface.   At any point O on the surface, the meridional plane through that point is one of the planes of principal curvature, and the meridian is one of the lines of curvature, the radius of curvature of which is denoted by r_1.   The other plane of principal curvature is normal to the meridional plane, and also being normal to the tangent plane contains the normal oz.   The intercept of this normal plane on the surface is the curve JOH, the radius of curvature of which is the distance OL, which will be denoted by r_2.

For purposes of analysis, it is convenient to define the middle surface of the shell by the lines of curvature, one family of which is the meridians and the other of which is the parallels of latitude intercepted on the surface by planes which are normal to the axis of revolution.   A differential element of the middle surface isolated by pairs of these parametric curves is shown in Fig. 17.10b and positioned by the angles θ and ϕ. Note further that the radius of curvature of the parallel is r_0.

Suppose that the distributed loading on this shell is symmetrical with respect to the axis of revolution.   Thus, q_x, the circumferential component of the load, is zero, and q_y and q_z are functions only of ϕ.   In such a case, because of the symmetry of the loading and of the shell, the stress condition of the shell is independent of θ and varies only with ϕ.   Thus, there are no shearing forces $N_{\theta\phi}$ or $N_{\phi\theta}$.   The normal stress resultants in the circumferential and meridional directions are denoted by N_θ and N_ϕ as shown.

The membrane-theory solution may be obtained by applying Eqs. (17.26) and noting that

$$\alpha_x = \theta \qquad a_x = r_0 \qquad r_x = r_2 \qquad r_0 = r_2 \sin\phi \qquad N'_{xy} = N'_{\theta\phi} = 0$$
$$\alpha_y = \phi \qquad a_y = r_1 \qquad r_y = r_1 \qquad N'_x = N'_\theta \qquad\qquad N'_y = N'_\phi$$

Hence,

$$\frac{d}{d\phi}(N'_\phi r_0) - N'_\theta \frac{dr_0}{d\phi} + q_y r_0 r_1 = 0$$

$$N'_\theta \frac{\sin\phi}{r_0} + \frac{N'_\phi}{r_1} + q_z = 0 \qquad\qquad (17.27)$$

From Fig. 17.10c, note that

$$\frac{dr_0}{d\phi} d\phi = KE \simeq KI \cos\phi \simeq r_1 \cos\phi\, d\phi \qquad \therefore \frac{dr_0}{d\phi} \simeq r_1 \cos\phi \qquad (a)$$

The second of Eqs. (17.27) becomes

$$N'_\theta = -\frac{r_0}{\sin\phi}\left[\frac{N'_\phi}{r_1} + q_z\right] \qquad\qquad (17.28)$$

By substituting from (a) and Eq. (17.28) in the first of Eqs. (17.27) multiplied by $\sin\phi$, and then by integrating from O to ϕ, the following expression is obtained:

$$N'_\phi = -\frac{1}{2\pi r_0 \sin\phi} \int_0^\phi (q_y \sin\phi + q_z \cos\phi)(2\pi r_0) r_1\, d\phi$$

The integral in this expression may be interpreted as the total vertical load F applied above a certain latitude ϕ. Hence,

$$N'_\phi = - \frac{F}{2\pi r_0 \sin \phi}$$

and from Eq. (17.28),   (17.29)

$$N'_\theta = - \frac{F}{2\pi r_1 \sin^2 \phi} - q_z \frac{r_o}{\sin \phi}$$

The membrane-theory solution for a symmetrically loaded shell of revolution may be easily computed by substituting into Eqs. (17.29) the value F.

Application of general theory to shell analysis. The general theory of shell analysis is formulated above. The application of this theory is difficult and has been done successfully only for a limited number of cases. For a discussion of such solutions, the reader is referred to books such as Timoshenko and Woinowsky-Krieger's "Theory of Plates and Shells" and Girkman's "Flachentragwerke."

Usually a successive-approximation technique is used to obtain the solution. First, a membrane-theory solution is obtained, to give a first approximation of the membrane stress resultants, and the corresponding displacements are then computed. These displacements imply certain changes in curvature which, in turn, imply certain bending couples and radial shears. The radial shears would imply certain changes in the membrane stress resultants, and thus establish a second approximation of the membrane stress resultants. Such calculations may be continued through as many cycles as are necessary to obtain a satisfactory convergence on the exact answers. Such final answers would be realized in the shell only if the supports supplied the boundary forces implied by these answers. In general the supports do not do so; therefore further interacting forces and couples have to be introduced between the shell and its support to reconcile the discrepancies. Similar forces and couples would have to be introduced on internal sections at locations of load or geometry discontinuities to reconcile internal discrepancies in the continuity of the strains. It is these corrective forces and couples which must be applied at the boundaries, or at internal sections, that are the most difficult to compute. They also cause the major difference between the stresses obtained by the general theory and those obtained by simple membrane theory.

17.7 Analysis of Buckling Behavior. In the Foreword, various types of structural failure are discussed, and it is emphasized that a buckling failure is potentially very dangerous and may trigger the collapse of many types of engineering structures. It is very important, therefore, for a structural engineer to develop the capability to analyze buckling behavior.

The possibility of buckling exists in any compressed portion. It may take the form of buckling of the structure as a whole or the localized buckling of an individual member or component part thereof, which may or may not precipitate the failure of the entire structure. **The load at which buckling occurs depends upon the stiffness of a structure or portion thereof, rather than upon the strength of the material involved.** As a result, stress intensities, if involved, are involved only to the extent of identifying the point on the stress-strain curve at which the modulus (or the slope) of the stress-strain curve is desired. Hence, for a hypothetical linearly elastic material with an infinite elastic limit, stress intensity would never enter the buckling considerations. Of course, for a nonlinearly elastic material or an elastoplastic material, stress intensity is involved in defining stress-strain characteristics.

It is also interesting to note that buckling can occur without the material involved being subjected to compressive stresses. For example, consider a tubular column of circular cross section. The axial force at which the column buckled would be the same whether the tube were compressed by uniformly distributed axial loads applied directly to its end cross sections or whether the tube were filled with water and the loads applied to the fluid through pistons inserted in each end so that the only stresses induced in the tube would be hoop tensions.

Fundamentally, the analysis of buckling behavior is simply an investigation of whether or not the equilibrium configuration of a system is stable. **The stability or instability of the system depends upon the answer to the following question: If a system is displaced slightly from its equilibrium position, does it tend to return to its original position or does it tend to displace further when the disturbance is removed? If it returns, the system is stable; if it displaces further, it is unstable.**

Methods of evaluating elastic buckling behavior. Several approaches may be used to obtain the answer to the fundamental question stated above regarding the stability of an equilibrium position. For purposes of simplifying the discussion and the computations involved, consider the simple idealized system shown in Fig. 17.11a. Assume that the compressed bar ab is weightless but perfectly rigid and nondeformable and that the only way that the system can deflect is for the spring ac to elongate. Initially it is assumed that the spring possesses the linearly elastic force-deflection characteristics[1] shown in Fig. 17.11b (though later in the discussion the effect of the nonlinear characteristics shown by the dashed line is considered).

---

[1] The spring stiffness factor k is equal to the force required to stretch the spring a unit distance and has units of pounds per inch.

The buckling behavior of this system may be studied by one of the following three methods:

Method I: Equilibrium Method. Assume that the member is initially perfectly vertical and concentrically loaded by the force P, so that there is no tendency for the bar to rotate about point b and nominally it is in equilibrium in its original vertical position. However, is there some value of P (called the critical value and denoted by P_{cr}) for which

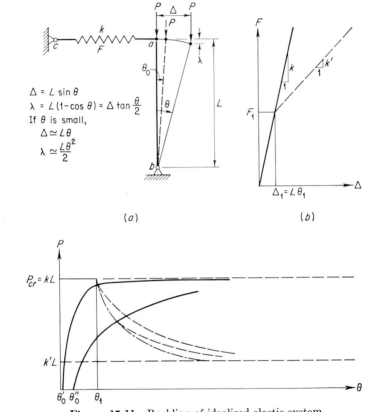

$$\Delta = L \sin \theta$$
$$\lambda = L(1-\cos \theta) = \Delta \tan \frac{\theta}{2}$$
If θ is small,
$$\Delta \simeq L\theta$$
$$\lambda \simeq \frac{L\theta^2}{2}$$

(a)

(b)

(c)

Figure 17.11   Buckling of idealized elastic system

the bar would also be in equilibrium in an alternative inclined position to which it is moved by a disturbance? If so, for equilibrium in the inclined position, $\Sigma M_b = 0$. Therefore, $P\Delta = FL \cos \theta \simeq FL$, if θ is small. But $F = k\Delta$; therefore, $P\Delta = (k\Delta)L$, or $P = kL$. Hence, if $P = kL$, the inclined position is also a possible alternative equilibrium position. This value of P is the critical value, or $P_{cr} = kL$. Note that the value of θ is indeterminate provided that it is small. In other words, the value of P_{cr} is independent of Δ (that is, of θ) and remains the same for any slightly inclined position of bar ab. This solution is represented by the horizontal line shown in Fig. 17.11c. Physically, when P reaches the value P_{cr}, the nominal vertical position is an unstable one, because at this load the bar could also be in equilibrium at any one of an infinite number of slightly inclined positions. That is, at P_{cr}, the system is unstable and buckling is possible.

Method II: Energy Method. This method involves a consideration of the energy changes that occur as a system is displaced from its nominal equilibrium position into a nearby possible alternative position. Consider again the vertical member shown in Fig. 17.11a, which nominally is in equilibrium in this vertical position when acted upon by a concentric load P. Suppose that the bar is rotated slightly to the alternative position defined by θ. During this rotation, the load P does work denoted by ΔW_E and equal to $P\lambda$ or $PL\theta^2/2$. Also, strain energy denoted by ΔW_I is stored in the spring of an amount equal to $F\Delta/2$ or $k\Delta^2/2$ or $kL^2\theta^2/2$. If ΔW_I is greater than ΔW_E, the disturbance has to do work *against* the spring to get the system into this position; therefore, when the disturbance is removed, the energy stored in the spring will pull the bar back to its original vertical position. If ΔW_I is less than ΔW_E, the disturbance has to work *with* the spring to prevent the bar from rotating more and more; and if it were removed, the system would collapse. If ΔW_I is exactly equal to ΔW_E, the system is in a *neutral* and *indifferent* condition, in which the system can be displaced from its nominal vertical position without the disturbance doing any work. This is the buckling condition which delineates the end of stability of the system and the start of instability. Therefore, when P is equal to P_{cr}, ΔW_E is equal to ΔW_I. Hence, $P_{cr}L\theta^2/2 = kL^2\theta^2/2$ and, therefore, $P_{cr} = kL$, thereby checking the value found by method I.

Method III: Load-deflection Curve Method. The critical value of P corresponding to the buckling condition can be identified simply by studying the characteristics of the load-deflection curve for the system, when the system is assumed to have some slight imperfection. For example, in this present case assume that the bar initially is not perfectly vertical but has some slight inclination θ_o. In this initial position, however, the spring is unstressed. Now, as P is applied, the member rotates about the base. For equilibrium at any particular load, $P\Delta = FL$, where now $F = k(\theta - \theta_o)L$. Therefore, $P = kL(1 - \theta_o/\theta)$. If kL is replaced by P_{cr}, then $P = P_{cr}(1 - \theta_o/\theta)$. Using this equation, the solid-line load-deflection curve shown in Fig. 17.11c may be drawn. Note that, as P approaches P_{cr}, θ approaches infinity. In other words, as P approaches P_{cr}, the system begins to lose its capability to resist rotation and very large rotation (or buckling) is imminent.

In the above considerations, the spring is assumed to be linearly elastic, with an indefinite elastic limit. It is also interesting to consider the effect of nonlinear elastic spring characteristics such as indicated by the dashed line in Fig. 17.11b, where the stiffness is reduced to k' when the force in the spring exceeds F_1 or $k\Delta_1$. For such a spring, the above solutions are valid only up to the point where θ equals $(\theta_1 + \theta_o)$, in which expression θ_1 is equal to Δ_1/L. Application of method III to this case leads to the following results: If $\Delta_o \leq \Delta \leq (\Delta_o + \Delta_1)$, or $0 \leq F \leq F_1$, or $\theta_o \leq \theta \leq (\theta_o + \theta_1)$,

$$P = kL\left(1 - \frac{\theta_o}{\theta}\right) \tag{a}$$

from which, when $\theta = (\theta_o + \theta_1)$,

$$[P]_{\theta_o+\theta_1} = kL \, \frac{\theta_1}{\theta_o + \theta_1}$$

However, if $\Delta \geq (\Delta_o + \Delta_1)$,

$$F = kL\theta_1 + k'L(\theta - \theta_1 - \theta_o)$$

but, for equilibrium,

$$P\Delta = FL \qquad \text{or} \qquad P = \frac{F}{\theta}$$

Therefore, if $\theta \geq (\theta_o + \theta_1)$,

$$P = \frac{kL\theta_1}{\theta} + k'L\left[1 - \frac{\theta_1 + \theta_o}{\theta}\right] \tag{b}$$

Curves plotted in accordance with Eqs. (a) and (b) are plotted in Fig. 17.11c for two values of θ_o smaller than θ_1: θ_o' and θ_o''. When the spring force reaches F_1, such curves break down sharply, as shown by the dashed-line portions, and become asymptotic to the horizontal line corresponding to $P = k'L$.

The nonlinear spring characteristics used in this hypothetical problem are actually quite representative of the stiffness characteristics of actual structural members, which are characterized by an initial stiff portion up to a certain elastic limit, above which the stiffness decreases markedly. The above results indicate that the critical load kL associated with the initial stiffness k can be approached only if the initial imperfection θ_o is small compared with θ_1. For larger imperfections, it is dangerous to count on the system to carry more than $k'L$.*

Buckling of columns.   Elastic buckling of structures and structural elements may be evaluated by any of the three approaches used above.

---

* In the periodical and textbook literature, a number of authors have reported some very valuable studies of buckling phenomena using simplified mathematical models such as that in Fig. 17.11.   For example, D. C. Drucker and E. T. Onat, On the Concept of Stability of Inelastic Systems, *J. Aeronaut. Sci.*, pp. 543–548, August, 1954; and F. R. Shanley, "Strength of Materials," McGraw-Hill Book Company, Inc., New York, 1957.

The mathematical details become more cumbersome to handle, but the fundamental concepts still are valid. To illustrate, method I is used below to study the buckling characteristics of the simple column shown in Fig. 17.12.

This column, hinged at both ends, is assumed to be a *perfect* compressed member which is homogeneous, linearly elastic, without initial curvature or eccentricity, and not subjected to any lateral loads. It is assumed to be constrained to deflect in the plane of the paper. Nominally, such a member simply undergoes only axial strain and remains unbent. Under certain conditions, the straight form, however, may not be the only deformed position which satisfies the equilibrium requirements for the member. Consider the possibility of the laterally bent position shown in Fig. 17.12. If the column is to be in equilibrium in this position, the differential equation of the elastic curve must be satisfied, or

$$\frac{d^2v}{dx^2} = -\frac{M}{EI} = -\frac{Pv}{EI}$$

Therefore,

$$\frac{d^2v}{dx^2} + \frac{P}{EI}v = 0$$

the solution of which is

Figure 17.12
Buckling of
simple column

$$v = A \cos\sqrt{\frac{P}{EI}}\,x + B \sin\sqrt{\frac{P}{EI}}\,x$$

If such a deflection occurred, the boundary conditions at a and b would have to be satisfied:

when $x = 0$, $[v]_{x=0} = 0 = A(1) + 0$ $\therefore A = 0$

when $x = L$, $[v]_{x=L} = 0 = 0 + B \sin\sqrt{\frac{P}{EI}}\,L$

To satisfy the latter condition, either B or $\sin \sqrt{(P/EI)}\,L$ has to be zero. If B equals zero, then no lateral deflection would be possible. However, if $\sin \sqrt{(P/EI)}\,L = 0$, then B does not have to be zero and could, in fact, have any value, in which case

$$v = B \sin\frac{\pi}{L}x$$

In other words, if the axial load P has such a value that $\sqrt{(P/EI)}L = \pi$, or if $P = (\pi^2/L^2)EI$, the straight form of the column is no longer the only equilibrium position, since at this load a laterally bent (or buckled) position is also possible. This value of the load is called the critical load P_{cr}. Sometimes it is called the *Euler load* after Leonhard Euler, who first developed the theory for the elastic buckling of flexible columns over two hundred years ago.

If the exact buckled shape were used in applying method II, the *energy method*, to this problem, exactly the same value would be obtained for the critical buckling load. If the column were assumed to have initial curvature, an eccentricity, or a lateral loading, method III could be used to obtain a plot of the axial load vs. the lateral deflection of the column.

Figure 17.13 Buckling curves of typical columns (no eccentricity, initial curvature, or other imperfections)

Such a plot would show that, as P approached P_{cr}, the lateral deflection would approach infinity—again indicating instability or buckling when $P = (\pi^2/L^2)EI$.

Actually these solutions are based on the assumption of linearly elastic behavior and are not valid if the proportional limit of the material is exceeded. If the stresses exceed this limit, the buckling load P_{cr} of a column which is hinged at both ends, concentrically loaded, and without initial curvature is found to be $(\pi^2/L^2)E_t I$, where E_t is the *tangent modulus* (or slope of the stress-strain curve at the stress corresponding to P_{cr}/A). The buckling curve (P_{cr}/A vs. L/r)* for such a column is shown in Fig. 17.13. Also shown for comparison are curves for a cantilever column and for a column which is fixed against rotation at both ends. If the material were linearly elastic with an infinite elastic limit, the dashed-line extensions would be valid and are shown for comparison with the buckling curves corresponding to the typical stress-strain curve for structural steel shown.

---

* In this sense, r is the radius of gyration of the cross-sectional area and is equal to $(I/A)^{1/2}$.

17.8   Evaluation of Dynamic Response.   In the past, the design of most civil engineering structures has been controlled by static (or substantially static) loading conditions.   Such dynamic loadings as were involved have made minor contributions to the total effect, so that the dynamic contribution was handled approximately by use of an equivalent static load, or by an impact factor, or by a modification of the factor of safety.

In recent years, a number of developments have led to a growing interest in a more precise evaluation of the contribution of dynamic loadings.   Among these have been the imposition on structures of heavier machinery and vehicles operating at higher speeds, the construction of higher towers and buildings and longer bridges involving more severe and important wind-loading conditions, the necessity of developing blast-resistant construction, and the desire to improve earthquake-resistant construction.   The growing interest in this area has stimulated the publication of many papers in the periodical literature and a number of books.[1]

Figure 17.14   Notation for step-by-step procedure

The response of a structure to dynamic loading depends upon the definition of the loading, the resistance of the structure to deflection, and since acceleration is involved, the mass of the structure.   Of course, if the supports of the structure are not immovable, their motion must also be defined in terms of time.

One of the best ways to develop a feeling and appreciation for dynamic response is to use a step-by-step numerical procedure to integrate the differential equations of motion.   Such procedures are generally applicable for any type of loading, and for elastic or elastoplastic structural resistance, in which cases more formal mathematical methods of solution become impractical or impossible to apply.   For multimass systems step-by-step numerical procedures become laborious but are adaptable to utilization of modern computational techniques and machines.

Consider the simple idealized system shown at rest by the solid lines

---

[1] Among the recent books dealing with structural dynamics are: S. Timoshenko, "Vibration Problems in Engineering," 3d ed., D. Van Nostrand Company, Inc., Princeton, N.J., 1955; G. L. Rogers, "Dynamics of Frame Structures," John Wiley & Sons, Inc., New York, 1959; C. H. Norris, R. J. Hansen, M. J. Holley, Jr., J. M. Biggs, S. Namyet, and J. K. Minami, "Structural Design for Dynamic Loads," McGraw-Hill Book Company, Inc., New York, 1959.

in Fig. 17.14. This system is allowed to move only in a horizontal translatory motion in the plane of the paper. This rigid body of weight W is restrained by a linearly elastic spring of stiffness k. Possible damping or frictional effects are ignored. Consider the dynamic response of this system to some known dynamic force P. The spring force kx is designated as R, as shown. If, at any time t_o, the displacement x_o were known, thereby defining the value of the spring force R_o, the net accelerating force acting on the mass would be $(P - R_o)$, and the acceleration $\ddot{x}_o$ at this instant would therefore be

$$\ddot{x}_o = \frac{P - R_o}{W/g}$$

If the velocity $\dot{x}_o$ at the time t_o were also known and if, during the following short interval of time Δt, the *acceleration were assumed to remain constant* at the value $\ddot{x}_o$, the velocity $\dot{x}_1$ at the end of this interval (that is, at time $t_o + \Delta t$) would be

$$\dot{x}_1 = \dot{x}_o + \ddot{x}_o \, \Delta t$$

In addition, the displacement x_1 at the end of the interval would be

$$x_1 = x_o + \dot{x}_o \, \Delta t + \ddot{x}_o \frac{(\Delta t)^2}{2}$$

Knowing this displacement x_1 defines a new value of the spring force R_1, and the accelerating force $(P - R_1)$ at the end of this interval. The above process could then be repeated for the next short time interval Δt to predict the velocity $\dot{x}_2$ and the displacement x_2 at the time $(t_o + 2\Delta t)$. By this step-by-step numerical process the motion of the mass could be tracked indefinitely. Obviously the accuracy of the above procedure depends on the length of the time interval and the degree of the approximation of the acceleration within it.

Figure 17.15 summarizes in a qualitative way the step-by-step development of the response of this simple system to a suddenly applied load. Suppose that, at $t = 0$, the system has no displacement or velocity. Consider the response for a series of intervals Δt, which are short compared with the natural period of the system. There being no displacement at $t = 0$, the spring force R is 0, and the accelerating force during the first interval is P_1. As the displacement increases, R gradually builds up, and the accelerating force, and hence the acceleration, decreases. When R exceeds P_1, the system starts decelerating. Subsequently the velocity is reduced to zero when the displacement reaches its maximum value of

$2P_1/k$. Then the mass starts rebounding and eventually reaches zero velocity and minimum deflection at its original starting position, thereby completing one complete cycle of this periodic response. Neglecting damping, the response continues, indefinitely, repeating the first cycle in a periodic fashion with a period equal to the natural period of the system.

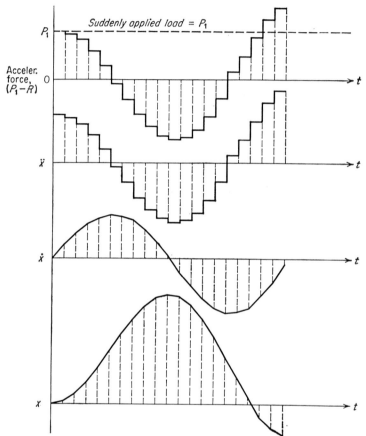

Figure 17.15 Step-by-step analysis of dynamic response of one-degree system to suddenly applied load

Of course, for a simple elastic system such as this, it is easy to solve the differential equation of motion involved for a general dynamic load P,

$$P = P_1 f(t)$$

where P_1 is the maximum value attained by the dynamic load. To derive the differential equation of motion for the undamped simple system shown in Fig. 17.14, apply d'Alembert's principle and add the inertia force $\ddot{x}W/g$ to the free-body sketch, showing it acting in the negative x direction. The condition for dynamic equilibrium $\Sigma H = 0$ for the isolated body is

$$P - kx - \frac{W}{g}\ddot{x} = 0$$

which may be rewritten as

$$\frac{d^2x}{dt^2} + \frac{kg}{W}x = \frac{P_1 g}{W}f(t)$$

The derivation is not included here, but the general solution of this equation to obtain the displacement x at any time t may be expressed in the following form:

$$x = x_o \cos \omega t + \frac{\dot{x}_o}{\omega}\sin \omega t + x_{st}\left[\omega \int_0^t f(t')\sin \omega(t - t')\,dt'\right] \quad (17.30)$$

where t' = any intermediate time between 0 and t
     x_o = initial displacement at $t = 0$
     $\dot{x}_o$ = initial velocity at $t = 0$
     x_{st} = P_1/k = static deflection of spring if P_1, the maximum value of dynamic load, were applied as a static load
     ω = $\sqrt{kg/W}$ = natural (circular) frequency of system

Note that, if the system were at rest at $t = 0$, then x_o and $\dot{x}_o$ would both be zero, and Eq. (17.30) would become

$$x = x_{st}(\text{DLF}) \quad (17.31)$$

where

$$\text{DLF} = \omega \int_0^t f(t')\sin \omega(t - t')\,dt' \quad (17.32)$$

and is called the *dynamic-load factor*. This factor is the value by which x_{st} should be multiplied at any time t in order to obtain the dynamic displacement at that time of a system which was initially at rest.

The dynamic-load factor for any given loading may be computed from Eq. (17.32). This factor is a function of time (that is, varies with time). Usually, the designer is most interested in the maximum value of the dynamic-load factor $\text{DLF}_{\max}$, since this value defines the maximum displacement of the system. The results for three typical dynamic loadings are summarized below:

a. Suddenly Applied Load

$$0 \leq t \quad P = P_1 \quad \therefore f(t) = 1$$
$$\text{DLF} = 1 - \cos \omega t \quad \text{DLF}_{\max} = 2$$

Figure 17.16   Dynamic-load factor for suddenly applied load

b. Gradually Applied Load

$$0 \leq t \leq t_1 \qquad P = P_1 \frac{t}{t_1} \qquad \therefore f(t) = \frac{t}{t_1}$$

$$t_1 \leq t \qquad P = P_1 \qquad \therefore f(t) = 1$$

$$0 \leq t \leq t_1 \qquad \text{DLF} = \frac{t}{t_1} - \frac{\sin \omega t}{\omega t_1} = \frac{t}{t_1} - \frac{T}{2\pi t_1} \sin \omega t$$

$$t_1 \leq t \qquad \text{DLF} = 1 + \frac{T}{2\pi t_1} [\sin \omega(t - t_1) - \sin \omega t]$$

Figure 17.17   Dynamic-load factor for gradually applied load

c. Rectangular Pulse Load

$$0 \leq t \leq t_1 \qquad P = P_1 \qquad \therefore f(t) = 1$$
$$t_1 \leq t \qquad P = 0 \qquad \therefore f(t) = 0$$
$$0 \leq t \leq t_1 \qquad \text{DLF} = 1 - \cos \omega t$$

$$t_1 \leq t \qquad \text{DLF} = 2 \sin \frac{\omega t_1}{2} \sin \omega \left(t - \frac{t_1}{2} \right)$$

Figure 17.18   Dynamic-load factor for rectangular-pulse load

To study the dynamic behavior of a structure, one must be able to define its position at any instant.   If at any instant the position of a structure can be defined by *one* number, or *one* coordinate, the structure is said to have 1 *degree of freedom*.   The simple system considered above illustrates such a case.   The two-mass system shown in Fig. 17.19b represents a structure with 2 *degrees of freedom*, since *two* distances x_1 and x_2 are required to define the position of the system at any instant. The beam shown in Fig. 17.19c has an *infinite number of degrees of freedom* because the definition of its positions requires enumerating an infinite number of vertical ordinates of its deflection curve.

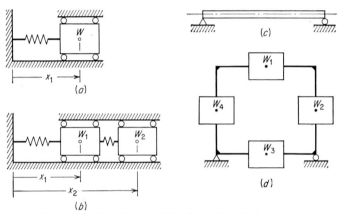

Figure 17.19   Degree of freedom of typical systems

Consider the rigid frame shown in Fig. 17.19d, which is constrained to deflect in the plane of the paper.   Assume that the weight of the members is small compared with the concentrated masses shown, which are assumed to be concentrated at a point at mid-lengths of the members. Also assume that the rotation of each mass is small and therefore can be neglected.   Consider only the effect of bending deformation of the structure.   On this basis *five* deflections (horizontal deflection of masses 1, 2, and 4 and vertical deflection of masses 1 and 3) completely define the configuration of the frame, and therefore the structure is said to have 5 *degrees of freedom*.

The present discussion will not be extended to include the multi-degree-of-freedom system which is representative of actual structures.   The reader should refer to the references noted for such a discussion.   It will be found that a general method can be developed for evaluating the dynamic response of linearly elastic multi-degree-of-freedom systems, which utilizes many of the basic ideas discussed above for the simple 1-degree system.   This method involves first determining the natural frequency and deflected shape of each of the *normal modes of vibration* of the system, there being as many such modes as there are degrees of freedom of the system.   The dynamic response of the system to a given dynamic load is then evaluated by superimposing proper contributions of each of the various normal modes of vibration.   The contribution of each mode depends on the *participation factor* and the *dynamic-load factor* for that mode.   The participation factor depends upon the characteristic shape of the mode in comparison with the distribution of the dynamic load over the structure.   The dynamic-load factor depends upon the natural frequency of the mode and the time variation of the dynamic load.

18

Model Analysis of Structures

18.1 Application of Model Analysis. In the field of structural engineering, the use of models has steadily increased in the last 40 years. Today, model analysis of structures not only is extremely important as a tool for research and development but also forms an important supplement to the mathematical methods used in the actual design of structures. European engineers such as Nervi, Oberti, Torroja, and Rocha often use models in arriving at their designs. Perhaps the most widely publicized use of models in this latter respect has been in connection with the design of most of the important and well-known suspension bridges erected in recent years. Further evidence of the importance of model analysis in the field of structural design is furnished by the well-equipped laboratories that have been established by several governmental agencies. There are also many academic institutions that possess fine model-analysis laboratories established primarily for educational and research purposes.

Model analysis of structural problems encountered in either research or actual design may be used for one or more of three reasons: (1) because mathematical analysis of the problem concerned is virtually impossible; (2) because the analysis, though possible, is so complex and tedious that the model analysis offers an advantageous short cut; (3) because the importance of the problem is such that verification of the mathematical solution by model test is warranted. The stress distribution in an irregularly shaped member may be investigated by use of a model for the first reason; a model test may serve as the basis for the analysis of a complex building frame or of a shell roof for the second reason; a model study of the proposed design of a suspension bridge may come under the third classification.

The objective of tests of a structural model may generally be placed in one of the following four categories: (1) stress analysis of the model, (2) determination of stress distribution, (3) determination of critical or buckling loads, (4) analysis of the characteristics of the normal modes of vibration.   As used in this chapter, **stress analysis** means the determination of the axial force, the shear force, and the bending moment acting on any cross section of the model, whereas **stress distribution** is the term used to designate the manner in which the stress intensities vary across any cross section of a member.

18.2   Standard Methods of Model Stress Analysis.   Certain methods are commonly used for the stress analysis of a model, among them being the *brass-wire model method*, the *Beggs method*, the *Eney deformeter*, the *Gottschalk Continostat*, the *moment indicator*, and the *moment deformeter*.   All these methods are discussed in Chap. 19. The *photoelastic method* is also used to a limited extent in the stress analysis of structural models, but its principal application is in the solution of stress-distribution problems.

18.3   Design of Models.   Whenever a reduced-scale model is used to study an actual structure, it is necessary, of course, for the model to be designed so that full-scale behavior of the prototype may be deduced from the observations of the behavior of the model.   For this to be accomplished, the dimensions of the model and the characteristics of the material used in its construction must bear certain definite relations to the dimensions and material of the prototype. **The principles governing the relationship between a model and its prototype are called the principles of similitude.**   Certain of these principles govern the design of the model, and others establish the means of extrapolating the results of the model tests to predict the performance of the prototype.

The determination of the principles of similitude is discussed briefly in Chap. 19.[1]

The choice of the proper material for the construction of models is of great importance.   Not only must the material be such that its structural action is suitable to its use, but one should also bear in mind the ease with which it can be fabricated for a small model.   For many models, the materials of the prototype may be used.   Steel is often used, and reinforced concrete may be used if the model is sufficiently large so that reinforcement can be detailed and placed properly.

It is often desirable to use a material having a lower modulus of elasticity than the material of the prototype so that deformations which are large enough to be measured accurately may be obtained without the application of forces which are too great.   The use of Duralumin or brass

---

[1] See also R. D. Conrad, Structural Models.   Part I: Theory, *U.S. Navy Dept., Bur. Construction and Repair, C and R Bull.* 13, 1938; G. E. Beggs, R. E. Davis, and H. E. Davis, "Tests on Structural Models of Proposed San Francisco–Oakland Suspension Bridge," University of California Press, Berkeley, 1933.

in place of steel is sometimes convenient for this reason.   Brass has the additional advantage that it may be soldered easily, thus facilitating the construction of the model.

Celluloid is one of the most widely used materials in the construction of the models used in conjunction with the more common model methods of stress analysis; its properties are discussed in more detail in the next article.

The selection of the scale of a model depends on many factors, some of the more important of which are the properties of the materials available for its construction, the capacity of the equipment to be used in loading the model, the dimensions of the instruments to be used in testing the model, the limitations of machinery to be used in fabricating the model, and the funds and time available for the experimental program. As the scale of a model is reduced, it becomes increasingly difficult to maintain geometric similarity, and the duplication of all the details of the prototype is physically impossible.   Some details of the design are obviously unimportant and may be omitted from the model.   In other cases, the details of the structural connections have a great influence on the result, and a large enough scale must be used so that the structural action of the model is adequate.

18.4 Properties of Model Materials. The properties of model materials, such as steel, brass, Duralumin, wood, and concrete, are well known and need not be reviewed here.   Celluloid is widely used for structural models and has, in common with certain other plastic materials, certain properties that are not well known and require further discussion.

Celluloid (or cellulose nitrate) has some very desirable properties as a model material, but it also has some that are very undesirable. It is very readily machined, has a low modulus of elasticity, is homogeneous, and may be readily welded by using acetone.   On the other hand, its elastic properties change decidedly with age, temperature, and humidity.   More serious still, celluloid creeps under a constant load; i.e., if a load is applied, while some 85 per cent of the deformation occurs within a few seconds, the remaining 15 per cent takes place more slowly. It is necessary to wait an appreciable period, in the neighborhood of 15 min, before motion is essentially complete.   Even then, small movements will still occur.

This creep phenomenon may be more easily understood by referring to Fig. 18.1.   Suppose that a weight W is hung on the celluloid member shown.   Almost instantaneously, the member will undergo about 85 per cent of its total elongation, but the remaining 15 per cent will take place gradually, as shown in Fig. 18.1b.   If the member is loaded instead with a weight of $2W$, the elongation will vary with time, as is also shown in Fig. 18.1b.   The elongation that takes place up to certain times after loading, such as $t = 1, 2, 5, 10$, etc., may be read off from the curves of Fig. 18.1b for various loads W, $2W$, $3W$, etc. If these elongations are plotted against the loads as shown in Fig. 18.1c, it is found that all the elongations measured at 1 min after loading lie along a straight line for all practical purposes. The same is true of the elongations measured at

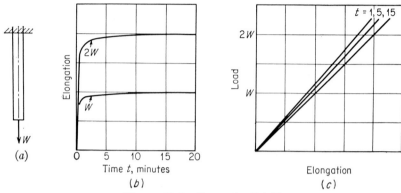

Time t, minutes

(a) (b) (c)

Figure 18.1   Creep of celluloid

times $t = 2, 5, 10$, etc. All these straight lines likewise pass through the origin. This latter plot discloses a very important characteristic of the creep of celluloid. At any particular instant after loading, the instantaneous elongation (or strain) is directly proportional to the load (or stress intensity); i.e., at any instant the material is following Hooke's

Figure 18.2   Celluloid cantilever subjected to (a) constant load, (b) constant displacement

law and has an instantaneous modulus of elasticity E_t. The effect of creep is to lower this instantaneous value of the modulus with time.

It is extremely important that the creep of celluloid has this characteristic; otherwise, the usefulness of the material for structural models would be impaired. In view of the creep of celluloid, if a constant load W is applied to the end of a cantilever beam, the elastic curve progressively assumes different positions as the time after loading increases, as shown in Fig. 18.2a. Of course, after about 15 min, the rate of creep has become so small that the beam may be considered to have come to rest. Suppose, however, that a fixed deflection Δ_b is introduced at the end of the beam, as shown in Fig. 18.2b. The force P_t applied to the beam by the pin maintaining the fixed deflection at b decreases with time owing to the creep and the resultant lowering of the instantaneous modulus E_t. Since, at a given instant, E_t does not vary with the stress intensity and is therefore constant for the entire beam, the deflection at point b may be expressed as $\Delta_b = K_b(P_t/E_t)$, where K_b is a constant that depends only on the dimensions of the beam.   Hence, $P_t/E_t = \Delta_b/K_b = C$, a constant that does not vary with time.   The deflection at any point n may be expressed as $\Delta_n = K_n(P_t/E_t) = K_nC$, also constant and independent of time, since K_n is a constant depending only on the dimensions of the beam and the location of point n.   It is apparent, therefore, that not only does the end of the cantilever remain fixed in position but the entire elastic curve of the beam also does

so.   It may therefore be concluded that the deflected position of a celluloid model will not change with time if a fixed deformation is applied to the model instead of a constant load.

18.5   Use of Spring Balance to Overcome Creep.

It is shown in the previous article that the deflected shape of a celluloid model does not change with time if a fixed deflection is introduced at one point on the model.   Owing to creep, however, the effective modulus of celluloid does change with time, and therefore the external forces and internal stresses of the model likewise change

Figure 18.3   Use of celluloid spring balance

with time.   Thus, it is difficult to interpret the strains and deflections, even though they do not change with time and therefore may be measured without difficulty.   In other words, we cannot conclude simply from the measured strains that a certain load will produce certain stresses in the model—all we know is that some unknown load produces certain strains and deflections.

Through the use of a so-called celluloid "spring balance," we may circumvent this difficulty, however, and interpret the measurements of the strains and deflections.   Such balances may be designed in a number of different forms and shapes, depending on the problem at hand. Suppose, for example, that we wish to analyze the celluloid model of the rigid frame shown in Fig. 18.3 when it is acted upon by a horizontal force H at the top of the right column.   To do this, the model may be connected to a balance, as shown in Fig. 18.3a.   Then, by pulling point d to the right, a horizontal deflection Δ may be applied to the combined system of model and balance.

On the assumption that the steel straps ab and cd may be considered as being infinitely rigid in comparison with the celluloid model and spring balance, part of this total deflection Δ is introduced into the model and the remainder into the spring balance.   Thus

$$\Delta = \Delta_m + \Delta_s \qquad (a)$$

If both the balance and the model have been made out of the same piece of celluloid, it is legitimate to assume that the instantaneous modulus E_t is the same for both.   Recognizing that the instantaneous value of the tension in both straps is the same and equal to P_t and, therefore, that the deforming force on both model and balance is also the same and equal to P_t, we may express the deflections Δ_m and Δ_s as follows:

$$\Delta_m = K_m \frac{P_t}{E_t} \qquad (b)$$

$$\Delta_s = K_s \frac{P_t}{E_t} \qquad (c)$$

where K_m and K_s are constants, the value of which depends only on the geometry and dimensions of the model and balance, respectively.
   Substituting in Eq. (a) from Eqs. (b) and (c), we find that

$$\frac{P_t}{E_t} = \frac{\Delta}{K_m + K_s} \qquad (d)$$

and therefore conclude that the ratio of P_t to E_t remains constant and does not change with time.   In other words, while both P_t and E_t change with time, they always bear a constant relationship to each other. Substituting now from Eq. (d) back into Eqs. (b) and (c), we find that

$$\Delta_m = \frac{K_m \Delta}{K_m + K_s} \qquad (e)$$

$$\Delta_s = \frac{K_s \Delta}{K_m + K_s} \qquad (f)$$

Since the right-hand sides of both these equations contain only constants that do not change with time, both Δ_m and Δ_s remain constant and do not change with time.   In other words, by using a celluloid spring balance in this manner and introducing a fixed deflection Δ into the combined system of model and balance, we produce a deformation of both balance and model that remains constant and does not change with time.
   Suppose that the model has been deformed in this manner and that the resulting strains in it have been measured.   Suppose that we then wish to interpret these strains so as to obtain the stresses in the model due to a horizontal force H.   While the stresses in the model vary with time, we may express the instantaneous value of the stress intensity, σ_t, in

terms of E_t and its corresponding strain e. Thus,

$$\sigma_t = E_t e \qquad (g)$$

From Eq. (c),

$$E_t = \frac{K_s}{\Delta_s} P_t \qquad (h)$$

Therefore,

$$\sigma_t = \frac{K_s}{\Delta_s} e P_t \qquad (i)$$

Assume that K_s, the constant of the spring balance, has been either computed or determined previously from a calibration test. The desired stress intensity σ_t has been expressed, therefore, in terms of the known constant K_s, the measured quantities e and Δ_s, and the unknown value of P_t. By assigning various values to P_t, the corresponding stress intensities may be obtained. If $P_t = H$, the corresponding stress intensity σ_H is found to be

$$\sigma_H = \frac{K_s e}{\Delta_s} H \qquad (j)$$

In this manner, the strain measurements may be interpreted to give the stresses in terms of a horizontal force H.

The use of the spring balance is discussed further in subsequent articles. The determination of the constant of the spring balance by calibration test is also discussed in detail later. The purpose of the present discussion is simply to introduce the idea of the balance and illustrate how it may be used to overcome the difficulties associated with the creep properties of celluloid.

18.6 Planning a Model Analysis. It is difficult, if not impossible, to give a complete list of instructions that will cover the planning of the model analysis of any and all problems that might be encountered. There are, however, certain factors that are more or less common to most such problems and that should therefore be discussed.

The first factor that should be considered is the purpose of the proposed model study. If the model is being used to check the design of an actual structure, then the principles of similitude must be established for the given problem and observed as closely as is possible and practical in designing and constructing the model. Contrasted to this type of model study is the case where the model is being used to develop or study the mathematical theory for a certain type of problem. In such cases, the model may be considered as actually a small-sized structure for which the mathematical results are computed and compared with the experimental results. In other words, model and prototype are synonymous, and similitude is not a factor. When models are used in this manner, a number of different models should be selected so that the relative dimensions of the various elements are varied sufficiently to cover the entire range that might be encountered in large-sized structures of this type.

The next step in planning a model study is to select the most appropriate method of model analysis for the particular problem at hand.   Quite often the choice of the method is limited by such factors as availability of equipment and suitable model material or experience of the laboratory personnel.   Assuming that there are no such limitations, the method of analysis may be selected simply on the basis of the advantages and disadvantages of the various methods applicable to the problem at hand.

Once the method of analysis is selected, the limiting dimensions of the model may then be established.   To illustrate how to do this, suppose that it has been decided to use the Beggs method for the stress analysis of a given problem.   First, the width of the model at any point where the deformeter gage is to be attached should not exceed $\frac{3}{4}$ in., which is the normal capacity of the clamping device on the gage.   On the other hand, the minimum width at any point in the model should preferably be not less than $\frac{1}{4}$ in.   This is controlled by the working tolerances that should be permitted in constructing celluloid models.   Such models can be finished quite easily to satisfy a tolerance of ± 0.002 in.   If the width of a member is less than $\frac{1}{4}$ in., the tolerance in the width will cause a variation in the moment of inertia of more than ± 2 per cent, which is about the maximum that should be permitted.   The length scale and the thickness of the members should be selected so that the model is neither too stiff nor too flexible.   If the model is too stiff, the springs of the deformeter gage will not be strong enough to deform the model.   If the model is too flexible, some of the compression members may buckle.

Similar factors are involved in establishing the limiting dimensions of any model.   Careful consideration must be given to the limitations imposed by the proposed methods of measuring strains and deflections or by the proposed technique of loading or deforming the model.   Of course, the more experience one has, the easier it is to make such decisions.

In planning a model study, the fact is often overlooked that some of the most informative model studies can be conducted with relatively simple models.   Elaborate, complex, and expensive models may be impressive, but they do not necessarily produce the most valuable results. If it still seems necessary and desirable to make such a model, precede such a study with enough studies of simplified models to be sure that the proposed model and method of analysis will yield satisfactory results.

18.7   Interpretation of Model Results.   The first step in interpreting model results comes when the experimental data are actually being measured and recorded.   One should continually be studying the data as they are accumulated, being sure that the data from duplicate tests are consistent, checking to see that the measurements from point to point vary in a reasonable and orderly manner, taking precautions to see that constant test conditions and techniques are being maintained, etc. In this way, if questionable or unexpected data are being obtained, the measurements may be checked and verified before the test setup is altered. It is often helpful to make rough plots of data as they are being obtained in order to "spot" quickly any inconsistent measurements.

After the test data have been analyzed and the test results computed, the information should be plotted or tabulated in such a manner that its reasonableness may be estimated. The best way of judging the results, of course, is to apply any physical checks available. For example, in any static problem, the test results must satisfy the laws of static equilibrium: $\Sigma F_x = 0$, $\Sigma F_y = 0$, and $\Sigma M = 0$. Of course, static checks may

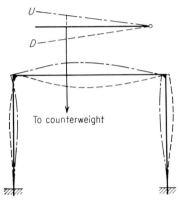

Figure 18.4   Imperfections in loading arrangement

be applied to the entire model or any portion of it. Such checks are extremely useful. There is perhaps no better way of judging the reliability of model results for a static problem.

It is often difficult to load a model exactly as specified. For example, suppose that the model shown in Fig. 18.4 is analyzed for a vertical load by means of the moment indicator. To do this, the deforming device is arranged as indicated. Just how successful we are in applying the desired vertical load is indicated by the model results. Suppose that the joints are in equilibrium under the experimental end moments in the members but that the shears in the columns which are computed by statics from these end moments are not equal and opposite. This indicates that the load which was actually applied to the model had a horizontal as well as a vertical component. To correct these results for this error in loading we now analyze the model for a horizontal load. Then, using this information we can adjust the values of the first test so as to remove the effect of the undesired horizontal component of the load. In this manner, therefore, the laws of statics may often be used to assist us in correcting for the effect of errors in loading.

Whenever the results obtained from a model are to be extrapolated in order to predict the behavior of its prototype, the principles of similitude must be fulfilled in designing, constructing, and testing the model. The requirements of these principles can seldom be met exactly, and in almost all practical cases it will be found that the behavior of a model differs to some extent from that of its prototype. **Scale effect is defined as the degree to which a prediction made from a model test will not be fulfilled in the full-scale structure.** This effect may be caused by unavoidable inaccuracies in test conditions. As the scale of a model is reduced, it becomes impossible to reproduce all the details of the prototype, and such elimination also may contribute to the effect. The excellence of the workmanship in building the model must increase as the scale is reduced in order to minimize such results.

It is evident that scale effect may arise from a variety of sources, some of which are beyond control. It should always be suspected. If the purpose of the test is to provide an accurate indication of the behavior in full scale, similar models of different scales may be built and tested and the laws of behavior determined empirically from the results of the series of model tests.

19

Model Methods of Stress Analysis

19.1   General.   One of the most frequent uses of structural models is to obtain the stress analysis of a model of a statically indeterminate structure.   Numerous methods[1] and techniques have been developed for this purpose.   In using some of these methods, the required results may be obtained by loading the model in the same manner as the prototype.   The elastic deformation of the model is then similar to that of the prototype, and strain measurements then lead to the required results.   Such a method is called a **direct method of model stress analysis.**   Suspension-bridge model studies are usually carried out in this manner; the moment indicator is also used in a direct manner.

Contrasted to direct methods of model analysis are those methods in which the model is loaded in a manner bearing no direct relation to the actual loading on the prototype.   Such methods are called **indirect methods.**   Usually they involve first finding influence lines for the model.   These results may be extrapolated to the prototype, and the stresses in the prototype due to the given condition of loading may then be computed from the extrapolated influence lines.   The methods of using the Beggs deformeter and the moment deformeter are examples of indirect methods of model analysis.

19.2   Theory of Certain Indirect Methods.   Certain of the indirect model methods of stress analysis are merely different experimental techniques of applying Müller-Breslau's principle, which is

---

[1] C. B. McCullough and E. S. Thayer, "Elastic Arch Bridges," chap. VII, John Wiley & Sons, Inc., New York, 1931; J. B. Wilbur, Structural Analysis Laboratory Research, *Mass. Inst. Tech., Dept. Civil Sanitary Eng., Ser.* 65, 1938, *Ser.* 68, 1939, *Ser.* 73, 1940, *Ser.* 80, 1941; C. H. Norris, Model Analysis of Structures, *Exptl. Stress Analysis*, vol. 1, no. 2, July, 1944; J. B. Wilbur and C. H. Norris, Model Analysis of Structures, "Handbook of Experimental Stress Analysis," chap. 15, John Wiley & Sons, Inc., 1950.

stated in Art. 14.3. The spline method, the brass-wire model method, the Beggs method, and the Gottschalk Continostat all are examples of such methods.

In the general case for any stress element X_a, this principle may be stated mathematically by the following equation:

$$X_a = - \frac{\Delta_{na}(1)}{\Delta_{aa}} \qquad (19.1)$$

It is important to note the sign convention of this equation, namely: X_a is plus when in the same sense as the introduced deflection Δ_{aa}, and Δ_{na} is plus when in the same sense as the applied unit load, the influence of which is given by the ordinates of the influence line. Note further that X_a may represent either a force or a couple. If X_a is a force, the corresponding Δ_{aa} is a linear deflection; but if X_a is a couple, the corresponding Δ_{aa} is an angular rotation.

According to Müller-Breslau's principle, the influence line for any reaction element X_a can be obtained experimentally by applying the following procedure: Make a model of the structure, and temporarily remove the support restraint that supplies this reaction element to the model. Now introduce a displacement Δ_{aa} in the direction of the removed restraint. This will deform the model into the shape of the influence line for the reaction element X_a. To obtain the absolute magnitude of any ordinate, measure the deflection Δ_{na} which is produced at that point, and divide it by the introduced displacement Δ_{aa}. Since any suitable constant displacement Δ_{aa} may be introduced and the force necessary to produce this displacement is not involved in the calculations, influence lines may be determined in this manner from celluloid models, if this is desirable, without encountering any difficulty due to creep.

19.3 Instruments for Measurement of Deflections. Practically all the model methods of stress analysis involve measuring linear deflections of the model. Such deflections are commonly measured by one of the following methods: steel scale or cross-section paper, dial gage, micrometer barrel, or filar micrometer microscope.

If the deflections of a model are rather large, they do not have to be measured by precise methods. In such cases, a steel scale, graduated in hundredths of an inch, or ordinary cross-section paper may be mounted adjacent to a model and the deflection measured in this manner with the aid of a magnifying glass. Cross-section paper is quite useful for such purposes, for on inspection it will be found that the lines are not solid but actually are composed of a series of dots spaced about a fiftieth of an inch apart.

When the deflections are small, it is necessary to use one of the more precise methods of measurements. Dial gages graduated in thousandths of an inch may be used. Such gages have the disadvantage, however, that the spring attached to the plunger applies sufficient force to alter the deflections of a flexible model by an appreciable amount. In such cases where a dial gage cannot be used for this reason, it will be necessary to use either a micrometer or a microscope.

The principal disadvantage involved in using a micrometer is that it is difficult to establish the exact point of contact between the model and the micrometer. This difficulty may be overcome by using some

Figure 19.1 Contact indicator

Figure 19.2 Field of micrometer microscope

type of contact indicator. The simplest type of indicator is a battery-and-lamp system in which the model and micrometer are part of the circuit and the micrometer acts as the switch which closes the circuit by making contact with the model. A much improved contact indicator using a 6E5 "magic-eye" radio tube has been suggested.[1] The wiring diagram for this device is shown in Fig. 19.1. In this arrangement, the contacts on the model and micrometer are connected to the grid circuit of the tube, and their coming together causes the magic-eye cathode-ray target to become completely illuminated. This device is very sensitive and will establish the point of contact of polished-steel contacts within three or four millionths of an inch.

All things considered, the filar micrometer microscope is perhaps the most useful instrument for measuring model deflections. The type of microscope supplied with the Beggs deformeter apparatus is very convenient. The apparent field of view of this microscope is shown in Fig. 19.2. There are two orthogonal cross hairs, which may be moved across the field by turning the micrometer head. There is likewise an

[1] B. Mills, A Sensitive Contact Indicator, *Rev. Sci. Instr.*, vol. 12, no. 2, p. 105, February, 1941.

index, which moves with the cross hairs along a fixed scale that makes an angle of 45° with each of the cross hairs.   One complete turn of the micrometer head causes the index to move one full division along the fixed scale.   By bringing the cross hairs tangent to two successive positions of the target, it is possible to obtain the movement of the target from the difference of the micrometer readings for the two settings.   This arrangement of the cross hairs and the fixed scale makes it possible to read both the horizontal and the vertical movements of the target with one orientation of the microscope.   The value of one of the micrometer divisions in inches may easily be calibrated by observing with the microscope a known movement of a target placed on the plunger of a dial gage.

After a little practice, almost anyone can learn to use a micrometer microscope successfully.   There are certain important rules that should be observed, however, viz.:

1. Choose clear, well-defined, and readily identified targets.
2. Adjust the eyepiece carefully to eliminate parallax.
3. Focus the microscope on the target as sharply as possible.
4. Orient the cross hairs accurately.
5. Do not unnecessarily touch the microscope or the table on which it is mounted.

If parallax is present, the image of the target will not lie in the plane of the cross hairs and this will lead to difficulty in reproducing readings.   Poor focusing not only makes it difficult to bring the cross hairs tangent to the target but also in effect changes the magnification of the microscope and therefore changes its calibration factor.

Figure 19.3   Orientation error

Poor orientation leads to errors of the type shown in Fig. 19.3.   Suppose that the target a moves to a'.   To obtain the vertical component d of this movement, the cross hair XX should be oriented in a horizontal direction.   The difference between the two solid-line positions of cross hair XX will then give the correct distance d.   Suppose, however, that the cross hair is oriented poorly and is set at an angle β to the horizontal, as indicated by the dashed-line positions $X'X'$.   The difference between the two positions of $X'X'$ will then indicate that the supposedly vertical movement is the distance d'.   From the sketch,

$$d' = \cos \beta (d + c \tan \beta) = d \cos \beta + c \sin \beta \qquad (a)$$

This equation may now be used to study the effect of poor orientation:

If $c = 0$ and $\beta = 1°$, $d' = 0.9999d$ ∴ 0.0% error
If $c = 0.5d$ and $\beta = 1°$, $d' = 1.0086d$ ∴ 0.9% error
If $c = 5d$ and $\beta = 1°$, $d' = 1.0871d$ ∴ 8.7% error

This comparison shows that, if the resultant movement of a point is essentially in the same direction as the component which is being measured, an error in orientation does not have much effect on the measurement.   If, however, the resultant movement of a point is such that the component being measured is small in comparison with the component normal to this, then a small error in orientation makes an appreciable error in the measurement.

19.4 Certain Indirect Methods. Perhaps the simplest method utilizing Müller-Breslau's principle is the spline method of obtaining influence lines for the reactions of continuous beams. The procedure consists simply in selecting a long flexible spline of steel, brass, or wood and laying it down on a board on which a piece of cross-section paper has been mounted. The spline may be held in place between two nails, driven into the board on each side of the spline at the support points. A vertical displacement may then be introduced at the reaction the influence line for which is desired. The elastic curve of the spline in such a case may be marked on the paper and the influence-line ordinates obtained by reading the deflection ordinates on the cross-section paper and dividing each of them by the introduced displacement.

Very good accuracy may be obtained by using a ⅛-in.-square steel spline and introducing deflections of about one-sixth of the span length either way from its mean position. Introducing equal displacements both ways from the undeflected position of a model and measuring the movement of a point between these two deflected positions constitute a technique used in many methods of model analysis. Such a technique not only has the advantage of producing larger deflections without the possibility of overstressing the model but also in some cases minimizes errors in the measurements due to changing the geometry of the model.

Figure 19.4 Plus-and-minus displacement technique

It happens that this technique does not affect the geometrical error encountered in the case of the reaction influence lines of a continuous beam. This technique is effective, however, in the case shown in Fig. 19.4. In this case, the influence line for the horizontal reaction at point a may be obtained by introducing a horizontal displacement either to the right or to the left at this point. In either case, deflecting the column into a curve causes a small drop of the top of the column δ_b, which is greatly exaggerated in the sketch. As a result, a point n would drop to the position of n' owing simply to the rotation of chord bc of the elastic curve of the girder. Thus, if the deflection of point n were measured from n to n_L, it would be too large by the amount nn'; or if it were measured from n to n_R when the introduced displacement was to the right at point a, the deflection of n would be too small by the same amount nn'.

Note, however, that, if point a were displaced from L to R and the resulting displacement of n were measured from n_L to n_R, the error nn' due to the change in geometry would have been eliminated from this measurement. The displacement from n_L to n_R would give, therefore, the correct value for the deflection Δ_{na} corresponding to an introduced displacement of a of Δ_{aa}. Introducing equal displacements both ways from the mean position therefore eliminates certain errors resulting from changing the geometry of the structure. This technique is not a "cure-all," however, and does not eliminate all errors due to changing the geometry of a structure.

The so-called brass-wire model method[1] is simply a more or less generalized version of the spline method, in which the models are fabricated out of brass wire. A rather large variety of two- and three-dimensional models can be built up in this manner. Even members with varying moments of inertia may be simulated by soldering end to end a number of small pieces of different-sized brass wires. Brass wires may normally be obtained in a wide range of gage sizes; and, of course, brass may easily be soldered to facilitate fabrication. Simple templates may be improvised to introduce the displacements, and the resulting deflections may be measured by using a magnifying glass in combination with cross-section paper or a steel scale, by a micrometer barrel, or by some other simple device.

The Gottschalk Continostat[2] and the Eney deformeter[3] are two other well-known indirect methods. They are described in the references given below.

All the methods referred to above utilize rather simple models and simple means of introducing displacements and measuring the resulting deflections. To obtain suitable accuracy, it is necessary to introduce somewhat large deformations so that the lack of precision in the measuring devices does not introduce too large an error in the results. As a result in certain cases, errors due to changes in geometry may become significant and may be impossible to minimize. In such cases, it may be necessary to use a method utilizing more refined instruments and techniques.

19.5   The Beggs Method.   The Beggs method[4] is the most general and usually the most satisfactory experimental method of those based

[1] Anders Bull, Brass Wire Models Used to Solve Indeterminate Structures, *Eng. News-Record*, vol. 99, no. 23, Dec. 8, 1927.

[2] Otto Gottschalk, Mechanical Calculation of Elastic Systems, *J. Franklin Inst.*, vol. 202, no. 1, pp. 61–88, July, 1926.

[3] W. J. Eney, New Deformeter Apparatus, *Eng. News-Record*, Feb. 16, 1939, p. 221; Model Analysis of Continuous Girders, *Civil Eng.*, vol. 11, no. 9, p. 521, September, 1941.

[4] G. E. Beggs, An Accurate Mechanical Solution of Statically Indeterminate Struc-

on Müller-Breslau's principle.   It was developed by the late Prof. George
E. Beggs of Princeton University.   The equipment consists of a set of
deformeter gages and plugs for introducing the deformations and a
micrometer microscope for measuring the resulting deflections.   In
order to obtain influence lines for reactions, the deformeter gage is used
to replace the support of the model at that point, one half of the gage
being attached to the model and the other half to the mounting surface.

Figure 19.5   Beggs's method

To obtain influence lines for internal moments, shears, and axial forces,
it is necessary to cut the model and connect one half of the deformeter
gage to each side of the cut.   By inserting different types of plugs between
the two halves of the gage, an axial, shear, or angular deformation may
be introduced into the model, thus deflecting it into the shape of the
corresponding influence line.   A typical application of the Beggs method
is shown in Fig. 19.5.

   This method has the advantage that a more reliable and accurate
means is used for introducing the deformations and a more precise
instrument is used for measuring the deflections that are produced.
This enables one to introduce smaller deformations and thus reduce errors
due to changing the geometry of the structure.   The models used with
the Beggs method are ordinarily made from celluloid or a high-grade

tures by Use of Paper Models and Special Gages, *Proc. ACI*, vol. 18, pp. 58–82, 1922;
Discussion of "Design of a Multiple-arch System," *Trans. ASCE*, vol. 88, pp. 1208–
1230, 1925; The Use of Models in the Solution of Indeterminate Structures, *J. Franklin
Inst.*, vol. 203, no. 3, pp. 375–386, March, 1927.

cardboard. Since the deformeter gages introduce constant deformations rather than apply constant loads to the structure, no trouble is encountered from the creep characteristics of celluloid. The method can be used without modification for any planar structure, regardless of whether the members are straight or curved or of constant or varying moment of inertia.

The usual precautions must be observed in using the microscope in this method. Care must also be taken in mounting the deformeter gages

to be sure that the long axis of the gage is normal to the axis of the member. If the gage is not so mounted, the influence data obtained for the shear and axial force will be in error. In Fig. 19.6, if the gage is mounted in the direction indicated by the dashed line, the test data will give the values of the thrust T_t and shear S_t perpendicular and parallel to this direction. To obtain the true thrust and shear T and S, it is necessary to measure the angle ϕ and convert the test data as indicated below:

Figure 19.6 Mounting errors

$$T = T_t \cos \phi + S_t \sin \phi \qquad S = S_t \cos \phi - T_t \sin \phi$$

It should be apparent that such an error in the orientation of the gage does not affect the data obtained for the moment at this point.

One should also be careful to attach the model to the gage so that the axis of the member lies at the center of the gage. If this is not done, the influence-line ordinates for the moment at this point will be in error; for the angular deformation introduced by the gage not only rotates the cross section of the model but also introduces an axial displacement of its centroid.

The Beggs plugs may be calibrated in the following manner: Attach a strip to one half of the gage, and fasten the other half to the mounting surface. Insert the various plugs into the gage, and measure the resulting displacement of a target on the strip with the microscope. In this manner, the deformations introduced by the various plugs may be calibrated in micro-units and thence converted to inch units, if desired, using the calibration constant of the microscope.

19.6 The Moment Deformeter. The moment deformeter[1] is an instrument which deforms a model so that it takes the shape of the influence line for the bending moment at the section located at the center of the instrument. This deformation is accomplished without cutting the model as is necessary in using the Beggs method.

---

[1] Norris, *loc. cit.*; Wilbur and Norris, *loc. cit.*

The action of this instrument depends upon a relationship that exists between bending moment and deflection. Consider a segment ab of a member, this segment being initially straight and having a constant EI. Suppose that a load P is applied at point o, as shown in Fig. 19.7. The effect of the load P is to deform the structure and produce bending moments throughout. The bending moments thus produced at the ends of this segment are M_a and M_b, which are assumed to act as shown. The bending-moment diagram for this portion may then easily be drawn. By means of

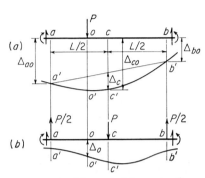

Figure 19.7 Moment-deflection relationship

Figure 19.8 Moment-deformeter theory

the moment-area theorems, Δ_c, the deflection of point c on the elastic curve from the chord ab, may be computed and the resulting expression simplified to

$$\Delta_c = \frac{M_c L^2}{8EI} - \frac{Pd^3}{12EI} \tag{19.2}$$

Thus the moment at c due to the load P acting at any point o in the segment ab is found to be

$$M_c = \frac{8EI}{L^2}\Delta_c + \frac{2}{3}\frac{Pd^3}{L^2} \tag{19.3a}$$

where d is the distance from point o to either end a or b, whichever is closer. If the load P is applied at a point outside the segment ab, the second term of Eq. (19.3a) vanishes and

$$M_c = \frac{8EI}{L^2}\Delta_c \tag{19.3b}$$

Thus it is apparent that the bending moment at c could easily be computed if the deflection Δ_c could easily be measured on a model.

There is a convenient way of obtaining Δ_c that may be explained by the following considerations: First consider the structure to be acted upon by the force P applied at point o. This causes the structure to be deformed; the deflected shape of the segment ab is shown in Fig. 19.8a. Next consider the structure to be acted upon by the special force system shown in Fig. 19.8b. The deflected shape of the segment ab under such conditions is also shown in this sketch. Applying Betti's law to this situation, we know that the virtual work done by the external force system in sketch a during the deformation produced by the external force system shown in sketch b is equal to the virtual work done by the system in sketch b during the deformation produced by the system in sketch a; therefore,

$$(P)(\Delta_o) = -\left(\frac{P}{2}\right)(\Delta_{ao}) + (P)(\Delta_{co}) - \left(\frac{P}{2}\right)(\Delta_{bo})$$

or

$$\Delta_o = \Delta_{co} - \frac{\Delta_{ao} + \Delta_{bo}}{2} \tag{a}$$

From the geometry of Fig. 19.8a, it is apparent that

$$\Delta_c = \Delta_{co} - \frac{\Delta_{ao} + \Delta_{bo}}{2} \tag{b}$$

and therefore, from Eqs. (a) and (b), it may be concluded that

$$\Delta_o = \Delta_c \tag{19.4}$$

Thus, if a system of loads such as that shown in Fig. 19.8b is applied to a segment ab, the model deforms so that it takes the shape of the influence line for Δ_c.

In the development leading to Eqs. (19.3a) and (19.3b), M_c denotes the bending moment at c caused by a load P acting on the model. If m_c denotes the bending moment at c due to a unit value of P, then

$$m_c = \frac{M_c}{P} \tag{19.5}$$

and, from Eq. (19.3a), the following relation is apparent:

$$m_c = \frac{8EI}{L^2}\frac{\Delta_c}{P} + \frac{2}{3}\frac{d^3}{L^2} \tag{19.6}$$

If the values of Δ_c are obtained by using the loading condition shown in Fig. 19.8b, then, by Eq. (19.4),

$$m_c = \frac{8EI}{L^2}\frac{\Delta_o}{P} + \frac{2}{3}\frac{d^3}{L^2} \tag{19.7a}$$

As before, when Δ_o is measured at a point o outside the segment ab, the second term in Eq. (19.7a) vanishes and

$$m_c = \frac{8EI}{L^2}\frac{\Delta_o}{P} \tag{19.7b}$$

Thus, for the portion of the model lying outside the segment ab, if the loading of Fig. 19.8b is applied, the deformed model takes the shape not only of the influence line for Δ_c but also of the influence line for m_c. To obtain the actual ordinates for m_c at points o outside the segment ab, values of Δ_o must be multiplied by $8EI/L^2P$, where E, I, L, and P refer to the segment ab. To obtain the actual ordinates for m_c at points o within the segment ab, values of Δ_o are substituted into Eq. (19.7a).

To determine the values of the influence-line ordinates, one must know, in addition to Δ_o, the values of E, I, L, d, and P. With the exception of P and E, all these are easily determined. When a celluloid model is used, it is necessary to apply a fixed deformation corresponding to the type of loading shown in Fig. 19.8b instead of constant loads P and $P/2$. A moment deformeter that embodies the principles shown diagrammatically in Fig. 19.9 may be shown to produce a deformed shape of both the model and the balance beam that does not change with time and thus effectively eliminates creep. If a plug that has a diameter larger by an amount Δ than the undeformed distance between the model and balance beam is forced into place between the two pieces, a deformed shape of both balance and model will be produced that will not change with time. This assumes that both model and balance have been made out of the same piece of celluloid and therefore have the same creep characteristics. It also assumes that the frame of the instrument is made out of metal and is heavy enough to be assumed rigid as compared with the flexible celluloid members. The pressure P_t applied by this plug to the model and balance will, of course, change with time, proportionally to the change in effective modulus E_t, but the elastic curve of both members will not change.

If, in addition to measuring the deflections Δ_o at the various points o on the model, the deflection δ_s of the balance is also measured, then upon recalling the discussion in Art. 18.5, the following relationships are apparent:

$$\delta_s = K_s \frac{P_t}{E_t} \quad \text{or} \quad \frac{E_t}{P_t} = \frac{K_s}{\delta_s} \quad (19.8)$$

where K_s is a geometrical constant of the balance beam, which depends on its dimensions and the manner in which it is attached to the instrument frame. Thus, if K_s is computed and δ_s is measured, the ratio of E_t to P_t will be known not only for the balance beam but also for the model, provided that

Figure 19.9 Simplified moment deformeter with balance beam

both balance beam and model are made from the same sheet of celluloid.

Upon substituting from Eq. (19.8), Eqs. (19.7a) and (19.7b) may be written in the following form for use on a celluloid model where δ_s has been measured on the balance beam of the instrument. The influence-line ordinates for the bending moment at c are obtained from Eq. (19.9a) for points o within the segment ab,

$$m_c = \frac{8IK_s}{L^2} \frac{\Delta_o}{\delta_s} + \frac{2}{3} \frac{d^3}{L^2} \quad (19.9a)$$

and from Eq. (19.9b) for points o outside the segment ab,

$$m_c = \frac{8IK_s}{L^2} \frac{\Delta_o}{\delta_s} \quad (19.9b)$$

The value of K_s may be computed, but the accuracy of the result may not be good because of the uncertain fixity conditions at the points of attachment of the balance beam. As a result, it is more satisfactory to obtain K_s by a calibration test run on a statically determinate cantilever beam, where the bending moments are known by statics.

The latest model of the moment deformeter is shown mounted on a celluloid model in Fig. 19.10. It will be noted that the principle of this instrument is essentially the same as that shown in simplified form in Fig. 19.9. The deflections δ_s and Δ_o are measured with the same type of micrometer microscope as that used in the Beggs method.

This instrument provides an effective means of obtaining influence

Figure 19.10   Moment deformeter

lines for bending moments at internal sections of a model without the
necessity of cutting the model.   The method does have the disadvantage
that, in order to use the above simple interpretation of the measurements,
it is necessary to apply the instrument to a segment of the model which
is initially straight and has a constant I.

19.7   The Moment Indicator.   The moment indicator[1] is a convenient instrument that furnishes a direct method of obtaining bending
moments in a model.   The theory of this instrument is based upon the
Manderla-Winkler equations, which are used primarily in the analysis of
secondary stresses in trusses.   These equations are applicable to a
member or a portion of a member which is initially straight and has
constant E and I and to which no external loads are applied between the
ends of the portion under consideration.

The Manderla-Winkler equations are simply expressions for the
moments acting on the ends of a member in terms of the slopes of the
elastic curve of these two ends of the member.   Let M_{AB} be the moment
acting on the A end of member AB and M_{BA} be the moment on the B
end, the end moments being positive when clockwise on the end of the
member.   Also, let τ_A and τ_B be the slopes of the tangents to the elastic
curve at points A and B, respectively.   Such slopes are measured with

[1] A. C. Ruge and E. O. Schmidt, Mechanical Structural Analysis by the Moment
Indicator, *Proc. ASCE*, October, 1938.

reference to the chord AB of the elastic curve and are positive when the tangent rotates clockwise with reference to the chord. The Manderla-Winkler equations may be derived by means of the moment-area theorems and may be stated as follows:

$$M_{AB} = \frac{2EI}{L}\,(2\tau_A + \tau_B) \qquad M_{BA} = \frac{2EI}{L}\,(\tau_A + 2\tau_B) \qquad (19.10)$$

Keeping these relationships in mind, we may now proceed to the development of the theory of the moment indicator.

Referring to Fig. 19.11, suppose that two arms are attached at points A and B of a member. As the model is loaded and deformed by loads applied outside this segment, the two arms will rotate through the same angles as the tangents to the elastic curve at their point of attachment. Upon recognizing that the rotations are actually through small angles, the following relative movements of the targets a and a' and b and b' may easily be computed. Let Δ_a and Δ_b represent the relative movements of the targets, being positive when the targets move apart; then

Figure 19.11 Moment-indicator theory

$$\Delta_a = \frac{2L}{3}\,\tau_A + \frac{L}{3}\,\tau_B = \frac{L}{3}\,(2\tau_A + \tau_B)$$
$$\Delta_b = \frac{L}{3}\,\tau_A + \frac{2L}{3}\,\tau_B = \frac{L}{3}\,(\tau_A + 2\tau_B)$$

$$(19.11)$$

Upon substituting from Eqs. (19.11) in Eqs. (19.10), the following expressions are obtained for the end moments at points A and B:

$$M_{AB} = \frac{6EI}{L^2}\,\Delta_a \qquad M_{BA} = \frac{6EI}{L^2}\,\Delta_b \qquad (19.12)$$

in which a positive Δ (or a relative movement apart) indicates a positive end moment (or clockwise on the end of the segment). Hence if Δ_a and Δ_b are measured with a microscope and if E is known, the moments can be determined at the points of attachment of the moment indicator.

Here again, if celluloid is used as the model material, the creep problem must be overcome. Of course, constant loads cannot be applied to a celluloid model, for its deflection will change with time. If, however, a fixed deformation is applied to the model at the point and in the direction

of the specified loading, the deflected position of the model will not change
with time. The movements of the targets of the moment indicator may
then be measured without difficulty with a microscope. However, it
would still be impossible to compute the end moments from Eqs. (19.12),
for E is unknown and changing with time. Further, the corresponding
load on the model is also unknown and is changing with time in direct
proportion to the change in E. In such a case, however, it is possible to
obtain the relative value of the moments, for they are proportional to
the product of I and the moment-indicator deflections.

Quite often these relative values of the end moments may be converted
into absolute values in terms of the load, through the use of conditions
of static equilibrium. Consider as an example
the simple frame shown in Fig. 19.12. Suppose
that the moment indicator has been mounted in
turn on each column and thus relative values of
the moments at two points on each column have
been obtained for some fixed horizontal displacement imposed at the top of column 1-2. In this
case, the relative value of the end moments in
each column may be extrapolated from the relative values measured at
the points of attachment of the indicator. Let these relative values at
the ends of the columns be m_{12}, m_{21}, etc.; then the absolute values may
be expressed as

Figure 19.12 Equilib-
rium considerations

$$M_{12} = Cm_{12} \qquad M_{34} = Cm_{34}$$
$$M_{21} = Cm_{21} \qquad M_{43} = Cm_{43}$$

If each column is isolated as a free body, this enables us to compute the
shear in each column in terms of the unknown constant C. The girder
may likewise be isolated as a free body by cutting it free from the columns
just below the column tops. Since the shears on the stub ends of the
columns have been expressed in terms of C, the statics equation $\Sigma F_x = 0$
applied to the isolated girder now enables us to find C in terms of P.
Having C in terms of P, we may obtain without difficulty the absolute
values of the end moments in terms of P.

The above procedure of converting relative values into absolute values
of moments can often be done very easily. There are cases, however,
when either there are no suitable equations of statics available or, if
such equations are available, to solve them is too laborious. In such
cases, the use of a celluloid spring balance in the loading system leads
to a direct solution for the absolute values of the moments in the model.

The use of a spring balance to overcome creep is discussed in Art. 18.5.
In Fig. 18.3, the balance is shown connected to the same type of model
as shown in Fig. 19.12. Suppose that a moment indicator were mounted

on the model in Fig. 18.3 and that readings were taken on the targets of both the indicator and the spring balance. Referring to Eq. (h) in Art. 18.5, we recall that, having measured Δ_s, E may then be expressed as

$$E = \frac{K_s}{\Delta_s} P \qquad (19.13)$$

Substituting from Eq. (19.13) in Eqs. (19.12),

$$M_{AB} = \frac{6IK_s}{L^2} \frac{\Delta_a}{\Delta_s} P \qquad (19.14)$$

By using the celluloid spring balance in this manner, therefore, it is easy to obtain the absolute values of the moments in terms of the load P.

This presumes, of course, that the constant K_s of the balance is known. The value of this constant can be computed, but it can be obtained more accurately from a calibration test on a statically determinate cantilever beam such as that shown in Fig. 19.13. Upon attaching the indicator as shown, the deflections Δ_a and Δ_s may be measured with the microscope. Knowing that the moment M_{AB} is equal to P times d, we can then easily back-figure K_s by applying Eq. (19.14).

Figure 19.13 Calibration of moment indicator

The moment indicator provides a very satisfactory model solution for many problems. A typical setup of the moment indicator in combination with a celluloid spring balance is shown in Fig. 19.14. It should be recalled that the theory of the moment indicator is based on the Manderla-Winkler equations. In order to use the above simple interpretation of the measurement, it is necessary, therefore, to apply the indicator to a portion of a member that is initially straight and has a constant I. It is possible to interpret the indicator readings in cases where I varies within the portion, but the computations would be very cumbersome.

19.8 Principles of Similitude. The principles of similitude governing the relationships between a model and its prototype may be determined by either of two approaches. The conditions of similarity may be expressed in mathematical form by means of established laws of structural mechanics and the principles of similitude rigorously deduced from them; or the principles may be deduced by using the methods of dimensional analysis. The first method is generally employed for structural models since the mathematical laws that structures follow

Figure 19.14 Moment indicator

are usually well known. However, in cases where the mathematical laws are not known but the factors affecting the phenomena are known, the principles of similitude may be determined by the dimensional-analysis approach.

19.9 Derivation of Principles of Similitude Using Established Laws of Structural Mechanics. To illustrate the derivation of the

Figure 19.15 Principles of similitude

principle of similitude by this approach, consider the problem of extrapolating influence-line data from a model to its prototype. For this purpose, consider a beam which is statically indeterminate to the first degree, such as that shown in Fig. 19.15.

Suppose that we wished to obtain the influence lines for R_a, the vertical reaction at a, and for M_b, the moment at b. In either case, we may apply Müller-Breslau's principle and thereby obtain the desired influence lines as indicated in Fig. 19.15. Of course, this procedure may be applied either to the prototype or to its model. Upon applying this procedure to the prototype, the expressions for the ordinates of these two influence lines are

$$R_a^P = -\frac{\Delta_{na}^P}{\Delta_{aa}^P}\,(1) \qquad (19.15)$$

and

$$M_b^P = -\frac{\Delta_{nb}^P}{\Delta_{bb}^P}\,(1) \qquad (19.16)$$

where the index P indicates that these quantities refer to the prototype.

On the other hand, upon applying Müller-Breslau's procedure to the model, the ordinates for the two influence lines for the model are

$$R_a^M = -\frac{\Delta_{na}^M}{\Delta_{aa}^M}\,(1) \qquad (19.17)$$

and

$$M_b^M = -\frac{\Delta_{nb}^M}{\Delta_{bb}^M}\,(1) \qquad (19.18)$$

where the index M refers to the model. Of course, if the principles of similarity between model and prototype are known, the ordinates of these influence lines may be measured experimentally on a small-scale model and then these results extrapolated to the prototype. In other words, to do this we need to know the relation between R_a^M and R_a^P and between M_b^M and M_b^P.

From Eqs. (19.15) to (19.18), it is apparent that these relationships between the reactions or moments on the model and those on the prototype depend upon the relationship between deflections. The relationship between deflections of the model and the prototype may be investigated by considering the computations of such deflections by the method of virtual work. To compute beam deflections, the law of virtual work may be expressed as

$$\sum Q\delta = \int M_P M_Q \frac{dx}{EI} \qquad (19.19)$$

If a force F^P acts at point a of the primary structure of the prototype, as shown in Fig. 19.15b, the vertical deflection of point n may be computed from

$$(1)\,(\Delta_{na}^P) = \int M_P^P M_Q^P \frac{dx^P}{E^P I^P} \qquad (19.20)$$

In the same manner, Eq. (19.19) may be applied to compute a similar deflection on the model, due to a force F^M at a, or

$$\text{(1)} \ (\Delta_{na}^M) = \int M_P^M M_Q^M \frac{dx^M}{E^M I^M} \tag{19.21}$$

Suppose that the model has been constructed so that the following relations exist between the model and prototype:

$$L^M = kL^P \qquad I^M = \alpha I^P \qquad E^M = \beta E^P \qquad F^M = \gamma F^P \tag{19.22}$$

In view of these relations, it is apparent that the following additional relations are true for the statically determinate primary structure shown in Fig. 19.15b:

$$M_P^M = k\gamma M_P^P \qquad M_Q^M = kM_Q^P \tag{19.23}$$

Substituting in Eq. (19.21) from Eqs. (19.22) and (19.23) and comparing with Eq. (19.20),

$$\text{(1)} \ (\Delta_{na}^M) = \frac{k^3\gamma}{\alpha\beta} \int M_P^P M_Q^P \frac{dx^P}{E^P I^P} = \frac{k^3\gamma}{\alpha\beta} \text{(1)}(\Delta_{na}^P)$$

Therefore,

$$\Delta_{na}^P = \frac{\alpha\beta}{k^3\gamma} \Delta_{na}^M \tag{19.24}$$

These relationships are true for any of the vertical deflections in Fig. 19.15b. Substituting therefore in Eq. (19.15) from Eq. (19.24) and comparing with Eq. (19.17),

$$R_a^P = R_a^M \tag{19.25}$$

and therefore the corresponding influence-line ordinates for R_a are exactly the same for both model and prototype.

In a similar manner, the vertical deflection Δ_{nb} and the relative angular rotation Δ_{bb} of the primary structure shown in Fig. 19.15d may be investigated for model and prototype. In this case, of course, the deflections are caused by couples T^P on the prototype and couples T^M on the model. Proceeding as before with the exception that we shall let

$$T^M = \gamma T^P$$

we shall find that

$$\Delta_{nb}^P = \frac{\alpha\beta}{k^2\gamma} \Delta_{nb}^M \tag{19.26}$$

$$\Delta_{bb}^P = \frac{\alpha\beta}{k\gamma} \Delta_{bb}^M \tag{19.27}$$

Substituting in Eq. (19.16) from Eqs. (19.26) and (19.27) and comparing with Eq. (19.18),

$$M_b^P = \frac{1}{k} M_b^M \tag{19.28}$$

and therefore the influence-line ordinates for M_b on the model should be multiplied by $1/k$ to obtain the corresponding ordinates on the prototype.

Of course, this discussion is limited to a beam that is indeterminate to the first degree, but it could now be extended successively to include beams or frames which were indeterminate to the second, third, or any degree. Such considerations would lead to the following general conclusion for any indeterminate beam or frame, the stress analysis of which can be carried out satisfactorily by considering only the effect of bending deformation:

A model should be dimensioned so that the axial lengths of its members are k times those of the prototype, the moments of inertia of its cross sections are α times those of the prototype, and the modulus of elasticity of the model is β times that of the prototype. If this is done, then the ordinates of the influence line for any reactive force, shear, or axial force on the prototype are equal to the corresponding ordinates on the model; but the ordinates of the influence line for any moment on the prototype are equal to 1/k times the corresponding ordinates on the model.

In this manner, the principles of similitude may be developed for models of trusses and other types of structures, provided that the solution of the problem can be formulated mathematically.

20
Other Uses of Structural Models

20.1 General. Model analysis has been extremely helpful in solving stress-distribution problems, i.e., in determining the manner in which the stress intensities vary across the cross sections of a member. Several experimental methods are available for solving such problems; among these, the two most important at the present time are the photoelastic method and the approach based on first measuring surface strains.

The photoelastic method has been used extensively in recent years, particularly by the mechanical engineer, to study the complex stress distributions that he often encounters in the design of machine elements. The civil engineer to a less, but still important, extent has used this method in analyzing similar problems for structural elements.

The art of measuring surface strains has developed tremendously since 1938. Wartime research produced astounding techniques for measuring such strains under both static and dynamic loading conditions. Numerous types of mechanical and electrical strain gages have been developed. Today that most generally used is the so-called SR-4 wire-resistance strain gage.[1]

Model analysis is used most commonly to study either stress analysis or stress-distribution problems. In addition, however, models are also frequently used to determine buckling loads or vibrational characteristics.

20.2 Photoelastic Method—General. Relatively simple stress-distribution problems can be handled successfully by mathematical methods. There are innumerable practical problems, however, where mathematical methods are inadequate and recourse to experimental procedures is necessary. The photoelastic method[2] is one of the most

---

[1] Produced and distributed by the Baldwin-Lima-Hamilton Corporation.

[2] The following are excellent references on the photoelastic method: E. G. Coker and L. N. G. Filon, "A Treatise on Photoelasticity," Cambridge University Press,

useful of these experimental procedures and is widely used to solve for the stress distribution in such locations as those around holes and notches, in riveted and welded joints, or in other irregularly shaped structural elements.

The photoelastic method is based upon the fact that, when certain transparent materials are stressed, their optical properties are changed. It is possible to measure these changes and relate them to the state of stress in the material. Thus, by making a model from a suitable transparent material and loading it in the same manner as the prototype, certain optical effects may be measured and interpreted to give the stress distribution in the model.

In a plane (two-dimensional) stress problem, the complete condition of stress at any point may be defined in terms of the magnitudes and directions of the two principal stress intensities. Since the two principal stresses are perpendicular to each other, the magnitudes of the two principal stress intensities and the direction of one of them are sufficient to define the condition of stress. Three independent quantities must be determined, therefore, at each and every point of a body subjected to a condition of plane stress, in order to define the stress distribution in the body completely.

When the photoelastic method is used for such problems, it is usually most convenient to determine three slightly different independent quantities at the various points, viz., the algebraic difference between the principal stress intensities, their algebraic sum, and the direction of one of them. From these data, it is easy to compute the normal and shear stress intensities on any plane through a point.

The photoelastic method is likewise applicable to three-dimensional stress systems. In such cases, however, the experimental techniques and the interpretation of the results are quite complex. This discussion will therefore be limited to the two-dimensional application of the method.

20.3   Review of Certain Principles of Optics.   Before the fundamental theory of two-dimensional photoelasticity can be developed, it is necessary to review briefly certain ideas of physical optics. The photoelastic phenomena may be explained satisfactorily by means of the ether-wave theory of light. In this theory, light is assumed to result from the transverse vibration, in a plane containing the ray, of all

London, 1931 (this is the classic reference book on photoelasticity); M. M. Frocht, "Photoelasticity," John Wiley & Sons, Inc., New York, 1941 (this book is an excellent textbook on photoelasticity and contains a number of valuable illustrative examples and photographs); R. D. Mindlin, Review of the Photoelastic Method of Stress Analysis, *J. Applied Phys.*, vol. 10, nos. 4 and 5, April, May, 1939 (these two articles give an excellent summary of the photoelastic method and contain a very good bibliography on the subject).

the particles lying along the ray. It is further assumed that at any instant all these particles lie along a sine curve, the *amplitude* of which is $2a$ and the wavelength of which is λ. Thus, a particle m is assumed to oscillate between the positions A and B as shown in Fig. 20.1 and some other particle n between positions C and D. Suppose that particles m and n lie as shown on the solid sine curve at time $t = 0$. Suppose further that, at some other time t, the particles have moved to the position m_1 and n_1 and now lie on the dashed-line sine curve. It is clear that the effect of the transverse movement of the particles has been to cause the sine curve connecting them to move to the right along the ray a distance Δz.

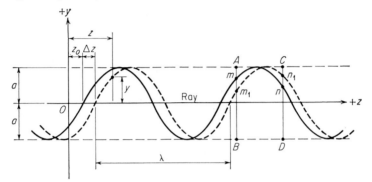

Figure 20.1   Ether-wave theory of light

The rate of the apparent movement of the sine curve along the ray is called the *velocity of light* and is constant for a given medium through which the ray is passing. For one complete wave of the sine curve to pass a given point, it is necessary for the various particles to undergo one complete cycle of transverse vibration. The frequency of the waves passing a given point is therefore the same as the frequency of the transverse vibration of the individual particles. The *frequency* of the vibration of the particles, f, determines the *color of light* and is constant for any given color regardless of the medium through which the ray may be passing. White light is composed of waves of all frequencies.

The velocity of light is equal to the product of the length of one complete wave and the frequency with which the waves pass a given point, or

$$v = \lambda f \tag{20.1}$$

Since the frequency for any given color of light remains constant, the wavelength of that color varies directly with the velocity, which in turn depends upon the medium through which the light is passing.

The *intensity of light* is proportional to the amplitude of the transverse vibration of the particles. If there is no transverse vibration, i.e., if the amplitude is zero, the intensity of light is zero—that is, there is no light.

In subsequent discussions, it will be necessary to use an expression for the instantaneous transverse position of a particle vibrating at a section located a distance z from the origin. In Fig. 20.1, the transverse displacement y of this particle at any time t may be evaluated as follows:

$$y = a \sin \frac{2\pi}{\lambda} [z - (z_o + \Delta z)] \tag{a}$$

However, Δz is the distance the sine curve has moved since $t = 0$ and therefore is equal to

$$\Delta z = vt = \lambda ft \tag{b}$$

Substituting in Eq. (a) from Eq. (b),

$$y = a \sin \left[\frac{2\pi}{\lambda} (z - z_o) - 2\pi ft \right] \tag{20.2}$$

From this equation, it is apparent that the transverse vibration of such particles is a simple harmonic motion.

Polarized light is another term that should be defined.   A ray of ordinary light consists of waves vibrating in all the planes that can be passed through the ray.   If, however, the vibrations are controlled in some manner, the light is said to be *polarized*. If the vibrations are constrained to one plane only, the light is said to be *plane-polarized*.   Such light need not be monochromatic and may be produced by passing ordinary light through a Nicol prism, a Polaroid sheet, or some other device.

If, on the other hand, the light is the resultant of two waves of equal amplitude and wavelength but vibrating in perpendicular planes and one-quarter of a wavelength out of phase, it is said to be *circularly polarized*.   Such light may be produced by passing a ray of plane-polarized monochromatic light through a *quarter-wave plate*. The quarter-wave plate is a sheet of mica or cellophane or some other permanently doubly refractive material, the axes of which are set at 45° to the plane of polarization of the incident ray of plane-polarized light.   The thickness of the quarter-wave plate is such that one of the two component waves is slowed up a quarter of a wavelength with respect to the other.   The two component waves emerge on the far side of the quarter-wave plate one-quarter of a wavelength out of phase, equal in amplitude, and vibrating in perpendicular planes and therefore combine to produce circularly polarized light.

Double refraction is a property possessed permanently by certain crystalline substances such as mica.   Such materials may be considered to break an incident ray of plane-polarized light down into two rectangular components.   These two components travel through the material at different velocities and therefore may be out of phase when they emerge on the far side.   **Other materials such as bakelite and celluloid become temporarily doubly refractive when stressed, breaking an incident ray down into two components that travel through the material in the planes of the two principal stresses.   This property is the basis of the photoelastic method of stress determination.**

Two light waves having the same intensity and wavelength and vibrating in the same plane may, of course, be superimposed.   The phenomenon associated with such superposition is called *interference*.   If these two waves are in phase, they will reinforce each other and produce a combined wave of greater intensity.   If, however, the two waves are one-half wavelength out of phase, they will cancel each other and total darkness will result.   As the phase difference is varied from zero to $\lambda/2$ to λ, etc., the intensity of the combined effect varies through various stages of interference from brilliance to darkness to brilliance, etc.   For white light, the phase difference that eliminates a color of one wavelength will not completely eliminate colors of other wavelengths.   The combined light will therefore have a color that depends upon the color eliminated.

20.4 Photoelastic Method—Fundamental Theory.   The principal apparatus used in applying photoelasticity to two-dimensional problems is called a *polariscope*.   The simplest type of polariscope is

shown diagrammatically in Fig. 20.2.   The essential parts of this polariscope are the light source and two devices for producing plane-polarized
light, one called the *polarizer* and the other the *analyzer.*

The light coming from the light source is vibrating in various planes,
but after passing through the polarizer it is converted into plane-polarized light vibrating, in this case, in a vertical direction.   This plane-
polarized light then passes through the loaded bakelite model, which, as
a result of its stressed condition, has temporarily become doubly refractive.   The plane-polarized light is therefore broken down into two

Light   Polarizer   Loaded   Analyzer
source   model

Figure 20.2   Polariscope

rectangular components vibrating in the planes of the principal stresses
and traveling through the model at different velocities.   Since one of
these components has been retarded with respect to the other, they may
be partly or completely out of phase when they emerge on the far side
of the model.   The amount by which they are out of phase may be
measured by putting them into interference with one another.   This can
be done by passing them through the analyzer, which permits only the
horizontal components of the incident waves to pass through, thus putting
them into interference with one another in a plane normal to the plane
of polarization of the polarizer.   If these horizontal components are in
phase with each other, there will be maximum brilliance; but if they are a
half wavelength out of phase, there will be complete interference, or
darkness.   The resulting pattern that one sees coming through the
analyzer may be related quantitatively to the state of stress in the model.

Consider the differential particle of the model shown in Fig. 20.3a.   Suppose that
this particle has been isolated so that its sides are planes of principal stress.   It is so
small that the principal stress intensities σ_x and σ_y may be assumed to be uniformly
distributed over its sides.   Suppose that a ray of *plane-polarized monochromatic light*
of amplitude $2a$ and vibrating in a plane OP strikes the particle.   Because of the doubly
refractive properties of the stressed bakelite in the planes of principal stress, this ray
will be broken down into two rectangular components, one of which goes through the

particle vibrating in the plane YOZ and the other in the plane XOZ. The amplitudes of these two components will be $2a \cos \alpha$ and $2a \sin \alpha$, respectively.

Consider now the component vibrating in the plane YOZ and shown in Fig. 20.3b. Suppose first that this component is traveling through air; in this case, the instantaneous position of the particles will lie on the solid-line sine curve. However, when this component passes through the stressed bakelite, it is retarded and hence its wavelength is shortened from λ to λ_y. If all the medium were bakelite, the instantaneous position of the particles would lie on the dashed-line sine curve. In the actual case, though, the instantaneous positions of the particles are located on the solid-line sine curve up to the model, on the dashed-line sine curve through the model, and on the dot-dash sine curve to the right of the model, where the wave returns to air as a medium and resumes a wavelength of λ.

Figure 20.3　Photoelasticity theory

In order to evaluate the instantaneous displacement y of a particle located a distance z from the origin and on the dot-dash sine curve, it is first necessary to compute the distances z' and z''. First,

$$\frac{z'}{\lambda_y} = \frac{z_n}{\lambda} \quad \text{or} \quad z' = \frac{\lambda_y}{\lambda} z_n \tag{a}$$

Also,

$$\frac{z'' + z_f}{\lambda} = \frac{z' + b}{\lambda_y} \quad \text{or} \quad z'' = \frac{\lambda}{\lambda_y}(z' + b) - z_f \tag{b}$$

Substituting in Eq. (b) from Eq. (a) and rewriting, using Eq. (20.1),

$$z'' = \frac{b}{\lambda_y}\lambda - b = \frac{b}{v_y}f\lambda - b = f\lambda t_y - b \tag{c}$$

where v_y is the velocity of the light through the bakelite in the YOZ plane and t_y is the time it takes it to pass through the model. However, using Eq. (20.2),

$$y = a \cos \alpha \sin\left[\frac{2\pi}{\lambda}(z + z'') - 2\pi ft\right] \tag{d}$$

Substituting from Eq. (c) and simplifying,

$$y = a \cos \alpha \sin\left[\frac{2\pi}{\lambda}(z - b) - 2\pi f(t - t_y)\right] \tag{20.3}$$

In a similar manner, the instantaneous displacement x of the wave vibrating in the XOZ plane may be evaluated and found to be

$$x = a \sin \alpha \sin \left[\frac{2\pi}{\lambda} (z - b) - 2\pi f(t - t_x) \right] \tag{20.4}$$

When these two waves are passed through the analyzer and put into interference with one another, the resultant displacement s obtained from the superposition of these two components is

$$s = y \sin \alpha - x \cos \alpha \tag{20.5}$$

Substituting in Eq. (20.5) from Eqs. (20.3) and (20.4) and simplifying,

$$s = a \sin 2\alpha \sin [\pi f(t_y - t_x)] \cos \left[\frac{2\pi}{\lambda} (z - b) - 2\pi f \left(t - \frac{t_y + t_x}{2} \right) \right] \tag{20.6}$$

It is apparent from Eq. (20.6) that the resulting displacement is a harmonic vibration, the amplitude of which is

$$\text{Amplitude} = 2a \sin 2\alpha \sin [\pi f(t_y - t_x)] \tag{20.7}$$

This expression may be put in slightly different form, since

$$t_y - t_x = \frac{b}{v_y} - \frac{b}{v_x} = b \frac{v_x - v_y}{v_z v_y} \approx \frac{b}{v_b^2} (v_x - v_y) \tag{e}$$

The latter simplification is permissible since v_x and v_y are essentially the same as v_b (the velocity of light through unstressed bakelite), and therefore the denominator may be replaced by v_b^2. Experiments show that $v_x - v_y$ is proportional to the difference in the principal stresses, and hence Eq. (e) may be written thus:

$$t_y - t_x = \frac{kb}{v_b^2} (\sigma_y - \sigma_x) \tag{f}$$

Now, by using Eq. (f), Eq. (20.7) may be rewritten as follows:

$$\text{Amplitude} = 2a \sin 2\alpha \sin \left[\frac{\pi f k b}{v_b^2} (\sigma_y - \sigma_x) \right] \tag{20.8}$$

This is the fundamental equation of two-dimensional photoelasticity, since from it we can determine the amplitude and hence the intensity of the light that comes through the analyzer.

Inspection of Eq. (20.8) reveals that the intensity may be zero for either or both of two reasons. First, the amplitude will be zero if $\sin 2\alpha$ equals zero. This will be so when α is a multiple of $\pi/2$, in other words, when the plane of polarization of the polarizer coincides with the direction of either of the principal stresses. Thus, regardless of the color of light or the magnitudes of the principal stresses, every point on the model where the direction of one of the principal stresses coincides with the plane of polarization of the polarizer will be black. There will be a number of points at which the principal stresses have the same direction. They will all be joined together by a black line, called an *isoclinic*.

Second, the amplitude is also dependent on the difference of the principal stresses, which affects the value of $\sin\,[(\pi fkb/v_b^2)(\sigma_y - \sigma_x)]$. When the model is unloaded and unstressed, the value of this term, and hence the amplitude, is zero; i.e., an unstressed model appears black all over when viewed through the analyzer. If we focus our attention on a particular point in the model and gradually apply the load, we notice this point getting lighter and lighter, attaining maximum brilliance when the value of $(\pi fkb/v_b^2)(\sigma_y - \sigma_x)$ equals $\pi/2$ so that the sine of this angle equals unity. Further increase in load, however, makes the point get darker and darker until it is black again when the stresses are such that $(\pi fkb/v_b^2)(\sigma_y - \sigma_x)$ equals π. Further increase of load causes the point to undergo additional cycles from black through brilliance and back to black again. All this discussion presumes that the model is being viewed with monochromatic (or one-color) light, as is assumed at the beginning of this article.

As we view this one particular point on the model, there are other points going through the same number of cycles. In fact, when this particular point is black, the other points are also black; all together, they form a black line, called an *isochromatic*. At all points along such an isochromatic, the difference in principal stresses must therefore be the same. Of course, at this particular instant there are other series of points that have undergone a different number of cycles, and each of these series forms another black isochromatic line. Thus, the model as a whole at a given instant appears to have several black isochromatic lines on a white background, as shown in Fig. 20.4. The various different isochromatics are designated as being the first-order isochromatic, second-order isochromatic, etc., depending on the number of cycles of black through brilliance to black that have occurred along that particular line.

It is easy to evaluate the difference in principal stress along the nth-order isochromatic, because we know that along this isochromatic every point has undergone n cycles, or

$$\frac{\pi fkb}{v_b^2}\,(\sigma_y - \sigma_x) = n\pi$$

Hence,

$$\sigma_y - \sigma_x = \frac{n}{b}\frac{v_b^2}{fk} \tag{20.9}$$

Knowing n and the thickness of the model b and certain constants of the light and model material, we may evaluate $\sigma_y - \sigma_x$ from this equation.

From the theory developed in this article, we now see how the photoelastic phenomena can be related quantitatively to the condition of stress in the model. How to use this information in solving a stress-distribution problem is discussed in the next article. Before doing so, however, several additional factors should be noted.

We have found that, when we observe a bakelite model through the analyzer, using monochromatic light, we see two different types of lines, isoclinics and isochromatics, both of which are black lines on a light background. The question immediately arises as to how we are able to tell one from the other. If we used white light instead of monochromatic, the isoclinic would still be black, for it does not depend on the frequency of the light. The isochromatic lines, however, would assume the colors

Figure 20.4   Isochromatics for simple beam

of the spectrum instead of being black, for only when the difference in the principal stresses is zero can there be complete interference for all frequencies simultaneously. Since such a situation usually exists at isolated points, there is seldom a black isochromatic—usually they are colored lines. By using white light, therefore, it is usually easy to identify the isoclinics.

For convenience, isochromatics are usually photographed, and for this purpose it is most satisfactory to use monochromatic light so that the isochromatics are black lines on a light background. It is desirable, however, to eliminate the isoclinic from the photograph. This can be accomplished by using circularly polarized monochromatic light. In such a case, the theory may be developed as is done above for plane-polarized light, and the amplitude of the resulting vibration seen through the analyzer will be found to be

$$\text{Amplitude} = 2a \, \sin \left[\frac{\pi f k b}{v_b^2} (\sigma_y - \sigma_x) \right] \tag{20.10}$$

This expression is the same as Eq. (20.8) except that the sin 2α term has disappeared and there is no directional effect. In practice, circularly polarized light is produced by introducing one quarter-wave plate on each side of the model. Actually, however, the same effect could be produced by rotating the polarizer and analyzer, these being always kept crossed. If we did this, the isoclinic line would move around the model as the plane of polarization was rotated. We can visualize, however, that, if we rotated the polarizer and analyzer fast enough, the isoclinic would disappear, in much the same way as the spokes of a wheel do if the latter is whirled fast enough. This is one way of visualizing the effect of circularly polarized light.

20.5 Stress Distribution Determined by Photoelastic Method. In the previous article, it is shown that the optical pattern which one views through the analyzer can be interpreted to give the direction of the principal stresses and the differences between them. This gives us two independent quantities concerning the condition of stress at any point in the model. In this article, we discuss how to obtain a third independent quantity and how to use this information to obtain the complete stress distribution in a two-dimensional system.

The polariscopes actually used in experimental work may be arranged in several different ways. The essential parts, however, are those shown in Fig. 20.2, with certain refinements added so that plane-polarized white light, plane-polarized monochromatic light, or circularly polarized mono-chromatic light may be obtained easily when desired. A mercury-vapor lamp with a suitable filter is widely used for monochromatic light, and the mercury-vapor lamp without the filter or an incandescent-filament lamp is used for white light. The polarizer and analyzer are fitted with quarter-wave plates arranged so that it is easy to change from plane- to circularly polarized light. A suitable lens system should be provided so that the model is in a field of parallel light. The loading machine should be arranged so that the entire loading device and model can be moved and aligned without removing or varying the load. The camera used with the polariscope should be a plate-type camera fitted with a screen for viewing the image.

With a polariscope such as this, it is a simple matter to set up a model and photograph the isochromatics (or isochromatic fringes) by using circularly polarized monochromatic light. A photograph of the iso-chromatics of a simple end-supported beam loaded by a concentrated load at mid-span is shown in Fig. 20.4. The fringe orders on such a photograph may be identified by watching the model as the load is applied and counting the number of cycles at certain points. Knowing the fringe orders n, we may use Eq. (20.9) to compute the difference in the principal stresses at various points in the model.

For such computations, it is convenient to change the form of Eq. (20.9) and denote the two principal stresses by p and q instead of σ_y and σ_x, or

$$p - q = \frac{n}{b}\, \text{OC} \tag{20.11}$$

where OC = optical constant of model material = v_b^2/fk. The optical constant for a given material may be determined from an auxiliary test on a tension specimen where $p - q$ is known.

While, in general, the isochromatics give us only the difference between the principal stresses, such information is sufficient to compute the edge stresses of a model. At a free unloaded edge, there is no shear or normal stress on the boundary surface, and therefore the boundary is a principal plane on which the principal stress is zero. At such points, the other principal stress is parallel to the boundary and is therefore numerically equal to the edge value of $p - q$ obtained from the isochromatics. In many problems, the maximum stresses occur at the edges of the model so that the investigation does not need to be carried beyond photograph-ing the isochromatics.

Isoclinics are obtained by using plane-polarized white light and may be sketched on a piece of tracing paper mounted on the screen of the camera. The plane of polarization of the polarizer is set successively at various positions between the vertical and horizontal, the polarizer and analyzer being kept crossed at all times. For each of these positions, the corresponding isoclinic on the image is sketched on the tracing paper. We thus obtain a sketch from which we can determine the direction of the principal stresses at any point in the model, since we know that at the points lying along any particular isoclinic, such as the 20° isoclinic, one of the principal stresses is in a direction which is 20° to the vertical and the other principal stress is perpendicular to that.

If, in addition to knowing $p - q$ and the direction of the principal stresses at any point in a model, we know $p + q$, that is, the sum of the principal stresses, it will then be easy to compute the normal and shear stress intensity on any plane through any point in the model. By considering the equilibrium of the small particle shown in Fig. 20.5, suitable equations may be derived for the normal stress σ_y and the shear stress τ_{xy} on a plane the normal of which makes an angle θ with the direction of the principal stress p at point O. The perpendicular sides of this element are principal planes of stress, and it is assumed that the length of the hypotenuse and the thickness of the particle are both unity. From $\Sigma F_y = 0$,

$$(\sigma_y)(1)(1) - (p)(\cos \theta)(1)(\cos \theta) - (q)(\sin \theta)(1)(\sin \theta) = 0$$

which simplifies to

$$\sigma_y = \frac{p + q}{2} + \frac{p - q}{2} \cos 2\theta \qquad (20.12)$$

Likewise, from $\Sigma F_x = 0$, we find that

$$\tau_{xy} = -\frac{p - q}{2} \sin 2\theta \qquad (20.13)$$

From these equations, it is now apparent that both σ_y and τ_{xy} can be computed if $p + q$ is also known.

Several methods are available for determining $p + q$, one of the best of which is measuring the change in thickness of the model. The change in thickness of a plate depends upon the principal stresses in the plane of the plate in exactly the same way as the contraction of the cross section of a tension specimen depends upon the axial stress in the specimen.

$$\Delta b = -\frac{\nu b}{E}(p + q) \qquad (20.14)$$

Figure 20.5   Principal stresses

Several lateral extensometers have been developed specifically for measuring Δb. The de Forest–Anderson extensometer[1] is one of the best of these. With such instruments, $p + q$ may be measured at certain specific points, and by means of this information, curves may be drawn to assist in interpolating the values of $p + q$ at other points.

The values of $p + q$ may also be determined by several other experimental procedures or by an iterative numerical method suggested by Liebmann for solving problems involving Laplace's equation. Instead of determining $p + q$ by one of the methods that have been suggested, it would be possible to compute the separate values of p and q simply through the information that can be obtained from the isochromatics and the isoclinics. To do this, however, involves some rather tedious graphical and analytical computations not required by the other methods.

[1] A. V. de Forest and A. R. Anderson, A New Lateral Extensometer, *Proc. Tenth Semi-annual Eastern Photoelasticity Conf.*, December, 1939.

The use of the photoelastic method in stress-distribution problems may be summarized as follows:

1. *To determine edge stress intensities,* only isochromatics are required.

2. *To determine shear stress intensities on any plane at every point,* isochromatics and isoclinics are required. Note, however, that maximum shear stress at a point can be determined simply from the isochromatics since

$$\tau_{max} = -\frac{p - q}{2}$$

3. *To determine both normal and shear stress intensities on any plane at every point,* in addition to isochromatics and isoclinics, the value of $p + q$ or some third independent quantity must be determined for every point.

20.6 Strain Measurement. It is impossible to discuss the art of strain measurement in the limited space available here.[1] Many different strain gages have been developed, but the principles on which they are based are limited in number. The various instruments may be classified in one of the following groups: mechanical gages; optical gages; electric resistance gages; electric inductance gages; or electric capacity gages. At the present time, the most widely used strain gage is the SR-4 resistance wire gage.

One should note, however, that the minimum size of a structural model may be controlled by the method selected for the strain measurements. Of course, if the strain varies linearly along a gage line, the average strain over any gage length will be exactly equal to the strain at the mid-point of the gage. If, however, the strain varies in a distinctly nonlinear manner, the average strain may be considerably different from the strain at the mid-point of the gage. It is necessary, therefore, to design the model large enough or to select a strain gage with a gage length small enough so that the strain variation between the gage points is essentially linear. If proper consideration is not given to this matter, the results of the model study may not be sufficiently accurate.

20.7 Stress Distribution by Surface-strain Measurement. When a thin flat plate is loaded by forces acting in the plane of the plate, a condition of plane stress is developed in the plate, i.e., the stresses developed in the plate may be assumed to act parallel to the plane of the plate and the stress intensities to remain constant through the thickness of the plate. Such a condition of stress is the one most commonly encountered in structural members. In such cases, the complete state of stress throughout the interior of the plate is defined as soon as the stress condition is determined on the surface.

---

[1] The reader is referred to M. Hetenyi (ed.), "Handbook of Experimental Stress Analysis," John Wiley & Sons, Inc., New York, 1950.

In the case of a thick plate or in the most general case of a stressed body, a three-dimensional stress system is involved, and the stresses vary through the thickness of the plate. Determining the surface stresses in such problems, therefore, does not enable one to define the condition of stress in the interior. Fortunately, however, in such cases the maximum stresses usually occur at the surface, and hence determining these surface stresses gives a practical solution to many problems.

The surface stresses at a point on the unloaded surface of any body form a two-dimensional stress system. As stated in Art. 20.2, the complete condition of stress at such a point may be defined in terms of three unknowns, the magnitude of the two principal stress intensities and the direction of one of them. Of course, stresses cannot be measured directly, but we can measure surface strains. If three independent linear strains are measured, it is then possible to compute the principal strains and their directions. By using the physical relations between stress and strain, these principal strains can be converted into the principal stresses. The directions of the principal stresses and the principal strains are the same. Once the magnitude and directions of the principal

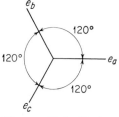

Figure 20.6 Equiangular strain rosette

stresses are known, the normal and shear stress intensities on any plane through a point can be computed.

The gage lines of the three linear strains that must be measured may be chosen in such a way as to simplify the computation of the principal strains and stresses.[1] One such arrangement, known as the *equiangular strain rosette*,[2] is shown in Fig. 20.6. The three linear strains e_a, e_b, and e_c are measured along gage lines that make angles of 120° with each other. Then it can be shown that the major (or algebraically larger) principal strain ϵ_1 and the minor (or algebraically smaller) principal strain ϵ_2 may be computed from the following formula:

$$\epsilon_1 = A_1 + B_1 \qquad \epsilon_2 = A_1 - B_1 \qquad (20.15)$$

where $A_1 = \frac{1}{3}(e_a + e_b + e_c)$

$$B_1 = \frac{\sqrt{2}}{3} \sqrt{(e_a - e_b)^2 + (e_b - e_c)^2 + (e_c - e_a)^2} \qquad (20.16)$$

All strains, when they are elongations, should be considered plus. The direction of the major principal strain ϵ_1 is given by an angle α_1, which is

[1] W. M. Murray, An Adjunct to the Strain Rosette, *Exptl. Stress Analysis*, vol. 1, no. 1, pp. 128–133.

[2] R. D. Mindlin, The Equiangular Strain Rosette, *Civil Eng.*, vol. 8, no. 8, pp. 546–547, August, 1938.

measured counterclockwise from the e_a gage line, where

$$\tan 2\alpha_1 = \frac{\sqrt{3}\,(e_c - e_b)}{2e_a - e_b - e_c} \tag{20.17}$$

The quadrant in which the angle $2\alpha_1$ lies can be identified by noting the signs of both numerator and denominator when the numerical values of the strains are substituted in Eq. (20.17). The direction of the minor principal strain ϵ_2 is located by an angle $\alpha_1 + 90°$ measured counterclockwise from the e_a gage line.

Another suitable arrangement is known as the *rectangular strain rosette* and is shown in Fig. 20.7. In this case the principal strains may be computed from the following formulas:

$$\epsilon_1 = A_2 + B_2 \qquad \epsilon_2 = A_2 - B_2 \tag{20.18}$$

where

$$A_2 = \frac{e_a + e_c}{2} \tag{20.19}$$

$$B_2 = \tfrac{1}{2}\sqrt{(2e_b - e_a - e_c)^2 + (e_a - e_c)^2}$$

The direction of the major principal strain ϵ_1 is given by the following angle α_1, which is measured counterclockwise from the e_a gage line,

Figure 20.7
Rectangular
strain rosette

$$\tan 2\alpha_1 = \frac{2e_b - e_a - e_c}{e_a - e_c} \tag{20.20}$$

whereas the direction of the minor principal strain ϵ_2 makes an angle of $\alpha_1 + 90°$ with the e_a gage line.

The principal strains having been computed from the above equations, the major and minor principal stress intensities, σ_1 and σ_2, respectively, may be computed from the following equations:

$$\sigma_1 = \frac{E}{1 - \nu^2}\,(\epsilon_1 + \nu\epsilon_2)$$
$$\sigma_2 = \frac{E}{1 - \nu^2}\,(\nu\epsilon_1 + \epsilon_2) \tag{20.21}$$

where E is the modulus of elasticity of the material and ν is Poisson's ratio. For either type of rosette, the principal stresses may be computed directly without first computing the principal strains by using the following equations, which have been obtained by substituting either Eqs. (20.15) or (20.18) in Eqs. (20.21):

$$\sigma_1 = E\left(\frac{A}{1 - \nu} + \frac{B}{1 + \nu}\right)$$
$$\sigma_2 = E\left(\frac{A}{1 - \nu} - \frac{B}{1 + \nu}\right) \tag{20.22}$$

The directions of σ_1 and ϵ_1 and of σ_2 and ϵ_2 are the same.

In certain cases, it is convenient to establish the directions of the principal stresses and strains by some auxiliary means such as symmetry or through the use of brittle lacquer or Stress Coat. If this is done, then the two principal strains may be measured in these directions, the strain readings required at every point being thus reduced from three to two.

20.8 Determination of Buckling Loads. Structural models may also be used advantageously to determine critical or buckling loads of columns, beams, and other structural elements. Such information may be obtained most readily by running tests under loads that are somewhat less than the buckling load and then interpreting the test data by Southwell's method[1] or some adaptation of it. In such tests, the load is applied in a series of increments, and certain deflections are measured after each increment of loading. By plotting this information in a certain manner, the plotted points lie on a straight line the slope of which may be interpreted to give the critical buckling load. The chief advantage of this procedure is that necessary data may be obtained from measurements taken at loads smaller than the buckling load, and as a result the model is not destroyed in conducting the test. The model may be retested, therefore, after any desired modifications in its design have been made.

In Southwell's original paper, the theoretical proof of his method was given only for the case of a simple strut. He demonstrated that, if the ratio of lateral deflection to the corresponding axial load was plotted as an ordinate against the deflection itself as an abscissa, the plotted points would lie along a straight line the inverse slope of which was equal to the critical load of the strut.

Subsequently Lundquist[2] suggested a modification of Southwell's procedure. Donnell[3] and other investigators have suggested and applied variations of Southwell's method for more complex types of buckling. These studies indicate that this procedure or some variation of it may be applied to all cases in which buckling does not introduce appreciable second-order stresses.

[1] R. V. Southwell, On the Analysis of Experimental Observations in Problems of Elastic Stability, *Proc. Roy. Soc. (London)*, vol. 135A, p. 601, 1932.

[2] E. E. Lundquist, Generalized Analysis of Experimental Observations in Problems of Elastic Stability, *NACA Tech. Note* 658.

[3] L. H. Donnell, "On the Application of Southwell's Method for the Analysis of Buckling Tests," Contributions to the Mechanics of Solids, Dedicated to S. Timoshenko, p. 27, The Macmillan Company, New York, 1938.

Problem Answers

Following are the answers (or partial answers) to the problems preceded by an asterisk.

Chapter 1

1.2

Span =	20 ft	M_I =	9.00 kip-ft
	30 ft		20.25 kip-ft
	40 ft		36.00 kip-ft
	50 ft		53.63 kip-ft
	60 ft		72.90 kip-ft
	70 ft		94.08 kip-ft
	80 ft		117.12 kip-ft
	90 ft		141.55 kip-ft
	100 ft		166.67 kip-ft

1.3   Vertical surfaces: P_N = 400 lb per ft
Inclined surfaces: P_N = 292 lb per ft windward
= 308 lb per ft leeward

1.5   Stress = 7.29 kips per sq in.

Chapter 2

2.1   (e) unstable; (f) unstable; (i) stable, indeterminate; (l) stable, determinate; (m) unstable; (n) stable, determinate; (o) unstable; (t) stable, externally indeterminate; (u) stable, determinate; if β is such that EF does not pass through D; (v) stable, determinate

2.2   (a) R_{ax} = 0, R_{ay} = 26.0 kips up; R_{by} = 46 kips up

(b) R_{ax} = 0, R_{ay} = 2.0 kips up, M_a = 16.6 kip-ft c.c.

(c) R_{ax} = 30.0 kips to left, R_{ay} = 22.92 kips up;
R_{by} = 90.42 kips up; R_{ey} = 54.26 kips up;
R_{fx} = 22.19 kips to right; R_{fy} = 42.32 kips down

(d) R_{ax} = 10.00 kips to left, R_{ay} = 16.36 kips up;
R_{by} = 13.64 kips up

(e) R_{ax} = 40.0 kips to left, R_{ay} = 23.6 kips up;
R_{dx} = 40.0 kips to right, R_{dy} = 6.0 kips down;
R_{by} = 22.3 kips up

636

     (f) $R_{ax} = 5.5$ kips to left, $R_{ay} = 4.\dot{6}$ kips up,
        $M_a = 30.0$ kip-ft c.c.; $R_{dx} = 1.0$ kips to right,
        $R_{dy} = 7.\dot{3}$ kips up
    (g) $R_{ax} = 0$, $R_{ay} = 8.5$ kips up, $M_a = 30.0$ kip-ft c.c.;
       $R_{dx} = 10.0$ kips to left, $R_{dy} = 7.5$ kips up

2.3   (a) $R_{ax} = 1.48$ kips to right, $R_{ay} = 71.03$ kips up;
       $R_{bx} = 25.48$ kips to left, $R_{by} = 50.97$ kips up
    (b) $R_{ax} = 56.0$ kips to left, $R_{ay} = 42.0$ kips up;
       $R_{bx} = 24.0$ kips to left, $R_{by} = 12.0$ kips down;
       $R_{ex} = 80.0$ kips to right, $R_{ey} = 30.0$ kips up
    (c) $R_{ax} = 3.51$ kips to left, $R_{ay} = 4.39$ kips up;
       $R_{bx} = 14.07$ kips to left, $R_{by} = 17.59$ kips down;
       $R_{fx} = 32.42$ kips to left, $R_{fy} = 64.85$ kips up;
       $R_{gx} = 0$, $R_{gy} = 68.3$ kips up
    (d) $R_{cx} = 26.\dot{6}$ kips to left, $R_{cy} = 11.85$ kips down;
       $R_{dy} = 11.85$ kips up

Chapter 3

3.2   Shear in lb: left of $A = -1,350$; right of $A = +5,400$; left of $B = -9,000$;
     right of $B = +5,850$
     Moment in lb-ft at: $A = -1,800$; midway between A and $B = +16,200$;
     $B = -9,000$

3.3   Shear in kips at: $a = +15$; $b = -15$; right of $c = +5.417$; $d = +5.417$
     Moment in kip-ft at: midway between a and $b = +50$; $c = -100$; 9 ft right
     of $c = -75.83$

3.5   Shear in kips at: $A = -20.0$; right of $C = +50.0$; left of $D = +100.0$;
     $B = +20.0$
     Moment in kip-ft at: $C = -180, -292$; $D = +608, -120$; $B = +40$

3.6   Shear in kips at: $a = +26.46$; right of $b = -24.57$; right of $c = +26.46$;
     $d = -15.53$
     Moment in kip-ft at: $a = -16.0$; $b = +195.73, +291.97$; $c = -2.87, +93.40$

3.9   Shear in kips at: $a = +45.3$; 20 ft right of $a = +15.3$; 20 ft left of $b = -18.7$;
     $b = -52.7$
     Moment in kip-ft at: 9 ft right of $a = +407.7$; 24 ft right of $a = +637.2$;
     9 ft left of $b = 316.2$

Chapter 4

4.2   (a) determinate, stable; (b) indeterminate to first-degree reactions, stable; (c)
     determinate, stable; (d) indeterminate to first-degree reactions, stable; (e)
     indeterminate to first-degree bar stresses, stable; (f) unstable; (g) unstable;
     (h) determinate, stable; (k) determinate, stable; (l) indeterminate to first-
     degree bar stresses, stable; (m) unstable

4.3   (A) $a = +18.03$, $b = -8.3$, $c = +25.0$, $d = -18.03$
     (B) $a = -43.75$, $b = +24.04$, $c = +2.083$
     (C) $a = +3.535$, $b = +29.20$, $c = +17.50$, $d = -15.00$
     (D) $a = -1.41$, $b = -5.89$, $c = -5.17$, $d = +28.18$
     (E) $a = -20.00$, $b = +24.74$, $c = +32.50$, $d = +38.89$
     (F) $a = -45.44$, $b = -41.76$, $c = -5.04$, $d = +59.85$, $e = +26.89$
     (G) $a = -22.36$, $b = -56.57$, $c = 0.0$, $d = +60.00$, $e = -20.00$

4.5   (a) Member: $HI = -65.086$; $DE = +65.086$; $Fg = -13.017$; $cD = +45.56$
     (b) Geometrically unstable

      (c) Geometrically unstable

      (d) Member: $Bc = -16.406$; $cd = -24.745$; $De - +4.841$; $fg = -5.156$

4.6   (a) Member: $BD = -28.125$; $Bc = +1.563$; $ab = +27.188$

      Member BD: Shear at: $B = +5.0$, $D = -5.0$

                  Moment at: $B = 0$, $C = +150$, $D = 0$

      (b) Member: $CE = +5.625$; $bC = +8.125$; $Ab = -5.0$

      Member AC: Shear at: $A = +4.00$; $C = -4.00$

                  Moment at: $A = 0$, under load $= +120.0$; $C = 0$

      Member CE: Shear at: $C = +2.5$; $E = -2.5$

                  Moment at: $C = 0$; under load $= +75$; $E = 0$

Chapter 6

6.1   (a) Ordinate at: left end $= +0.25$; left of $a = -0.5$; right of $a = +0.5$

      (b) Ordinate at: left end $= -2.5$; $b = 0$; $a = +5.0$; right end $= -5.0$

      (c) Influence line varies linearly from $+1.25$ at left end to -0.5 at right end

6.2   (a) 14,062.5 lb; (b) $+50,000$ lb-ft, -40.625 lb-ft

      (c) $+10,312.5$ lb, $-3,750$ lb; (d) $+68,750$ lb-ft

6.5   (a) Influence line varies linearly from -0.75 at C to 0.0 at E to -0.75 at G

      (b) Influence line varies linearly from 0.0 at E to -15.0 at G

6.9 $+1,068$ kip-ft

6.10 $+28.2$ kips

6.12 $+56.25$ kip-ft

6.14 Bar $a = -112,500$ lb; bar $b = +30,300$ lb, $-17,045$ lb

6.15 (a) Influence line varies linearly from 0.0 at left to -1.25 at panel point 3 to 0.0 at right end, panel point 7

      (b) Influence line varies linearly from 0.0 at left to $+0.833$ at panel point 3 to -0.125 at panel point 4 to 0.0 at right end

      (c) Influence line varies linearly from 0.0 at left to $+0.300$ at panel point 5 to -0.750 at panel point 6 to 0.0 at right end

      (d) Influence line varies linearly from 0.0 at left to $+0.333$ at panel point 4 to 0.0 at right end

Chapter 7

7.2   Member: $L_0L_1 = +4,310$, -20; $U_1U_2 = +1,530$, $-3,610$; $U_2L_2 = +1,000$, $-3,760$ lb

7.3   (a) Member: $L_0L_1 = +93.1$; $U_1U_2 = -148.9$; $U_1L_2 = +101.6$ kips

      (b) Member: $U_2L_3 = -14.3$, $+56.5$; $U_2L_2 = -48.3$, $+6.0$ kips. No other members exhibit reversal of stress

7.4   Counters L_2U_3 and U_3L_4 are required

7.6   (a) Member: $L_0L_1 = -105.0$; $U_1L_2 = +84.85$; $U_2U_3 = +45.0$ kips

      (b) Member: $L_2L_3 = -31.62$; $U_1U_2 = +45.0$, -10.0; $L_2U_3 = -49.50$ kips

      (c) No

Chapter 8

8.1   (a) Influence line varies linearly from 0.0 at E to $+1.33$ at B to 0.0 at C

      (b) Cantilever reaction $= 888.8L = R_1$

      Simple span reaction $= 750.0L = R_2$. $R_1/R_2 = 1.185$

8.2   (a) Influence line varies linearly from 0.0 midway between i and b to 1.0 at b to 0.0 at a

      (b) Influence line varies linearly from 0.0 at h to 1.5 at b to 0.0 at a

      (c) Influence line varies linearly from 0.0 at b to 1.8 at a to 0.0 at f

      (d) 747,000 lb

8.4   Influence line varies linearly from $+1.0$ at A to -0.5 at B to 0.0 at C

8.8   Influence line varies linearly from 0.0 at a to $+0.215$ at b to -1.720 at e to 0.0 at i

8.10   Influence line varies linearly from 0.0 at a to $+0.220$ at b to -1.761 at e to 0.0 at i

8.11 $Bc = +19{,}110$ lb, $-16{,}930$ lb

Chapter 9

9.2 $R_{ay} = 1{,}000$ lb down; $R_{az} = 866$ lb up; $R_{by} = 1{,}000$ lb up; $R_{bz} = 866$ lb down; $R_{cy} = 0$; $R_{cx} = 1{,}000$ lb to left

9.3   Bar: $ab = -500$; $bc = +1{,}000$; $ca = -1{,}000$; $ed = -1{,}000$; $eb = -1{,}000$; $ea = +1{,}414$ lb; all others $= 0$

9.4 $R_{ay} = 1{,}154$ down; $R_{az} = 250$ up; $R_{by} = 577$ up; $R_{bz} = 750$ down; $R_{cy} = 577$ up; $R_{cx} = 866$ lb to left
  Bar: $ab = -433$; $bc = +866$; $ca = -289$; $ed = eb = -577$; $da = +577$; $dc = -815$; $ca = +815$ lb; all others $= 0$

9.5   (a) 11 bars, 8 reactions, 6 joints, therefore indeterminate to first degree
  (b) $R_{ay} = 5{,}000$ down; $R_{az} = 5{,}000$ to left; $R_{by} = 5{,}000$ up; $R_{bx} = 0$; $R_{cy} = 5{,}000$ down; $R_{cx} = 0$; $R_{dy} = 5{,}000$ up; $R_{dz} = 5{,}000$ lb to left
  Bar: $ef = -5{,}000$; $ed = -7{,}500$; $af = +7{,}500$;
    $ec = +5{,}600$; $bf = -5{,}600$; $bd = +2{,}500$;
    $ca = -2{,}500$ lb; all others $= 0$

9.7   (a) Bar: $ab = -8.45$ kips; $bc = 0$; $ca = 0$
  (b) Joint, d: $Z = -0.41$, $X = +6.34$, $Y = -7.04$; e: $Z = -0.41$, $X = +0.70$; $Y = -7.04$; f: $Z = +5.81$; $X = +2.96$; $Y = -5.92$ kips
  (c) $R_{lx} = 10.00$ to left; $R_{ly} = 19.43$ up; $R_{jz} = 3.37$ up; $R_{jy} = 22.22$ down; $R_{kz} = 8.37$ down; $R_{ky} = 22.79$ kips up

Chapter 10

10.2   (a) 0.8.   (b) 3,200 kips.   (c) 611 ft.   (d) 609 ft.

10.6   (a) Maximum cable tension $= 538.5$ kips; bottom chord carries no stress
  (b) (1) Influence line varies linearly from 0.0 at either end to $+2.50$ at mid-span
    (2) Influence line varies linearly from 0.0 at either end to $+0.10$ at mid-span
    (3) Influence line varies linearly from 0.0 at left end of span to -0.192 at second panel point to $+1.032$ at third panel point to -0.495 at mid-span to 0.0 at right end of span
  (c) 2.84 sq in.

Chapter 11

11.1   (a) $+47{,}812.8$ lb; (b) $\mp 8{,}437.5$ lb, $\pm 3{,}750$ lb

11.2   (a) $+46.\dot{6}$ kips; (b) $+33.00$ kips; (c) $-31.\dot{6}$ kips

11.6   (a) Shear in lb: from base to knee $= +2{,}500$; above knee $= -3{,}750$
    Moment in lb-ft at: base $= -18{,}750$; knee $= +18{,}750$; top $= 0.0$
  (b) Axial force: in left post, $-2{,}846$ lb; in right post, $+2{,}846$ lb
    Shear: in left post, $3{,}750$ lb to right; in right post, $3{,}750$ lb to right; force in left knee brace $= +8{,}520$; in right knee brace $= -8{,}520$ lb

11.9   Bending moment at supports, from left to right: 15.0, 30.0, 30.0, 15.0 kip-ft

11.10   Bending moment at supports, from left to right: 13.5, 31.5, 31.5, 13.5 kip-ft

11.11   Bending moment at supports, from left to right: 23.80, 25.45, 25.45, 23.80 kip-ft

Chapter 12

12.2   0.0390 ft to right
12.3   0.375 in. to right
12.5   0.00642 ft down
12.7   (a) 0.0774 ft down; (b) 0.75 in. up, 0 in. horizontal
12.8   1.905 in. up
12.9   0.01695 ft, down and to right at 27.7° to vertical
12.12 (a) 0.00585 ft down; (b) 0.003635 radian counterclockwise
12.14 0.000877 ft down
12.17 (a) At a, $115/EI$ down; at c, $17.5/EI$ up; at d, $10/EI$ down; at b, $23.33/EI$
           counterclockwise; and at c, $6.67/EI$ clockwise.   (b) At a, 0.02204 in.; at b,
           0.000373 radian
12.20 0.021 ft down
12.22 0.00698 ft up at 8.56 ft from a
12.25 0.01182 ft down at 5.1 ft from a
12.27 $1,440/EI$ down at 12 ft from a
12.28 Joint h; 0.82 in. down, 0.31 in. to right, etc.

Chapter 13

13.1   At A, 83^k up and 44^k to left; at B, 44^k to right; and at C, 17^k up
13.3 $F_{ad} = +3.06^k$
13.4 $F_{ab} = +14.4^k$; $F_{ed} = -15.6^k$; $F_{bc} = +16.1^k$; etc.
13.5   (a) 58.65^k to right; (b) 222.5^k to left; (c) 391^k to right
13.10 M at base of column, $270^{k'}$ causing tension in left-hand fibers
13.11 $R_{ax} = 0$; $R_{ay} = 31.1^k$ up; $M_a = 195.4^{k'}$ counterclockwise; $R_{dy} = 28.9^k$ up
13.12 $R_{ax} = 18.3^k$ to right; $R_{ay} = 30^k$ up; $R_{cx} = 18.3^k$ to left; $R_{cy} = 10^k$ up
13.13 Shear constant and equal to 3^k. $M_A = 15^{k'}$ tension in outer fibers; $M_B = 15^{k'}$
           tension in inner fibers
13.15 Shear A to load $= +5.31^k$; shear load to $B = -4.69^k$; $M_A = 17.81^{k'}$; M at
           load $= +14.07^{k'}$
13.17 $F_{L1b} = +47.0^k$
13.22 Slope-deflection signs. $M_{AB} = -275^{k'}$; $M_{BA} = +170^{k'}$; $M_{BD} = -70^{k'}$;
           $M_{DB} = -35^{k'}$
13.23 Slope-deflection signs. $M_{ab} = -160^{k'}$; $M_{ba} = -20^{k'}$; $M_{bc} = -90^{k'}$; $M_{be} =$
           $-80^{k'}$; $M_{eb} = -40^{k'}$
13.25 Slope-deflection signs. $M_{AB} = -164.6^{k'}$; $M_{BA} = -150.2^{k'}$; $M_{BC} = +150.2^{k'}$;
           $M_{CB} = +147.4^{k'}$; $M_{CD} = -147.4^{k'}$; $M_{DC} = -163.5^{k'}$
13.29 Slope-deflection signs. $M_{AB} = -180.8^{k'}$; $M_{BA} = +88.3^{k'}$; $M_{BD} = -28.3^{k'}$;
           $M_{DB} = -10.3^{k'}$; $M_{DE} = +5.1^{k'}$; $M_{DF} = +5.1^{k'}$
13.31 Slope-deflection signs. $M_{AB} = -338^{k'}$; $M_{BA} = -340^{k'}$; $M_{BC} = +294^{k'}$;
           $M_{BD} = +46^{k'}$; $M_{DB} = +98.6^{k'}$; $M_{DE} = -98.6^{k'}$
13.32 Slope-deflection signs. $M_{AB} = +26.8^{k'}$; $M_{AD} = -26.8^{k'}$; $M_{DA} = -33.2^{k'}$;
           $M_{DC} = +10.4^{k'}$; $M_{DE} = +15.2^{k'}$; $M_{DG} = +7.7^{k'}$
13.34 Slope-deflection signs. $M_{AB} = -158.2^{k'}$; $M_{BA} = -123.6^{k'}$; $M_{CD} = -223.6^{k'}$;
           $M_{DC} = -208.2^{k'}$
13.35 Slope-deflection signs. $M_{AB} = -69.2^{k'}$; $M_{BA} = -55.6^{k'}$; $M_{CD} = -233.4^{k'}$;
           $M_{DC} = -167.6^{k'}$
13.39 Slope-deflection signs. $M_{BA} = -M_{BC} = +8.6^{k'}$; $M_{CB} = +8.6^{k'}$; $M_{CD} =$
           $-37.2^{k'}$; $M_{CE} = +28.7^{k'}$; $M_{EC} = +23.9^{k'}$

Name Index

Subject Index